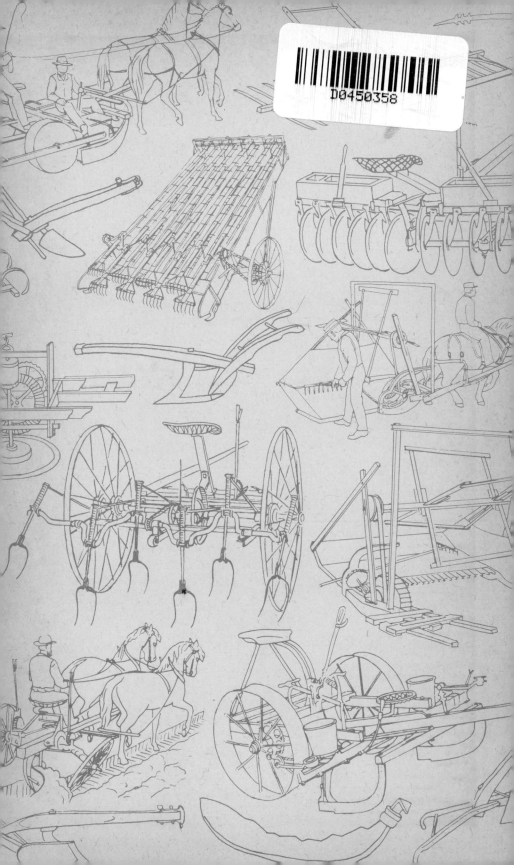

The Yearbook of Agriculture

1960

*The Yearbook of Agriculture, 1960*

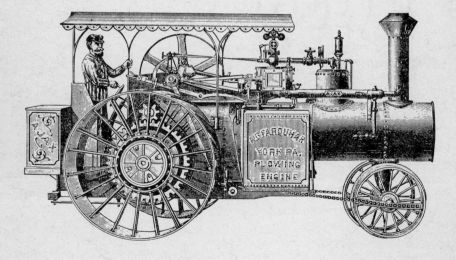

THE UNITED STATES GOVERNMENT PRINTING OFFICE

# Power
# to
# Produce

THE UNITED STATES DEPARTMENT OF AGRICULTURE • Washington, D.C.

# Foreword

EZRA TAFT BENSON

*Secretary of Agriculture*

THE VALUE OF THIS BOOK is that it pictures on a wide screen and in sharp focus the technological revolution that now is changing not only agriculture but our way of living.

The revolution is all around us. We see, hear, and feel evidences of it in new and more efficient machines, sources of power, ways of getting work done; in better ways of transporting, processing, storing, and marketing food; and in the wiser and more effective use of resources.

The revolution gives us new benefits every month, even every day— better food and more of it, improved industrial products, less work, more leisure. It can give us the elements of a more purposeful existence and the power to live more abundantly.

All this, and more, is described here in an effort to enlarge the knowledge and wisdom with which daily we face the demands of our personal lives and our national fortunes.

The mere possession of tools, gadgets, machines, packages, things is not enough. Wisdom requires an understanding of what the march of technology can do to people and for people.

We must make the most of the extra food technological advances provide.

It must be made available for sale in all markets, at home and abroad. It should be shared with the needy wherever possible. It should be, as President Eisenhower has said, "Food for Peace."

The extra efficiency in farming that results from such advances must be used wisely and energetically in maintaining and strengthening the family farm.

The changes wrought in farming operations by technology require our understanding and the necessity of helping many farm families, young and old, to adjust to the full impact of the technological revolution.

The proper recognition of the men responsible for our advances will

v

make certain even wider horizons for science and engineering in the future.

These are not merely rhetorical statements. They put in a broad and proper framework the revolution of which we are a part. They remind us of our obligations as fellow members of the human race. They indicate how much we have to know and do in an age that gives us much and demands much.

Truly ours is a choice land. Grateful to the Almighty for our many blessings and opportunities, let us be ever devoted to the spiritual and moral principles upon which all lasting progress must inevitably rest.

# Preface

ALFRED STEFFERUD

*Editor of the Yearbook*

POWER IS TOOLS, machines, wheels, levers, oil, energy, structures, the strength in muscles.

Power is communication, information, transportation, administration.

Power is ability to think, plan, invent, adapt, use, act, produce.

Power comes from the sun, the earth's stored riches, man's long experience, the sciences that we describe as technology or engineering and that have expanded with revolutionary force in the past few years.

We examine many aspects of power in this book, but we do not cover all agricultural technologies. We devote ourselves mainly to a more limited, but common, view of technology: The application and control of power in several forms, the use of a growing variety of materials, and the improvement in technical processes to raise the productivity and efficiency of economic activities and to reduce their requirements of human labor.

We consider the history, potentialities, and physical effects of power but not, except at times in passing, the social, political, and humanitarian problems that the possession of power may bring.

We believe a knowledge of our subject is important to everybody, for it is a big part of the world we live and work in. An understanding of our great power to produce—besides its practical values—helps us understand the complex situation of American agriculture.

Our photographs were supplied by Louis C. Jones, Director, New York State Historical Association and its Farmers' Museum, Cooperstown, N.Y.; Edward C. Kendall, Curator of Agriculture, Museum of History and Technology in the Smithsonian Institution's United States National Museum, Washington, D.C.; the writers of the chapters; Photographic Division, Office of Information, the United States Department of Agriculture, Washington, D.C.; and the manufacturers of implements.

The use of a photograph does not necessarily imply endorsement by the Department of Agriculture of the machine or product that is illustrated or disapproval of other machines and concerns.

The Committee Members for the 1960 Yearbook of Agriculture are:

Walter M. Carleton, CHAIRMAN, *Agricultural Research Service*
Wallace Ashby, *Agricultural Research Service*
J. L. Butt, *American Society of Agricultural Engineers*
Edward P. Cliff, *Forest Service*
William C. Crow, *Agricultural Marketing Service*
E. M. Dieffenbach, *Agricultural Research Service*
T. W. Edminster, *Agricultural Research Service*
C. J. Francis, *Soil Conservation Service*
Edward H. Graham, *Soil Conservation Service*
Joseph G. Knapp, *Farmer Cooperative Service*
Morris P. Leaming, *Agricultural Conservation Program Service*
Samuel P. Lyle, *Federal Extension Service*
John R. Matchett, *Agricultural Research Service*
Eugene G. McKibben, *Agricultural Research Service*
Robert D. Partridge, *Rural Electrification Administration*
W. T. Pentzer, *Agricultural Marketing Service*
Harold E. Pinches, *Agricultural Research Service*
Barton C. Reynolds, *Agricultural Research Service*
Alfred Stefferud, *Office of Information*
Lenore S. Thye, *Agricultural Research Service*
Austin Zingg, *Agricultural Research Service*

# Contents

# Power on the Land

# Power in the Harvest

# Power and Livestock

# Power in the Market

# Power and Efficiency

# Power and Its Effects

# Power in the Future

# Power to Produce

# Power
# in
# the Past

## Revolution
## in Agriculture

Harold E. Pinches

THE MAJORITY of all men who have ever lived have been bound to drudgery on the land. We are breaking away from that servitude.

Technological developments in agriculture have made us beneficiaries of a great breakthrough in the age-old struggle for greater abundance and, especially, for more assured supplies of our physical necessities.

Only where agricultural productivity has advanced faster than a people's needs have the economic conditions been created necessary to release larger and larger segments of the population from limited production on the land and thereby enable more and more persons to advance in intellectual, cultural, and social development above static folkways.

Where population increases without offsetting advances in agricultural productivity—except where trade and commerce or military conquest draw upon the products of foreign soils—increasing pressures on the sources of livelihood follow. The scale of living declines. Starvation appears. Famine threatens.

We have made substantial gains in the race between agricultural technology and population. This progress is not limited to the United States, but we have made the most profound and portentous advance in the world.

How did we come to our present level of physical well-being?

How secure is our progress?

What must be done to go on to higher levels?

Many technologies may contribute to agricultural productivity. Technology in its broadest sense is any practice that is an application of the findings of science. Thus agriculture embraces soils technology, horticultural technology, dairy technology, and so on over a wide range of sciences.

Discussion of the technological adaptations in agriculture of the findings of those many sciences would be a vast undertaking beyond the scope of a single book.

Utilization of energy and materials to offset natural hazards, or to multiply the effectiveness and value of farmers' labors, is the special concerns of engineering research and development. We note here technological advances of such importance that we may call them the "revolution of engineering in agriculture," but we must note also that only recently compared to other industries have significant amounts of engineering research and development been applied in agriculture.

Men's efforts to supplement their own strength with outside forces go back into unrecorded history. Men long ago trapped the winds to move their boats. Later, as engineering knowledge expanded, they turned to the energy stored in fossil fuels—coal and oil—to drive larger and larger boats. Now we have boats, powered by fissioning atoms, that cruise swiftly beneath the surface untroubled by wind or weather.

Travel over land was held down to the pace of running horses, which men had to use until they built "iron horses." Now we have millions of them as locomotives, streetcars, automobiles, buses, and trucks. They also draw on the great stores of energy in fossil fuels.

These developments and the things men learned in other phases of the Industrial Revolution have enabled men to give power to wings with which to fly far above difficulties of terrain and their own structures and faster than the turning of the earth.

Lately we have learned how to accumulate and control such awful concentrations of energy that man can hurl his instruments—perhaps even himself—away from his home on earth to the moon and beyond into interstellar space.

WHY THEN were men so slow to put mechanical power and devices to work at mankind's fundamental and, in total, most massive tasks: Tilling the soil, harvesting its products, and storing and converting part of them into livestock products?

Looking behind the farm machines and structures and other attributes and products of current agricultural technology, what were the elements that so delayed its development?

There are no simple or certain answers.

Yet there are some reasonable explanations in persistent influences and relationships, which aid understanding of how we got what we have, what has been accomplished, and the nature and size of the tasks ahead.

Attempts to introduce more power into agriculture were made long ago in many countries.

Animals have been used for a long time for limited amounts of mobile farm power, often for purposes and with equipment much the same centuries ago as today. Windmills and water wheels were developed for such stationary operations as milling flour, grinding feed, and pumping water for irrigation.

Such developments notwithstanding, there are several obstacles which are peculiar to farming and country life that have retarded technological progress in agriculture.

Perhaps the most important of them is in the nature itself of agricultural operations, nearly all of which can be done "by hand"—stirring the soil, planting seeds, gathering the harvest, feeding animals, milking cows, gathering eggs.

Each of these and many other operations can be done by a man alone with only his own strength and simple handtools. Men did them that way before civilization dawned and still do in many places.

Even where jobs were too big for one man, there was no urgent need for innovation as was obviously necessary, for example, to travel faster than by running horses. The answer for larger operations was multiplication of manpower by adding man to man in gangs.

Then, too, there was usually an adequate labor force—adequate in that what was attempted was adjusted to the capacities of those who lived on the land.

But men did seek means to augment the capacity of human muscles for some types of work. They turned to the power in the muscles of cattle, buffalo, camels, elephants, horses.

Here is a very important point, though: Inherent in those very animals were obstacles to bringing capacities and methods on the land comparable to capacities and methods used in manufacturing industries.

The work animals were more than power for plowing, hauling, and carrying men and goods. They furnished milk and meat, fibers, and hides. Even their bones had uses. Moreover, as long as land was available beyond men's direct needs, work animals could feed on otherwise unused plants and thus convert the outpouring of the sun's energy into usable power and useful products.

To the usefulness of work animals, further, were added feelings of understanding, even affection, of man for his animals. These immediate values and feelings obscured or put off recognition of the need for more and different power. They, men and animals, lived and worked together and were adjusted to the conditions and vagaries of nature in their own parts of the world.

Also influential was the fact that new ways of working seldom had to be learned in working with animals. Each young person had to learn what his father knew, of course, but much of what had to be learned was picked up easily as children and animals grew up together. Knowledge, equipment, and methods of use could be passed on from generation to generation. The animals would always be the same; there were, and would be, no "new models."

MAN-STRENGTH hand operations and work animals were, then, major factors in retarding the coming of an "industrial revolution" on the land, but there were other factors even more powerful: The ordinary physical and economic conditions under which most farm operations are done.

Farmwork is dispersed. Most of it cannot be concentrated, as under the roof of a factory.

Much farmwork is seasonal. All but a few operations are carried on for only a few days or, at most, a few weeks each year. These short seasons of use of any equipment impose severe limitations on investments of capital. They also limit what may be done in division of labor and attainment of skills through specialization.

The operating requirements for a farm field machine are extreme. It must be mobile, but seldom does it operate on graded, firm-surfaced terrain. Its functional operations require a high degree of precision while working on fragile, easily spoiled organic materials or an easily damaged soil structure.

And then there are economic restraints. Economic needs are satisfied—or attempts made to satisfy them—in response to and in proportion to recognition of human wants. For example, most persons want to have electricity available instantly, day or night. Such a situation contains enough consciously felt need or want to lead to a pooling of resources, even to borrowing against future income, to obtain a powerplant and distribution system. Its function is to generate a single unvarying product for daily use in perpetuity. For that product there is adequate experience to project the probability of increasing demand.

Such conditions lead to and justify large outlays for engineering research and development; precision manufacture and assembly; massive, long-life construction in generating machinery, accessory equipment, and buildings. They may be used so efficiently and so long that very large investments in them can be made profitably.

Not so with a combine-harvester, for example. It is a bulky machine, which works only while mobile, yet it must roll lightly over yielding agricultural soils. Tossed about and twisted by uneven surface of soil and terrain, it still must do a high-precision job of separating the grain from the straw cleanly and without damaging the grain. But it can be used only a few days or weeks annually. It cannot be put to other contraseasonal work without extensive modification. Nor can many of its component parts or much of the specific engineering or any considerable part of the manufacturing tooling be transferred to other machines.

The scene of a combine's working is distant, transitory, and only a few persons see it in operation. All people in a community depend on efficient, timely, and secure harvest of wheat, but they will not feel the lack thereof so directly or recognize a need for efficient harvest machines so clearly as they would the lack of, say, a needed bridge. All in the community are affected in both instances. But a sense of urgency and therefore willingness to devote substantial efforts to secure needed improvements usually will be stronger for something like a bridge whose immediate benefits are apparent to everyone.

AGAINST SUCH difficulties and obstacles—human, technical, economic, and social—technologies properly evaluated as revolutionary have been adopted in American agriculture.

They did not, however, come in one great, sweeping change in a short time. Their present effect is the sum of many changes that have come piecemeal, scattered in small units over vast territories, and of many events and innovations scattered in time over perhaps a generation in any area and often involving imbalances of old and new on any farm.

We can fix no single date or decade as the start of this agricultural revolution through technology.

But it is clear that the revolution in agricultural work, in work methods and productivity per man, got under way about the middle of the 19th century with the development of several new types of machines for use with horses.

Many experimenters during the first half of the 19th century sought better horse-drawn tillage implements and horse-powered machines to replace hand labor in planting and harvesting crops.

Shortage of labor and high grain prices during the Civil War speeded up the adoption of machine methods, especially for harvesting small grains. The numbers of horses and mules rose rapidly during the next half century.

Agriculture, as it advanced in waves of settlement across the American continent, surged up to an unprecedented level of productivity, derived from new technologies based on the use of horses and mules and the fertility of new soils.

That development did not end suddenly, but the virtual end of that era may be identified as the First World War or the years immediately after.

Horse and mule numbers at that time were the highest in our history— more than 25 million—but the rate of technological progress had slowed down. The availability of good new land had dwindled to insignificance. One-fourth of the harvested crop acreage was being used to produce feed for power animals.

If methods had not been changed, many more horses, more men to work them, and much more land to grow feed for them would be required for today's net agricultural output. The American economy of the 1960's could not be supported by an animal-powered agriculture on our essentially fixed—in fact, slowly shrinking—land base. National progress on all fronts would have been retarded seriously had not agriculture received new forms of power and sources of energy not restricted by biological limitations.

With the adoption of mechanical forms of power in engines, tractors, and electric motors and development of more and more types of adapted equipment to use that power, American agriculture entered a new era of sharply rising productivity.

Adaptations of internal-combustion engines in the form of tractors provided adequate mobile power on the land for the first time. Automobiles and trucks reduced barriers of separation and distance. Central-station electricity was extended to nearly all farms.

But more was required than merely putting electric motors to do what formerly had been done by hand or simply substituting tractors for horses. A tractor is not just a gas engine on wheels or a modified automotive truck. Neither is it simply a "pulling machine" to take the place of horses. Those ideas were tried in many ways during the long time—30 to 40 years—it took for the gradual evolution of successful designs.

Few important machines have required overcoming so many false starts and failures as dogged the early developments of farm tractors. Difficult problems of engines, bearings, gears, and such mechanical elements had to be licked. But more difficult were the problems of how to secure adequate ruggedness for working long hours at heavy loads over yielding soils and varying terrain, but in an overall design compact and nimble enough for practical use and not so heavy that most of the engine's power would be used to move only the tractor itself.

Yet these problems were only problems of mechanical design. Still more important were the difficulties of learning what a tractor ought to be and what it ought to do. It involved drastic innovations and the introduction of off-farm elements lacking the natural relationships that had existed for centuries between man and animals or the equally natural use of simple handtools.

New methods for each farm operation had to be devised before it could be mechanized. Adapted equipment had to be developed.

But as methods and equipment were developed, they enlarged the range of practical tractor operations and at the same time the breadth of ideas of what could be done by mechanical power. This led, in turn, to further advances in efficiency and adaptability of tractors and associated implements. Then came attempts at horseless farming. Without this important final step, agriculture would have been burdened with dual power systems, part animal, part mechanical.

The concept of farming without horses, which swept across the country after the First World War, was derided, denounced, and resisted by many who solemnly predicted various evils that would befall agriculture and the Nation in the wake of mechanical power instead of animal power on American farms. Enough had been done by 1925, however, in developing combinations of tractors and integrated implements to do satisfactorily all of the major farm operations, that horseless farming began to be demonstrated as practical.

Automotive equipment meanwhile had been driving horses off the highways. American farmers had 50 thousand automobiles in 1910. Only 15 years later, farm automobiles and trucks together had increased to nearly 4 million.

Tractors were accepted more slowly and numbered little more than 500 thousand in 1925. But in the next 10 years the number of farm tractors doubled. In the next decade it more than doubled again.

During the period when farmers were adopting automobiles and trucks and shifting to horseless farming, a third major development got under way that ultimately would affect all farms.

Beginning about 1925, rural electrification was being tested, demonstrated, and shown to be practical and economical for an ever-increasing variety of farm uses of electricity. Some farms on lines built primarily to serve towns and villages had electricity quite early, but still only 205 thousand were receiving central-station electricity in 1925. By 1935, their number had increased nearly tenfold, and a tremendous nationwide effort was extending electric lines to about 300 thousand additional farms each year.

Looking back, we can see that motorized farm transport, mechanical power in the fields, and farm electrification were proved and practical and were being widely adopted by 1935.

The great changeover was in full swing.

The groundwork, the experimentation, the seeking of new ways occupied the first three decades of this century.

THE SECOND THREE decades have brought a substantially complete technological transformation of American agricultural operations and processes.

Commonly apprehended aspects of this transformation are the substitution of mechanical power for human labor or animal power and the use of larger amounts of energy, materials, and equipment to modify or control the physical conditions of agricultural production.

But much that is involved we cannot easily see in farmers' equipment or methods. The extension of telephone, radio, and television to farms, delivery of daily papers, rural-centered and urban-centered magazines, and market information services, all combined to break down the comparative social and commercial isolation of farmers.

All-weather roads took from distance its former importance as a factor restricting farming activities.

As all-weather roads were extended, automobiles and trucks became increasingly important factors for change in types of farming and the organization of farm enterprises. Farmers acquired more certain and speedier access to local markets and economical access to more distant markets. This fostered many changes in types, quantities, or qualities of agricultural products from many areas.

Farms and farm operations have become more accessible to industries and industrial and commercial services. Machinery and facilities dependent on nonfarm sources of energy are being used. Agriculture has been changed from a comparatively self-sufficient status to an expanding market for products of many industries.

These two-directional changes and interchanges, farm-to-market and industry-to-farm, are not finished.

Farmers are shifting increasingly from production of a variety of products to specialization aimed at a particular market or at more efficient use of expensive equipment. At the same time, more and more functions, once typically on-farm activities of the farmer or some member of his family, are being transferred to services performed by off-farm agencies. Each year is bringing greater use of special-purpose equipment and facilities and increasing specialization of activities and functions, both within and for agriculture. They are stimulated by continuing improvements in transportation and communication.

We may speculate but probably will underestimate the full impact of these forces yet to come as thousands of miles of the nationwide system of superhighways are built.

THE OVERALL industrial and economic effects of the technological advances in agriculture have been abundant supplies of food; large supplies of raw materials for many industries that would not have been available under a low-powered agriculture; and release of vast amounts of manpower from agriculture to other industries and services.

The great advance of this Nation industrially and economically in the past hundred years required a supply of manpower increasing more rapidly than would have been available only from natural reproduction of the existing working population. We have had, throughout our national history, a shortage of labor relative to our needs and opportunities for development of the rich resources of this continent.

The need for more manpower for our industries, service occupations, and professions was filled for many years by immigration. Since about the time when the inflow of people from overseas was restricted by national legislation, a great internal source was created by the technological revolution in American agriculture. That has been one of the most valuable fruits of this revolution.

The characteristic nature of American farms—freeholdings of large acreages compared to generally much smaller holdings elsewhere—fostered interest in equipment with more capacity and power than hand- and animal-powered devices. Also, it usually favored improvement of output per man rather than per acre as the quickest and cheapest route to higher income.

Increasing efficiency of production reduced the number of men required for any given output. Transfers of some functions to off-farm services had a similar effect. Reductions in physical and social isolation of farmers and their families stimulated millions of persons to seek employment elsewhere than on local farms. This drained off from the more productive agricultural areas what otherwise would have been a surplus of farm labor and raised farm wage rates so sharply as to induce persistent search by farmers for equipment and power substitutes for labor— promoting, in turn, further technological change.

The conjunction of these forces and resources during a well-advanced phase of the general Industrial Revolution resulted in a great forward surge in agricultural technologies and productivity. This advance had no previous counterpart. It was not possible earlier in this country or elsewhere. American agriculture, through a period of many decades, benefited from increasingly efficient technologies while drawing on an adventitious element of productivity in the fertility of abundant new land.

As a Nation, we were able to get the jump on our basic needs.

We were able to form production capital rapidly, both within agriculture and to serve agriculture. This has been a century-long process of profound importance to the Nation, to every person in this country and, indeed, to many in other countries.

LOOKING BACK to earlier times, we see that a very large total of capital was accumulated in agriculture in millions of horses and mules, the machinery and harness and conveyances used with them, and barns for their shelter or storage of feed.

Then, too, there were the many off-farm industrial and commercial establishments behind them: The factories and tooling for manufacture of horse machinery, harness, and supplementary feeds; community facilities for collection of commodities like milk for transport to urban markets; and, not least important, the blacksmith shops in every community.

There were many other formations of capital—for example, the development of herds of cattle and facilities for their care, or the clearing, drainage, or other improvement of the land itself. None of these was there when the country was opened to settlement. Nearly all had to be accumulated from the productivity of agriculture in their areas of use.

These capital facilities, in turn, made agriculture more productive. But such capital had to be saved, as does all capital; it had to be possible of saving over and above subsistence needs.

The immensity of some of these earlier accumulations of production capital and of subsequent developments may be told with a few figures.

In 1910: Value of farm horses and mules, 2.7 billion dollars; machinery and equipment, 1.3 billion dollars; a total value of farm power and operating equipment of 4 billion dollars.

By 1940: Value of horses and mules was down to 1.3 billion dollars; machinery and equipment (including by that date considerable power machinery), up to 3.1 billion dollars; a total of 4.4 billion dollars.

In 1959: The value of farm tractors alone, 3.4 billion dollars; other farm machinery, 8.2 billion dollars; a total of 11.6 billion dollars. If to this last figure were added the value of motortrucks, plus 40 percent of the value of automobiles (the usually ascribed business value of farmers' automobiles), the total inventory of farm power equipment in 1959 was nearly 16 billion dollars.

If we adjust the values of this equipment at different dates to offset changes in the value of the dollar, farm mechanical equipment increased in volume by 2.5 times in the 20 years between 1940 and 1960. During the same period the number of farmworkers declined sharply.

The result of these two divergent trends was that the amount of power equipment per farmworker has been nearly quadrupled since 1940.

These figures show only changes in what we might call the power operating equipment, but this is not even all of the significant on-farm capital equipment. Moreover, they do not include many off-farm types of capital resources that are contributing to modern agriculture's strength and productivity, two of which we should note especially.

One is the rapidly growing and vast total of resources of the off-farm agencies that are providing an increasing variety of specialized services in agricultural production, transportation, or distribution. Some are in lieu of functions once done by farmers. Others are additions to our total national agricultural inputs to provide us more assured supplies or new or better products, or are personal and household services to enhance the scale of living of farm families.

The other notable accumulations of off-farm capital are the ones related directly to the implementation and maintenance of farm techniques now in use and to research and development leading to introduction of new or more advanced technologies. These are the billions of dollars invested in industrial organizations that manufacture, distribute, or service all of the farm production equipment and operations. Among them are farm machinery companies; some specialized electrical equipment manufacturers and parts of other companies producing also for the nonagricultural market; large segments of the petroleum industries; producers of a wide variety of chemicals; some parts of nearly all agencies generating and distributing electricity; many producers of building materials and of fabricated structures; and so on through a long list that grows every year in scope and diversity.

These capital resources and the activities carried out and products derived therefrom are as much part of our modern agricultural technology as are the direct resources visibly located on farms. They, just as much as a farm barn or new fence around a pasture, are devoted to and supported by the productivity of agriculture. Some may have been established in part by investment of outside capital. In the end, however, they must be justified by and the investments serviced by enhanced agricultural productivity.

WE HAVE BEEN concerned so far almost entirely with American events, but we should recognize that substantial technological progress is being made in some other countries, including western Europe, Canada, Australia, and the Soviet Union.

There has been less exchange of information and discussion of principles between agricultural engineers and technologists of different countries than has prevailed for many years among scientists in biological and chemical fields. Some steps have been taken recently by agricultural engineers toward reducing barriers of languages and distance. Reciprocal exchanges will enrich and strengthen agricultural technologies here and elsewhere.

Technological revolution in agriculture could be worldwide before long. Specific practices or details of machines or structures probably will not become universal. But fundamental physical principles are the same everywhere. They require only to be developed in ways suited to the economic conditions and social relationships in each country.

Such developments will not come easily in all areas. The difference between normal production and subsistence needs is very small in many countries. That limited margin may be dissipated quickly by natural disasters or over a few years by population growth.

Nevertheless, these difficulties may be faced confidently. The common problem in those countries is how to secure enough capital to step up productivity far enough ahead of immediate needs to save some for reinvestment in facilities for greater productivity. Yet this is only a question of finding or forming working capital. The time-consuming processes of trial and error and research that were required to advance our technologies have developed and demonstrated principles which show the way for rapid technological progress elsewhere.

TECHNOLOGICAL ADVANCES are manifested in use of new types of machines, new forms of power, modified practices, and so on. But to appraise fully how far we have come and may yet go beyond the limitations of hand- and animal-powered agriculture, we must look at more than tangible capital resources or current technological advances. Behind such advances are their sources and supports: Accumulations of knowledge and organized research.

Some technical developments may seem to be brilliant inventions, but most are the products of persistent testing, recording results, projecting and building possible improvements, and more testing.

As this process is carried on year after year, the accumulation of knowledge advances technical skills and the art of engineering pertinent to a particular field. With acquisition of still more knowledge and experience, engineering art and personal "know-how" can be reduced to engineering science and basic physical principles.

Design, testing, and projection of new devices or practices can then proceed more objectively and confidently, along routes more productive but often less spectacular than invention.

This process is cumulative and expansive. Each successful development, each principle newly discovered or more accurately stated, opens the way for further advances, sometimes along several new paths previously too difficult or unperceived.

It is impossible to overestimate the importance of this progressive accumulation of knowledge and understanding. There would have been much less technological advance—certainly no technological revolution—in agriculture except for this continued endeavor to push out in widening reaches the boundaries of man's knowledge of the forces and elements in his environment and how to control them.

This revolution is not finished even in the United States. It is continuing without any foreseeable end. We must expect it to accelerate. Its future form cannot be discerned, particularly as to details, but we can project a few almost-certain trends over considerable time.

As more businesses and industries turn to agriculture as an important sphere of economic activity, more technically trained manpower and resources will be devoted to development of products and equipment to be used in agricultural processes; to specialized services of supply and production operations (sometimes obviating farmer-owned equipment, sometimes providing farm labor equivalents); and to collection, primary processing, or distribution of agricultural products.

As purchasing and marketing organizations more effectively extend specifications for products back to the producers, whether through contracts or otherwise, they will become concerned with supporting technologies.

ADVANCES in agricultural productivity—that is, reductions of the real costs of a given output—will come, as in other industries, from organized research and development. There will continue to be isolated inventions and discoveries, but even these usually will be sparked by practical concern with problems similar to the subjects of organized research and industrial or commercial developments.

The folklore of America's growth and the literature of our past abound with references to the skills and contributions of local smiths, woodworkers, and other artisans. But future economic progress and national growth and stability will require larger and larger research expenditures and the employment of ever greater numbers of scientists and engineers devoting full time to technological development.

In addition to programed agricultural research and development, there will be borrowings and adaptations from the basic automotive and electrical industries; from general advances in structural design and fabrications; advances in metals, plastics, and chemicals; in heavy-duty, high-capacity equipment and in methods for transport of materials and industrial construction; in instrumentation and control devices; and so on through many other fields of technical and scientific development. Future technological advances of American agriculture, as in the past, will in part stem from and be determined in form and timing by the nature, sequence, and degrees of adoption of general technical advances throughout the whole economy.

IN SUM, the elements for change at work in American agriculture are compelling and self-regenerating concepts never before present so forcefully anywhere in the world:

Using in agriculture any needed amount of power or energy in concentrated, untiring, compatible, and controllable forms and amounts;

Recognizing as only temporary limits what ingenuity and engineering research and industrial development have presently made practical;

Tackling new tasks with optimism founded on current accumulations of applicable experience and knowledge;

Facing the future with conscious purpose and determination to discover and implement better, more efficient, and less onerous ways of doing man's fundamental work.

# A Stout Man
# To Bear On

Dorothy R. Rush

HOW FAR WE HAVE COME we see when we read what men wrote about the implements they themselves used on farms a hundred years or so ago.

They wrote for the Yearbooks of Agriculture and the forerunners of the Yearbooks, and they wrote with awareness, hope and pride or asperity, and a commendable directness.

One of them was Charles L. Flint, Secretary of the Massachusetts Board of Agriculture, whose article, "A Hundred Years' Progress," appeared in *Report of the Commissioner of Agriculture for the Year 1872.*

"One of the chief obstacles the early colonists had to encounter, to add to the hardships of their lot in the cultivation of the soil, was the difficulty of procuring suitable implements," he wrote.

"A few, no doubt, were brought with them, but all could not obtain them in this way, and the only metal they had was made of bog-ore, and that was so brittle as to break easily and put a stop to their day's work. Most of their tools were made of wood, rude enough in construction, heavy of necessity, and little fit for the purpose for which they were made. The process of casting steel was then unknown. It was discovered in Sheffield, England, but not till the middle of the last century, and then kept a secret there for some years. The few rude farming-tools they had were, for the most part, of home manufacture, or made by the neighboring blacksmith as a part of his multifarious business, there being little idea of the division of labor, and no machinery by which any particular implement could be exactly duplicated.

"But it is recorded that as early as 1617 some plows were set to work in the Virginia colony, for in that year the governor complained to the company that the colony 'did suffer for want of skillful husbandmen and means to set their plows on work; having as good ground as any man can desire, and about forty bulls and oxen, but they wanted men to bring them to labor, and iron for the plows, and harness for the cattle. Some thirty or forty acres we had sown with one plow, but it stood so long on the ground before it was reaped it was most shaken, and the rest spoiled with the cattle and rats in the barn.'

"A contemporary resident of that colony says, in 1648, 'We have now going near upon a hundred and fifty plows,' and they were drawn by oxen. In 1637 there were but thirty-seven plows in the colony of Massachusetts Bay, and for twelve years after the landing of the Pilgrims the farmers had no plows, but were compelled to tear up the bushes with their hands, or with clumsy hoes and mattocks. It afterwards became the custom, in the Massachusetts colony, for some one owning a plow to go about and do the plowing for the farmers over a considerable extent of territory, and a town sometimes paid a bounty to any one who would keep a plow in repair for the purpose of going about to work in this way. The massive old wooden plow required a strong team, a stout man to bear on, another to hold, and a third to drive. The work it did was slow and laborious. The other tools were a heavy spade, a clumsy wooden fork, and, later, a harrow. I have had in my possession specimens of these forks two hundred years old. It is difficult to see how they could have done very effective work.

"The plows used by the French settlers upon the 'American bottom,' of Illinois, from the time of their occupation, in 1682, down to the war of 1812, were made of wood, with a small point of iron fastened upon the wood by strips of rawhide. The beams rested upon an axle and small wooden wheels. They were drawn by oxen yoked by the horns, the yokes being straight and fastened to the horns by raw-leather straps, a pole extending back from the yoke to the axle. These plows were large and clumsy, and no small plow was in use among them to plow corn till about the year 1815. They used carts that had not a particle of iron about them.

"Among the forms of the old wooden plow that achieved something more than a local reputation during the last century was that known as the 'Carey plow.' It was more extensively used than any other, though its particular form varied very much according to the skill of each blacksmith or wheelwright who made it. The land-side and the standard were made of wood, and it had a wooden mold-board, often roughly plated over with pieces of old saw-plate, tin, or sheet-iron. It had a clumsy wrought-iron share, while the handles were upright, held in place by two wooden pins. It took a strong man to hold it, and about double the strength of team now required to do the same amount of work. The 'bar-share plow,' sometimes called the 'bull-plow,' was also used. A flat bar forming the land-side, with an immense clump of iron, shaped like half of a lance-head, into the upper part of which a kind of colter was fastened, which served as a point. It had a wooden mold-board fitted to the iron-work in the most bungling manner. A sharp-pointed shovel, held with the reverse side up, and drawn forward with the point in the ground, would give an idea of its work. Then there was the 'shovel-plow,' in very general use in the middle and southern colonies, a roughly hewn stick was used for a beam, and into this another stick was framed, upon the end of which there was a piece of iron, shaped a little like a sharp-pointed shovel. The two rough handles were nailed or pinned to the sides of the beam.

"A plow known as the 'hog-plow' was also used in some parts of the country in the last and the early part of the present century, so called probably on account of its rooting propensity. Specimens of this plow were taken to Canada in 1808 for use there, which would seem to indicate that it was thought to be one of the best plows then made. These old forms of the wooden plow continued to be used with little or no improvement till some time after the beginning of the present century. The wooden plow was liable to rapid decay."

"The other implements of husbandry," Mr. Flint went on, "were very few and very rude.

"The thrashing was done with the flail. The winnowing was done by the wind. Slow and laborious hand-labor

for nearly all the processes of the farm was the rule, and machine-labor the exception, till a comparatively recent date. Indeed, it has been said that a strong man could have carried on his shoulders all the implements used on his farm, except, perhaps, the old wooden cart and the harrow, previous to the beginning of the present century, and we know that the number as well as the variety of these tools was extremely small. . . .

"We are now prepared to appreciate the condition of our agriculture at the time of the outbreak of the Revolution. We have seen that the settlers had but poor and inefficient tools, poor and profitless cattle, poor and meager crops, and poor and miserable ideas of farming. They had no agricultural journals, no newspapers of any kind, and few books, except the old family Bible. There were less than a dozen papers published in the country at the middle of the last century. There was not one in New England at the beginning of that century, but four in 1750, and these had but a very limited circulation in the rural districts. There was little communication from town to town. The facilities for travel were extremely limited. It was before the days of stages even, and the liberalizing influence which modern travel and social intercourse exert. Everything was favorable to the growth of prejudice and of narrow-minded views."

Farm production was brought close to a standstill during the Revolution. Agricultural societies were organized gradually within the next few years, and with them came exhibitions. The Massachusetts Society held its first exhibition at Brighton in 1816. There was a plowing match.

Mr. Flint continued: "The plow-maker, however, happened to be there with his eyes open, and there can be no doubt that this and similar exhibitions which soon followed gave a new impetus to the progress of agricultural mechanics. Improvements in the plow had begun, even before the close of the last century. A patent had been granted for a cast-iron plow to Charles Newbold, of Burlington, New Jersey, in 1797, combining the mold-board, share, and land-side, all cast together, and it was regarded by intelligent plow-makers as so great an improvement that Peacock, in his patent of 1807, paid the original inventor the sum of $500 for the right to combine certain parts of Newbold's plow with his own. The importance of this implement was so great as to command the attention and study of scientific men, to improve its form and construction, and Thomas Jefferson, in 1798, applied himself to the task, and wrote a treatise upon the requisite form of the mold-board, according to scientific principles, calculating the exact form and size, and especially the curvature to lessen the friction. . . .

"There can be no doubt that the saving to the country from these improvements in the plow, within the last half century, amounts to many millions of dollars a year in the cost of teams, and some millions in the cost of plows, or that the aggregate of crops has been increased by them many millions of bushels. The plow has also been modified to adapt it to a much greater variety of soils. In the mode of manufacture, too, a vast improvement has taken place. Half a century ago it was made sometimes on the farm, sometimes by the village blacksmith, and the wheelwright. The work is now concentrated in few establishments. . . .

"But, perhaps, the most important of modern agricultural inventions are the grain-harvesters, the reapers, the mowers, the thrashers, and the horse-rakes. The sickle, which was in almost universal use till within a very recent date, is undoubtedly one of the most ancient of all our farming implements. Reaping by the use of it was always slow and laborious, while from the fact that many of our grains would ripen at the same time, there was a vastly greater loss from this cause than there is at the present time. . . . Nothing was more surprising to the mercantile community of Europe than the fact that we could continue to export such vast quantities of wheat and other bread-stuffs through the midst of the late rebellion, with a million or two of able-bodied men in arms. The secret of it was the general use of farm machinery. The number of two-horse reapers in operation throughout the country, in the harvest of 1861, performed an amount of work equal to about a million of men. The result was that our capacity for farm production was not materially disturbed."

Part II, *Agriculture*, of the Annual Report of the Commissioner of Patents was the forerunner of the present Yearbook of Agriculture. Most of the material came from farmers and others to whom the Commissioner of Patents had sent circulars requesting information.

John N. Rottiers, Jefferson County, New York, wrote in the report for 1849: "The inventive genius of mechanics, by improving the various implements of husbandry, has done much for the tillers of the soil. Their newly invented horse-powers, their threshers and separators, their seed-sowers and grain-crushers, and other valuable machines, do much to expedite the labors of the farm; and the time is fast approaching when the husbandman will have more leisure for mental cultivation, and the science of farming will be much better understood than it now is. The products of the land, instead of being lessened under an improved system of tillage, will constantly be increased, and the tiller of the soil, fully satisfied with his vocation, will bless Providence that made him a farmer."

Obed Hussey patented a reaper in 1833. Cyrus McCormick patented one in 1834. Even so, some farmers were still using the scythe and cradle in 1850.

In the report for that year, Edmund Ruffin, Esq., of Virginia, wrote an article on the management of wheat harvests.

The Virginia patriot, editor, and

farmer, whose writings aroused great interest in scientific farming, wrote: "I use for reaping only the scythe and cradle. Since coming to my present farm, I have had great difficulty in getting the wood-work of cradles made heavy enough. Cradles made as light as usual hereabout are more laborious to work in good wheat, and less efficient, than heavier cradles. My scythemen complained loudly of the lightness of the ordinary cradles, which I was compelled to use for several years. . . .

"It would doubtless be an improvement if we could introduce here, for all heavy wheat, the 'strewing' instead of 'handling'—and also the cradles best suited for the former practice. Perhaps a still greater benefit may be found in the substitution of reaping-machines—which even now are used by most of the good farmers of my neighborhood. But because of their great liability to get out of order, the difficulties of working them, and especially my own ignorance of machinery, I have feared to attempt the use of a reaping-machine."

The Annual Report for 1848 listed 33 agricultural implements that were patented that year. They were for plows and cultivators, seed planters, bog cutter, grain and grass cutters, horse rakes, and corn shellers.

The Annual Report for 1860 listed 917 agricultural discoveries or inventions in that year. The list included such things as beehives, butterworker, machine for printing butter, locks and ties for cotton bales, cultivators, churns, cornhuskers, cane coverers, device to prevent horses from cribbing, corn shellers, cornstalk cutters, machine for cleaning cottonseed, sugar-crushing apparatus, apparatus for cleaning, drying, and polishing coffee, machine for cleaning rice, seed drills, ditching machines, mode of laying tile drains, apparatus for evaporating saccharine juices, hay elevators, flowerpots, fodder cutters, fertilizers, a machine for making picket fence and one for pointing fence rails, cotton

gins, grain binders, grain cleaners, hop frames, harvesters, harrows, device for preventing hogs from rooting, hemp brakes, hominy machines, rice hullers, mowing machines, cider mills, coffee mills, flour mills, plows, planters, cotton presses, cheese presses, combination reaping and mowing machines, horse rakes, seeding machines, furnace for evaporating sugar juices, stump extractors, grain separators, smut machine, threshing machines, winnowing machines, machine for burring wool, grain-weighing machines, and ox yoke fastenings.

THE COST OF LABOR averaged about the same throughout the States in 1849. According to William Bacon, of Richmond, Massachusetts: "Men get from ten to sixteen dollars per month and boarded, for six months commencing in April."

John N. Rottiers, Jefferson County, New York, reported: "The usual price of hired hands on farms is from ten to fifteen dollars per month, with board, which is worth one dollar twenty-five per week. In haying, we pay from seventy-five cents to one dollar per day; and in harvest for cradling, one dollar or one and a half per day, with board."

In New Castle County, Delaware, Dr. Allen Vorhees Lesley listed the wages as: "Labor with board 50 cents per day, $8 to $12 per month; without board 75 cents per day, $14 to $20 per month. Harvest ranges from $1 to $1 50 per day. Board from $6 50 to $7 50 per month."

Thomas Affleck, of Washington, Mississippi, wrote in 1849: "Negroes hire out readily at $15 per month for common out-door labor; the owner clothing them, paying physicians' bills, if any, taxes, &c.; the employer boarding them. When hired by the year on plantations, which is rarely done, the employer pays about $70 to $75 for a full hand, paying all expenses, in sickness and in health, unless perhaps taxes, and supporting the children if any.

"White laborers, when making levees, canals, ditches, &c., receive $1 per day and board with quan. suf. of whiskey. Few owners will put their negroes at such work in the swamps, mainly on account of its unhealthiness. At work in the mills they have from $10 to $15 per month, and board. Carpenters $30 to $50. Gardeners from $20 to $50. Overseers $250 to $800 according to number of hands on the place, and the experience and competency of the overseer.

"The number who have gone, or are going to California, has somewhat raised the wages of overseers. Intelligent young men from the North and West, who are pretty good farmers, would find employment in this capacity; being content with moderate wages for a couple of years, under the eye of experienced planters on their home places."

"The cost of labor is about one hundred and thirty dollars per year and board," Wm. S. Wright, of Sugar Grove, Ohio, found. "Cost of boarding, five dollars per month."

J. W. Scott, of Adrian, Michigan, said: "The most common labor with board is worth from $50 to $75 a year. A higher quality, in which some care and responsibility are added, is worth $100 to $120. When hired by the day 75 cents in summer, and 50 cents in winter, with board, is about the average; without board 20 cents should be added. The cost of boarding a laborer is from $1 to $1 50 per week."

THE FIRST ROADS in our country were merely trails and passable only on horseback.

"The public roads were bad," wrote Mr. Flint, "and over these the freight of the country, whatever it was, had to be moved in wagons made to be capable of the hardest usage. The modern light carriage would have been comparatively useless in a new country. . . . The mail contracts, even over a very large part of the country, when the post system was instituted, were based on a speed below four and five miles per hour. But there were no mails previous to 1780; and in 1791, the first year of the mail-service, there were but eighty-nine post-offices in the whole country, and less than two thousand miles of post-roads, and on these nine-tenths of the mail-service was done on horseback, the stage-service being very small."

Mr. William Parry, of Burlington County, New Jersey, wrote in the 1850 report: "The extensive cultivation of perishable articles is necessarily confined to the vicinity of large cities, and situations having steam communication with them. Our land being a sandy loam, is very favorable for the early ripening of fruits and vegetables, and, situated within a few miles of Philadelphia, and having railroad communication with New York, fruits and other perishable crops, gathered one evening, may be served out in either market the next morning. As a consequence, the farmers in this section of New Jersey find the raising of fruits and vegetables for the great markets, Philadelphia and New York, to be the most profitable use to which their lands can be applied, and vast quantities of such produce are daily despatched, by cars, steamboats, and sloops, during the market season."

Another aspect was cited by Wilmot S. Gibbs, of Chestnut Grove Post Office, Chester District, South Carolina: "The farmers are just becoming aware of the importance of apples to their stocks, but their orchards are quite too small yet, to draw any comparison between the use of apples and corn for stock; none are raised for exportation—freight has been too high; but I do hope that the completion of the South Carolina and Charlotte Railroad will bring with it a reduction of freight, and all the benefits attending such improvements, and so enable us to obtain a market for the various little articles we could raise, and an additional incitement to improve our orchards."

a well (with an old-fashioned pump in it) where soft water can be obtained by digging, is probably the next best source of supply, as it, too, is always cool and lively. Every part of the kitchen, the wash and bake house, the dairy and barn can be supplied from the pump by the aid of pipes, saving much labor at small cost.

"The roofs of barn and dwelling will furnish an ample supply of rain water for any farmer's use, and, next to pure spring or well water, it is the most healthful for drinking and bathing, as well as best for cooking and washing.

"Due care and caution should be used in the selection and use of pipes for conveying and distributing water to the buildings. Where suitable timber is cheap, the large pipes (or mains) may be most easily and cheaply made of logs. Iron is probably the next in cheapness in some sections. Earthen mains, when properly vitrified (hard-burnt and glazed) are sometimes preferred. And for distributing pipes where zinc or tinned pipes cannot be afforded, lead is the most common material—and against the action of vegetable matter, and of some kinds of water, on this mineral, the utmost caution should be used. . . . It is water stagnant in a lead pipe which causes mischief, so that every faucet should be allowed to run the water waste for at least one minute the first thing in the morning, especially in the kitchen. . . ."

Israel Goodwin, East Montpelier, Vermont, in 1850 told how to make and store butter:

"I keep but 5 cows; the average of butter made from them the past year is a trifle over 200 lbs. Three calves had all the milk they would take, until six weeks old, and raised two; sold the butter we had to spare to people near us, for 16 cts. per lb. It is the variable practice, as far as my knowledge extends, with those that make butter, to set the milk about 36 hours, which is long enough for the cream to rise, which is then taken off and churned.

None, in this vicinity, churn the mill Our practice is to churn in the morn ing. When the weather is warm, an the butter comes soft, we wash it i cold water till the buttermilk will no color the water; salt the butter, set in a cool place till the next morning, then work it over with the hand. Some make use of the butter-worker, but I think a woman's hand, if it is clean and expeditiously used, is the best butter-worker I have ever seen. The butter is then put in tubs, usually made of spruce or fir, holding from 30 to 60 lbs.; fill to within two inches of the top; fit a cotton or linen cloth, the size of the tub-cover, with good, strong brine; let the cover fit tight, so as to exclude all the air, if possible. The mode of churning is very uniform; the churn used is the float, or sometimes the barrel-churn, made by Ruggles, Nourse & Co., of Boston; but, where the business is small, the old dash is preferable."

Farmers in 1850 had different methods of curing and storing pork. Henry Miller, Jun., of Ashland, Ohio, wrote "My method of putting up and curin pork for home consumption is, first t salt slightly in open casks, and let stand one week, then pour off th brine, for it is generally bloody, an would taint the meat; then pour c strong fresh brine, and put on weig enough to keep every particle of me perfectly submerged. Let it stand 4 c 6 weeks, according to the size of th pork, then hang it up and smoke wit green hickory or sugar wood, until shows a rich yellow color, then pac down in clean oats."

J. Hendershott, P.M., of Springfield Ohio, wrote: "The cheapest method for producing pork is by feeding th hogs with ground grains in slop. With clover pasturage in summer, and apples in the fall, 10 bushels of corn will produce 100 to 130 lbs. of pork. Sugar-curing, with a little saltpetre; and when cured and smoked, take ground pepper and mix with good molasses, and rub in well upon the soft or fleshy parts; then enclose in a canvas bag, and hang in a dry place."

The problem of disposing of surplus products existed in 1852, too.

F. J. Cope, of Hemphill, Pennsylvania, added this postscript to his reply to the circular distributed by the Commissioner of Patents. (Such replies were the basis of the agriculture section of the annual report.) "Now that the home market for our surplus products is in a great degree destroyed by a mistaken policy, are the farmers of the country to be left to shift for themselves in all future time?

"When the vast wilderness of the West shall be made to 'bloom and blossom as the rose,' and when 'two blades of grass shall be made to grow where but one grew before,' who is to consume this immense addition to our productive industry?

"Are these things not worthy of the consideration of those we send to represent us at the American capital?"

COSTS OF PRODUCTION always have bulked large in farmers' concerns.

S. Hale, of Cheshire County, New Hampshire, wrote in 1850: "An intelligent, aged, and successful farmer has given me the following account of his mode of raising corn, its cost, product, &c. He ploughs his land (always sward) in the spring, about 7 inches deep, turning it well over, then harrows and furrows it. He then puts on 20 cartloads of dung to the acre, all into the hills. The dung used, say in 1850, was made in the winter of 1848–49, remained in the yard during the summer of 1849, was hauled into the field in the fall, placed in large heaps, and shovelled over once or twice during the next spring. He uses great care in covering the corn and dung; hoes the corn twice, and harvests in October. He is never troubled with the wireworm, and attributes his exemption to planting on sward land.

"The cost he estimates as follows:

| | | |
|---|---|---|
| Ploughing, per acre | | $2.00 |
| Harrowing " | | .75 |
| Furrowing " | | .25 |

| | | |
|---|---|---|
| Twenty loads of dung | | $20.00 |
| Putting dung in hills | | 2.00 |
| Planting corn | | 1.00 |
| Hoeing corn twice | | 4.00 |
| Cutting up corn | | 1.00 |
| Husking corn | | 4.00 |
| Harvesting corn | | 1.00 |
| Total | | $36.00 |
| Corn fodder | $10.00 | |
| Manure left in soil | 10.00 | |
| | | 20.00 |
| Net Cost | | $16.00 |
| Product, 75 bushels, at 70 cents | | 52.50 |
| Income per acre | | $36.50" |

Jacob L. Kintner, of Rock Haven, Indiana, wrote about the cost of producing timothy hay:

"As to the cost of raising hay, I consider that, when sown with wheat, the cost of setting an acre of grass will consist of the following items, viz.: Two gallons of seed at 50 cents per gallon, $1, and the sowing of the same, at a cost of 25 cents, make the sum of $1.25 per acre, without rolling, which should be done in the month of February or March preceding the mowing; for, if the roller were passed over the ground when the sowing was done, it would assist the vegetation of the grass-seed very much, by compressing the soil, thereby retaining the moisture. The cost of rolling, per acre, would be, for driver 75 cents per day, and team $1.25, making $2 per day. Eight acres would be a fair day's work, making the cost 25 cents per acre. Harvesting the hay is estimated at $2 per ton, and baling $1. Thus, one acre of grass, producing two tons of hay, would cost as follows:—

| | |
|---|---|
| Seed | $1.00 |
| Sowing | 0.25 |
| Rolling | 0.25 |
| Harvesting | 4.00 |
| Baling | 2.00 |
| | $7.50 |

"The average price of baled hay, at the river, is $10 per ton, amounting to $20 per acre, deducting expenses, $7.50, leaves $12.50 as the net proceeds of an acre of grass. I consider my grass crop worth to me, on an average, $10 per acre."

*Egyptian plowing*

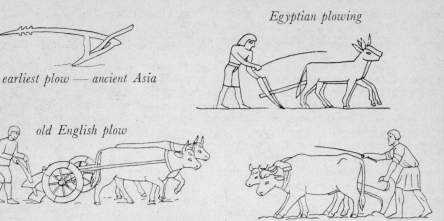

*earliest plow — ancient Asia*

*old English plow*

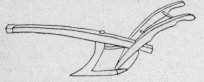

*ancient Roman plow*

*Charles Newbold's plow*

*Oliver's patent 1873*

*wooden moldboard plow from Pennsylvania*

*steel plow 1837*

*Daniel Webster's plow*

*riding sulky plow about 1881*

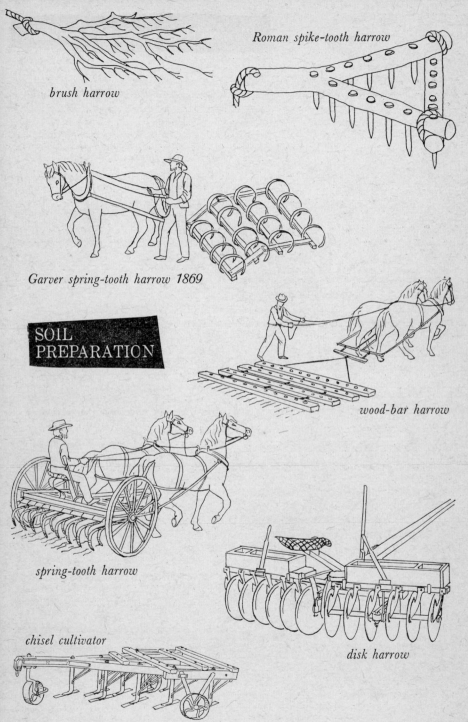

brush harrow

Roman spike-tooth harrow

Garver spring-tooth harrow 1869

SOIL PREPARATION

wood-bar harrow

spring-tooth harrow

chisel cultivator

disk harrow

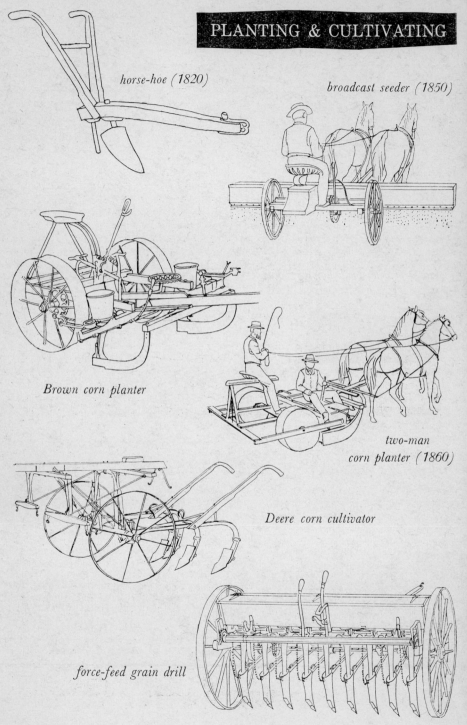

## PLANTING & CULTIVATING

*horse-hoe (1820)*

*broadcast seeder (1850)*

*Brown corn planter*

*two-man
corn planter (1860)*

*Deere corn cultivator*

*force-feed grain drill*

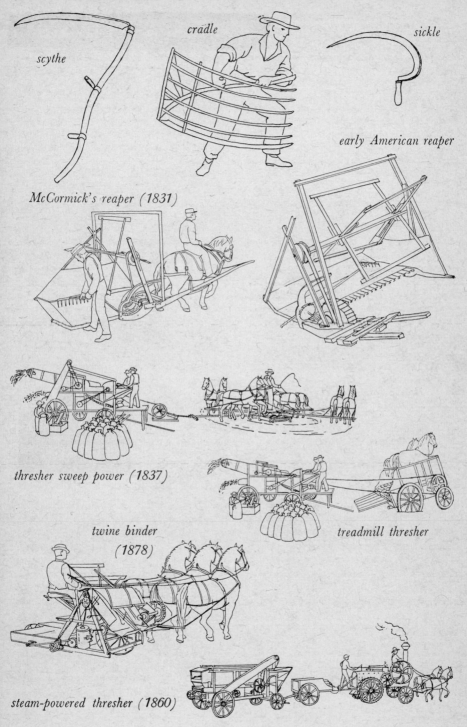

scythe

cradle

sickle

early American reaper

McCormick's reaper (1831)

thresher sweep power (1837)

twine binder
(1878)

treadmill thresher

steam-powered thresher (1860)

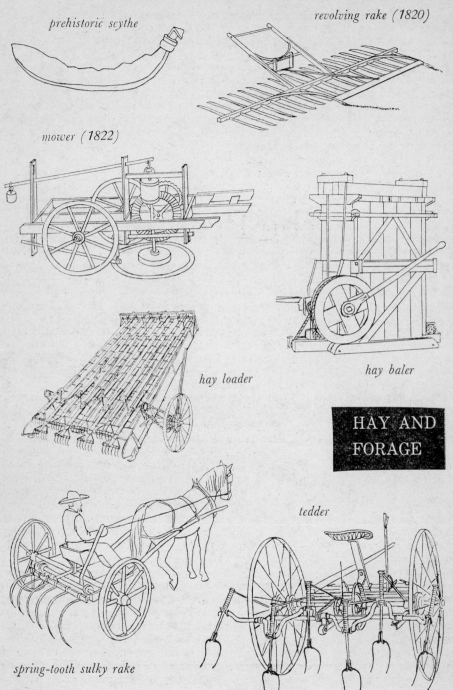

*prehistoric scythe*

*revolving rake (1820)*

*mower (1822)*

*hay loader*

*hay baler*

HAY AND
FORAGE

*tedder*

*spring-tooth sulky rake*

# Power

# in

# the Present

## The Development of the Tractor

E. M. Dieffenbach and R. B. Gray

A FARMER in 1910 needed 135 hours to produce 100 bushels of corn, 106 hours for 100 bushels of wheat, and 276 for a bale of cotton.

The average for the United States in 1960 was about 23 man-hours to produce 100 bushels of corn, 17 for 100 bushels of wheat, and 77 for a bale of cotton.

A reason for this big drop in the American farmer's labor requirement was the development of the tractor.

Tractors were perfected because of the need for mechanical power for the new machines that were being invented and produced for farmers.

Cyrus McCormick invented his reaper in 1831. It soon created a demand for belt power with which to thresh the mechanically harvested grain crops. By 1860 more than 50 shops from Maine to California were building threshers under license from the Pitts Brothers, American inventors who patented a thresher in 1837.

Steel plows, mowers, shellers, fodder cutters, and other machines were offered to the farmer soon thereafter.

The reaper and the thresher made obsolete the flail, which had been in common use for centuries in all parts of the world for beating out the grain from the heads. First it was a whip, sometimes with two or more lashes. The later versions consisted of a wood handle with a shorter stick hung at the end so as to swing freely.

Work animals also became obsolete, in a manner of speaking, in time. Used with sweeps and treadmills, they provided some power, but not enough for operating the threshers and other belt-driven machines. Manufacturers of threshers and other machines undertook therefore the production of movable steam engines.

The early steam engines furnished belt power, but they had to be pulled from place to place by horses or oxen. One of the first to be produced in the United States was the Forty-Niner. It was built in Philadelphia in 1849 by A. L. Archambault in 4-, 10-, and 30-horsepower sizes. The smallest of these weighed 2 tons, or a thousand pounds per horsepower.

The Baker and Hamilton Co. marketed a movable threshing engine in 1880. The boiler had a jacket of 2-inch staves, held in place by brass bands, and could burn wood, coal, or straw. It had an Ames engine and Laufenburg boiler and was built by the Ames Iron Works of Oswego, N.Y. Henry Ames was one of the early builders and advocates of steampower on the farm, and he founded a factory to make movable engines in 1854.

The next step in the evolution of farm power was the conversion of the portable steam engine into a self-propelled steam traction engine.

The first ones were developed primarily for plowing. Obed Hussey of Baltimore invented and put into operation a "steam plow" in 1855. J. S. Fawkes of Christiana, Pa., produced a more successful steam plowing outfit in 1858. Its frame was of iron, 8 feet wide and 12 feet long, and rested on the axle of a roller (driver) 6 feet in diameter and 6 feet wide.

President Abraham Lincoln, in an address before the Wisconsin State Agricultural Society at Milwaukee, in 1859, said:

"The successful application of steampower to farm work is a desideratum—especially a steam plow. It is not enough that a machine operated by steam will really plow. To be successful, it must, all things considered, plow better than can be done by animal power. It must do all the work as well,

and cheaper, or more rapidly, so as to get through more perfectly in season; or in some way afford an advantage over plowing with animals, else it is no success."

Philander Standish built the Standish steam rotary plow, the Mayflower, at Pacheco, Calif., in 1868. It was offered for sale in several sizes, ranging from 10 to 60 horsepower. Operating speed was 1.7 to 3.4 miles an hour, and the plowing rate was up to 5 acres an hour.

Also in 1868 Owen Redmond of Rochester, N.Y., patented a steam plow. A report of the Commissioner of Agriculture in 1870 announced that "a gang of six plows, designed to go with the engine, has since been constructed, intended to be operated by one man, who also might be the fireman."

While the main efforts in providing self-propulsion systems for steam tractors seemed to center largely around the use of wheel propulsion, many inventors were at work devising methods for providing better traction through the application of tracks and other devices. They worked out many unusual ideas.

Gideon Morgan of Calhoun, Tenn., received a patent for a wheel substitute in 1850. The language of his patent was for an improvement in track-type tractor design; the development of the crawler-type tractor in the United States therefore must have begun before 1850.

R. J. Nunn of Savannah, Ga., patented an "improvement in land conveyance" in 1867. It was essentially two or more bands running over a series of grooved rollers that were mounted in a frame and driven through a larger roller powered by a steam engine.

Thomas S. Minnis of Meadville, Pa., in 1867 patented a locomotive for plowing and in 1870 a steam tractor mounted on three tracks—two in the rear and one in front. Each rear track was driven by a steam engine, attached at the rear, through pinion and drive gear.

According to Hal Higgins, an authority on power farming, "Iowa's first 'dirt farming tractor' was this Minnis Crawler from Pennsylvania that came out to the raw prairie within sight of the new Iowa State Agricultural College as the first students started attending classes within sight of its smoke."

Robert C. Parvin of Illinois in 1873 built a steam tractor propelled by an endless chain of steel plates to which "feet," shod with 2-inch plank, were attached. It pulled six plows.

Charles H. Stratton, Moscow, Pa., in 1893 produced a steam-powered traction engine designed especially "to travel readily over plowed ground, for cross plowing, and other work." The front end was supported by wheels on a pivoted axle and the rear by a pair of compactly arranged tracks actuated through gears and pinions from the horizontal engine. Besides driving the tracks, the engine could be used to drive a shaft that could be used to drive threshers or other machines—a so-called power takeoff.

One of the first attempts to manufacture track-type tractors commercially was made by Alvin O. Lombard of Waterville, Me., in the early 1890's. He patented one of the first practical track-type tractors in 1901. Lombard adopted the ball tread idea of John B. Linn of Cleveland.

Lombard substituted rollers for the balls. He built a workable tractor and sold a number of machines. The unit was "designed specially for transporting lumber and logs over the rough roads and even cross country in the Maine woods." It embodied half-track construction. The front was supported by runners in winter and wheels in the summer. Two power-driven tracks were in the rear.

Another track tractor was the Centiped Log Hauler manufactured by the Phoenix Manufacturing Co., Eau Claire, Wis. It resembled the Lombard machine, but it used a vertical instead of horizontal engine.

Other early inventors tried to solve the problems of traction by making the driving wheels wider and wider.

Daniel Best sold his first steamer, a three-wheeler with vertical boiler, in 1889. One big-wheel outfit which was made by the Best Manufacturing Co. in 1900 for the Middle River Farming Co., Stockton, Calif., had two wood-covered drive wheels 15 feet wide and 9 feet in diameter. The outfit weighed 41 tons.

The Stockton Wheel Co. (later the Holt Manufacturing Co.) built its first steam traction engine (of a track type) in 1890. Topography, soil, and their large acreages led farmers on the Pacific Coast to accept this type of tractor more readily than farmers in other sections.

Benjamin Holt successfully demonstrated his first track-type tractor near Stockton in 1904 after considerable experimentation, in which he devised a pair of rough wooden tracks that he installed on a steam engine from which the wheels had been removed.

He made use of three clutches—the master clutch, for connecting the power source, and the track clutches. When the track clutch was released on one side, the power applied through the track clutch on the other side caused the tractor to pivot around the declutched track. Application of brakes on the declutched side increased the speed of turning. This method of transmission continues to be used by the Caterpillar Tractor Co. and has been adopted by most other manufacturers of tracklaying tractors.

Only eight of the track-type Holt steamers were built. He had already made experiments to replace steam-power by gasoline, and one model tractor of the track type, which burned gasoline, was produced in 1907.

Inventors between 1870 and 1880 devised a suitable gearing for the rear wheels of portable steam engines of the wheel type and also a chain or belt drive from the engine flywheel to a countershaft of this gearing to provide self-propulsion.

The bevel gear and inclined shaft developed by C. and G. Cooper of

Mt. Vernon, Ohio, was also a popular method of drive. It enabled the farmer to convert his portable steam engine into a traction engine in the field.

A United States patent was issued in 1880 for a steering device, although English tractors were fitted with steering gears as early as 1863. There followed the introduction of a clutch and gear train between the engine and rear wheels.

The steering gears on these early steamers were not at first considered reliable by some manufacturers, and operators were cautioned about their use on public highways.

The suggestion was made that it might be safer to guide the machine with a team of horses. Some said horses were not frightened when they met a traction engine preceded by a steering team. Others felt that the additional horsepower provided by the team was advantageous—some of the reasons why horse steering remained for a while.

Many farmers started buying self-propelled steam engines in the late 1870's. About 3 thousand steam tractors and almost that many steam threshers were built in 1890. Several plow manufacturers advertised multiple-bottom steam tractor plows or gangs in 1894. By 1900 more than 30 firms were manufacturing 5 thousand large steam traction engines a year.

These tractors were improvements over earlier models. The gearing, shafting, and other wearing parts were built to withstand the immense strains imposed upon them in pulling large threshers and plowing many furrows at one time. Big wheat farms and ranches in the Dakotas, Colorado, Montana, Nebraska, Kansas, California, and western Canada were using steam traction engines.

About this time the Geiser and Friede companies, both of Waynesboro, Pa., offered steam lifts for engine gangs. This development indicated, even this early, that thought was being given to cutting down labor requirements in plowing and to lighten-

ing the burden of manually lifting the plows by levers, which always were giving trouble.

Before the abandonment of the steamer and the acceptance of the gasoline tractor, many improvements had been made, and the performance of the huge self-propelled powerplants was the pride of the traction-engine engineers who pioneered in the ultimate placing of power in the hands of the 6 million farmers in this country.

As a matter of fact, the interest is still so great that organizations, such as the National Thresher Reunion in Ohio, Rough and Tumble Engineers Association in Pennsylvania, Midwest Old Settlers and Threshers Association in Iowa, and others, composed largely of oldtimer steam buffs, hold annual picnics for their many members.

For these reunions they doll up old traction engines and use them to drive threshers or pull plows. Some of the machines run idle; some are driven by the kids under supervision. The enthusiasts swap yarns of the harrowing experiences when one man's outfit broke through a wooden bridge, another got mired down while crossing a sand creek, and another broke a piston rod so that the piston crashed.

At least one periodical, the Iron-Men Album Magazine, Enola, Pa., is devoted almost entirely to these steam-engine men of a half century ago.

THE STEAM TRACTION engines, pioneers in mechanization, often weighed more than 45 thousand pounds and developed more than 120 horsepower. They operated with a steam pressure of 150 to 200 pounds per square inch.

Both the horizontal-tube boiler (the more popular) and the vertical-tube boiler were used in these early vehicles. The two types were different in form but had many operative points in common.

The horizontal-type boiler was constructed mainly with direct flue, with return flue, or with firebox return flue. The direct-flue boiler was known as the locomotive firebox, straight-flue boiler. The flues passed horizontally from the firebox at the rear to the smokebox in front.

The products of combustion in the return-flue boiler traveled first through the main flue to the combustion chamber in the front end of the boiler and then back through the many small flues to the smokebox in the rear.

Little space was provided under the grates of all three types to catch ashes and cinders. Grates were always in danger of burning out. This danger was overcome in the firebox return-flue boiler, in which water surrounded the heated surfaces, the grate area was larger, and the boiler had a larger heating surface.

Boilers of the vertical type had a cylindrical shell with a firebox at the lower end. Fire flues extended vertically from the flue sheet above the fire to the top of the boiler or horizontal water tubes placed in courses, so that each course was at right angles to the course next below and next above. These tubes and circulation plates maintained constant circulation.

Of the two main approaches in constructing the steam traction engine, one was to make the boiler the central structure and attach all other parts— engine, drive gears, steering gear, main truck—to it. The other was to provide a separate framework on which to mount the boiler and attach all the parts.

To spare the engine from damage from heavy shocks and jars on rough roads, heavy coil springs were placed between the boiler and front and rear axles. Springs in the steering gear helped prevent breakage when the front wheels hit an obstruction.

The early engine usually was mounted on the boiler, called top-mounted, and the boiler was mounted on the truck. Sometimes the engines in the locomotive type were mounted under the boiler.

One common method of mounting the boilers, known as side mounting, was to attach stub axles of the drivers to brackets placed at about the middle of the sides of the firebox. In another type, known as rear mounting, one continuous axle was located back of the firebox. A continuous axle was often mounted ahead of the firebox on return-flue boilers. It was known as under mounting.

The power of the steam traction engine was transmitted usually to the traction wheels by a simple train of spur gears made of cast iron. A driving pinion attached to the friction clutch engaged an intermediate gear, which in turn engaged a large compensating gear on the countershaft. Pinions on either end of the countershaft drove large master gears, which were fastened in the drive wheels by rigid or spring connections.

Traction engines first were geared with one forward speed to make 2 or 3 miles an hour on the road. Later some—especially on those used in hilly country—were geared with two forward speeds, one slow and one fast.

The front or steering wheels often were of steel, with the outer ends of the spokes riveted to a flange inside the rim, and the inner ends riveted to arms on the hub. A flange, or collar, around the middle of the outside of the front wheels tended to prevent lateral slippage. Steering was done by guiding the front wheels with a chain, winding shaft (roller), worm gear, and hand wheel. Sometimes power from the engine helped in steering.

The rear traction, or drive, wheels usually had steel tires, round or flat spokes, and a cast-iron hub. Cleats of steel or iron were mounted diagonally on the outside of the rims to increase traction. On rims that were cast, the cleats were part of the cast.

EARLY ATTEMPTS to develop gasoline tractors were sparked by the need to reduce the size of the threshing crews.

Such crews included two men to operate the steam engine, two to haul coal and water, two to operate the thresher, a waterboy, and several men to haul bundles to the thresher and the grain away by horses and wagons.

Not the least of the problems was to feed them. Days, maybe weeks, before the threshing crew was due at a farm, the farmer's wife started to plan and prepare the gargantuan meals she was going to serve them—hams, a side of beef, chickens, fried potatoes, gallons of milk, at least three kinds of pie, maybe homemade ice cream. Her reputation as a cook was at stake, she knew, and the feasts she fixed were something to be proud of and marvel at. Still in our language are terms that recall her and them—"a meal fit for a threshing crew" and "eat like a bunch of threshers."

Most of the first attempts to develop liquid-fuel tractors consisted of mounting a stationary gasoline engine on a chassis patterned after that of the steam traction engine. This combination became the self-propelled gas engine.

Experimenters even built a gasoline tractor that looked like a steam traction engine with the rather strange idea that thereby they would not scare the horses so much. Also with horses in mind (why, we do not know), some put a whistle on the rig.

BEFORE A TRACTOR could be fully realized, there had to be a promising internal-combustion engine. The early experimenters used gunpowder, turpentine, and natural and artificial gas for fuel.

The discovery of petroleum fuel in quantity speeded the development of the gasoline engine. In 1859, at Titusville, Pa., Edwin L. Drake drilled his first oil well and got the petroleum product that paved the way for the creation of a great industry. The internal-combustion engine made rapid strides when petroleum fuel was available.

About the first internal-combustion engine on record was the one credited to Abbe Hautefeuille, a French physicist, who in 1678 conceived the idea of burning a small amount of gunpowder in a chamber. While he continued experimenting, other French, Dutch,

English, and American engineers developed many and various ideas for producing power.

Finally Nicholas Otto, a German, devised a practical power unit of the internal-combustion type. It had one cylinder. Counting the movement of the piston in one direction as one stroke, his engine made four piston strokes per explosion in the same manner as the four-cycle ("Otto cycle") engines used today in all American-made automobiles. Those in the cars have more cylinders, but they are four cycle.

This development did not begin to assume importance until 1876, when it reached a reasonably satisfactory stage. The patents of the Otto cycle engine, however, were so basic in character that not until they expired in 1890 did other companies start to work on similar engines.

One hundred firms in the United States were making internal-combustion engines by 1899.

Another early and important development was the compression-ignition engine. It was the work of Rudolph Diesel, a German scientist, who patented his first engine in 1892. Before inventing the engine that bears his name, he had considerable experience with air compressors and with internal-combustion engines with spark ignition. He used coal dust, a useless byproduct in mining, which was blown into the cylinder with compressed air. He found out that it was not feasible to use coal dust as a fuel.

Before long Diesel came out with an oil-burning, compression-ignition engine that proved successful. His idea was adopted quickly as a source of power. In the diesel engine, the fuel is injected after compression is practically completed, and is ignited by the heat of compression of the air supplied for combustion.

PROBABLY THE FIRST gasoline tractor that was an operating success was the one built in 1892 by John Froelich. A good businessman, he ran a grain elevator, a well-drilling outfit, and a threshing outfit powered with a steam traction engine. He wanted to build a smaller tractor—one that would run on gasoline.

He mounted a single-cylinder, vertical-type gasoline engine, made by the Van Duzen Gas and Gasoline Engine Co. of Cincinnati, on a Robinson running gear equipped with a traction arrangement of his own manufacture. It completed a 50-day threshing run belted to a Case 40 x 58 thresher, pulled the thresher over rough ground, and operated in temperatures of $-3°$ to $100°$ F. The Froelich was the forerunner of the John Deere tractors.

Some of the other tractors of this period were the Patterson, 1892; the Hockett (Sterling), 1893; the Van Duzen, the Otto, and the Lambert, in 1894; the Huber, 1898; and the Morton in 1899. The Patterson became the foundation for the Case line of tractors, and Morton became the forerunner of the International Harvester line.

C. W. Hart and C. H. Parr built their first tractor model in 1902. Their second model a year later was considerably improved. Their 30–60 "Old Reliable" appeared in 1907; in 1909 came the Hart-Parr 15–30, a tricycle type. Even their early models were designed for pulling (drawbar work) rather than for belt work—they made their transmissions rugged to withstand the heavy strains of plowing.

Hart and Parr formed a company that was to become a part of the Oliver Corp. They established in 1905 the first business in the United States devoted exclusively to making tractors.

Other tractors were the Electric Wheel, 1904; the Dissinger, 1904; the Eason-Wysong Auto-Tractor, 1905; and the Ohio, 1905.

The Ohio Manufacturing Co. later bought the patent rights for the Morton and in 1905 built a few tractors for the International Harvester Co., which in 1907 built its first tractor. Like the Ohio tractor, it was friction drive for both forward and reverse.

Other models were the Waterous in 1906, the Transit and the Ford in 1907, and the Russell, Olds, Joy-McVicker, and the Geiser in 1909. The Ford tractor of 1907, an experimental machine made by the Ford Motor Co. of Detroit, used parts of a Ford car and a binder. The front wheels and axle and steering were from the car. The rear wheels were binder bullwheels.

The origin of the word "tractor" was originally credited to the Hart-Parr Co. in 1906 to replace the longer expression "gasoline traction engine," which W. H. Williams, the company's sales manager, who wrote the advertisements, considered too cumbersome. The word actually was coined previously and was used in 1890 in patent No. 425,600, issued on a tractor invented by George H. Edwards of Chicago.

Although tractors powered with internal-combustion engines had been manufactured for about 20 years, people generally had no chance to compare field operations of steam and gasoline tractors until the first Winnipeg trial in 1908, conducted under the auspices of the Winnipeg Industrial Exhibition in Canada. In that and in tests in 1909–1912, representatives of many countries witnessed the competition of gasoline tractors plowing in the same fields with steam tractors.

The first Winnipeg trials were mainly contests of hauling and plowing for comparison of such factors as the thousand foot-pounds hauled per pint of fuel and the pints of fuel used per acre. The trials became more comprehensive with the years, until in 1912 the score sheet included an economy brake test, maximum brake test, plowing test, and a rating on design and construction. The contests showed, even at that early stage, the possibilities of the gasoline tractor. The interest created by the trials encouraged experimenters and manufacturers to continue their pioneer efforts.

Most of the gasoline tractors before 1910 had automatic intake valves, hit-and-miss governors, and make-and-break ignition systems. Electric current for ignition usually was supplied by dry batteries for starting and low-voltage, direct-current magneto or generator (auto sparker) for furnishing current thereafter. In a few, a low-voltage oscillating magneto furnished the spark for starting and running.

The frames of the wheel tractors were built up of channel iron, to which the engine and other parts were bolted. Most large drive gears were of cast iron, exposed to the dust and dirt, and wore rapidly. The built-up drive-wheels, often 6 feet and sometimes 8 feet in diameter, turned on a one-piece "dead," or floating, axle. Selective-type transmission, where there were any gears to select (many had only one speed forward), was common, although friction drive and planetary-gear transmissions were not uncommon. Clutches varied.

Makers of steam tractors and makers of gasoline tractors competed strongly during 1910–1920, when the number of tractor manufacturing companies increased from 15 to more than 160 and existing companies began to present more than one model. The president of a gasoline tractor company said that when he first went into business the manufacturers of steam tractors refused to load their machines on the same freight cars with gasoline tractors.

The International Harvester Co. in 1910 produced its 45-horsepower Mogul, which had a two-cylinder horizontal opposed engine, with gear drive forward and friction reverse; in 1911, the 45-horsepower Titan, with a two-cylinder twin horizontal engine, with gear drive forward and reverse; in 1912, the 15–30 single-cylinder Mogul; in 1914, the 10–20 Titan with a twin horizontal-cylinder engine, and the 8–16 Mogul with a one-cylinder horizontal engine and planetary-gear drive forward and reverse; and in 1915, the 15–30 Titan, with four-cylinder horizontal engine. The 8–16 International, with a four-cylinder vertical engine, the first to bear the company's name, appeared in 1918. It was one of the early attempts to design a machine suitable for smaller farms.

The International Harvester Co. introduced a practical power takeoff for its tractors in 1918. It permitted direct transmission power from the engine to such equipment as mowers, small combines, and sprayers. That was an important development. Most tractor manufacturers soon had their tractors so equipped, and they started to fit many of their field machines for power takeoff drive.

Deere & Co. brought out the Waterloo Boy in 1916 and a twin horizontal-cylinder kerosene-burning engine and 180-degree crankshaft, and so inaugurated a basic engine design that is to be found in most of its current models. The machine performed well at the National Tractor Demonstration in 1918 at Wichita, Kans.

The Bear, produced by the Wallis Tractor Co. in 1912, proved to be the advance guard of the Massey-Harris line. It had one front steering wheel, a directional vane, and two rear driving wheels.

The Wallis Cub appeared in 1913. It also was a three-wheeler, but it had a more compact design and introduced a revolutionary development— a frameless-type construction. The one-piece, U-shaped crankcase and transmission housing of boiler-plate steel was the backbone of the machine. The industry liked it, and soon designs by various manufacturers were introduced.

THE FORD MOTOR CO., after considerable experimentation, in 1917 started production of the Fordson. It also was of unit-frame construction but of cast iron instead of boiler-plate steel. The tractor was light for its power and relatively low in price. This unit-frame type was practicable. Most manufacturers soon adopted the idea.

This Fordson development came at an opportune time—the year the United States became involved in the First World War. Boatloads of horses were being shipped abroad. Labor was becoming scarce. Materials were restricted. Power became more vital than ever. The manufacture of more than 34 thousand Fordsons in 1918 and 100 thousand by 1925 (25 and 75 percent, respectively, of the tractors produced by all companies) helped greatly to meet difficulties caused by the war. After 1925, with returning normalcy and the increasing interest in the general-purpose tractor, production of the Fordson dropped, and its manufacture was discontinued in this country in 1928.

The J. I. Case Co., which had built its first machine in 1892, resumed building tractors in 1911, when the Case 30–60 appeared. It produced in 1912 the Case 20–40, which performed exceedingly well at the Winnipeg Trials that year. Case built its first tractor with a four-cylinder vertical engine in 1915. It had three wheels—a single front steering wheel, the right rear a driver, and the left rear an idler. Case produced the 9–18 model in 1918 and in 1919 the 15–27, both of one-piece frame, or unit, construction.

The Allis-Chalmers Co. built its first tractor in 1914. It had three wheels and 10–18 horsepower. In 1916 Allis-Chalmers introduced a cultivating tractor of 6–12 horsepower, which also could pull a plow. The company soon became an active contender in the business.

A significant development in 1913 was the introduction of the Bull tractor by the Bull Tractor Co. of Minneapolis. It was powered by a small engine of 12 horsepower. It started a trend toward smaller units, which practically all manufacturers followed. Several hundred machines were sold in its first year; within a year Bull ranked first among all tractor manufacturers in the number produced. Its relative position declined from year to year, though, and in 1918 it ceased production. This tractor had one drive wheel, making a differential unnecessary, and an idler wheel mounted on a crank axle on the left side for leveling.

The Minneapolis Steel & Machinery

Co. and the Minneapolis Threshing Machine Co. started producing tractors in 1911. In 1914 the Moline Plow Co. started production of the Moline-Universal, which was one of the earliest practical approaches to a general-purpose tractor. A later edition of the Moline-Universal, the Model D in 1917, probably was the first tractor to make use of a storage battery for ignition, starting, and lighting. The three companies merged in 1929 into the Minneapolis-Moline Power Implement Co., which later became the Minneapolis-Moline Co.

THE LARGE TRACTOR, seemingly the predominant type in 1910–1920, could not accomplish the many tasks necessary to mechanize the farm—it could only plow, drive threshers, and pull large headers. Much thought had been given to the problem. Manufacturers began experimenting with light tractors suitable only for cultivating, and some eight or ten companies produced them.

Light tractors did not fill the need, however, for two tractors thus were necessary on the farm, and that was beyond the farmer's needs and pocketbook.

A machine was needed that would plow and thresh and with proper attachments would also cultivate, sow, and perform other field operations—an all-purpose tractor.

Experimentation continued meanwhile on track-type tractors. Various models appeared: The Bullock Creeping Grip (1910) by the Bullock Tractor Co. of Chicago; the Yuba (1912) by the Yuba Manufacturing Co., Marysville, Calif., with the tracks mounted on "balls that rolled in a race"; an improved model (1912) by Holt; the Killen-Strait (1914) by the Killen-Strait Manufacturing Co., Appleton, Wis., with two track drivers in the rear and one front steering track; the Bates Steel Mule C (1916) by the Bates Machinery and Tractor Co., Joliet, Ill., with a single track in the rear for driving and two widely spaced front steering wheels; the Trundaar (1916) by the Buckeye Manufacturing Co., Anderson, Ind.; the Leader (1917) by the Dayton-Dowd Co.; the Bear (1918) by the Bear Tractor Co., N.Y.; the Cleveland H (1918), later to be made by the Oliver Corp.; the Monarch (1918) by the Monarch Tractor Co., Watertown, Wis., later to merge with the Allis-Chalmers Manufacturing Co.; and the Best (1913) by the C. L. Best Gas Traction Co., San Leandro, Calif., which in 1925 combined with the Holt Manufacturing Co. to form the Caterpillar Tractor Co.

It is of interest that during the First World War the Holt Caterpillar tractor was important as an artillery and supply tractor and also was the inspiration of Gen. E. D. Swinton, a Briton, who invented the tank, which worked havoc among enemy troops and installations. This tank consisted of two large motor-driven tracks, one on each side, between which was mounted an armor-plated housing, which protected the crew, turret, and guns.

TRACTORS in 1920, considered collectively, embodied fundamental principles of engineering and design that exist, perhaps in more refined form, in today's tractors.

The one-piece cast-iron frame, replaceable wearing parts, force-feed and pressure-gun lubrication, enclosed transmission, carburetor manifolding, air cleaner, electric lighting and starting, high-tension magneto ignition with impulse starter, enclosed cooling system, antifriction bearings, alloy and heat-treated steels, and the power takeoff had all been introduced. Some experiments had been made with rubber tires. The light-weight, low-price tractor had been designed and widely accepted. Several fairly successful motor cultivator-type units were on the market.

The advantages of the tractor as a farm power unit had been well established. More than 160 companies produced 200 thousand units. (Fifteen companies made 4 thousand tractors

in 1910. The number of manufacturers reached a peak of 186 in 1921.)

Many makes and types of tractors were on the market. Many turned out to be impracticable, and often the farmers were the scapegoats—many fence corners harbored so-called tractors, abandoned as useless, often even before they were fully paid for.

The farm equipment industry and others began to work for a standardized rating of tractors. Nebraska in 1919 passed a bill that in effect required that all makes and models of tractors to be sold in Nebraska pass certain tests.

The Nebraska Tractor Law specifies: ". . . Each and every tractor presented for testing, shall be a stock model and shall not be equipped with any special appliance or apparatus not regularly supplied to the trade. . . .

"Such tests shall consist of endurance, official rating of horsepower for continuous load, and consumption of fuel per hour or per acre of farm operations. The results of such tests shall be open at all times to public inspection. . . ."

The tests began in 1920. With modifications, they have continued since, except during the war. The test codes used in Nebraska were developed by engineers in the University of Nebraska, the Society of Automotive Engineers, and the American Society of Agricultural Engineers.

The tests, which have been used all over this country and in many other countries, have provided standards for rating tractors, have speeded up improvements on many of them, and have eliminated many that were inferior in design and performance.

A DROP IN production of tractors occurred during the postwar depression. Manufacturers, instead of just marking time, took this chance to incorporate new features. In the keen competition that followed, the tractor was improved steadily, although a number of companies had to discontinue business.

The depression brought a big drop in prices: Fordson tractors sold for 395 dollars in 1932—a 35-percent drop from the price in 1921. The Moline tractor, which sold for 1,325 dollars in 1920, was reduced to 650 dollars. One result was that many farmers who otherwise would not have been able to take advantage of power farming got good equipment.

Attention had to be given to air cleaners used on the engines. Dust that enters the engine from the intake can damage the working parts—particularly the pistons, rings, and cylinders.

Many makes and types of air cleaners appeared. They differed in ability to remove dust, the degree to which their use imposed vacuum or choking on the carburetor intake, and their effect on the maximum power to be obtained from the engine.

To determine the dust separation efficiency, vacuum imposition, and effect on power, tests were made at the University of California at Davis. The dust-separating efficiency of the 26 cleaners tested in 1922 varied between 42.7 percent and 99.8 percent. Fifteen cleaners had more than 95 percent efficiency.

THE INTERNATIONAL HARVESTER CO. in 1924 produced the Farmall, probably the first successful attempt to build a real all-purpose tractor. It could plow (two-plow size), cultivate four rows, and, as attachments were developed, do other jobs. It probably did more than any other to broaden the usefulness of the tractor and thus to further mechanization on the farm.

The Farmall had high rear-axle clearance; small, closely spaced front wheels to run between rows for cultivation; and a hitch for attaching a cultivator or other equipment. Industry accepted it readily. Soon similar machines appeared, designated as General-Purpose, Universal, All-Around, Row-Crop, Ro-Trac, Do-All, and so on.

Deere & Co. in 1923 offered the rugged Model D tractor, which became one of the company's standbys.

It produced in 1928 its first general-purpose tractor, the 10–20, with arched front axle and high-clearance rear axle and three-row planting and cultivating equipment. Deere in 1929 put on the market its GP tricycle tractor, equipped with a mechanical power lift for lifting integrally mounted implements. It was the first tractor so equipped.

Several companies developed refinements: The Oliver tricycle row-crop tractor, with tiptoe wheels; the Massey-Harris FWD (four-wheel drive); the Allis-Chalmers all-crop, and the Case.

Mechanical power farming slowed down in 1931, but even in that depression year several more companies offered row-crop machines, among them Huber, Caterpillar (a high-clearance, track-type machine), and Sears, Roebuck and Co.

Another advance in 1931 was Caterpillar's Diesel 65, the first diesel-powered tractor in the United States to be put on the market. It was an important step, and several companies, after experiments, put out diesel-powered tractors in 1934. Most of the tractor companies now have diesel-powered tractors in their lines.

THE WHEEL TRACTOR was rough to ride. A farmer, after a day on one, was well shaken up; he had had it.

Relief came in pneumatic tires, which made riding easier and reduced vibration. They also meant less wear on tractor parts, permitted higher speeds in the fields and on roads, and reduced rolling resistance—all in all, more efficient operation.

Citrus growers in Florida, having noted that the tractors damaged the roots of the trees, in 1928 or so started putting discarded casings (without inner tubes) on steel wheels. That seemed to help.

Tiremakers watched this development, and in 1931 the B. F. Goodrich Co. developed a zero-pressure tire. It consisted of a rubber arch built on a perforated steel base for attachment

## CHANGING SOURCES OF FARM POWER
### TRACTORS, HORSES, AND MULES

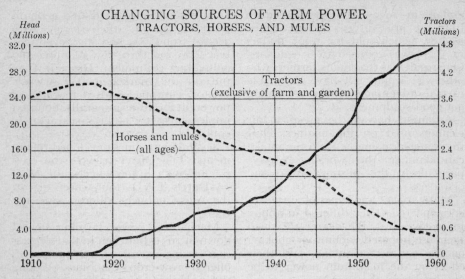

to standard steel tire drive wheels. The tire was not under air pressure and so was not subject to puncture.

A few companies experimented with pneumatic rubber tires. The Firestone Tire and Rubber Co. fitted an Allis-Chalmers tractor with pneumatic tires. Their advantages were evident, and rubber tires soon were accepted. Fourteen percent of the wheel tractors were mounted on rubber by 1935; by 1940, 85 percent; and by 1950, nearly 100 percent.

The advantage of using water in tires to add weight for better traction became clear. The water could replace the iron weights on the wheels, which often caused trouble, especially under high road speeds. An antifreezing solution had to be provided when tractors were used during freezing weather. Commercial calcium chloride added to the water made an economical and satisfactory solution.

Case tractors were equipped in 1935 with a motor lift for lifting or lowering implements. Pressure on a trip button would cause the implement to be lowered. Tripping the button again raised the implement. The lift was driven by engine power through an enclosed worm and gear operated by a starter button near the driver's heel.

Among the tools developed for use with the motor lift were two- and four-row corn and cotton cultivators, two-row potato cultivators, ten-row truck crop seeders and cultivators, six-row beet planters and cultivators, four-row corn and cotton planters, three-row middlebusters, two-row listers, and 7-foot mower attachments.

ALLIS-CHALMERS in 1938 made a one-plow, general-purpose tractor, Model B, that weighed less than 2 thousand pounds. It sold for 495 dollars at the factory—the first small farm tractor, mounted on rubber, to sell for less than 500 dollars.

Another development that improved the usefulness of tractors was the three-point hydraulic hitch developed by Harry Ferguson in Ireland and brought to this country in 1939 after many tests. It was a revolution in implement control. It strongly influenced the whole trend of design of tractors and equipment.

After a demonstration before Henry Ford, a working agreement was established between Mr. Ford and Mr. Ferguson for mass production of a tractor incorporating the Ferguson system.

Hydraulic systems have become

standard or optional equipment on practically all models of tractors. The hydraulic system includes an oil receptacle, pump, valves, and a control lever within reach of the driver, connected by means of high-pressure hose to a power cylinder (a piston within a cylinder), which can be located on any part of the tractor or trailed implement where a control is desired. The hydraulic systems can control mounted and drawn implements, govern the depth of tillage implements, operate loaders, and activate power steering. Sometimes they can be used to increase the traction of the rear wheels by transferring a part of the weight of the implement to the rear wheels of the tractor.

THE MINNEAPOLIS-MOLINE CO. in 1941 introduced the first standard tractor fitted at the factory for burning another type of fuel for tractors—LP (liquefied petroleum) gas. Some companies previously had offered kits for converting the tractors in the field from gasoline or kerosene to LP gas.

This LP gas, a light end of the crude oil, had been largely a waste product until means had been developed to liquefy it by compression. When the cost of the two fuels is similar per unit of work, LP gas has advantages in that it burns cleaner and causes less oil dilution. Gasoline is usually more readily available, and the engine is easier to start with it on cold days.

All major manufacturers of wheel tractors produced one or more LP gas-burning models in 1960.

Experimental work on tractors was again curtailed during the Second World War. Few new models appeared. Many tractor plants were converted to make war materials. Tractor production increased rapidly after the war; 793,497 tractors were made for farm use in 1951.

A marked improvement in the extremely important power takeoff, which we mentioned, was offered by the Cockshutt Plow Co., Brantford, Ontario, in 1947.

It was a continuous-running power takeoff (direct engine-driven power takeoff), which continued to operate even when the clutch was released. Heretofore, machinery operated by the regular power takeoff, such as sprayers, drawn cornpickers, and combines, would stop when the clutch was released. The continuous-running power takeoff allows one to stop the travel of the tractor without stopping the power takeoff. The same can be done with the independent power takeoff, which was developed later.

All major manufacturers of farm tractors now furnish one or more models of their tractors with either continuous-running or independent power takeoff.

Another use of hydraulic control came in 1947, when Allis-Chalmers offered its Model WD tractor, fitted with a device for power adjusting the rear wheel tread. It permitted the operator to use the engine power for changing the spacing of the rear wheels while sitting on the tractor seat. He was spared the strenuous and time-costly job of making tread alterations by the hand-and-jack method.

All but one of the major American manufacturers of tractors offered models with power-adjusted rear wheel tread as standard or optional equipment in 1959.

THE INTERNATIONAL HARVESTER CO. in 1954 announced a new source of farm electrical power, the Electrall, that can be mounted on its tractors. It is an electric generator driven by the tractor engine. Besides supplying electric power for tractor-drawn machinery, such as hay balers, and for farming operations where the utility companies' wires did not reach, it can also serve as a standby unit in case of failure of electric service.

It is provided with outlets that supply three types of current: 220-volt, three-phase 60-cycle alternating current, mainly for driving electric motors; 120-volt, single-phase current to attach to house wiring circuits; and

## TRACTORS MANUFACTURED IN THE UNITED STATES, 1909-1958
(Exclusive of steam and garden) for agricultural, industrial, and military use

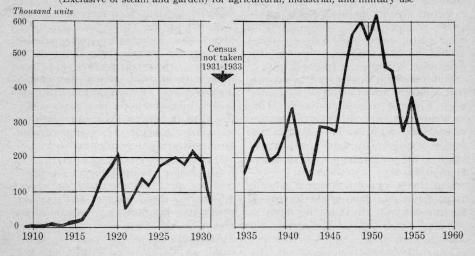

*Thousand units*

220-volt single-phase current for such heavy requirements as the electric range.

Later a trailing model of the Electrall was announced, mounted on a two-wheeled trailer and driven from the power takeoff of the tractor.

AMONG THE MAJOR improvements in the transmission systems since 1954 are those that permit "on-the-go" shifts, a greater range of travel speeds, and automatic adjustment of speed to draft requirements.

International Harvester put a new torque amplifier on the Farmall Super M-TA. A lever near the driver allows the operator instantly to reduce the travel speed 33 percent when the going gets difficult and at the same time increase the drawbar pull in any selected gear without stopping, or declutching, or shifting and without touching the governor control or throttle setting.

Another example of a new power transmission is the one announced in 1958 by the J. I. Case Co. A direct-drive clutch, a torque converter, and a master clutch give the tractor operator the option of the hydraulic torque converter or mechanical direct drive.

Still another example of new transmission is the "Select-O-Speed" an-

nounced by Ford in 1959. The transmission is a 10-speed, fully selective power shift unit. It is controlled by one small hand lever. There is no clutch pedal, and yet shifting can be made with the tractor in motion with almost no interruption.

WE FEEL we should mention self-propelled machines although they are not tractors—they take the place of tractors where they are used. Their propelling power unit is an integral part of the implement.

The self-propelled combine—harvester-thresher—appeared in commercial production in 1944. About one-fifth of the million combines on farms in the United States were of this type in 1958.

The Massey-Harris Co. received special authority in 1944 from Government war agencies to make and distribute 500 self-propelled combines to experienced operators. This Harvest Brigade began operations early in May in Texas and California and worked north. By the end of the season they had harvested more than a million acres, or an average of more than 2 thousand acres for each combine.

Self-propelled units are easier to operate and have faster working speeds than trailed machines. They lose less time in opening fields and moving between jobs. Because they cost more, single-purpose self-propelled machines must have a relatively larger annual use to be comparable to the trailed units in cost.

Self-propelled machines, sprayers, cornpickers, hay balers, windrowers, and forage harvesters also were made in 1960.

Another machine is the self-propelled chassis, on which various harvesting units can be mounted interchangeably.

The Minneapolis-Moline Co. in 1945 presented details for the Uni-Farmor system, which provided a chassis or Uni-Tractor equipped with a power unit upon which several types of machines could be mounted. The company had four separate and interchangeable harvesting machines ready in 1954 for use with the Uni-Tractor: A combine, cornpicker, cornpicker-sheller, and forage harvester. Several other manufacturers started to make units that could be used with the Uni-Tractor, including forage harvesters, a sugar beet harvester, and an applicator of anhydrous ammonia.

ATTACHMENTS of several types have been developed to make the operation of the tractor more automatic.

One kind of tractor guide uses the last plow furrow of the previous round as a guide to steer the tractor. The guides are most successful in large, level fields.

A Department of Agriculture engineer in the Texas High Plains reported: "Some farmers in the Amarillo and Lubbock area use guides for flat breaking and planting. For flat breaking, the operator makes the first few rounds driving the tractor. Then he plows 24 hours a day, and comes back to the field only to refuel. This is accomplished with disks mounted ahead of the front wheels and running in the furrow. If the guide or tractor gets out of the furrow, the ignition is automatically cut off. For planting, the

disks are mounted in front of the front wheels of the row-crop tractor and stay in the lister furrow. The operator watches his cotton boxes while going down the row and gets back on the tractor seat to turn it around at the end of the row."

Tractor guides of the furrow type have been commercially available from manufacturers of tractor accessories for many years. Five were listed in a 1959 directory of farm machinery manufacturers.

The International Harvester Co. in 1931 equipped one of their Farmall 30 tractors so that it could be controlled by radio. The tractor was demonstrated to thousands of people at the Century of Progress exposition in Chicago in 1933.

A member of the staff of the Department of Agricultural Engineering in the University of Nebraska in 1958 equipped a farm tractor with radio controls, by means of which the tractor could be started, stopped, and steered and its gears shifted. The operator was some distance away.

Another development for guiding tractors is an automatic pilot. It is actuated by lightweight feelers that can sense the position of the crop row to be cultivated, the windrow to be baled, or the distance to any other row to be followed. This pilot was not intended to replace the operator but to be an aid to make his work better and easier.

Two research engineers who had worked independently announced in 1958 that they had developed an automatic tractor pilot—L. A. Liljedahl, of the Department of Agriculture, and C. B. Richey, of the Ford Motor Co.

The Ford Motor Co. demonstrated a self-steering tractor at its testing center at Birmingham, Mich., in 1958. The sensing antenna for the steering controls is between the front wheels of the tractor and picks up its signals from a small wire buried under the test track. A second antenna receives start and stop signals over the same wire to control the clutch and brake.

Engineers of the University of Reading, England, in 1959 demonstrated a tractor controlled by a wire laid along the ground or just under the surface. Controls were available for steering, starting and stopping, operating the clutch, power takeoff, horn, and other mechanisms.

These and similar controls, which depend on a wire for guidance, may be useful on a test track or for performing certain operations that are repeated frequently in the barnyard or other fixed course. We question their value for work in the fields.

THE EFFICIENCY of tractors has been improved greatly over the years. One measure of that is the amount of fuel used.

Tests at the University of Nebraska showed that in 1920 the average wheel-type tractor tested delivered 5 drawbar horsepower-hours per gallon of gasoline or distillate. The average wheel tractor tested in 1959 delivered 10 horsepower-hours to the gallon. The average wheel-type tractor with diesel engine delivered 10 drawbar horsepower-hours per gallon of fuel in 1935 and 13.3 horsepower-hours per gallon in 1959.

A reason for the greater efficiency has been the use of higher compression ratios in many of the gasoline-burning engines and the increased use of diesel engines. (The compression ratio is the relation of the volume within the cylinder when the piston is at its bottom dead center to the volume when at the top.)

The compression ratios of spark-ignition engines in 1941 varied from about 4 to 6; in 1959 the compression ratios of spark-ignition engines varied from about 4 to 8.5. Compression ratios of current diesel tractor engines vary from about 15.5 to about 22. (American automobile engines in 1960 had compression ratios from about 8 to 10.5.)

MANY OTHER IMPROVEMENTS have been made in tractors.

Valves have been improved by the use of better alloys, and their life has been lengthened by the use of rotators and valve seat inserts.

Valve guides and spark plugs have been improved.

Bearings are precision manufactured to carry greater loads with less susceptibility to fatigue and greater resistance to corrosion.

Better oils and methods of lubrication have been provided, as have improved ignition and cooling systems.

Such improvements give the farmer more power from his tractor with little or no increase in cost or weight.

The electric starter, rubber tires, motor lift, hydraulic controls, and easily attached hitches are among the pieces of equipment that have made operation easier.

Many improvements contribute to the operator's comfort. Deere & Co. came out in 1946 with a Powr-Trol unit to be attached to trailing implements so that they could be lifted and lowered by hydraulic power from the tractor. Hydraulic remote controls were common enough by 1949 so that standards on them were adopted by the American Society of Agricultural Engineers and the Society of Automotive Engineers.

Power steering in automobiles inspired power steering in tractors. Allis-Chalmers put power steering attachments on the WD-45 (wheel type) tractor in 1956. All major American manufacturers offered at least one model with power steering as standard or optional equipment in 1960.

Seats on tractors used to be simple things of steel which soon became quite uncomfortable to the driver. Now they are of foam rubber or are equipped with springs, some of which are adjustable to the operator's weight. Some tractors are equipped with umbrellas, windshields, air-conditioned cabs, and radios. They are a matter not only of comfort, although that is important when days are from sunup to sundown, the thermometer stays at 100°, and clouds of dust fill eyes, nose, and mouth.

They increase efficiency and safety and are a matter of common sense, for a valuable crop, expensive machinery, and a man's life may be involved.

SAFETY is more important than comfort. In a great number of farm accidents, tractors have been a factor. The National Safety Council, professional engineering societies, manufacturers, and individuals have worked constantly for greater safety.

An important step was the adoption of standards for the location of the tractor hitch to help prevent the rearing of the tractor when under load. Design standards have been adopted also for the power takeoff and for safety lighting for combinations of farm tractors and implements. The improvements in hitches and the wide adoption of hydraulic power also have done much toward making the tractor safer to operate.

Nevertheless, every farmer should pay more attention to safety. The tractor replaces the horse, but the use of some horsesense would help prevent accidents. Only a fool works in front of the cutterbar of a mower, binder, or combine when the tractor engine is running, drives too close to a ditch, or hitches a load to the rear axle and jumps into it with the full power of the tractor. The load should be hitched to the drawbar, and the clutch should be eased in.

The manufacturers put protective guards on machines for a purpose— they should be kept there.

Professional engineering societies and industry groups have contributed greatly to the development of the tractor. Among them are the American Society of Agricultural Engineers; the Society of Automotive Engineers; the Farm Equipment Institute, which has a membership of more than 100 manufacturers of tractors, bearings, pistons, steel, aluminum, and tires; and the Tire and Rim Association, Inc., whose members are makers of tires, rims, wheels, and related parts.

Manufacturers of tractors have found it highly desirable to adopt certain standards to provide for the interchangeability of various brands of implements between tractors.

One example: It would not be hard to imagine the confusion that would be created if the tractor power takeoffs were not uniform in speed, location, and drive shaft. The adoption of these standards in manufacture is voluntary on the manufacturers' part, but they cooperate with the professional societies and other organizations that strive to achieve uniformity of many of the components of their units. Hydraulic control, power takeoff, lighting, and wheels are examples of components covered by standards and recommendations sponsored by joint action of the American Society of Agricultural Engineers and the Society of Automotive Engineers.

To develop some of the recommendations for standardization is not always a simple task. One, for example, recommended preferred drive wheel tire and rim sizes for general-purpose farm tractors. The recommendation was developed chiefly by four groups, the American Society of Agricultural Engineers, the Society of Automotive Engineers, the Farm Equipment Institute, and the Tire and Rim Association. Besides adopting certain standards that pertain to their own industry, tractor manufacturers also adopt some of the standards developed for automobile and other manufacturers so that there is general uniformity in certain components, such as pistons, antifriction bearings, oil filters, spark plugs, bolts, and screws.

THE USUAL channel of distribution of farm tractors and repair parts involves manufacturer, branch, dealer, and farmer.

The manufacturer owns the branch. It is in an important regional center and carries a large stock of the equipment and repair parts that may be needed in the territory.

The local dealer, selected or approved by the manufacturer, usually sells and services the full line of farm machinery of the manufacturer for which there is a demand in his community. He is an important link in the distribution of tractors and other farm machines. He must be a good merchant and he must also know the functions of each implement he sells and the size and type of equipment required. He has to be able to furnish good service to keep them running. His repair shop is much more than the old type of blacksmith shop. It is equipped to service and repair gasoline and diesel engines, combines, and others of the more complicated, precision-built implements that have become commonplace in farm operation.

Prompt service is so important in connection with tractors and other important farm machinery that many successful dealers have service shops at their retail stores and provide specially equipped trucks whose drivers can make repairs and adjustments in the field In emergency, repair parts are delivered by air from the factory or branch.

All of the large manufacturers of tractors have grown to their present stature by developing new and improved types of tractors and other farm equipment and by acquiring other companies engaged in the manufacture of items which they wished to add to their lines. Expansion enabled them to increase their volume and provide complete lines to offer to distributors and dealers.

ONE 1960 DIRECTORY of American manufacturers of farm machinery listed 13 manufacturers of crawler tractors and 35 builders of wheel-type tractors. Nine full-line companies made a large percentage of the machines. We give a few details about each of them.

The International Harvester Co., Chicago, the largest manufacturer of agricultural machinery in the United States in 1960, was incorporated originally in 1902 and began producing tractors in 1906. Several large firms were merged to form it. The company maintains a dozen or more factories in this country and several in Canada and other countries. Tractors are manufactured at plants in Chicago, Louisville, and Rock Island.

Deere & Co., Moline, Ill., the largest manufacturer of steel plows and our second largest manufacturer of agricultural machinery, bought the Waterloo Gasoline Engine Co. in 1918 and began to build tractors. The name of the gasoline engine company was changed to John Deere Tractor Co. in 1926 and later to Deere & Co. Back of this tractor company was an organization originally established by John Deere in 1837.

The J. I. Case Co., Racine, Wis., the third largest, was incorporated in 1880 as the J. I. Case Threshing Machine Co. The business was originally established by Jerome I. Case in 1842. The J. I. Case Threshing Machine Co. was actively engaged in the building of steam tractors in the 1890's and was among the first to turn to the gasoline tractor. The plant at Racine was enlarged in 1912 to permit the production of tractors. Engines were bought from the Davis Motor Co., Milwaukee. In 1913 they started building their own engines. In 1919 it merged with the Grand Detour Plow Co. It purchased the implement plant of the Emerson-Brantingham Corp. at Rockford, Ill., in 1928, when the J. I. Case Plow Co. of Racine was taken over by the Massey-Harris Co. of Toronto. The J. I. Case Plow Co. sold the rights to use of the name "Case" and "J. I. Case" to the J. I. Case Threshing Machine Co. of Racine. Thus an end came to years of confusion caused to these two concerns that had the same name but were not connected with each other.

The Massey-Harris Co., an amalgamation in 1891 of the Massey and Harris companies, Canadian manufacturers of agricultural machinery and tractors, extended its holdings in this country through the purchase of the

J. I. Case Plow Co. at Racine in 1928. The J. I. Case Plow Co., incorporated in 1919, was a consolidation of the J. I. Case Plow Works Co. and the Wallis Tractor Co., both of Racine. The plow company, established in 1876, engaged primarily in the manufacture of plows and tillage equipment. The Wallis Tractor Co. was organized in 1912 to manufacture farm tractors. Harry Ferguson, Inc., merged with the Massey-Harris Co. in 1953, and the resulting company became Massey-Harris-Ferguson, Inc. "Harris" was dropped from the name in 1958, and the firm became Massey-Ferguson, Inc., with United States headquarters in Racine.

The Oliver Farm Equipment Co., incorporated in 1929, acquired the business and property of six manufacturers to become a full-line agricultural implement company. Chief among these were the Oliver Chilled Plow Works of South Bend, Ind., the Nichols and Shepard Co. of Battle Creek, Mich., the Hart-Parr Co. of Charles City, Iowa, and the American Seeding Machine Co. of Springfield, Ohio. When this consolidation was effected, efforts were concentrated on the well-known Hart-Parr tractor, and the Nichols and Shepard factory was converted into one building harvesting and threshing machines. The tractors were produced under the name of Oliver Hart-Parr. The Cleveland Tractor Co., which had been making a tracklaying tractor under the name of "Cletrac," in 1944 combined with the Oliver Farm Equipment Co. to form the Oliver Corp., and all of the equipment and tractors are produced under the name of Oliver.

Formation of the Minneapolis-Moline Power Implement Co., incorporated in 1929, was the result of a merger of the Minneapolis Steel and Machinery Co., the Minneapolis Threshing Co., the Moline Implement Co. The Minneapolis Steel and Machinery Co., organized in 1902, had been building Twin City tractors since 1908, and at the time of merger was engaged in the manufacture of threshing machines and tractors. The principal products of the other two companies included tillage implements, which, combined with the tractor and threshing machine companies, gave another full-line agricultural implement company.

The Allis-Chalmers Manufacturing Co. was incorporated in 1913. Its expansion through the acquisition of eight manufacturing concerns widened its scope to embrace a diversified line of power machinery. It began to manufacture farm tractors shortly after the beginning of the First World War. In 1928 it took over the Monarch Tractor Co. (incorporated in 1918) and has since manufactured tracklaying tractors under the name Allis-Chalmers. The Advance-Rumely Co., makers of threshing machines and farm tractors, was acquired in 1931.

The Caterpillar Tractor Co., Peoria, Ill., was formed by a merger of the C. L. Best Tractor Co. of San Leandro, Calif., and the Holt Manufacturing Co., which had plants at Stockton and Peoria. The latter firm was the originator and holder of the Caterpillar trademark. The Best Co. was organized in 1910 and the Holt Co. in 1892, a successor to earlier Holt firms dating from 1869. Benjamin Holt built the first practical crawler tractor in 1904 at Stockton. The Holt Manufacturing Co. purchased the interests of Daniel Best in 1908, and the latter retired from business. C. L. Best, a son of Daniel Best, formed his company in 1910 and in 1913 started producing tracklayers in his father's old plant at San Leandro. Stiff competition ensued between the two interests until the merger. In 1928 the Caterpillar Tractor Co. acquired the Russell Grader Manufacturing Co. of Minneapolis, a manufacturer of roadbuilding machines for more than 20 years. The products of the Caterpillar Tractor Co. then included tracklaying tractors, combined harvesters, stationary engines, and a varied line of roadbuilding equipment.

The Ford Motor Co., Tractor

and Implement Division, Birmingham, Mich., was one of the major producers of wheel-type farm tractors in 1960. The Ford Motor Co. produced its first tractor for the trade in 1917 under the name Fordson. The name Ford could not then be used because it had already been given to a tractor manufactured by a group that included a young man by the name of Ford. The production of Fordson tractors increased rapidly to a yearly peak in 1925. Thereafter production declined, and the production of Fordsons in the United States ceased in 1928.

The Ford Motor Co. again started the mass production of tractors in 1939. Henry Ford made a working agreement with Harry Ferguson of Ireland, whereby Ford tractors were made which used the Ferguson system of a combined linkage and hydraulic control. The oral agreement between Mr. Ford and Mr. Ferguson was terminated late in 1946. Thereafter Ford continued to manufacture tractors, making use of the three-point suspension and hydraulic system. Harry Ferguson, Inc., also continued to manufacture tractors with a three-point suspension and hydraulic system, making use of engines from another manufacturer.

NEVER BEFORE has such a wide selection of sizes and types of tractors been available to the American farmer as in 1960.

Among the wheel tractors are sizes that pull a 12-inch plow and sizes that can pull eight 16-inch plows. Speeds of only 1 mile an hour are available for special jobs.

Most of the wheel tractors made in this country use gasoline or distillate as fuel, but each major manufacturer makes at least one model with a diesel engine and at least one model that burns liquid petroleum. Nearly all of the track-type tractors use diesel engines, but one manufacturer, the Oliver Corp., makes three models in the smaller sizes that burn gasoline.

Every major line includes all-purpose

tractors—those to which cultivators, planters, and other field equipment can be attached readily. These models are designated in various ways by the manufacturers with such names as General Purpose, Farmall, and Universal. All-purpose tractors usually have three wheels, the front wheels of the others are adjustable as to tread. Other models are available that have higher crop clearance than usual and are sometimes listed under such designations as Hi-Crop.

SMALL FOUR-WHEEL tractors of the riding type usually are of less than one 12-inch plow capacity. Many have appeared on the market since the war, and are popular with part-time farmers and others who have occasional need for a small tractor. Most of them have a single-cylinder, air-cooled engine.

Power is usually transmitted from the engine to the drive wheels by combinations of belt, chain, and gears, although some have gear and worm transmission. Many attachments are available—plows, rotary tillers, harrows, seeders, cultivators, sprayers, sickle bars, rotary mowers, and snowplows.

A variety of garden tractors and motor tillers also are available. They are of the walking type. They usually have one or two wheels, but motor tillers may have no wheels that touch the ground.

Many farmers use garden tractors for odd jobs for which larger tractors are too cumbersome and uneconomical. Commercial vegetable growers also use garden tractors, but most are bought by suburban homeowners.

Nearly 40 thousand garden tractors of the walking type were shipped by American manufacturers in 1958. Nearly 3 thousand had 2 horsepower or less, and more than 37 thousand had more than 2 horsepower. Of the 174 thousand motor tillers shipped by the manufacturers in 1958, more than 152 thousand had more than 2 horsepower.

All of these garden tractors have a single-cylinder, air-cooled engine, which usually is started by a rope. Most of those with an engine of up to 2 or 3 horsepower do not have a clutch for releasing the engine; instead, the engine is released from the drive wheels by loosening the belt, either by means of an idler pulley or by tilting the engine. Many attachments are available for garden tractors—rotary tiller, harrow, cultivator, seeder, mower, hayrake, cart, grader, fertilizer spreader, and snowplow.

Ordinarily it would be advisable to select a make that is available locally. Then one could see and maybe operate the machine before purchasing it. A 1- to 2-horsepower engine will be large enough for light work, such as cultivation, but for plowing with a conventional plow and extensive land preparation, a tractor with an engine of at least 3 to 4 horsepower will be required.

As to the future, we expect more widespread adoption of many of the improvements now limited to particular models.

The trend in automobiles leads us to expect the development of fuels and engines that will use higher octane gasoline.

There may be radical changes in engine design. Ford, for example, began work in 1954 on a free-piston engine that uses heated gases to drive a turbine and does not require many of the parts of a conventional engine. It shows promise of fuel economy, and it is adaptable to a wide range of fuels.

Nuclear power is an intriguing possibility. A small unit suitable for powering tractors may be in the offing using the principles in use in large installations. With nuclear power, it may be necessary to refuel only once a year.

Also possible is a reversible tractor, on which the seat and controls can be easily and quickly reversed. Reversing a tractor and the attached equipment would save turning at the row ends and give a more unrestricted view for cultivation. The operator would have certain implements in full view.

Another possibility is a tractor with hydraulic drive, which would be driven by two hydraulic motors, one in each drive wheel. The National Institute of Agricultural Engineering in England has developed an experimental model of such a tractor.

Perhaps the self-propelled chassis, with its own power unit, will become more competitive with the conventional tractors of today.

Electric tractors are mentioned sometimes. Storage batteries for power have not been satisfactory, nor has electricity from powerlines through cables. Future development of an electric tractor will probably depend on efficient transmission of current without wires or the development of an efficient long-life battery much superior to those now available.

Tractors of the future will be easier to use. More of them will have power steering, scientifically designed seating, and an automatic pilot to guide the tractor along the crop or other row to be followed.

# Using Wheels To Move Farm Loads

Jordan H. Levin

Wheels we tend to take for granted, as we do some other things that are common, useful, and old.

The story of wheels, though, is almost the story of civilization and surely the story of agriculture.

The importance of wheels is that a man can use them to multiply the work of his arms, legs, back, and even his brain.

Wheels move materials, animals, and people slowly or fast and up and down from where they are to where they should be. Agricultural production, like some other production, is largely a series of such handling or carrying operations.

A man can pick up and carry a burden that weighs as much as he does. With a two-wheeled cart or handtruck, however, he can move four or five times his own weight. With special handling equipment mounted on wheels and run by mechanical power instead of human or animal power, a man can pick up, move, and set down tons of material.

The invention or the discovery of the wheel—very likely in the Bronze Age, 3500–1000 B.C.—was a step forward for mankind. Men no longer had to transport their goods on their backs, or, as was usually the case, on their women's backs.

Wheeled carts were an improvement on the sled, drag, or skid, which were pulled by human beings or animals. (A flat-bottomed drag without runners is called a stoneboat because of its extensive use in transporting stones from fields.) The friction between the sleds and the ground was so large that the power needed to move even small loads was great.

The American Indians were ingenious in many ways, but they had not discovered the wheel. The first white settlers in the 17th century brought the wheel to this country. Wagons and carts were the first wheeled carriers used.

It was in the covered wagon that the pioneer farmer transported his family and possessions from the Atlantic to the Pacific. It was also in a wagon that the 19th century farmer took his wheat to market. The sulky, or wheeled, plow was invented about 1850, and soon other farm implements were mounted on wheels instead of skids.

TREMENDOUS improvements in wheeled vehicles have been made to meet the needs of modern agriculture. The two-wheeled cart and wagon have grown up.

And the wheels themselves have changed. The earliest wheels were made of solid wood or of separate pieces fastened together.

Next the wooden wheel with an iron rim was developed.

Iron and steel wheels were used in the early 1900's.

The rubber tire came into general use on tractors and other farm equipment in the late 1930's. One of the main advantages of the pneumatic rubber tire, as compared with steel wheels, is the reduced rolling resistance. Other advantages of rubber-tired wheels are higher operating speeds, less vibration, better flotation of equipment, and less power required to move the same loads. Many different types of tires have been developed. They differ in the tread, number of plies, size, and so on.

The size of the wheels also has changed. Before roads were improved, wheels were narrow and large in diameter. Today wheels tend to be wider and of small diameter. Because wheels on most agricultural equipment are used for off-the-road purposes, where the ground is uneven, wheels of larger diameters may still be the best.

Improvements have also been made in the bearings that carry the wheels. High-grade roller or ball bearings reduce the axle friction to about one-tenth of that of plain bearings.

The development of rural road systems accelerated the development of wheeled vehicles. Without surfaced rural roads the extensive use of automobiles and farm trucks would not be possible.

THE AUTOMOBILE has had a profound effect on American agriculture. The "horseless carriage" appeared on American farms between 1900 and 1910; by 1920 there were 2,146,000 of them; in 1940, 4,140,000. Although the number of people on farms decreased by 50 percent from 1940 to 1957, the number of automobiles increased slightly to 4,260,000. It was estimated that 80 percent of all farm families had automobiles in 1960. These automobiles are used for farm business purposes 50 percent of the time.

The automobile carries most of the 3.5 million hired farmworkers to their jobs. Automobiles make it possible for the owner to live away from the farm and for hired and part-time workers to come from distant homes.

Automobiles also are used for picking up supplies and moving them to farms, moving small parts of equipment about the farm, and transporting feed, fertilizer, and the harvested crops.

The automobile helps the farm manager supervise work and inspect the farm. Some farmers now have two-way radios in their cars or trucks. On many cattle ranches, small, multipurpose, cross-country two- or four-passenger vehicles equipped with four-wheel drive are being used for rounding up cattle. Jeeps can haul up to 1,200 pounds.

Motortrucks appeared on American farms between 1915 and 1920. In 1960 there were more than 3 million trucks on farms—about one for every 375 acres of farmland in the United States.

Nearly all the incoming supplies arrive at a farm by truck. The farmer picks up his seed, fertilizer, machine parts, and other materials in town and transports them to the farm. Commercial trucks deliver fertilizer, gasoline, oil, and feed directly to the farmstead.

Trucks go into the fields as part of the harvest equipment and haul potatoes, onions, beets, grain, and other crops to storages, warehouses, markets, or packing and processing plants.

Trucks are available for almost every agricultural need. At least a dozen companies make a wide assortment of trucks for farm use. They range in capacity from .5 to 2.5 tons and larger for moving cattle and crops.

Because trucks often operate in soft ground and rough terrain, units are available with four-wheel drive. Various transmissions are available from the standard three-speed to the eight forward-speed units.

Trucks are available with single, double-reduction, two-speed or dual ratio, underdrive, and overdrive axles.

The pickup is a light, all-purpose truck. Other types of bodies are platform, flat-deck, stake, dump, hopper, tank and closed van, cattle, and refrigerator trucks. The pickup truck is the most used multipurpose piece of equipment on many farms. Often it replaces the family automobile.

The flat-deck truck is used extensively for carrying loads that are palletized or handled in bulk boxes. A pallet is a platform on which a number of smaller containers can be placed and handled as a unit load with forklift equipment. A bulk box is essentially a combination pallet and box and has a capacity of 15 to 40 bushels.

Both pallets and bulk boxes have come into widespread use for handling fruit and vegetables. Pallets or bulk boxes can be stacked two or three high on flat-deck trucks. They can be loaded and unloaded quickly, since both sides of a flat-deck bed are readily accessible to forklift equipment. Platform trucks are used also for carrying baled hay, sacked materials, and other farm equipment.

Stake trucks are used for carrying loads that are in units and are handled one at a time. They are used also in moving farm machines. They usually are loaded from the rear. The side and end racks keep the loads from shifting or falling off the truck during transit.

Hopper and dump trucks have come into widespread use for carrying agricultural loads that are handled in bulk. An example is the potato bulk truck, used commonly in sections where potatoes are harvested mechanically.

The bulk truck is driven along the side of the harvester, which digs the potatoes and elevates them into the truck. The filled truck moves to the storage, and another takes its place. These trucks usually are unloaded by tilting the whole bed or by using a conveyor, which forms the bottom of the load-carrying bed.

Hopper trucks are used also for

carrying fertilizer, lime, onions, grains, and other farm products.

Tank trucks are used now for carrying milk, water, and other liquids.

Even cherries can be transported in water in tank trucks at less cost than in lugs; money is saved thereby and quality is retained well. More than 50 million pounds of tart cherries were handled in water in 1959. Pickles and brined sweet cherries are also handled in tank trucks.

Closed van trucks usually are used for moving perishables in cold weather. Refrigerated trucks carry perishables in hot weather. Neither type is common for on-the-farm use, but they are used extensively in handling farm products off the farm.

Cattle trucks, common in the Midwest and Southwest, are designed especially for moving hogs, sheep, and cattle but often are used for hauling poultry, grain, cotton, and other crops.

A TRAILER, cart, or wagon is a load-carrying unit on wheels that is pulled by a separate power source, as a truck or tractor.

Millions of trailers and wagons were in use on American farms in 1960. More than 50 companies manufacture such equipment. Trailers and wagons are available and suitable for almost every farm handling purpose. Pulled by tractors, they can be moved in places where it is impractical or impossible to drive trucks.

Trailers have two or four wheels. Some two-wheeled trailers are small service units. Some have large capacity. Two-wheeled trailers require balanced loads, but they trail well and are more maneuverable than four-wheeled units.

Four-wheeled trailers come in many sizes and are adapted to relatively high speeds. They are easy to hitch and unhitch and therefore are better for use where they may be loaded or unloaded while detached from the tractor.

Trailers or wagon beds (the load-carrying surface) can be had in almost any size and style. They are 4 to 10 feet wide. Narrow trailers can be used for hauling grapes or other crops where the rows are spaced close together.

Trailer beds are of three types—flat-bed trailer, the bulk trailer, and tank trailers.

Flat-deck beds are used for material that is in containers or is self-supporting—fruit, vegetables, and machinery, for example. Such trailers are low to the ground, so that the 40- to 100-pound field crates or sacks of fruit or vegetables can be lifted from the ground easily by hand. Flat-bed trailers also are used for handling baled hay. Flat-deck units are ideal for handling loads on pallets and in bulk boxes.

Tilt-bed, flat-deck trailers or units with an endgate, which can be lowered to the ground to form a ramp, are useful for moving farm machinery.

An example of the trailers that have been designed especially for moving equipment is the large trailer used in the Florida citrus industry. The crop is harvested by special crews who move from grove to grove. Each time they move, tractors, orchard carts, bulk loaders, and such must be moved. One or two trailers can carry all the equipment needed by one crew.

The bulk trailers are used for carrying agricultural loads that can be carried without a container. This type of wagon or trailer comes in various types depending on the crop it is to handle. They have beds into which loose materials can be put and moved. They carry grain, shelled corn, cotton, chopped hay, oranges, potatoes, and sugar beets.

Most bulk bed trailers are unloaded mechanically. For free-flowing materials, such as grain, the tilting or gravity method of unloading is satisfactory. Trailers are often dumped by means of external hoists or special hydraulic dumpers. In sugar beet and sugarcane operations, the wagon or trailer is often picked up mechanically and rotated 90 degrees, and the crop is dumped out.

Other trailers contain their own built-in tilting bed. The beds are usually tilted by a hydraulic cylinder operated from the tractor hydraulic system. Some modern trailers have integral hydraulic systems and power lifts. The hydraulic pump may also be driven from the tractor power takeoff.

Gravity-unloading trailers have a sloped bottom. They usually are unloaded by raising a gate on one side of the trailer and permitting the grain to flow out. Sometimes the trailers are placed on a dock, which is sloped to aid unloading.

Self-unloading wagons or bulk trailers are available for unloading at a controlled rate. The potatoes, grain, or other materials are placed on a canvas or a conveyor on the bed of the trailer. An electric motor or gasoline engine of one-half or three-fourths horsepower usually is coupled to the rear roller, which moves the canvas and causes the load to run off the conveyor. The rear roller in some self-unloading trailers is driven by the tractor power takeoff. The speed at which the rear roller turns determines the rate at which the load is removed from the trailer.

Tank trailers are in limited use for specialized operations. When the water source is at some distance from where spray equipment is being used, feeder tank trailers often are used to carry water to the equipment. This makes it possible to keep the expensive air-blast sprayer in use and thereby apply the chemicals quickly in order to control insects and diseases. Tank trailers are also used to carry water to cattle, for irrigation purposes, and for harvest and cattle crews to drink.

TRACTOR-INTEGRATED and mounted load-carrying equipment has come into general use in the past few years. A number of tractor attachments have been developed for handling and carrying farm loads.

Most modern tractors have three-point hydraulic hitches. A transport box or platform can be easily attached (and removed) to three-point hydraulic hitches. They are inexpensive and useful for carrying loads up to 1,500 pounds.

No forklift attachments were available for farm tractors in 1950. Because of the adoption of palletized and bulk box handling of fruit and vegetables and other products, the demand for this type of equipment has grown, and more than 25 companies began to manufacture such units. One man and a tractor equipped with forklift attachments on both the front and rear of a tractor can pick up and carry out of the orchard 1,500 bushels of apples in an 8-hour day. To do the same job with trailers would take six men, three tractors, and three trailers.

Growers who have tractors that are equipped with three-point hydraulic hitches can adapt them for handling pallets and bulk boxes by bolting forks to the hitch.

Forks may be bolted also to buck rakes or hayloaders. If this equipment is used, it is desirable to add a third cylinder, which enables the operator to keep the forks level while they are being raised.

Lift attachments that make it possible to lift the forks 12 to 14 feet and also tilt them are available for both the front and rear ends of practically every tractor of standard make. These units operate in the same way as those found on industrial forklift trucks. Power steering is desirable when the lift attachment is placed on the front end of the tractor.

Units are available that convert the tractor into a relatively permanent forklift unit. The lifting unit (hydraulic cylinder and forks) is attached to the rear of the tractor. The tractor gear box, steering mechanism, and driver's seat are all reversed. The driver faces the load, and most of the travel is in that direction. Such units can lift and carry 2-ton loads. Since the weight is over the drive wheels of the tractor, the units have good traction.

Handling fruit, vegetables, fertilizer,

spray material, and small farm machinery with forklift equipment saves time, money, and labor. It is estimated that in 1959 a thousand forklift attachments were in use in Michigan orchards.

Many types of tractor front-mounted loaders are available, and thousands are in use. They have taken the backache out of such work as loading manure and handling feed and hay.

Practically all front-mounted loaders are operated hydraulically. For handling manure, dirt, gravel, and other loose materials, a bucket or scoop is used. Forks are used for hay. Special units are made for stacking hay. Others are used as a sweep-rake.

Agricultural loads are carried on wheels about the farmstead. Most of the equipment is of a specialized nature. Probably the simplest are the two-wheeled cart and the wheelbarrow. These devices consist of one or two wheels and a material-holding section and handles. The unit is pushed or pulled. Two-wheeled carts or wheelbarrows have been used for many years, and they are still very useful about the farmstead, storage, and packinghouse. They are used for handling feed on poultry and dairy farms. Some have been designed for handling milk cans; others, for holding hoppers and for spreading lime or phosphate on barn floors. Still others have been made for carrying loose or baled hay or straw.

Two-wheeled handtrucks are used for handling boxes of fruit and vegetables at loading areas, cold storages, and packinghouses. One type of two-wheeled handtruck, the stevedore type, has an L-shaped frame mounted on wheels and a pair of handles separated by stretchers. The load is carried by the lower end of the unit on a metal blade. Another type is the two-wheeled clamp truck.

Dollies and four-wheeled handtrucks are common and have many uses. They are pushed by hand and usually require a smooth surface.

Some other load-carrying equipment mounted on wheels and used about the farmstead are grain elevators, auger-type grain loaders, and bag loaders. They are composed of various types of conveyors, which move materials from one level to another. Mounted on wheels, they can be moved from one location to another.

Spray equipment may have tank capacities of several gallons. Modern airblast sprayers have a capacity of 500 gallons, or almost 2 tons, of material. An airblast unit can make 16 trips to the orchard a day—one rig therefore moves 32 tons of water and chemicals a day. Thousands of such units are in use.

More than 22 million tons of commercial fertilizer are used each year on American farms. Fertilizer placement equipment mounted on wheels has been developed for carrying this vast tonnage quickly and effectively to the field.

A large amount of manure is applied to the soil each year. It is heavy and disagreeable to handle. Almost every farm that produces several tons of manure each year should have a manure spreader. This machine carries in a box, which is mounted on wheels, barnyard manure to the fields, shreds it, and spreads it uniformly. The capacity of spreaders is 2 to 5 tons.

Various types of lime spreaders are available. Lime spreaders are usually mounted on two wheels and have capacities of 800 to 1,000 pounds.

Farmers are beginning to use anhydrous ammonia and other forms of so-called "liquid nitrogen" fertilizer. The application equipment contains a load-carrying tank, which moves the gaseous or liquid fertilizer to the fields.

In a sense, seeders and planters are load-carrying equipment mounted on wheels. Many tons of seed, seed pieces, and plants are moved to the field on such equipment each year.

Several types of two- and four-wheeled dollies and trailers have been made for carrying millions of feet of aluminum pipe, used in irrigation, from one location to another.

Straddle trucks and trailers, which have been used for carrying lumber, are beginning to be used to carry fruit, and their use will probably expand to other crops. They also are being used to move farm machinery from field to field over paved roads. A straddle truck or trailer is a high-clearance vehicle that can drive over a load of palletized crates or bulk boxes which have been set on bolsters. The load is picked up from the bolsters with hydraulically operated raising and carrying shoes. A straddle truck or trailer can pick up or set down loads of 5 to 6 tons in 10 to 20 seconds. They can carry their loads at speeds up to 40 to 50 miles an hour. Their large wheels permit them to go into fields and orchards to pick up their loads.

# A Machine Is Produced

## C. B. Richey

DOE & ROE CO., INC., decided 5 years ago that they should do something about the problem of harvesting and handling forage.

I made up the name of the company, and the hay concentrator they worked on is hypothetical, but the problem is real and so are the steps a manufacturer takes in producing a new machine.

The decision itself was not a simple one.

Doe & Roe, like other manufacturers of farm equipment, ordinarily do not put in production a new design to replace an older model unless they feel it offers more value to the farmer for its manufacturing cost and will maintain or improve their business—that is, that it will maintain or increase sales compared to the superseded model (which may have been losing ground to competitive machines) because it offers a better value for the money and also may permit lower manufacturing costs as a result of a more efficient design and use of materials.

Doe & Roe know that if they are to stay in business they must build machines (at a profit) that offer values at least equal to competitive machines.

Values involve efficiency of operation and durability.

Efficiency of operation includes three factors:

Quality of the work done (pulverization and trash coverage when plowing or getting all the grain and no foreign material when combining);

efficient use of power (light draft in a plow because of the shape of the bottom, or a low power requirement in a field forage harvester because of an efficiently designed cutterhead);

and efficient use of human labor (minimum number of man-hours per unit of work done; minimum size of crew; minimum of nonoperating time obtained by having convenient controls and adjustments, freedom from clogging, minimum lubrication, quick attachment, and so on; minimum operator fatigue, achieved by having low muscular effort, good visibility, comfortable position and ride, and safety).

Durability, or the amount of work accomplished before the machine wears out, includes four points:

Freedom from breakage (parts of adequate strength and overload releases);

resistance to wear (wearing parts of wear-resistant materials, bearings of proper load capacity, easy and adequate lubrication, dirt excluded from bearings, gears, et cetera);

resistance to chemical deterioration (corrosion-resistant materials, protective coatings or treatments for vulnerable materials);

low repair cost (adjustments to compensate for wear; a design to permit easy replacement of wearing parts; provisions for intricate assemblies, such as diesel pumps, and simplicity of construction).

A NEW MACHINE usually is evolutionary—an improved model of an existing type.

Occasionally it may be revolutionary—a new type that offers a new and better method of doing the job and makes obsolete the machine or machines that use the old method.

An example of a revolutionary development is the small combine, which was introduced in the Midwest in the 1930's and quickly made obsolete the binder and thresher because it was more convenient and lowered the costs.

Evolutionary machines usually appear at a fairly predictable rate and often do not give the manufacturer a marked competitive advantage.

Revolutionary machines can sometimes change the balance of power in the industry with devastating suddenness.

In between them are machines that do the same job with a new and simpler mechanism that makes them cheaper and more trouble-free than older machines. An example is the flail-type forage harvester, which utilizes a single machine component, the rotor cylinder, to cut off, chop, and throw the forage into the wagon.

Doe & Roe has a product engineering unit that develops production designs, releases drawings to the factory for production, and continues to make desirable changes and improvements after machines are in production.

Specifications for new designs of evolutionary machines usually are based on the following information:

Features of successful competitive machines;

surveys of customer satisfaction; service experience with current machines as to weaknesses and shortcomings;

market analysis;

trends indicated by advanced practices based on research findings of agricultural scientists;

and technological developments that make available new materials, fabrication techniques, or components.

The sales, service, and product engineering offices agree as to such specifications. (Some companies have a product planning group, which collects the information and coordinates the development of specifications for a new machine.)

The product engineers then proceed to design and develop an efficient machine that meets the specifications and incorporates as many other improvements as possible within the specified cost limitations.

Revolutionary or unconventional new machines must be approached from a different standpoint and usually by a group of engineers who are not coping with production problems. Often such groups are placed into an advanced or research engineering activity separate from product engineering. Revolutionary developments do sometimes come out of product engineering groups, but generally the limitations imposed by working to specifications and meeting production deadlines leave little opportunity for revolutionary approaches of unproved worth.

Many revolutionary developments have started with mechanically minded farmers or small shops that are close to a local problem and have the mechanical ability to see and try a new approach. Their resources, however, seldom are adequate to perfect a new machine of considerable complexity, such as a hay baler or cottonpicker. As technology becomes more complex, the ability of the independent inventor to make significant improvements is diminished, and the large manufacturer must bear more responsibility for advancements.

THE IDEA of Doe & Roe's new machine, one of the revolutionary type, was incubated in the research or advanced engineering group.

The problem was that of harvesting and storing forage. The losses in feeding value caused by weather damage during field curing of hay have been estimated to average at least 25 percent. Weather damage is less with grass silage, but in making it about 2 pounds of water must be transported and stored for every pound of dry matter. Besides, both hay and silage are bulky materials, which require much more storage space than grain for their feeding value, and they are poorly adapted to mechanical conveying since they are not free flowing.

The top management of Doe & Roe agreed that this problem should be attacked. The chief research engineer assigned it to a small research engineering group, all of whom were agricultural engineers.

The group analyzed the problem and broke it down thus:

A. Possible solutions to curing problem: (1) Dehydrating green forage; (2) partial field curing with final drying on the wagon or in the barn; (3) protecting windrowed hay in field until curing is complete; (4) cutting off moisture supply from plant roots so the standing hay plant will dry out quickly by transpiration; (5) mechanical dewatering of green forage in field.

B. Possible solutions to bulk problem: (1) High density bales; (2) field wafers or pellets.

C. Possible solutions to conveying problem: (1) Grinding; (2) pelleting.

They attacked the curing problem first, because it was the most difficult and its solution could dictate the choices for the bulk and conveying problems. Dehydrating and partial field curing were both used, but the group rejected them on the basis of cost and inconvenience.

They experimented with plastic strips as protections for windrows at night and when rain threatened. The hay was cured without damage, but the cost of the plastic and the labor requirement were found to be too high.

Then they used a hot flame on the plant stalk near the ground as a means of rupturing the cells that carry water up from the roots. It stopped the flow of water, but the plants wilted and collapsed flat on the ground of their own weight, impeding both drying and subsequent harvest. That was disappointing, because calculations indicated that transpiration continuing at the normal rate would dry the plant in 30 minutes.

The engineers then experimented with applying high pressures to green forage to squeeze it dry. We assume here, for the purpose of our account, that they found it possible to squeeze the forage down to 15-percent moisture and that a dense stable briquette or pellet would be formed in the process.

(This actually has been tried, but only about half the water can be removed, reducing the moisture content from 75 percent to 60 percent, wet basis. Work by agricultural engineers in the University of Wisconsin has shown that stable briquettes can be formed from legumes under 25-percent moisture, wet basis, by applying a pressure of 3 thousand to 5 thousand pounds to the square inch.)

This hypothetical discovery opened up the possibility of developing a field machine that could process green forage into dry, stable, dense, free-flowing pellets, ideal for subsequent transport, storage, and handling.

The Doe & Roe engineers knew that if the first cost and operating costs of such a machine were not prohibitive, the machine would be truly revolutionary; it would make most other forage harvesting machines obsolete immediately.

NOW THEY NEEDED basic information for the design of the first experimental model.

They brought samples of green forage into the laboratory and measured the compressive force and energy required to dewater and form wafers. They studied the problem of openings in the pressure chamber that would allow the juice to escape but retain the forage. They also studied the optimum rate of applying pressure and the holding time necessary to get stable wafers.

The next step was to develop a suitable mechanism. It had to have capacity comparable to a small baler, and the power consumption should be such that costs of fuel would be in the same range as the cost of wire or twine for bales.

The mechanism also would have to be as simple as possible, although very large forces would be involved. They rejected a reciprocating plunger mechanism because of the difficulty of feeding a small cylindrical chamber and the high speeds needed to obtain adequate capacity.

They tried pressure rolls, but the moist green forage tended to mush out. Screw extrusion, as in the old-fashioned meat grinder, was suggested, and they made an experimental screw, housing, and die assembly.

Tests with green forage were successful, after many modifications, and they decided to build an experimental field machine using that mechanism.

Because torque required for the screw and pressures in the housing should be known before starting the new design, the Doe & Roe stress analysis unit, which serves all engineering, was asked to determine those figures by applying electric strain gages and taking measurements while the mechanism was in operation.

That detail completed the gathering of basic information for the design of the first field machine.

THE DESIGN of the first field machine was started in the fall, with the idea of having the machine ready for tryout by the next spring when green forage first became available.

The project engineer and his assistants made layout drawings of several different arrangements of the machine components, which included (besides the screw assembly) a frame and wheels, an engine, drive train, cutterbar and feeding mechanism, and

an elevator to dump the hay wafers into a wagon.

The machine needed a name, so they decided to call it a hay concentrator for the time being.

After agreeing on the most efficient arrangement of components, the project engineer and his assistants each took a part of the machine. They made layout drawings of their components and then detailed drawings of the individual parts. The parts were proportioned according to the operating load data and according to estimates of transport loads based on the probable weight of the complete machine. Strength calculations were made on all important parts for which load data were available.

Parts that would take the longest to make were drawn first and released to the shop for fabrication. Because castings took the longest time, the cast-steel screw and the gray cast-iron housing for the gear reduction drive to the screw were among the first to be designed and drawn. The screw housing was built up from welded steel parts, although that could be changed to a casting later if cost estimates indicated a saving.

The cutterbar and reel assembly from a production forage harvester were used with minor modifications. This saves time and money when an experimental machine is built primarily to test other components. For the same reason, a cornpicker elevator was used.

The drawings were completed in due course, parts were made, and the first machine was completely assembled. The engineers expedited the last parts through the shop and closely supervised the assembly of the machine, as that is easier than making detailed assembly drawings to guide the shop mechanics.

The hay concentrator was given a coat of bright, glossy paint. The engineers agreed that it looked very good.

Excitement ran high as the hay concentrator was taken to the field for the first time.

Because the screw had been tested previously and the cutterbar, reel, and elevator were production items, there was a certain amount of hope that the machine would work according to plan, although the engineers knew from experience that that was a lot to expect.

In the field, the machine was started. It went about 10 feet before the men noticed that the green forage was piling up at the feed rolls instead of going through into the screw chamber.

They cleaned out the machine. The start was repeated, the engineers watching closely.

After going through this process about ten times, they agreed on a course of action and took the machine back to the shop for modification.

At the next tryout, the machine took the forage enough further to reveal the next problem, and so on. The first wagonload of wafers was made eventually. That was indeed a milestone, but it had been so slow in coming that most of the excitement had been lost.

Testing of the first hay concentrator continued throughout the summer. It was not taken far from the shop because of the modifications and repairs needed. Because of those interruptions, only about 75 hours of actual use were attained.

Near the end of the season, strain gages were applied to various parts and load measurements were taken in the field for use in designing the next model.

THE SECOND DESIGN was started as soon as field testing of the first model was concluded. The same basic design was retained, but many modifications and improvements were made as a result of the summer's experience and on the basis of the new load information. A larger engine was used to give more capacity in the new model.

The engineers had to get approval to continue the project another year. The original project was for an investigation into improved forage harvesting. Now that a specific machine had evolved, further work on it had to be approved by top management.

The engineers had demonstrated the hay concentrator in favorable conditions to both high level and lower level personnel in an effort to convince them of its possibilities. Funds were approved to continue the project and for building two machines in order to broaden the test program.

The first of the second design machines was completed early in March. It was shipped to the Southwest, where the haying season was in full swing. It operated almost as well as the first machine did near the end of the season; indeed, as modifications and improvements continued, it sometimes ran for a half day without trouble. It became a problem to get enough hay to keep the machine busy, because most farmers did not have handling or storage facilities for wafers and did not want any more than they could feed daily.

As the season progressed, the two machines were tried in as many different conditions and kinds of hay as possible. It was found that immature crops with 80-percent moisture, wet basis, were not dried enough to wafer and that stemmy grasses, such as timothy and bromegrass, did not make durable wafers. On the other hand, the ability to harvest legume forage without weather damage, the ease of handling, and the economy of storage space were obvious advantages, and the engineers were encouraged by the interest of farmers in the machine.

Engineers from the forage harvesting section of the product engineering unit were invited to work with the machine in the field, because it would be placed in their hands, if and when it were to be readied for production. A successful transplanting of an experimental machine from the research activity to the product engineering activity requires the fullest cooperation of all hands.

In conferences of the research engineers, the forage harvesting product engineers, and the director of engineering, it was decided that the hay concentrator should be recommended for transfer to product engineering to be made ready for production.

The product planning unit was notified that a project would be requested. They proceeded to prepare a presentation on the hay concentrator, although they were somewhat at a loss because there were no competitive machines, no sales statistics, and no service experience.

The case for producing the hay concentrator was presented in due course to the top management. The sales manager was rather lukewarm; he had no proof that such a machine could be sold. The service manager knew from experience that he would get a brand new set of problems.

Nevertheless, the new project was approved, and a preproduction run of 50 machines was tentatively scheduled for the second year of the new project. That would allow the product engineers a year to get the machine ready for the preproduction run.

THE TRANSFER to product engineering was effected by giving the product engineers an up-to-date set of drawings for the second design and copies of all the test reports. They previously had a copy of the summary report covering the design and testing of the first machine. The research engineers also prepared a report covering the experience with the second design machines and recommendations for design changes in the next models.

The design of the production prototype, or sample, had to recognize several new factors that the research engineers had subordinated to functional considerations.

The product engineer had to design parts for the lowest total cost of manufacture, including tooling cost, at a production volume of 3 thousand a year for the first 5 years as estimated by the market analysts. The cost of the second experimental machine was estimated by the controller's cost estimating group, and a cost target was set for the production machines.

Servicing, adjusting, and repair operations were studied, and the design was modified to simplify those operations as much as possible. Almost all the grease fittings were eliminated by using enclosed gear boxes running in oil, sealed antifriction bearings, and self-lubricating plain bearings. Parts that might unavoidably wear out or break in service were designed for easy replacement.

The machine was studied and divided into subassemblies of convenient size.

Conferences with a specialist in packaging and shipping from the manufacturing engineering department led to a joint decision as to the degree of assembly and the shipping bundles required. Since this was a large, heavy, fairly complex machine, it was to be completely assembled on its own wheels, except for the header. The header was to be assembled complete, except for the reel parts, which were wired in the header.

The design was checked for the use of standard parts and components wherever possible. The research engineers had gone through this, for every standard part meant one less part to design and build. They had started with a standard combine header but found it necessary to make some changes for green forage.

The design was also checked for compliance with industry standards. Particular attention was paid to the hitch for the tractor and to the wagon hitch and wagon elevator.

Safety was also given more consideration by providing shields for exposed moving parts, eliminating sharp corners, and providing steps, handholds, and easily operated controls.

The product engineers studied the information on loads and forces, obtained from the previous designs by electric strain gage instrumentation and also the failures that occurred in field testing. Sometimes they requested help from the stress analysis laboratory in suggesting a more efficient design in a troublesome area.

The production design remained basically similar to the research machine. If a research machine is of a basically unsound design and requires rearrangement of structure and components for economic production, much ground is lost, because much of the research experience may not apply. An extra year may be required to overcome the functional difficulties often to be expected with an untried flow of material. Thus it is important that the research engineers start with a design that is simple and adapted to economic production methods.

Drawings for production must conform to company standards. Tolerances are opened up where possible, and complete finish and material specifications are given. All drawings must be approved as to material by the metallurgical laboratory in order to avoid nonstandard materials and heat treatments and to assure adequate strength of materials.

THE PRODUCT engineering activity is much larger than the research activity, partly because of the manpower required to look after the machines in production. Weaknesses must be corrected, field-tested improvements incorporated, and requests by the manufacturing unit for deviations from the engineering drawings must be analyzed and approved if they are permissible.

After a part has been released for production, any change may have far-reaching effects. A change must be approved not only by the engineering but by service, parts sales, purchasing, product planning, and manufacturing divisions. The procedures and paperwork necessary to keep changes from disrupting a large organization provide the product engineer with a large share of his daily work.

In preparing a new machine for production, the product engineer is the key man. He is responsible for designing, getting experimental models built, and making improvements indicated by results of test in the laboratory and field. He must approve all drawings before final release.

Hundreds of thousands of dollars are spent for tooling, instruction and parts books, sales training programs, and advertising before a new machine can bring in any revenue.

The product engineers must release a machine that is as nearly right as possible. This responsibility is not a light one.

Because of the larger size of the product engineering activity, more specialization is encountered. Most of the actual drafting is done by designers and detailers who spend most of their time at the drafting board. They work under supervision of the product engineers, who have usually come up through the drafting room. An engineering degree is desirable but not required of designers and detailers, but is usually one of the prerequisites for advancement to the position of product design engineer.

The mechanics of making up lists of parts, releasing experimental drawings to the shop for making experimental models, and releasing the final drawings for production was handled by a release group within Doe & Roe's product engineering division. The product design engineer supplied the necessary information.

TESTING of the production prototypes at Doe & Roe began as soon as the machines could be built from the completed drawings.

Three hay concentrators were to be built. The first one was completed in February and was shipped immediately to the Southwest in order to get as long a test season as possible. It was turned over to the field test section of the test engineering department.

An experienced field test specialist was sent with the machine. He located a farmer who had hay to harvest and was willing to have the hay concentrator used on part of his crop. At this stage, the machine was operated by the test man. As the hay concentrator became more reliable, it was turned over to the farmer for use. The test man called daily to check on the machine's operation and make necessary repairs.

One test man can often attend two or three machines in this stage of development. Copies of his daily reports on each machine were given to the product engineer. If he had troubles, the test man called the engineer to get approval for changes he thought necessary.

A product engineer was on hand when the machine concentrator was started. The new model showed the additional experience and thought that went into its design. It had only minor troubles. By the end of the first week it was running smoothly, and the engineer returned to his other duties, although he followed the test reports closely and visited the machine occasionally during the season.

The field test specialist reported on the new machine from the standpoint of the prospective user—on performance, hours of use, failures, awkward controls, inconvenient adjustments, sharp corners, and many other items.

Back at engineering headquarters, the second hay concentrator was turned over to the stress analysis section of the test engineering division. Modern experimental techniques of stress analysis make it possible to locate quickly points of stress concentration that otherwise may require several hundred hours of actual operation to cause visible fatigue failures. Thus much development time is saved. Points of maximum stress can be located by coating the parts with a brittle lacquer, which will show cracks when the metal part is stretched to a certain stress level well within its elastic limit. The closer the cracks, the higher the stress level and the more likelihood of fatigue failure. Thus critical areas are exposed, and the design can be modified to reduce the stress or to use stronger materials.

The running gear, frame, and wagon elevator of the hay concentrator were coated first. The machine was then drawn over standard bumps on the paved test track at maximum field speed. The coating was inspected carefully, and cracks, indicating highly stressed areas, were marked. The moving parts of the functional mechanisms were then coated. Arrangements were made to run hay through it in a building where temperature and humidity could be held relatively constant.

(The stress level at which the coating cracks varies with the temperature and humidity level, and a grade of coating must be selected for the temperature and humidity expected during the test.)

Fresh green hay was brought in and fed into the machine by hand at the maximum field rate for a short period. The machine was then stopped, and highly stressed areas were marked. Then the hay was fed fast enough to clog the machine, and the additional stressed areas were located and identified.

This gave a good picture of the operating stresses. Points of stress concentration that could cause fatigue failure were apparent. Borderline areas, particularly in drive train parts that cannot be easily and inexpensively strengthened, were fitted with electric strain gages, and recordings were taken while the machine was actually operating in the field. The strain gages gave a more accurate indication of stress than the brittle coating. A comparison of the stress with the strength characteristics of the material indicated whether the design was adequate.

In troublesome cases, it may be necessary to resort to a laboratory fatigue test on critical parts. A fixture is made to apply a vibrating load to the part in such a way as to stress it in the same way as field operation. If a part will withstand 6 million cycles, it should continue to run indefinitely, so few tests are longer than this. A vibration frequency of 5 cycles per second or more can often be used, thus making it possible to run a life test on a part in 350 hours or less. In many cases a part may need to withstand only 1 million cycles of stress for satisfactory life, and it is tested accordingly.

When these tests were complete, a report was issued by the stress analysis group and circulated to interested persons. The product engineers, however, had followed the stress tests closely and had made urgently recommended changes in the field insofar as possible.

By the time the third hay concentrator was completed, hay harvesting was about to start in the North, and it was operated in as many different types of hay as could be found. This machine also was used for functional tryout of various alternate designs of components. Occasionally it was demonstrated to sales and servicemen, who would be involved when it was put on the market.

The machine in the Southwest was kept operating in irrigated alfalfa throughout the entire season. Breakdowns occurred occasionally, but it accumulated 600 hours of use by the end of a season of 8 months.

Generally, a machine that will run 600 hours with only minor breakage will give satisfactory service during at least the first few years of normal usage.

The next job was to modify the production design in the light of the year's experience and then release the drawings for a preproduction run of 50 machines.

Drawings of the first production prototypes were previously released as "advanced information" to purchasing, cost estimating, quality control, and manufacturing departments, which went over the drawings for design details that could be improved from their point of view.

DESIGN REVIEW conferences were held with these departments before the design was considered final.

Purchasing representatives directed attention to materials that were nonstandard and hard to obtain. They also had suggestions for additional sources of commercially available components, such as hydraulic valves.

Cost estimators suggested various changes in design to lower costs, such as substituting castings for weldments and vice versa.

Quality-control and manufacturing people were quick to spot close tolerances that would be hard to hold with normal manufacturing techniques, and many tolerances were reevaluated.

Those who worked with manufacturing methods had gone through the fabricating processes for each piece and listed the type of tooling required. They pointed out the savings if tooling could be simplified and certain operations omitted: For the estimated volume, it would be cheaper, they said, to use extra labor to trim a piece of sheet metal with straight cuts and standard notching dies rather than to make a special die to blank it in one operation.

In a series of such conferences, every piece was gone over, and each department had a chance to make recommendations.

THE FINAL design for production then proceeded. It incorporated findings of field tests and laboratory tests and the design review suggestions. It was primarily a matter of making changes on the existing drawings, but myriad details were involved, and the final drawings had to be correct in every detail.

Since tooling and special machines would perhaps require several months to build, an attempt was made to release first the parts that would require the most tooling time.

The release of drawings for production is a fairly complex and time-consuming operation in a large organization because the information must be furnished to all the different groups involved in the manufacture and servicing of the new machine and their activities must be scheduled for proper coordination. It so happened that the header for the hay concentrator would be made in a different plant than the remainder; that further complicated the procedure.

THE PREPRODUCTION 50 machines were built on the tooling designed for full production in most cases, although temporary tooling was used for a few parts. The machines were spread over the major hay producing areas of the United States in order to get experience in all areas and types of hay.

Because of the great variation in crops and operating conditions, it has been found wise to proceed with caution in putting new farm machines on the market. Local manufacturers making a machine tailored to local conditions sometimes are able to compete successfully with full-line manufacturers who make one type of machine for the entire country. Potato and beet harvesting machines tend to fall in this category. A preproduction run of 50 machines brings out the problems in the various areas and in some instances points out areas for which the new machine should not be recommended. For instance, Doe & Roe's hypothetical hay concentrator turned out to have inadequate moisture-removing ability for the lush forage of 80–85-percent moisture in Florida.

The preproduction run of machines was sold at a loss because the manufacturing cost was much higher than for full production. That is considered, however, to be part of the development expense. In addition to determining functional adaptation to the various areas, this experience served to check out production tooling, locate design weaknesses, and instruct sales and service personnel in the use and adaptation of the machine.

If a new machine is a failure functionally or has serious mechanical weaknesses, a limited production run results in comparatively few machines to take back or rebuild. Losses are limited in this case, but serious financial losses and impairment of future sales can result if a firm undertakes a full year's production of an untried machine.

Then the product design engineers closely followed field reports on the 50 hay concentrators. They were called to the field by service personnel when serious functional difficulties were encountered.

They gained much additional experience, since opportunities for improvement still existed. Sometimes the engineers and servicemen made and tested modifications on the spot in order to get the machine to operate properly in a particular condition.

In general, the hay concentrator did very well. Because it offered advantages over previous methods, farmers were tolerant of minor difficulties.

The product design engineers made the needed changes in the design as quickly as possible. Sales estimates for the first year of full production were reevaluated in view of the season's experience, and production schedules were set up.

At last Doe & Roe's hypothetical hay concentrator was set for full production with reasonable assurance of meeting the farmer's needs and of being a profitable machine for the company.

It had been 5 years since the original experiments had started, a comparatively short time for a development of this size and importance.

At this point, the engineers would like to feel that production can proceed "happily ever after," but they know that this design will be competitive for only 8 or 10 years at the most and that they must soon have a new and better design coming along.

*Readers who wish to keep up with publications about machines and engineering may find helpful:*

*List of Available Publications of the United States Department of Agriculture.*

*Bibliography of Agriculture, the United States Department of Agriculture Library.*

*Agricultural Engineering, The American Society of Agricultural Engineers, St. Joseph, Mich.*

# The Place of Petroleum

Howard F. McColly

In the backwoods village of Titusville, Pa., in August of 1859, Edwin L. Drake drilled a hole 69.5 feet into the ground, and the first commercial oil well was brought in.

Colonel Drake was an investor in the Pennsylvania Rock Oil Co. He was employed in 1858 to conduct drilling operations on the company's Oil Creek property.

He thought he could find enough oil to light the lamps of America. He knew about the success of Samuel M. Kier, who 8 years earlier had set up a one-barrel still in Pittsburgh to produce the pale-yellow "carbon oil" for the lamps and lanterns of a young country.

The oil had always been there, waiting. It had been formed by sun and lush vegetation in prehistoric swamps and then trapped in the earth's strata. The word "petroleum" means rock oil, because it is derived from the Greek word "petros," meaning rock, and the Latin word "oleum," meaning oil.

Little use had been made of it. American Indians collected oil in pits and used it as medicine. White men skimmed it off pools and creeks. They called it Seneca oil or Genesee oil and sold the black stuff as a cure for rheumatism and other pains of man and beast.

The rock oil pumped up from salt wells was a nuisance and was dumped into nearby canals and ponds. Someone accidently "torched" the oil-covered water, and it burned beautifully—proof that the stuff might be good for something.

Now petroleum furnishes all the lubrication and three-fourths of the fuel for machines, which do much of the work in this country.

The oil industry celebrated the centennial of Colonel Drake's hole in 1959. In the 100 years, more than 1.7 million oil wells had been drilled in the United States; 569,273 of them were producing oil in 1959. In the century, the vast amounts of petroleum have enabled man to improve his position in the physical world more than in all previous history. Only about 35 percent of all work in the United States was performed by machines when Colonel Drake was drilling. The rest was done by human and animal muscles. The few steam engines, locomotives, and factory machines always were breaking down because they lacked proper lubricants.

Petroleum supplied axle grease and cup grease for lubrication and kerosene for lighting.

Kerosene also was used to kindle fires. Most coal stoves had a "coal oil" jar or can at the back with a corncob in it soaking to serve as fire starters. People often threw the oil on reluctant fires, and not all of them lived to tell about it.

Really modern farm kitchens had a kerosene cook range for summer. The coal range was idle until cool weather came.

Kerosene stoves often supplemented other heating plants on the farm. Many farm homes had a wick-heater to take the early "frost" out of the room until other fires could be kindled.

Proud was the poultryman who acquired an oil-fired, thermostatically controlled incubator for chicks. Many tales of woe were told during the time the early incubators, first invented in 1844, were undergoing development—for the fire had crept up and spoiled the hatch and sometimes set the building on fire, or the fire went out and the eggs were chilled. The incubator and the colony-type heated brooders, introduced in 1910, put the setting hen out of business.

Kerosene brooders for young farm animals enabled earlier production dates in the spring. The farmer no longer needed to stay up so many nights to care for his young animals.

Most early tank heaters burned coal, wood, or cobs, but many ranchers preferred kerosene burners because they saved work and were easy to regulate. Kerosene burners in water fountains for poultry and swine warmed the water or the mash and prevented freezing.

Orchard heaters—smudge pots—have saved many orchards and vineyards from frost damage. They raise slightly the temperature and, by making a smudge or smoke ceiling, retard the drift of cold air downward.

Oil heaters heated the milkhouses enough to prevent freezing and furnished enough hot water for cleaning utensils.

CRUDE OIL as it comes from the earth is a mixture of thousands of different hydrocarbon compounds. The proportion generally is about 86 percent of carbon to 14 percent of hydrogen. All these compounds can be burned. That is why crude oil is such a good fuel.

Refining processes break up crude oil into its components. The major products made from it are gasoline, kerosene, light and heavy fuel oils, lubricating oils, wax, asphalt, and coke. New developments in refining have increased by about 75 percent the yield of gasoline from crude oil.

The higher quality of today's gasoline has made possible improvements in the design of engines and greater efficiency in the form of drawbar work output per gallon of fuel. Tractors in 1935 gave more than 50 percent more horsepower-hours per gallon of fuel than in 1920. The pneumatic tire markedly raised the drawbar efficiency of tractors; that and further refinements in fuel and engines made tractors in 1960 more than 100 percent more efficient than the 1920 models.

Petroleum products provided more than two-thirds the total United States energy requirement in 1960. The

YIELDS FROM A BARREL OF CRUDE OIL

|  | 1957 | | 1918 | |
|---|---|---|---|---|
|  | Gallons per barrel | Percent Yield | Gallons per barrel | Percent Yield |
| Gasoline | 18.4 | 43.8 | 10.6 | 25.3 |
| Kerosene | 1.6 | 3.8 | 5.6 | 13.3 |
| Gas oil and distillates | 9.7 | 23.1 ⎫ | 22.5 | 53.5 |
| Residual fuel oil | 6.0 | 14.4 ⎭ | | |
| Other products and losses | 6.3 | 14.9 | 3.3 | 7.9 |
| Total | 42 | 100 | 42 | 100 |

PHYSICAL PROPERTIES OF FUELS

| Fuel | API Gravity, degrees | Weight, pounds per gallon | Heat Value | |
|---|---|---|---|---|
| | | | B.t.u. per gallon | B.t.u. per pound |
| Coal, bituminous | | | | 13,100 |
| Wood, elm | | | | 7,683 |
| Propane | 145 | 4.25 | 92,140 | 21,680 |
| Butane | 114 | 4.80 | 102,200 | 21,300 |
| Premium grade gasoline | 63 | 6.06 | 123,100 | 20,320 |
| Regular grade gasoline | 61 | 6.13 | 124,300 | 20,280 |
| Kerosene | 43 | 6.76 | 134,100 | 19,830 |
| Tractor fuel | 47 | 6.60 | 133,000 | 20,150 |
| Diesel fuel | 35 | 7.05 | 139,000 | 19,715 |

amount of energy derived from oil increased from 2,634 trillion to 17,290 trillion B.t.u. between 1920 and 1957. The total consumption of energy in the United States has more than doubled since 1920, but the energy from petroleum has increased 6.5 times. The energy from natural gas has increased 13.5 times.

The heating value (or, in engines, the heat of combustion) of a fuel is a measure of its worth. Heat units are expressed as British thermal units (B.t.u.).

Petroleum fuels contain more heat units per pound than such solid fuels as wood and coal. The combustion process consists of chemically combining oxygen of the air with carbon and hydrogen in the fuel. Heat is liberated in the process, and an increase in pressure results. The pressure increase in an engine takes place on the power or expansion stroke, and thus work is done.

THE EARLY FARM TRACTOR utilized the heavy, slow-running, low-compression, stationary engine placed in frames adapted from steam traction engines. Some of the early engines burned gasoline. Others burned kerosene.

Sixty years ago tractor engines had 1, 2, and 4 cylinders, rated at 10 to 30 horsepower and operated at 200 to 400 r.p.m. Gasoline-burning tractors had been manufactured since the early 1890's, but 15 companies produced steam tractors as late as 1920. Internal-combustion tractors and steam tractors competed in plowing matches in 1908–1912. The petroleum-fuel tractors were faster and more versatile than their steam competitors.

Because farmers wanted tractors that could use fuels cheaper than gasoline, the number of tractors burning kerosene and other low-volatility fuels predominated at first.

The volatility of a petroleum fuel is a measure of its ability to be vaporized for combustion. Thus it requires a higher temperature to vaporize kerosene than it does gasoline. Regular-grade gasoline is a better fuel than is needed for satisfactory operation of low-compression tractor engines.

Tractor engines that use low-grade fuels seldom detonate or knock on regular-grade gasoline even under the most severe conditions. Regular gasoline is used extensively as a tractor fuel, although it should be used in only high-compression tractor engines to obtain higher fuel-horsepower efficiency. Low-compression tractor engines operated on low-volatility fuels often have to be started and warmed up on gasoline.

About 40 percent of the tractor fuel in 1920 was gasoline.

The general-purpose tractors and the development of higher compression motors in the mid-1920's caused an increase in the use of gasoline. The introduction of pneumatic tires and increased production of higher compression motors meant that gasoline comprised about 69 percent of the tractor fuel in 1940.

Distillate, a variable and a poorly defined fuel, became a prominent tractor fuel in the early 1930's. Liquefied petroleum gas—LP gas—started to gain prominence as another type of tractor fuel in the 1940's. LP gas is propane or butane or both in varying proportions.

Kerosene, a leading tractor fuel in 1920 and the early 1930's, accounted for only 6 percent of the tractor fuel in 1940. Other fuels accounted for 25 percent. The use of gasoline for tractors has steadily increased since 1940. Fuel for all tractors in 1947 was approximately 80 percent gasoline, 3 percent kerosene, 6 percent distillate, 4 percent diesel fuel, and all other fuels 7 percent. In 1959, the approximate percentages were gasoline 85, LP gas 4, diesel 7, and all other fuels, including kerosene and distillate, 4.

Garden tractors, which use gasoline, in 1953 accounted for 7 percent of all tractors on farms, but used only 0.2 percent of the motor fuel used by tractors.

Automobiles ranked first among the users of petroleum fuel on farms in 1940 and earlier years. Tractors have been the largest single farm user of these fuels since 1940. There were approximately 4.3 million farm automobiles in 1959; in 1920 there were 2.1 million. There were an estimated 4.8 million tractors on United States farms in 1959, a threefold increase over 1940.

Farm motortrucks in 1957 numbered 2,900,000, almost three times the number in 1940. Consumption of gasoline by farm trucks totaled 1.2 billion gallons in 1957 and amounted to 17.5 percent of all fuels used in farm vehicles.

Commercial agricultural flying doubled in the decade from 1948 to 1957; the hours flown increased from 450,000 to 865,800. There are flying farmer organizations, which for the most part comprise owners of planes employed in the business rather than for recreation and pleasure.

Airplanes have been used for seeding, dusting, spraying, defoliation, fertilizing, supervision, frost protection, and other production uses. More than 61 million acres were treated from aircraft in 1957; more than 5,100 craft were utilized.

Motor fuel used by internal-combustion engines used for stationary work, self-propelled machines, chain saws, power lawnmowers, and auxiliary engines on machines amounted to about 400 million gallons in 1959. It was about 60 percent gasoline, 6 percent diesel fuel, 33 percent LP gas, and 1 percent all other fuels.

The total farm use of petroleum fuel, including LP gas, in 1953 was 8.8 billion gallons. The consumption in 1959 was more than 10 billion gallons. Farmers spend more than 2.5 billion dollars annually for petroleum products. The agricultural market takes about 10 percent of the domestic demand for petroleum products. The personal market, composed of passenger cars and oil burners, requires roughly 38 percent. The commercial and industrial market uses a little more than 48 percent. The rest, about 3.5 percent, goes to the Government-military market.

One-third to one-half the annual cost of owning and operating a tractor is for fuel.

Tractor engines are designed to use a variety of fuels, ranging from zero octane on up to premium grades of gasolines and the LP gases. Available are tractor engines that can burn high-octane, high-priced fuels with high efficiency, but they cannot burn low-test fuels. Other engines will burn cheap, low-test fuels or gasoline with relatively low power and efficiency. This is a complex situation, and many persons think there is no justification for the problem, and that all tractors should be high compression to follow the trend in car, truck, and airplane engines.

Two factors are responsible for this wide variation in requirements of tractor fuel. Low-test fuel was produced as a byproduct in the refinement of gasoline until a few years before the Second World War. This byproduct fuel was available to the farmer at low cost and gave economical power, even though performance and efficiency were lower.

Trends are probably away from a continuation of the byproduct status, because in recent years the price of diesel fuel has increased because of the rising consumption for heating purposes. The same is true for kerosene, which is used by jet engines.

A second important factor is the State tax refund procedure. Seventeen States in 1958 imposed gasoline taxes that were not exempt or refunded to the farmer when the fuel was used for agricultural purposes. Of the 27 States that gave refunds, 14 gave full refunds and 13 gave partial refunds, varying from 90 percent to all but a cent or two. Four States did not tax gasoline for agricultural uses. The tax rates vary from 4 to 7 cents a gallon. When a tax of more than a cent or two a gallon is levied, farmers turn from gasoline to nontaxed, low-test fuels for tractors.

Studies in Kansas showed that if a tax of 7 cents a gallon were added to gasoline, the fuel cost of plowing with a high-compression tractor was 77 percent higher than when nontaxed distillate was used. The cost increase was 29 percent if the gasoline was not taxed for tractor use.

The tractor manufacturer is encouraged to produce tractors of the low-compression, low-test-fuel type for the States where gasoline is not the predominate fuel, because of gasoline taxes. This means optional equipment or a compromise in designs of engines. It is not economical for the manufacturer or the farmer. The farmer does not benefit from engineering improvement and progress in engine design. However, continued distribution of the low-compression, low-test-fuel type of tractors in tax-refunding States results in inefficiencies because in those States most of the tractors operate on gasoline instead of on the lower volatile fuels for which they are designed.

As competition for fuel supplies increases because of the growing use in diesel locomotives, home furnaces, and aircraft, developments could easily make low-test or heavy fuels no longer a byproduct. Interest in low-compression tractors in all areas would wane, and a special problem would be created in States that tax gasoline used for agricultural purposes.

Farmers would be interested in higher compression tractors that use high-test gasoline or diesel engines that use diesel fuels if the tax on agricultural fuels were readjusted in those States that tax these fuels.

Diesel tractors have increased in numbers on farms. The performance characteristics of the engine and its economy of operation have been factors.

Some persons think that any compression-ignition engine is a diesel engine. Dr. Rudolph Diesel, the inventor, described the fundamental characteristic of his engine as the compression of a charge of air producing a temperature beyond the self-ignition point of the fuel, the subsequent fuel injection, and consequent instantaneous ignition of the fuel in this highly compressed hot air.

The operating principles of the diesel and the gasoline engine are basically the same. Both engines deliver power from the combustion of a mixture of fuel and air. Both engines are made in four-stroke cycle or two-stroke cycle. Because diesel engines have higher pressures, the construction is stronger and heavier. The significant differences are in the method of introducing and igniting the fuel charge. The gasoline engine employs a carburetor and spark-ignition system. The diesel uses a fuel-injection system and high compression.

Gasoline engines in tractors have a compression ratio in the neighborhood of $7:1$ or $8:1$. Diesels range from $14:1$ to $17:1$ or higher. The thermal efficiency of the gasoline engine is about 23 percent; that of the diesel, 32 percent.

Gasoline used in tractors weighs about 6 pounds a gallon. Diesel fuel weighs more than 7 pounds. Thus, the B.t.u.'s per gallon are about 124 thousand and 139 thousand, respectively. The diesel engine delivers about 15 or more brake horsepower-hours per gallon of fuel; the gasoline engine, 9 or 10. The low-speed torque of the diesel is better, but its idling and flexibility performance are poorer. The diesel has more exhaust smoke and little or no carbon monoxide. The gasoline engine has 3 to 6 percent of carbon monoxide.

Diesel tractors normally use diesel fuel, light furnace oil, or other designations. The fuel quality to use in every diesel engine is specified by the oil companies and the tractor manufacturers.

The choice of a diesel engine on a farm is governed by economic conditions. Diesel fuel normally costs less than gasoline, and since there is more energy in each gallon, a saving in fuel results. Diesels are more expensive than comparable gasoline tractors, however. Therefore the savings in fuel costs have to pay off the extra investment, although the price differential between diesel and gasoline tractors has tended to become narrower. As compression ratios increase in gasoline tractors, the cost has increased.

One must know two facts to determine the number of years it will take for fuel savings of a diesel tractor to pay off its higher price and fixed annual costs. One is the difference in price of fuel. The other is the number of hours a tractor is used in a year.

For example, the difference in price of a diesel tractor and a gasoline tractor may be put at 600 dollars and diesel fuel 3 cents a gallon less. If the tractor is to be used about 900 hours a year, it would have to be used more than 5 years to pay off the extra cost. On the basis of the same difference in fuel, the diesel would have to be kept more than 10 years to amortize the extra cost if it cost 750 dollars more.

LIQUEFIED PETROLEUM GAS—LP gas—sometimes is referred to as bottled gas. Both natural gas plants and oil refineries are sources of liquefied petroleum gases. The gases are stored and handled under pressure to keep them in liquid state. Pressure reducers and mixers are substituted for carburetion equipment for power use, and pressure reducers are used for heating purposes.

Farm consumption of LP gas in 1949 was estimated at 509 million gallons; in 1959 it was nearly one billion gallons—an increase of almost 100 percent. Much of the extra demand resulted from the use of gas in areas not served by gas from utility pipelines.

About 12 percent of American farmers used LP gas principally for heating houses in 1959. The percentages of farms using other fuels were: Fuel oil, kerosene, and other distillates, 23; natural and utility gas, 5; wood, 33; coal, 25; all others, including electricity, corncobs, and miscellaneous, 2. Thus petroleum products accounted

for about 40 percent of the farm household heating requirements.

About 65 percent of the LP gas used in 1959 was in farm homes, 25 percent as motor fuel, 6 percent as brooder fuel, and 4 percent in curing and drying crops, destroying weeds and brush, sterilizing dairy utensils, and other uses.

Household use of LP gas in 1959, about 34 percent of the total household petroleum fuel used, amounted to about 600 million gallons. Some is used in all States, but in the Southern Plains and the Delta States, it accounted for more than 80 percent of the liquid fuel used in farm homes. Household uses included cooking, heating water, heating, cooling, refrigeration, and processing of food.

LIGHT FUEL OILS are used in automatic household heating burners. Oil burners comprise almost one-half the domestic automatic-heating devices used in the United States. Farm household use of petroleum fuels in 1953 was estimated at 1,577 million gallons. About 14 percent of this was kerosene; 34 percent, LP gas; and about 52 percent, fuel oil and other distillates.

It was estimated that fuel oil met more than one-third of farm household heating requirements in 1959.

Almost 200 million gallons of petroleum fuels are used to cure and dry crops. More than two-thirds of this is kerosene; about one-third is LP gas, fuel oil, and other petroleum fuels.

More than 60 million gallons were used in equipment to control weeds and brush. About 10 percent of it was kerosene, and 90 percent was fuel oil, LP gas, and others. All other uses of petroleum, other than motor fuel, accounted for more than 60 million gallons.

In rural areas, where bacon rinds and tallow were once used to grease wagon axles, millions of gallons of lubricating oils and millions of pounds of greases are now used each year. These products lower maintenance costs and increase efficiency of motors.

Modern engines and machines require improved lubricants—clearances are reduced, speeds are increased, and loads made greater. Automotive lubricants increased in demand from a little more than 5 million barrels in 1920 to about 30 million barrels in 1958. Farm tractors and garden tractors very likely use about 120 million gallons of motor oil each year—an average of about 25 gallons per farm tractor annually.

GREASES are important lubricants for hard-to-reach bearings, in high-temperature operations, and in bearing housings that cannot be made oil-tight. Greases are used where splashing of fluid lubricants or dripping is objectionable and where bearings operate in dirty, dusty, or moist conditions.

Most greases are mixtures of metallic soaps in mineral oils. Wide ranges of performance characteristics are obtained by varying the properties of the mineral-oil base and the metallic soap. No longer may the farmer satisfy his needs with a pail of axle grease and a can of cup grease.

Several types of greases are required on the farm for the great variety of service needs of his engines and machines. Among them are cup, axle, fiber and sponge, graphite, extreme pressure, and tacky chassis greases. There is a trend toward the use of multipurpose greases, which are of the lithium soap class and are smooth and buttery in texture. They resist both water and high temperatures and may be used, if properly formulated, at temperatures of −90° to 350° F. They have good mechanical stability. Multipurpose greases will reduce the greases necessary on most farms to one or two types.

ASPHALTS are made by careful selection of crude oils, controlled air oxidation, and blending.

The products are inert to most chemicals and fumes. They resist weathering and permeation and absorption of water. They are tough and flexible, resist shock, and have good adhesion to materials used in construction.

Most asphalt is used for surfacing roads, but other uses are important. Roofing materials, floor coverings, preservatives, and livestock floors are common farm uses.

PETROCHEMICALS have been important to agriculture. Many of the new chemical insecticides, soil fumigants, weedkillers, fertilizers, plant and animal disease inhibitors, crop ripeners, and food preservatives contain petroleum or a derivative.

More than one-third of all insecticide and fungicide sprays have a petroleum base. Analysts predict that fully 40 percent of the Nation's total chemical output will be petroleum-derived by 1965.

RESEARCH ON OILS has yielded nitrogen fertilizer. Anhydrous ammonia is injected directly into the soil as a gas. More than 2 million tons of fertilizers, including anhydrous ammonia, aqua ammonia, ammonium nitrate, and urea, were used in 1958. All can be produced in petroleum refining processes.

Vapors of ethylene, propylene, and butylene will hasten the ripening of fruit. Seed potatoes treated with ethylene gas have produced an increased yield.

Defoliants—containing petroleum derivatives—cause plants to drop troublesome leaves and other growth and to ripen evenly for harvest. Defoliants have been used a good deal on cotton and edible beans and have improved the quality and grade of them.

Thin films of paraffin-type wax preserve fish, eggs, poultry, and many other products. Paraffin wax is obtained from petroleum. Paraffin wax preparations waterproof and vaporproof milk containers, cartons for cottage cheese, bread wrappers, cereal boxes, frozen food containers, and innumerable packages. Paraffin wax with thinners is used to coat silo interiors to prevent seepage of ensilage juices. It is painted or sprayed on and can be used also to waterproof masonry walls.

Paraffin waxes that are to be used in contact with food products are highly refined, but occasionally off-flavor objections are recorded for some foods.

Specially developed petroleum-derived sprays protect fruits with a rubbery web, which will stretch with growth and seal out insects and fungus growth. Others prevent premature dropping of fruit; uniform ripening and dropping can be promoted with other sprays.

PETROCHEMICALS preserve fruits, vegetables, grains, and other food products during shipment and storage. Some of these chemicals made from petroleum improve colors of fruit and vegetables and help preserve them in the market.

Detergents are important in the home and on the farm. They are added to lubricating oils, soaps, and other products. Those derived from petroleum are mainly alkyl-aryl sulfonates, with some alkyl sulfates.

Synthetic rubber employs in its manufacture the petroleum-derived chemicals butadiene and styrene. Tires, inner tubes, neoprene, and other compounds are extensively used for automobiles and machinery.

Nylon and other synthetic fibers are used for pump impellers, ropes, and coverings. Plastics are used for containers, floor coverings, feed and silo covers, vapor barriers, adhesives, paints, hoses, piping, tool handles, upholstery, and a multitude of other products. These fibers are made from petroleum or its derivatives.

MORE THAN 42 thousand businesses are engaged in producing, refining, transporting, and distributing wholesale petroleum and petroleum products. Nearly 12 thousand of them are fuel-oil dealers. More than 3 thousand are LP gas companies with one or more bulk plants.

Also, about 181 thousand service stations were in operation in 1960,

about 95 percent of them independently owned or operated by local businessmen.

The delivery of petroleum products by tank truck directly from the bulk plant or terminal is an important part of the bulk tank operation in rural areas. Thousands of farm equipment dealers service tractors in all parts of the country.

These dealers and their companies conduct schools, often in cooperation with State colleges and county agents, to train their employees and farmers in the most efficient use of tractors and power equipment.

THE 4-H CLUB tractor and machinery maintenance program is another area of common interest and cooperation sponsored in all States and Puerto Rico by eight oil companies. The program, started in 1944, generally has been conducted and directed by the Cooperative Extension Services of the State colleges of agriculture. The entire program is coordinated by the National Committee on Boys and Girls Club Work, Inc.

The original aims of the program were to provide training in the maintenance of farm equipment to help the farmer cut his costs for fuel and repairs and to develop a program that would appeal to older 4-H members. More than 750 thousand members were enrolled in 1959. Nearly 45 thousand volunteer leaders have been trained.

The leaders are selected by local groups and trained in State or district clinics, which usually are planned by State 4-H tractor committees and arranged by State 4-H leaders and extension agricultural engineers of the land-grant colleges.

Representatives of sponsoring oil companies and of farm equipment companies and dealerships also cooperate. Tractors and other equipment are furnished for demonstrations, contests, and other purposes. The companies have spent almost 2 million dollars for literature and leaders' expenses since the start of the program.

The 4-H Club tractor and machinery maintenance program stresses learning by doing. A basic objective of the program is to reduce waste in agricultural production caused by lack of proper service and care of equipment. Tractor repairs every year cost American farmers more than 500 million dollars, one-half of which could be saved by proper service and care. The annual farm bill for petroleum products is more than 2 billion dollars. About 10 percent of all fuel could be saved by proper care of equipment.

The Future Farmers of America (FFA), which operates through the vocational agriculture departments of high schools, has effective programs dealing with power, care of machinery, safety, production programs, and others. Farm equipment dealers, colleges, oil companies, teachers, and parents help conduct the program.

# Electricity
# Comes to Farms

John H. Rixse, Jr.

THE RURAL electric system has done much to increase farm production and to better farm living.

Insulated wires, a switch, a fuse, and a motor, a light, or an electrical appliance are all it takes for a farmer to make effective use of electricity.

Effective use means increasing production with less human labor, lightening the housewife's burden in the farm kitchen and laundry, and improving general living conditions.

Electricity must be dependable and available in adequate amounts at reasonable cost if the farmer is to benefit from it. An electric system, to supply power under those conditions, must be designed, maintained, and operated to meet the specific requirements and conditions of rural areas.

Electric generators on the farm, whether driven by engines or windmills, cannot meet the farmer's needs. Only service from a central station through a rural electric system can. Central-station service means the generation of electricity in large amounts at some central point and its transmission by wires directly to the farmer. The farmer's concern is to make wise and safe use of the electricity that is delivered to his door.

A quarter century of progress has put electricity at the door of nearly every farmer in America. Service from central stations was available to 10.9 percent of our farms in 1935. In 1940, 30 percent had service; in 1945, 45 percent; in 1950, 77 percent; in 1955, 92 percent; in 1960, 97 percent.

When George Westinghouse conceived the idea in 1886 of an electric system using an alternating current, electricity was theoretically within the reach of farmers on the fringe of towns. The outstanding characteristic of alternating current is that its voltage can be changed economically. The voltage can be "stepped-up" for transmission and then "stepped-down" for utilization, so that its transmission over long distances is practical.

California and New York had the first electrified farms. Many farms there and in the New England States had central-station electric service by 1935. The electrification of farms over the Nation was slow, however— zero in 1886, 1.6 percent in 1919, and 9.5 percent in 1929.

Many farmers who realized the value of electricity but were beyond the reach of the power system in towns and along electrified railways built their own electric systems. Power came from gasoline-driven generators, homemade water-wheel generators, windmill-driven generators, and battery systems. They could generate a limited amount of electricity, but they stimulated a desire for a more dependable and adequate source.

Interest grew meanwhile in the potential use of electric power on farms. Farmers, engineers, and scientists worked together. Study projects were set up at State experiment stations. Some farms became "laboratories." Research workers studied ways to increase the number of uses of electricity and improve uses already known. Engineers experimented with new materials and methods of building lines.

The Department of Agriculture, the land-grant colleges, the National Electric Light Association (NELA), and its successor, the Committee on the Relationship of Electricity to Agriculture (CREA), sponsored these investigations, studies, and developments. Experiment stations in Minnesota, Wisconsin, Michigan, Indiana, Iowa, California, and Maryland were among the leaders.

A project at Red Wing, Minn., brought central-station electricity to about 20 farm homes through the cooperation of the local utility company, the University of Minnesota, and 20 nationally known manufacturers. The aim was to find out how electricity could be used on the farm and whether the farmer could afford its cost. As the experiment continued, the use of power and the power bills went up sharply, but the farmers' returns increased more rapidly. The whole level of farm living was raised.

The main efforts between 1911 and 1935 looked to the wider use of electricity on farms that had electric service. Utility companies, manufacturers, and engineers developed techniques, materials, and equipment for lowering the cost of lines and transmitting power to more distant rural localities.

An example is the development of high-strength conductors known as Copperweld-Copper and ACSR. Copperweld conductor has a steel core coated by a thin layer of copper. ACSR is a composite conductor with a steel wire core, around which is

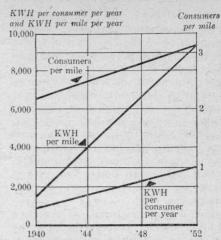

*A comparative study of the average use of energy and consumer trends on rural electric systems.*

stranded aluminum wire. Both conductors permit the structures, usually poles, to be more widely separated.

Early lines cost 2 thousand dollars or more a mile. By 1935, construction costs averaged about 1 thousand dollars a mile. Other advances were the use of higher voltages—6,900 volts instead of 2,400—and simplified single-bushing distribution transformers for use at the farm instead of the more expensive double-bushing transformers.

THE DEVELOPMENT of rural electrification after 1935 brought together the best of the many ideas for making electricity available to all farmers. It was stimulated by the establishment on May 11, 1935, of the Rural Electrification Administration.

REA was established initially by Executive Order 7037 of the President. The Rural Electrification Act of 1936 reestablished REA as a lending agency, and it was incorporated into the Department of Agriculture in 1939.

In the field of rural electrification, REA is empowered to make loans to qualified borrowers, with preference to nonprofit and cooperative associations and to public bodies. Loans cover the full cost of constructing powerlines and other facilities to serve persons in rural places who are without central-station service.

Lines constructed by REA borrowers are designed to serve entire rural areas, including less densely settled sections as well as the more populous areas. The "area coverage" policy became increasingly important as the rural electrification job progressed. The test was not whether an individual line or section was self-supporting but whether the entire system was feasible.

The percentage of farms having central-station service increased from 10.9 in 1935 to 97 in 1960. About half of them get electricity from REA-financed systems.

The rural electric systems financed by REA are relatively small. There were slightly more than 1 thousand such systems in 1960. Their average age was 13 years. They operated 1.5 million miles of line. They served 4.8 million consumers. Of 4.0 billion dollars borrowed from REA, 76 percent was invested in distribution lines. The remaining 24 percent was invested in generation facilities, transmission lines, and headquarters buildings.

REA itself operates no electric facilities. Its main functions are to lend money and assure repayment through appropriate loan-supporting activities. Loans are repaid from operating revenues of the locally owned, locally managed systems it finances.

When REA engineers first faced the problem of rapidly expanding rural electrification in 1935, they had a new combination of factors.

There was, first of all, a need for maximum economy in construction. The farmer was in no position to pay the bill for constructing lines that were as costly as those built in town. Lines had to be built at much lower cost.

The engineers also had to consider the long distances between consumers (an average of about three farmers to a mile); natural hazards like tornadoes, ice storms, windstorms, and lightning; the distances servicemen had to travel; the need for cross-country routing of pole lines; and the interference of trees and fast-growing brush with the lines.

Further, each farm had a demand and usage pattern that was quite different from the average home or small business in town.

These conditions demanded the adoption of the best techniques that had been developed by the electric power industry. Sometimes new equipment and methods were required.

A fundamental decision to meet these conditions was the adoption of a standard of 7,200 volts to ground, instead of the 2,400 that had been used most commonly by the industry. This increase in voltage meant that the same amount of power on the average could be transmitted nine times as far and nine times as many farmers could be reached.

It was decided to adopt a multi-grounded system: The neutral, or return, wire of the circuit was to be grounded every 1,000 to 1,500 feet and at every corner, every transformer, and every lightning arrester.

It was decided also to use the same neutral wire for the primary high-voltage circuit and also for the secondary, or service, voltage circuit. The practice elsewhere was to use two separate conductors.

These practices produced a new electrical system known as a 7,200/12,450-volt, multigrounded common primary-secondary neutral system. Less conductor was required because of the common neutral. Because the neutral was grounded frequently, one bushing was eliminated on the transformer. A bushing is required only for the connection of the high-voltage wire to the transformer. Because nearly every farm has a transformer in the yard, the voltage can be stepped down from 7,200 volts to 120/240 volts, which is safe and is required for utilization in the home and the barn.

Lightning is a problem in the country. Lightning does physical damage when it strikes and also introduces an undesired electrical surge, like a flood, in the system, which will destroy electrical equipment. To drain off the excess surge, lightning arresters are required. How best to provide this protection had concerned the engineers. The multigrounded neutral provided considerable relief in the basic electrical design.

Poles, which hold the conductor in the air away from people and objects and in a safe operating position, are expensive, but the heavy poles used in town are not needed for the light lines in rural areas. The use of high-strength conductors, such as Copperweld and ACSR, made it possible to put poles at 500- to 700-foot intervals, instead of 150 feet apart. Fewer poles meant fewer pole top pins and insulators. The pins and insulators were simplified.

Old systems required insulators in the down guy that must be put at every turn and corner in the line. The multigrounded neutral eliminated this one.

One transformer might serve 15 to 20 customers in cities, but every farm has its own transformer. The investment in transformers therefore is substantial, but the cost has been lowered by simplified transformers, made possible by new design and the new electrical systems. Transformers were made in small sizes specifically for rural use. They have a capacity of 1.5 to 3 kilovolt-ampere, compared to the smallest previously available, 5 kv.-a (approximately 5 thousand watts.)

Manufacturers and engineers also developed simple, reliable, self-reading cyclometer watt-hour meters, which were low in cost, rugged, and trouble free. Consumers could read their own meters and mail the reading to the office.

The application of production-line techniques to the construction of rural distribution lines did two things: It speeded construction, and it lowered costs.

A contractor would train crews of

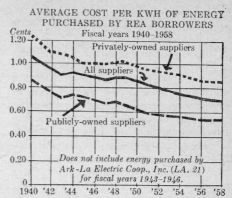

AVERAGE COST PER KWH OF ENERGY PURCHASED BY REA BORROWERS
Fiscal years 1940-1958

*Trends in the average cost of energy (cents per kilowatt-hour) purchased by REA borrowers for distribution.*

men for each of the operations, such as distributing poles, digging the pole holes, putting the hardware and other equipment on the pole before it was raised (thus eliminating the more costly practice of having a lineman climb the pole to install the hardware), raising the pole, backfilling the pole holes, stringing the conductor, pulling the conductor up to the proper tensions and sag, installing the transformer at the farm, and installing the service to the farm buildings.

Each crew, specially trained and equipped, would move down the line one after another, performing its function on a repetitive basis. A national construction average of 561 miles per working day was reached between 1947 and 1951. The peak was 707 miles a day in 1949.

These innovations in materials and practices reduced the cost of construction. The cost of a typical mile of rural line was brought down from an average of about 1 thousand dollars to as low as 5 hundred dollars. The reduction helped make rural electrification economically feasible.

The operation of the lines also presented new problems.

For example, the rural electric systems at first were sectionalized as utilities elsewhere were—that is, fuses

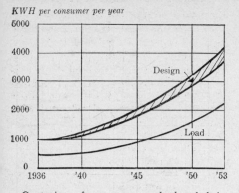

*KWH per consumer per year*

*Comparison of average system load and design capacity for rural electric systems.*

were used. In rural areas, however, that proved to be impractical. Tree limbs falling on wires, windstorms, and lightning could produce a short circuit or fault on a line, thus causing an extended interruption of service. To solve this problem, the automatic circuit recloser was developed by engineers and manufacturers.

These reclosers, now in almost universal use, allow three incidents, such as the blowing of a limb against the conductor. Each incident opens the line. After a certain number of seconds, the line closes again. This occurs three times. If the cause of the interruption still exists, the recloser locks open the fourth time. If the fault is temporary, the recloser will reset itself and will be ready to go through the entire cycle of operations when another fault occurs. The recloser thus separates permanent outages from temporary causes.

The problem of reviewing materials and making certain that they were adequate for rural service posed a challenge.

The answer was not in designing a new item but in establishing a procedure or technique. REA developed a technical standards committee to review all materials and equipment to determine their adequacy for use on REA-financed systems.

The materials had to meet minimum physical and electrical requirements. They had to be practical in cost and serviceability. Only those that met the general and technical requirements of a rural system could be considered.

The decisions regarding each item of material were made available to industry and the rural systems in a publication, "List of Materials Acceptable for Use on REA-Financed Electrification Systems." It is available from the Government Printing Office at a subscription price of 2 dollars, which includes one semiannual supplement.

Engineers adapted to everyday use the two-way radio systems, which had been developed during the Second World War. Among the rural electric systems, more than 10 thousand vehicles were equipped with two-way radios in 1960. The radios help operation and construction crews and also are an asset in time of emergency.

To INSURE reliable service, facilities and equipment—poles, reclosers, lines, and conductors—are inspected periodically.

Because rural lines are built across the countryside, through woods, and over fields, special attention must be given to maintaining adequately cleared rights-of-way. To insure reliable service and overall lower costs, it has been found that rights-of-way need to be cleared to widths of 30 to 50 feet. Since hand clearing is slow and expensive in many sections, chemical control of undesirable growth has been adopted widely.

To avoid interruptions of service to farms while doing the necessary work of construction and maintenance, crews do not take a line out of service. They know how to do the work on lines that are energized, or hot. They have special training and tools for that dangerous work.

Electric lines can cause interference in radio and TV reception. The farther the receiver is from the transmitter, the more noticeable the interference becomes. It arises from the relationship of materials and equipment on the poles and in the equipment, which creates a transmitting condition. If design is at fault, the condition can be eliminated. If it is due to a poorly maintained facility, it also can be eliminated. All equipment for rural electric systems therefore must meet exacting standards and must be maintained properly.

As farmers have increased their use of power, loads have grown and there has been need for work in rebuilding and "heavying-up" the rural lines to carry larger amounts of power. It had been customary to plan facilities for distribution systems 1 to 3 years ahead. That was replaced by engineering plans for a minimum of 10 years, keeping in mind facilities that would give good service and assist in repayment of investment in future years.

But long-range planning has become more than that: It now is looking ahead to the day when rural electric systems will have to serve four to six times the loads they now serve. On that basis, engineers arrive at a reasonable analysis of possible development of each system and a method of obtaining it. Each year's work and decisions can then be fitted into the project as it finally will emerge.

In the earlier days of the rural electrification program, there was often a shortage of wholesale power. In some places it was expensive. These conditions restricted the use farmers could make of electricity. The average cost of power from all sources has been going down continuously, however, and it is generally available in adequate amounts.

Power companies are the major source of power, but in some areas rural cooperatives have joined to build their own low-cost generation and transmission systems.

The costs of material and labor have continued to rise.

The need to develop new and simplified items of materials and equipment continues. One possibility studied by engineers and managers is the use of the digital computer to analyze

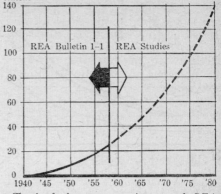

*Net KWH power requirements, billions*

REA Bulletin 1–1    REA Studies

*Trend of the energy requirements of REA-financed systems—actual requirements 1943–1958, estimated requirements 1959–1980.*

the mass of data needed in the operation of an electric system.

Safety is another continuing concern. The electric utility industry is one of the most hazardous. Careful design, construction, operation, and maintenance are vital in helping to avoid accidents and untoward incidents, but none can protect against carelessness, indifference, or ignorance. Considerable attention is being given to overcoming them.

Those who work in REA and rural electric systems have been asking themselves: Is effective use being made of the materials that have been developed recently? Can present equipment be redesigned for more effective service? Are new basic concepts needed? What are the possibilities of higher distribution voltages?

Despite the achievements in the systems, little progress has been made in improving the farmstead wiring. The need has long existed for a more effective distribution of electric power on the farm. A higher secondary or service voltage of 220/480 volts may be the answer.

Maintaining a steady load is the eternal problem of a distribution system. Electric loads are seasonal. Irrigation and air conditioning, for example, boost the summer load beyond that of the winter. The summer load can be balanced if the consumer uses electric heating. That means better utilization of electric facilities and a lower average cost for wholesale power—the objective of electric distributors everywhere.

# Farmers Use Electricity

T. E. Hienton and J. P. Schaenzer

OF ALL the many uses of electricity on farms, lighting the house comes first.

That use, like the others, can be made more effective.

The amount of light is important.

For the proper performance of various tasks, we can recommend four levels of illumination—low, medium, high, and very high.

At the low level are general lighting for living and dining rooms, bedrooms, halls, and stairways.

General reading and sewing, kitchen, and laundry are at the medium level.

Reading small type, studying, writing, and working at a bench and in a workshop are at the high level.

Sewing for long periods or on dark fabrics requires a very high level.

The use of bulbs of different wattage, such as 50, 100, and 150 watts, simplifies changing the illumination level desired for different activities.

Good lighting is the right kind and the right amount of light at the right place. Lamps must be well placed. There should be no glare and no shadows on your work. Distribution of light should be uniform, never spotty.

Shades are used to prevent glare and to direct light. They should have a white or light-colored lining and an open top to reflect the light downward. The height and position of a shade with respect to the lamp are important to prevent light from striking readers' eyes directly.

Individual rooms or areas in the house need special lighting. Shadow-free light is needed over stairways. A dining room that is used for study requires a fixture that will give good light on the table and distribute some through the rest of the room. In a kitchen, light is needed around the sides of the room where work is done. In the bathroom and bedroom, wall-mounted mirrors should have lamps on each side.

Dairy barns, milkhouses, general barns, brooder houses, and garages are most likely—next to farmhouses—to be wired.

Many chores are done in them. Good lighting makes for better and faster work. The time needed for stabling cows, cleaning mangers, and feeding hay and grain, for example, was found to be 84.5 minutes if done by lantern light and 55 minutes by electric light. Farmers in Wisconsin reported that good lights saved them an hour per man per day in doing chores.

The lights should be placed properly. Enough light behind the cows promotes cleanliness.

More illumination is needed in the feed alley than is ordinarily used when feed is weighed for individual cows.

A properly placed lamp with a swivel socket helps one to inspect the inside of bulk milk tanks for cleanliness.

A fluorescent fixture over the washtubs in the milkhouse makes it easier to be sure that the utensils are clean.

General illumination is necessary in the farm shop. Each major machine tool should have a special lamp, because work often is done at night in the shop or during bad weather. A good light over the shop bench is necessary. A rough service lamp is more suitable than the ordinary lamp for use on an extension cord to provide light under and around farm machines that are being repaired.

Incandescent lamps in haymows and feed and mixing rooms should be protected by dustproof fixtures to reduce the danger of fire and explosion.

ANOTHER USE of electricity is to extend the period of light to 13 hours in fall and winter so as to stimulate greater production of eggs.

The effect of increasing the light period is physiological. It does more than merely give the hens more time to eat.

Light is provided by mounting 60-watt incandescent lamps at the ceiling, 8 to 10 feet apart, midway between the front wall and droppings board. Incandescent units of one-half watt per square foot are adequate in large henhouses. A timeclock turns the lamps on before daylight or at dusk to give the required daylength.

Gradual increase in daylength (1 hour a week or month) is considered more effective in stimulating egg production than lengthening the lighted time abruptly.

Daylength for the turkey breeding flock is a factor in the fertility of males as well as in production of eggs. An 11-hour day is used in early winter and is increased gradually 1 hour a day each month. Restricting male turkeys to an 8-hour light-day before the breeding season extends their fertility periods.

Lighting installations in poultry houses should include a 12-inch shallow dome reflector with each lamp to distribute the light effectively. Lamps with built-in reflectors may be used where reflectors are not installed. Such lamps are not available in sizes smaller than 75 watts.

A SIMILAR DEVELOPMENT is the discovery of the response of plants to changes in daily durations of light and dark — photoperiodism — by W. W. Garner and H. A. Allard of the Department of Agriculture in 1920. Short-day plants, such as the chrysanthemum, flower best in late summer or fall when days are short. Long-day plants, such as the China-aster, flower best in midsummer when days are long. Indeterminate plants, such as the tomato, seem uninfluenced by daylength and flower throughout the growing season.

Daily duration of darkness, not of light, regulates flowering. Short-day plants therefore are really long-night plants. Long-day ones can be considered short-night plants.

The duration of darkness can be regulated effectively by artificial light, used either at the end of the day to shorten the dark period or, more economically, as a brief interruption in the middle of the dark period to divide it into two short periods.

Responses of various long-day, short-day, and indeterminate plants to supplemental light from unfiltered incandescent or fluorescent lamps were reported in 1958 by R. J. Downs, H. A. Borthwick, and A. A. Piringer of the Department of Agriculture.

The incandescent lamp is more efficient in accelerating the flowering of long-day plants and promoting more rapid vegetative growth of herbaceous and woody plants than fluorescent lamps.

The fluorescent lamp is considered to be the better source for fulfilling the high-intensity light requirements of artificially lighted growth rooms.

Electric lighting is utilized extensively in greenhouses and outdoors by commercial chrysanthemum growers to control time of flowering.

Home gardeners also utilize electric lamps to start plants from seed, root cuttings, or grow plants in the basement or other available space. Fluorescent lamps are a practical source of light for such installations. The lighting and other equipment can be readily assembled at home or bought as a complete unit. Provision must be made to regulate the air temperature surrounding the plants as the lamps supply considerable heat. This is done by enclosing the plants in some sort of chamber that can be heated or cooled as conditions require.

SOME ELECTRIC LAMPS attract night-flying insects. Adult insects of several species naturally fly to a flame or lamp. The carbon-filament electric lamp, invented in 1879 by Thomas A. Edison, furnished more visible light than other lamps, but the yellow color was only slightly more attractive to insects than the weak yellow light of the candle or kerosene lantern. The tungsten-filament lamp and the newer lamps that supply near-ultraviolet (black light) radiant energy are even more attractive to them.

European corn borers, adult tobacco and tomato hornworms, corn earworm moths, the pink bollworm, armyworm, and European chafer are among the insects of economic importance that are lured irresistibly to near-ultraviolet sources.

Traps equipped with black-light fluorescent lamps have been used throughout the country to detect the emergence and the abundance of many species of insects as a guide in control measures.

Designs for these insect survey traps have been developed through investigations of Federal and State agricultural engineers and entomologists in Indiana, Iowa, Texas, and Virginia since 1955. Other electric traps that use a black-light lamp are being developed in attempts to control various insects.

ELECTRIC LAMPS provide useful light in sorting and grading operations in agriculture.

Eggs are examined under the light from a clear-glass incandescent electric lamp, operated in combination with a lens and focus reflector. Automatic sorting of eggs for shell color has been made possible by a machine developed in the Department of Agriculture.

Stripping and sorting some varieties of tobacco, such as burley, broadleaf, Havana seed, and Type 32, is done effectively under lamps of proper color, uniformity, and intensity. The commonly accepted lighting unit is a combination of two types of 40-watt fluorescent lamps, one a daylight and the other a deluxe cool white. They provide a color combination determined by research to be suitable for grading these tobaccos.

LIGHT promotes safety.

Electric lamps, suitably placed in the yard, make working around the farmstead safer after dark and give protection against thieves and prowlers.

Every farmstead and estate should have at least a 200- or 300-watt incandescent lamp, mounted in a weatherproof fixture on a pole near the center of the farmstead. Lamps put at the sides or corners of buildings in angle reflectors give additional lighting for specific areas.

Manual control, with three- or four-way switches, enables one to turn the lamps on and off from two places or more.

Automatic control of lighting can be provided by installing a photoelectric cell or sunswitch, a type of switch that is sensitive to changes in light intensity and automatically turns the lamp on at dusk and off at dawn.

ELECTRIC MOTORS have replaced human, animal, wind, and internal-combustion engines for driving many machines on farms.

One of the first known farm installations of an electric motor was in 1898 in California to replace a gasoline engine for driving an irrigation pump, when the most important source of power for irrigation pumping was wind.

The use of electric motors has increased steadily as electric service and new machines became available. More than 500 thousand electric motors, totaling more than 6 million horsepower, were in use on farms in California in 1960.

At least 35 household appliances and more than 100 farm machines driven by electric motors are now in use on American farms. Among them are washing machines, refrigerators, food freezers, vacuum cleaners, food mixers, clocks, ironers, sewing machines, fuel pumps, fans, water pumps, grain and forage elevators, air compressors, milking machines, milk or egg coolers, drill presses, tool grinders, crop driers, and feeders for poultry and livestock.

RUNNING WATER in the house and farmstead saves labor, improves sanitation, promotes efficiency in livestock production, and provides fire protection.

One in 10 American farms had running water installations in 1920; 6 in 10 had them in 1960. Running water is not always pumped by electric power, but the advantage of automatic operation, provided by electric motor-driven pumps, has influenced many farmers to install such equipment—for example, 78 percent of farms in Illinois and 64.6 percent of farms in Kansas had pumps in 1958.

ELECTRIC WASHING MACHINES were used on 80 percent of American farms in 1960.

The machines save about 60 percent of the time needed to wash clothes on a washboard and about 25 percent of the time needed with a hand machine. The hand machine, in its time, was 10 to 38 percent more efficient than the washboard. Automatic or semiautomatic washing machines increase this saving in time even more.

Mechanical refrigerators, powered by electric motors, have filled an important need for satisfactory refrigeration in the farm home. Lacking ice delivery and desirous of properly caring for family foods, farm families welcomed the arrival of the electric refrigerator: Of 99,011 farmhouses included in a survey in 19 States in 1934, 22.9 percent of those with central-station electric service had mechanical refrigerators; 11 years

SOURCE OF POWER FOR
REA-FINANCED SYSTEMS

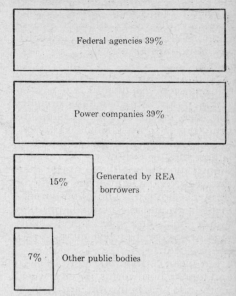

Federal agencies 39%

Power companies 39%

15%   Generated by REA
        borrowers

7%   Other public bodies

*Source of power supplied to REA-financed systems for distribution.*

later, 1,737,463 mechanical refrigerators (64.8 percent of farms reporting electric service from a powerline) were reported in the Census of Agriculture. A survey of 10,508 farms with electric service in Kansas in 1958 showed that 82 percent had electric refrigerators.

Interest in home freezers for the farm was stimulated during the Second World War by the need to preserve food. The construction of locker plants, beginning about 1935, had acquainted farm and town families with the use of community lockers for storing frozen meat and vegetables. Freezing food and storing it in a cabinet on the farm was just beginning to attract attention at the outbreak of the war. A few pilot-model home freezers had been installed experimentally on farms. Commercial manufacture of such units was just starting and was limited during the war by shortages of materials.

Consequently the interest of farmers

in the construction of such freezers at home was intensified in order to preserve all food as well as possible.

Plans were prepared for a two-temperature, walk-in refrigerator for the farm. They were based on the design and testing of units at the Agricultural Research Center and on Maryland farms. The plans were distributed by State agricultural extension services. Technical specifications for a package-unit freezer also were developed in the Department of Agriculture.

The number of home freezers on farms increased from 650 thousand in 1950 to 2 million in 1960.

Air-conditioning equipment includes room coolers and central systems that have a mechanical refrigeration unit driven by an electric motor. Window fans and attic fans may be helpful in making a house more comfortable, but they are not considered air-conditioning equipment.

Central systems include a single refrigeration compressor and a coil- and fan-unit to circulate cooled air in the house through ducts. The heat pump differs from such equipment in that it provides not only refrigeration but also heat, when the refrigeration cycle is reversed.

Room coolers are designed to cool one room, not several rooms. Those who try to cool two or more rooms with single-room units may get unsatisfactory results.

THE NUMBER of milking machines has increased sixtyfold on United States farms in the past half century. Of the estimated number (725 thousand in 1958) 63.6 percent were installed between 1940 and 1950. Census figures put the number of milking machines at 12 thousand in 1910 and 636 thousand in 1950.

The adoption of machine milking to replace hand milking has been due to shortage of labor, the need to raise the operator's efficiency, and the availability of electric power to operate the milkers.

A similarity exists between the increase in the number of milking machines and index numbers of production per man-hour for dairy cows. A report of work in Illinois, a 1957 publication by C. J. Fenzau and R. N. Van Arsdall (Agriculture Information Bulletin No. 153), said that machine milking reduces milking time to less than one-half that spent in milking by hand.

IRRIGATION PUMPS utilize more electric energy than any other farm motor application, particularly in the Western States, Arkansas, and Louisiana.

The extent of this load in California, compared to human effort, was reported in 1925 by L. J. Fletcher, of the California Agricultural Experiment Station: "If all the wells in California now equipped with electrically operated irrigation pumps were furnished with hand pumps instead, and all the men and boys over 15 years of age in the State were set to work pumping 10 hours each day, every day in the year, they would be able to deliver, altogether, less than one-third the water now furnished by electrically operated pumps during the irrigation season." There were more than 1,750,000 men and boys over 15 years in California in 1925, and there were 39,600 irrigation motors, totaling 656 thousand horsepower, in the State.

There were 156 thousand irrigation pumps in 19 Western States and Florida in 1950. Electric motors provided power for 67.3 percent of them. Since 1950, 28 thousand pump installations, of which 5 thousand were electric, have been made in the Texas Panhandle. Electric motors supplied power to 4 thousand irrigation pumps in the humid area (28 Southern and Eastern States) in 1955.

An increasing number of irrigation pumps is being installed in the humid area to offset the crop losses due to inadequate rainfall during critical periods of the growing season. Power units for these pumps may be internal-combustion engines or electric motors. Engine power has predominated in this area. The development of special single-phase motors of 20-horsepower capacity and the increasing availability of three-phase electric service to farms have meant greater use of electric motors. This shift parallels the one that occurred in the pump-irrigation areas of Western States between 1920 and 1930.

MATERIALS HANDLING on farms for production purposes and waste disposal has been a major time-consuming chore.

Research at the University of Massachusetts disclosed that a total of 19 tons of silage, grain, hay, bedding, milk, and manure are handled every year for each cow in a 40-cow herd.

Of the 19 tons, 6 are manure. Great progress has been made in the application of electric equipment to the removal and disposal of manure and wastes on the farm.

F. W. Duffee and L. A. Brooks, agricultural engineers at the University of Wisconsin, conducted studies of the time required by various methods of barn cleaning for a 30-cow dairy. The wheelbarrow took 174 hours per year to remove the manure; the litter carrier, 140 hours. Direct loading into the manure spreader made possible by the drive-through cowbarn still took 138 hours per year. When electricity was available, the semiautomatic cleaner came into being, and the time was cut to 72 hours. The automatic cleaner has cut the time still further, so that only 24 hours per year are required to clean a 30-cow dairy barn—one-seventh of the time a man used to take with a wheelbarrow.

Modern laying houses, such as the solar house at The Pennsylvania State University, designed by H. V. Walton and G. O. Bressler, employ electrically operated barn cleaners to remove the poultry droppings. Cleaners may be placed under a slatted floor or in a wire-covered pit under tiers of mechanical feeders and automatic waterers.

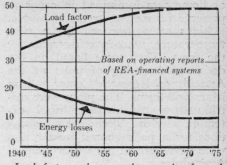

*Percent load factor and energy losses*

*Load factor and energy loss trends of rural electric systems.*

H. B. Puckett, an agricultural engineer at the University of Illinois, planned a system for automatically cleaning the floor of a hoghouse. A 2-horsepower pump supplies 10 gallons of water a minute at a pressure of 70 pounds per square inch. The loosened manure is washed down a 4-inch drain and into a septic tank, which has a drain field.

Waste disposal is a big problem on poultry farms. Agricultural engineers of the Department of Agriculture and the Connecticut and Maine Agricultural Experiment Stations developed a 1,500-gallon heated septic tank and drain field, which they found will meet the needs of a farm that has 10 thousand hens or 20 thousand broilers. To insure satisfactory digestion of the carcasses in about 11 days, the tank contents were heated electrically and held at 100° F. This took 2 to 3 kilowatt-hours per day.

Manure tanks or pits of large capacity have been built on farms of the Willamette Valley, Oregon. Into such a tank are flushed the manure from the barn and the paved barnyard as well as the wastes from the milking area and milkhouse washings. Some farmers empty the tank by pumping the manure into a tank wagon or trailer and haul it to the fields. Others add more water to the tank, mix it thoroughly, and pump it

These reminders of the way it used to be are a manifest of the mechanical revolution in farming: The growing use of power, new materials, and capital equipment instead of human labor to produce food and fibers.

From Diderot's old Encyclopedia came this view of practices recommended in France as the Industrial Revolution dawned two centuries ago. Horses should replace oxen for pulling such innovations as the harrow, roller, and a plow of the type invented by the Englishman Jethro Tull. A new, light seeder was more efficient than broadcasting seed. Narrow strips of land should be made into broad fields. Efforts should be coordinated. At first, many did not like the newfangled ideas: Why change the old ways?

Men and women with scythes and rakes made hay and harvested the grain, which was threshed later with flails. The first settlers in America brought tools and methods from the Old Countries. Their power to produce was limited.

In the Farmers' Museum of the New York State Historical Association in Cooperstown, N.Y., and the Smithsonian Institution in Washington, one can see tools the pioneers used, participate in a way in their daily work (including the making of butter), and gain insight into the progress since of farming and agricultural engineering.

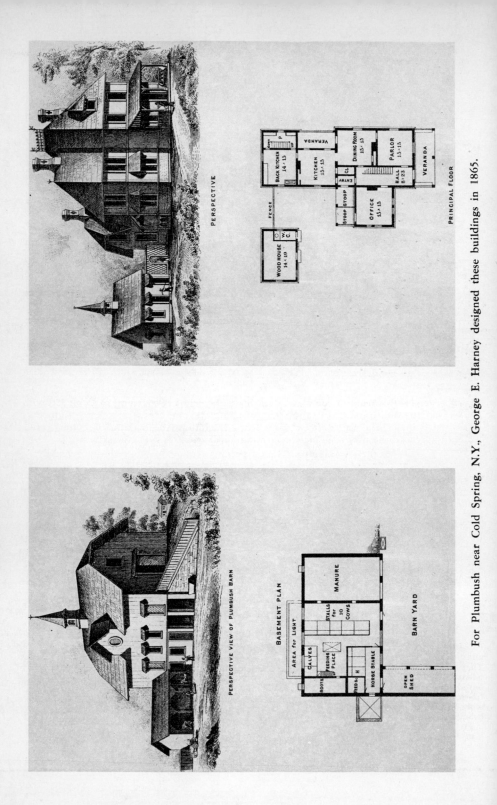

For Plumbush near Cold Spring, N.Y., George E. Harney designed these buildings in 1865.

# E. WHITMAN & CO'S
# DOUBLE GEARED HORSE POWER.

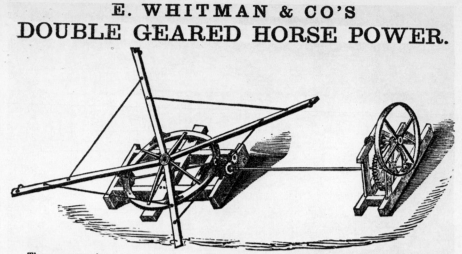

The accompanying cut represents a NEW HORSE POWER that was added to our stock in 1856, and which we take great pleasure in recommending. It is one of the most simple, durable, and strongest Powers in use. It is manufactured by us, and is warranted to be WELL made, of the best materials, and in the most substantial manner. It is a four-horse power, but has sufficient strength for six or eight horses, and we recommend it as one of the best Horse Powers in use in this country. Price $120.

☞ See Thresher on another page.

myl

---

# E. WHITMAN & CO'S
# Wrought Iron Railway Horse Power.

It is well known that these Powers are manufactured by us of Wrought Iron instead of Cast, and that all the materials are of the very best quality, which renders them strong and durable. They work much lighter than other Railway Powers, and will last four times as long. We are confident that no person acquainted with the merits of this power will purchase any other. The sales have regularly increased during the past fourteen years, and although no changes have been made in the general principle of the power, yet many slight improvements have been made, which make it more durable, and we recommend this power to our customers this season, as perfect in every particular, and cannot fail to please if properly managed.

PRICE OF DOUBLE POWER, $110——PRICE OF SINGLE POWER, $85.

myl                  E. WHITMAN & CO., 63 EXCHANGE PLACE, BALTIMORE.

# RANDALL'S REAPER, AS USED IN 1833.

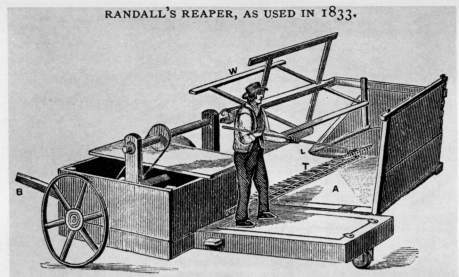

A. Platform which receives the cut grain.  B. Tongue to which the horses were attached.  L. Divider.  T. Cutters.  W. Reed.

Bell's Reaper, 1828.

N. Currier depicted this American Farm Scene in 1853.  A major advance was the sulky plow, which let the plowman ride, instead of walk.

Archambault, "The Forty-Niner," 1849.

Atlas Engine, 1881.

Froelich, 1892.

Hart-Parr No. 1, 1902.

Holt (steam), 1904.

International Harvester, 1906.

Big Four "30," 1910.

Man's genius produced the tractor to fill a great need and then improved it, step by step.

Case 20–40, 1912.

Wallis "Cub," 1913.

Bull, 1913.

Moline Universal, 1914.

Case (steam), 1915.

Heider, 1915.

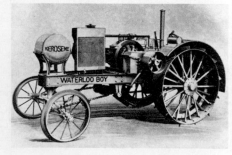

Waterloo Boy N 12–25, 1916.

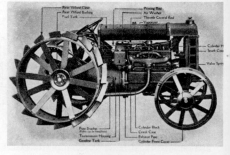

Fordson, 1917.

Best, 1918.

Twin City, 1919.

John Deere D, 1923.

McCormick-Deering Farmall, 1924.

Caterpillar 15, 1929.

Massey-Harris Four-Wheel Drive, 1930.

Oliver Tricycle Row Crop, 1930.

Allis-Chalmers B, 1938.

Developments came fast. They included the threshing rig, powered by a steam engine or tractor, horses, and many men. Trucks and highways opened many more markets.

The power to produce was multiplied by internal-combustion engines, which, in trucks and tractors, provided mobile power; petroleum products; central-station electricity; all-weather roads and better means of communication; more efficient buildings and farmsteads; machines for working the land; and countless other technologic developments. A few of the multipliers of power are illustrated in the pages that follow. Not all of them were big machines. This farmshop, powered by electricity, has equipment that enables a farmer to build simple machines and small buildings and make repairs.

Modern tractors have many uses. One is to dig postholes. Another is to mix concrete. In a mixer like this, which operates from the power takeoff of a utility tractor, a full one-bag batch can be loaded, mixed, transported, and dumped in minutes.

Tractors also can lift huge loads and cultivate gardens.

Many small machines, including powersaws, can save time, effort, and money. The extension of telephone, radio, and television and the delivery of newspapers, market bulletins, and magazines have ended the comparative isolation of farms. Intricate exchange facilities have been installed so farm communities can have modern dial telephones. All these have increased the power to produce.

through the irrigation system, so that the mixture can be distributed on the land by hand with a firehose.

MECHANICAL FEEDERS, which deliver grain or silage to animals from bins or other storages, are a development since 1950. They are driven by electric motors, which are controlled by time-clocks or manually.

Mechanical poultry feeders, used almost entirely for mash feeding, have come into greatest use. Nearly 65 thousand of them were in use in 1958.

Mechanical feeders for grain and silage are of more recent development, and fewer have been manufactured.

One of them, developed by E. F. Olver and R. N. Jones at the Pennsylvania Agricultural Experiment Station, can supply an accurate amount of concentrate to individual cows in stanchions. An automatic silage feeder was perfected in 1953. An automatic hog-feeding system was designed in 1957.

The movement by hand of grain, hay, silage, and other heavy, bulky objects used or produced on a farm takes a lot of energy.

Elevators, conveyors, and blowers to do that work have been available a long time, but new and improved machines with electric power available to drive them have increased their acceptance.

Portable elevators of various sizes meet different requirements for moving small grain, ear corn, baled or chopped hay, silage, and straw. Belt, chain, screw, and pneumatic conveyors of proper design handle some materials horizontally. Electric motor requirements vary from one-half to 5 horsepower, varying with type, size, and capacity.

SILO UNLOADERS eliminate twice-a-day trips up and down the silo chute to remove silage with a fork or shovel by human muscle.

The unloading machine is essentially a horizontal conveyor, suspended from the top of the silo, or supported

directly on the surface of the material by three or four wide-rimmed wheels. Both are known as top or surface unloaders. Another type, the bottom unloader, remains fixed at the bottom of the silo. Surface and bottom types are both driven by electric motors of 3 to 7.5 horsepower. Mechanical silo unloading saved one man-minute per 100 pounds of silage removed.

Difficulties in unloading grass silage and all frozen silages and poor performance of some old machines reduced unloading capacity in studies in Minnesota in 1957–1959. Six makes of new machines unloaded unfrozen corn silage at an average rate of 147 pounds a minute. Thirteen thousand silo unloaders were put into use in 1955–1958—more than 40 percent of them in 1958.

FARMERS began to install equipment for mechanical refrigeration to cool products in 1925.

Milk, eggs, fruit, and vegetables require quick cooling and cool storage to preserve their quality. It used to be done with ice. Refrigerating machinery for cooling milk was considered too expensive for the ordinary farmer until small electric refrigerators became more widely available in the early 1920's. By 1928, test results at several experiment stations disclosed that the costs of electric cooling, including labor, interest, depreciation, and power, could be less than for ice cooling.

Changes in the design of milk coolers began with the dry box and wet insulated concrete tank, progressed to commercial can coolers, and finally to bulk milk tanks. Lack of electric service forced many dairymen to install engine-driven milk coolers in the late 1930's, but they were replaced by electric-motor drive as electric lines were extended.

The first egg coolers were of some type of water-evaporating device and an electric fan. Before long the economy of mechanically refrigerating eggs was demonstrated.

Fruit and potato growers have installed mechanical refrigeration in their storage houses.

THE GENERATION of heat by the passage of electric current through a wire, the fundamental principle of electric cooking, has been known since the days of Benjamin Franklin, but we do not know who first applied this principle to electric cooking and heating appliances. Such devices were exhibited at the Crystal Palace in London in 1891, and an electrically cooked banquet was given in honor of the Lord Mayor of London in 1894.

Development of the electric range in this country is an outgrowth of socket appliances, the first of which was the electric iron.

A 1925 survey of 9,000 farms in California with electric service showed that 2,254 (25 percent) had electric ranges. Surveys in Illinois and Kansas in 1958 of 39,540 and 10,508 farms with electric service reported 43 and 37.5 percent, respectively, equipped with electric ranges.

Early users of electric ranges insisted on a range with a firebox in which corncobs or other locally available fuel could be burned to heat the kitchen during cold weather or water for laundry and bathing. As central heating systems were installed in farm homes, the demand for this combination range disappeared.

A few farm housewives in the Nation in 1960 had electronic ranges, which use radio-frequency energy, instead of those with common resistance-wire heating units.

ELECTRIC WATER HEATERS were used first in homes in 1920 or so.

Of the three types of electric water heaters—resistance (heat produced by electric current flowing through wire), induction (by transformer action), and carbon-electrode (electric current flowing through water from one electrode to another)—only the resistance type is commonly used in homes.

Electric water heaters were found in tests to be the highest in relative efficiency and convenience as well as operating cost and time required for heating.

Improved designs and low energy rates have increased the popularity of such heaters in farm homes.

Automatic washers and dishwashers have added to the hot water requirements and stimulated installations of water heaters.

About 30 percent of electrically equipped farmhouses had electric water heaters in 1959.

AUTOMATIC electric clothes driers have been installed in farmhouses mostly since 1950.

Studies at the Ohio Agricultural Experiment Station gave more satisfactory results for drying washed clothes in a drier than on an outside line, including time required for handling clothes after they were washed, loss of weight, and tensile strength. Shrinkage was greater for clothing dried in the drier than on the line. Electricity used averaged 2.7 kilowatt-hours and gas, 9.6 cubic feet for drying an 8-pound load. Additional electric energy was used for operating the electric motor on the gas drier.

Surveys of electric equipment on Illinois and Kansas farms reported 10.6 and 4.1 percent, respectively, with electric clothes driers in 1955 and 20 and 11 percent in 1958.

ELECTRIC CHICK BROODING was one of the first farm applications of electric heat. Development of such equipment began about 1920.

The early brooders, used primarily in mild climates, lacked sufficient heating capacity for winter brooding in colder climates, but several manufacturers have increased the heating capacity from 500 to about 1,000 watts.

Radiant-heat and underfloor-heat types of electric brooders also have been developed.

More than 750 thousand American farms had electric brooders—16 percent of those with electric service—in 1960.

A farmer in Minnesota discovered in 1927 that he saved one or two pigs in a litter when he suspended a household heater over his farrowing pens.

In an early trial of specially designed underheat and radiant-type pig brooders in California, pig losses during the first 10 days after birth with the brooders were about half the losses in unheated farrowing pens.

Lamb-brooding equipment, similar to that for pig brooding, was developed at the Washington Agricultural Experiment Station in 1940.

The use of such equipment increased rapidly during the war years; incandescent lamps were used for heat. Infrared lamps have provided the heat source in most pig brooders since then. The 1954 Census of Agriculture reported 117,987 farms with electric pig brooders.

AUTOMATIC WATERING of livestock and poultry proved to be economical before electric heaters became available to prevent winter freezing. Investigations at the Iowa Agricultural Experiment Station in 1926 established that giving heated water proved beneficial with fall pigs.

Pullets drank 25.4 percent more warmed water than cold water during freezing weather in investigations at the Oregon Agricultural Experiment Station.

Cows given free access to water were found to produce more milk and more butterfat than when permitted to drink twice a day.

Warm water increased the gain per steer by 8.9 pounds in a 112-day feeding trial and at the same time saved 39.3 pounds of hay, 29 pounds of silage, and 16 pounds of barley per 100 pounds of gain. Various types of electric water heaters have been developed by agricultural engineers.

We estimate that 297,700 farmers, 6 percent of those with electric service, had water heaters for livestock and poultry in 1960.

Electrically heated poultry waterers are of two general types—external and immersion. External heaters warm the container that holds the water. Immersion heaters warm the water directly; the heating element is placed in the water. Both types usually are equipped with a thermostat.

Livestock waterers heated electrically are available in several types. A combination cattle and hog waterer has a tank about 26 inches above ground level for cattle and a trough at a lower level for hogs. A large combination waterer handles up to 150 head of cattle and 250 hogs. Waterers designed for only one kind of livestock are of bowl or trough type. A general-purpose, bowl-type waterer serves 30 head of cattle or 60 hogs. Any electrically heated livestock waterer should be equipped with a thermostat, preferably one with a range of 5° F. between the on and off control points.

EXPERIMENTS with heating soil by electricity by G. Jacobsen, of Aker, Norway, to promote plant growth proved successful in 1922. First recognition of the feasibility of such heating resulted from his observation that vegetation growing over overloaded underground electric cables was greener and more advanced than elsewhere.

Glen Cushing, a Northwestern power company engineer, designed the first electric hotbed in the United States in 1925.

Harry L. Garver, then of the Washington Agricultural Experiment Station, in 1927 reported the results of research on electric soil heating.

Widespread interest in the possibilities developed almost immediately.

Types of heaters, their installation, and effects on seed germination and rooting of cuttings became the subjects of extensive research. Lead-sheathed cable, originally manufactured in Sweden, received general acceptance as most suitable for heating hotbeds and cutting benches. Heating cable, manufactured in the United States, became available in 1932, and 330 thousand feet, with 2 thousand thermostats, were sold in a few months. Plant growers in Northern States were first to install electric soil heating, but many in southern areas have also adopted it.

Several million feet of electric heating cable are now used each year. In greenhouses, cuttings are rooted more easily by bottom heat from such cable. Heat supplied by electric cable in hotbeds and coldframes helps to germinate seeds, grow plants for outdoor planting, and protect the plants from frost.

An asparagus grower in the Imperial Valley has several acres in which electric cable is buried under the asparagus crowns. The supplementary heat helps to grow asparagus outdoors in December—otherwise unheard of.

ELECTRIC HEATERS perform two important tasks in the milkhouse—heating water for washing dairy utensils and providing heat in the milkhouse during freezing weather.

Water heaters, of a nonpressure type, first became available about 1933. Units of 10- to 15-gallon capacity were installed on dairy farms, particularly where hot water was needed for washing milking machines. Increased demands for hot water created by bulk milk tank and pipeline milker installations are being met by heaters of larger capacity. They operate automatically under water-system pressure.

Several types of electric heaters—radiant and forced-air—and infrared lamps supply added heat in milkhouses during extremely cold weather to prevent water pipes from freezing or icing of the floor and to provide more comfortable working conditions for the dairyman.

Heat extracted from milk during cooling can be used to heat the milkhouse and also to preheat wash water for milking utensils.

M. C. Ahrens, at the Washington Agricultural Experiment Station, has developed methods and equipment for utilizing this waste heat to reduce energy required to heat water.

By this method as much water can be preheated as the amount of milk cooled in a bulk milk cooler. Water temperature is increased about 50° during preheating.

Water is preheated by recirculating it through a water-cooled condensing unit and preheat tank. A commercial unit to make this heat transfer was not available in 1960, but information about the necessary equipment was available from the Washington Agricultural Experiment Station and the Department of Agriculture.

ELECTRIC HOUSE HEATING has made substantial gains since 1950. An estimated 850 thousand dwelling units were using electricity for space heating in 1960.

At the beginning, most electrically heated homes were in areas of the Tennessee Valley Authority and the Pacific Northwest, where the costs of electric energy were low. Since 1950, because of greater knowledge of the proper application of effective insulation and improvements in electric heating units, people in all parts of the country have installed them successfully, even in Minnesota and Montana, where winters are severe. Another factor in the growth in many localities was that electric rates became competitive with those of flame fuels.

Acceptance of this new method of heating has been gaining in both the country and city. As evidence, Puget Sound Power and Light Company in a survey in 1959 disclosed that electric house heating was thought to be better than gas heating by three families to one. In 1958 the preference was 2 to 1.

Virginia Polytechnic Institute in Circular VFEC 12, "Heating Homes with Electricity," issued in 1957, gave other reasons for the growth—namely, the doubling of the cost of the common fuels since 1947 while the cost of electricity remained the same or actually went down in many areas. The first cost of electric heating

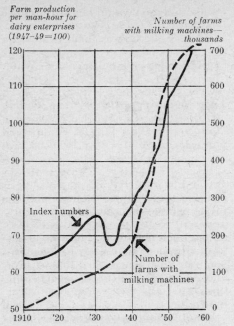

*Farm production per man-hour for dairy enterprises (1947–49=100)*

*Number of farms with milking machines— thousands*

Index numbers

Number of farms with milking machines

*Curves showing milking machines on farms and index numbers of farm production per man-hour for dairy enterprises, 1910–1958. The increase in index numbers parallels the increase in number of milking machines.*

equipment, plus the additional insulation recommended, compare favorably with any other system that provides comparable comfort, the circular said.

Landy B. Altman, Jr., and Leon F. Charity, Iowa State University, learned from a study of 12 well insulated farmhouses that electricity provides a satisfactory means of heating. Energy consumption averaged 16,303 kilowatt-hours for the 1956–1957 heating season for houses averaging 1,373 square feet of floor area. The average connected heating load per house, less basement, was 14.8 kilowatts.

Some of the advantages of electric heating are its cleanliness, even heat, safety, low maintenance cost, absence of noise and fumes, saving in space, individual control of room temperatures, and satisfactory humidity.

Users appreciate especially the thermostatic control installed with the unit heaters in each room. With

these the temperature of any room can be set at any level to meet the desire of the individual. Bedrooms can be kept cooler than living quarters. This control feature also adds to the economy of operation. Such temperature control is difficult or even impossible with any central heating system having one thermostat.

Many unit heaters with individual room control are used. Among them are the radiant panel, wall insert resistance heater, baseboard heater, floor furnace, and resistance wire embedded in the ceiling. Ceiling heat has been popular. A trend favoring baseboard units began in 1959.

So far we have considered the advantages of electric light, power, and heat—primarily individual pieces of electric equipment.

In the early days of electric service, many electric devices were manually controlled. We threw the switch to start the water pump. Then came automatic operation controlled with thermostats.

The water system is operated with an air-pressure switch, which starts the pump motor when the water is drawn from the tank and stops it as the volume of water increases in the tank and compresses the air.

More complex equipment came next, such as the combination automatic clothes washer-drier, the refrigerator-freezer, and the electric range with its many controls and security lights.

Today entire farming enterprises are completely electrified. All machines and equipment making up the completely assembled system to do the job are automatic in operation.

To illustrate: All the devices required in milk production are combined as a unit and operated electrically, with little or no attention.

When fast machine milking was first introduced, one man milking 20 cows an hour with two milking units was considered remarkable. With this method, however, the milking units were idle an average of 3 minutes between cows. When a third stall was used to get the cows ready for milking, the idle time dropped to less than 1 minute. Some dairymen soon were milking 30 cows per hour.

Next came various types, sizes, and shapes of milking parlors. The cows were on a platform, above a pit for the workers. With arms and udders at the same level, the number of cows milked in an hour was again increased.

The herringbone milking parlor was brought to this country from New Zealand in 1957. Researchers at Purdue University reported in 1958 that the number of cows milked during 1 man-hour in the herringbone milking parlor was higher than that of others where the number of units that can be handled by one man is less. He can handle four milking units in a two-sided herringbone parlor and milk up to 50 cows an hour, including machine stripping. With no machine stripping, five units can be handled and up to 60 cows milked an hour.

A California manufacturer in 1957 developed devices for further improvement of the milking method. They can be used with any conventional milking machine. The milk flows by vacuum to a small container. A pump below it pumps 1 pound of milk from it at a time, with little turbulence, through a clean-in-place pipe to the bulk milk cooler. The milk is recorded pound by pound on a dial. To get a sample for butterfat testing, a plastic bottle is attached. A red light flashes when the cow has nearly finished milking or a teat cup drops off.

Another manufacturer has developed a milker that drops off individual teat cups as milking in each quarter is finished.

An Idaho dairyman feeds grain and milks 120 cows in 2 hours in a 6-stanchion parlor. Milking, plus caring for the equipment, milking parlor and milkhouse, takes 10 hours each day. Another man feeds the roughage. The number of hours of work per cow per year is far below the 125-hour national average.

# Telephones for Farmers

E. C. Weitzell

FARM HOUSEHOLDS have a need for telephone service that may not be readily apparent to city people who live close among their neighbors. The need arises from distances that have to be overcome in emergencies like illness, fire, and accidents and in the social and business requirements of modern rural living.

Until Alexander Graham Bell's basic patents on receivers and transmitters expired in 1893 and 1894, the expansion and development of telephony was confined to the more densely populated urban centers.

The expiration opened the way for independent manufacturers and operating companies to share the telephone industry. During the next 5 years, more than 9 thousand independent systems were established in towns, villages, and rural areas.

The number of companies, mutual associations, and farmer-owned lines grew to more than 60 thousand by 1927. Most of them were organized by farm groups and local businessmen.

The manufacturing and supply industry also expanded rapidly. Some manufacturers of telephone equipment promoted and assisted the organization of operating systems as a part of their sales programs. Many small mutual and cooperative telephone companies existing today were started in this way.

Thousands of farm groups, some comprising only a few families, built their own pole lines to the nearest switchboard in order to get telephone service. They owned their own poles and wire, but depended on the exchange facilities of the nearby system. These outmoded "switcher lines" still persist in many rural communities in the Midwest.

Much of the early rural telephone service was financed by subscribers through stock or share subscription to locally owned companies and cooperatives. Many were crudely established, were not incorporated, and lacked attention to long-term needs. Adequate accounting, depreciation and replacement reserves, financial planning, and other requirements of sound management were infrequent.

The need for guidance and technical assistance was recognized by the Department of Agriculture in Farmers Bulletin No. 1245, "Farmers' Telephone Companies," in 1922. In general, obsolescence and the lack of maintenance and long-term financing led to the rapid deterioration of many rural telephone facilities. This situation grew worse in the 1930's.

In 1920, 38.7 percent of all farms had service—in 1935, only 20.6 percent. Expansion and development from that point was confined mostly to suburban and the more densely populated areas. The shortage of materials during the war interfered. The lack of suitable financing for the small rural companies was a major deterrent after 1946. Only 38.2 percent of the farms had telephones of any type by 1950—fewer than in 1920. Fewer than one-fourth of all farm telephones in 1950 were of the modern dial type.

All rural interests felt keenly the need for adequate telephone communication. Wartime demands emphasized the inadequacy of communication. Then the surge of technology that began to change the face of agriculture, rural industries, and rural living demanded adequate intercourse with all elements of the economy. People could no longer do with the old crank-type magneto telephones and the grounded circuits that served 50 years ago.

The drive for improvement occupied the attention of local farm and business groups. Progress was slow, however, except as the larger companies served some of the more densely populated areas around major population centers. The smaller independent companies were handicapped because of the lack of suitable long-term financing.

Most of the smaller companies had consumed their capital through depreciation, obsolescence, and lack of maintenance. Their rates were too low. They had no equity or financial record as a basis for obtaining capital from conventional private sources. Everywhere the old systems were being pressed to expand and improve their services.

An industry pioneer, E. C. Blomeyer, summarized the situation in his *Farm Telephone Story* (Independent Telephone Institute, Chicago, 1945).

"Many, if not most of them must also modernize, rehabilitate and convert or expand their plants to meet the farm and nonfarm service requirements of postwar years," he wrote. "Without government loans, where will they get the money with which to do these things? That is the real rural telephone problem in the Independent part of the telephone industry. . . . This proposition of financing the small Independent telephone companies is . . . not a matter of thousands of dollars but of millions."

This was typical of the analysis and comment that led the Congress to be concerned. The Congress on October 28, 1949, enacted an amendment to the Rural Electrification Act of 1936, providing a rural telephone loan program. It was "declared to be the policy of the Congress that adequate telephone service be made generally available in rural areas through the improvement and expansion of existing telephone facilities and the construction and operation of such additional facilities as are required to assure the availability of adequate telephone service to the widest practicable number of rural users of such service."

Accordingly, loans are made to telephone companies and cooperatives at 2 percent interest for periods of 35 years or less. Technical engineering and managerial assistance also are provided where needed.

The Rural Electrification Administration lent approximately 575 million dollars to 665 borrowers between 1949 and 1959 to finance the expansion and improvement of modern telephone facilities to serve 1,191,000 subscribers.

Up to July 1, 1959, 532 of the REA-financed companies and cooperatives had placed 2,064 new dial exchanges and 183 thousand miles of pole line in service. These completed facilities were providing modern dial service to about 700 thousand farm families and other subscribers in rural areas. This, together with new service provided by the remainder of the telephone industry, represents substantial progress in the provision of adequate rural communications.

Estimates of the Department indicate that more than 60 percent of all farms had telephone service of some sort by July 1959. Only a little better than 40 percent were dial, however; others awaited conversion to modern service. Close to 90 percent of the farms in the New England States had telephones. The Southeastern States had the lowest percentage of farms with telephone service in 1959.

The years between 1950, when the first REA telephone loans were made, and 1959 had the greatest gain in farm telephones of any decade in the history of the telephone industry. The job ahead is still sizable. It involves the expansion and modernization of more than 2 thousand manual exchanges in small towns and rural areas.

For some time now, there has been an increasing trend toward merger and consolidation of small companies and farmer-owned exchanges in order to establish larger and more efficient operating units. This is essential in providing a stable basis for feasible long-term financing.

Modern dial equipment is much more complicated and costly than the rather simple installations that served rural areas in the early years of this century. There is still a place in rural telephony for the small systems, but the larger companies that operate urban exchanges are finding it advantageous to expand their operations into rural areas.

Farmers are no longer satisfied merely to ring their neighbors down the road. They ask for efficient, round-the-clock telephone connection with merchants and markets and friends in cities scattered across the Nation. Improvement of the service is justified in part by their willingness to pay higher rates. The average monthly local farm telephone bill has gone up from 2.29 dollars in 1947–1949 to 4.08 dollars in 1958. Farmers know that a single telephone call may be worth many times the monthly bill.

To reach some isolated regions with adequate telephone service, new companies and nonprofit associations are being formed. The development of the less expensive telecommunications equipment is hastening the day when no rural establishment will be too far away to reach by telephone.

The "quickest way anywhere" by telephone is just as important to rural people as it is to those living in urban areas. The ability of farmers and other rural people to compete and participate in our economic affairs depends on their ability to overcome the impediments of time and space. The telephone puts price quotations, market information, supply houses, repair services, veterinarians, and transport services at the fingertip of the rural producer.

The modern home also needs the telephone. The rural household may be many miles from the consolidated school, the city church, amusement centers, and shopping facilities. The telephone shortens the distance.

# Radio and Television

Layne Beaty

IF IT's getting harder to tell the difference between a farm-dweller and a town-dweller, two of the reasons are radio and television.

The role of the Department of Agriculture in the development of agricultural communications through the broadcast mediums since the mid-1920's has been to encourage, cooperate, and supply timely, useful information to broadcasters. The cooperation had much to do with the progress and soundness of our agriculture.

Much of the agricultural information broadcast on radio and television originates with the officials, scientists, regulatory and service agencies, and market reporting services of the Department.

It reaches broadcasting stations, at their request, through the Associated Press and United Press International and other private news agencies and by direct mail and wire.

The majority of producers of farm products now can receive up-to-the-minute news of what commodities are bringing on the market and what the weather may be expected to be in the next hour, the next day, the next week.

AGRICULTURAL LEADERS have been heard to say, "If we didn't have radio now we'd just have to invent it."

Radio has become a workhorse of agricultural communications. It is the medium that brings news and information as soon as it is available on a day-in, day-out, work-a-day basis.

Probably no single group in the population has benefited more from the advances in radio broadcasting than people on the land.

Radio receivers in the beginning were big and complicated and had antennas outside the house. They have become smaller and so simple and easy to use that they no longer are the center of activity in the living room but are all over the house on desks, bedside tables, shelves in the kitchen, basement, workroom, barn, milkshed, pickup truck, automobile—sometimes in the tractor and shirt pockets.

The invention of the transistor, a tiny substitute for tubes, enabled manufacturers to reduce the size of receivers so that some battery-operated sets now fit snugly into pockets and handbags.

Partly because television emerged almost fullblown in the first decade after the Second World War (while it took radio 25 years to condition the public thoroughly to receiving broadcasts), radio has yielded the family gathering places to the television set and itself has become the more personal medium.

There were 4,142 radio broadcasting stations in January 1959 in the United States. Americans owned and used more than 98 million receiving sets in homes, 38 million in automobiles, and 10 million in public places, such as restaurants, barbershops, and garages.

We should note here that the broadcasting industry in the United States is commercially owned, except for stations owned and operated by educational institutions and a few State and municipal governments for educational and other purposes.

Of the stations that went on the air in the first years after the First World War, some still stand out, as they have through the years, for their contributions to agricultural advancement, their devotion to the informational needs of rural people, and their support of improved agricultural practices, community development, and home-making.

Station WHA, operated by the University of Wisconsin, in Madison, and

KDKA, Pittsburgh, were among the first stations to offer market and weather reports on a regular basis. KDKA celebrated its 35th year of market news broadcasting in May 1956. WHA and the experimental station that preceded it in Madison had done some market newscasting before then.

Both stations have continued to serve farmers with daily broadcasts designed especially for the farmers of their area and have given the Nation some outstanding talent. Milton E. Bliss broadcast over WHA a long time before he became agricultural representative of the National Broadcasting Company network and producer of the 31-year-old National Farm and Home Hour. Frank E. Mullen, once a writer for farm magazines in Nebraska and Iowa, got the idea of a network farm program when he worked for KDKA and, after joining NBC, worked out arrangements with the Department of Agriculture, which launched this daily program as a joint effort of the Department and the network. KDKA included a farm program director on its regular staff until 1957, when its programs were revised.

Of the many stations that have done outstanding service to agriculture, I cite a few.

WLS, Chicago, in the early 1920's tuned itself in on the agriculture of its section and broadcast throughout the day with the needs and likes of its rural listeners in mind—programs of farm news from the area and from Washington, farm advice, foot-pattin' music, markets, weather, sermons, interviews with farmers, interviews with visiting brides and bridegrooms (and regularly they came, on their honeymoons in Chicago, to visit Arthur C. Page and his WLS Dinner Bell Hour every weekday noon).

Cincinnati's WLW boomed out market news and weather, farm advice, and results of experiments on its own farm on a powerful signal heard over most of the continent in those early days of broadcasting. It still does.

WHAS, Louisville; WHO, Des Moines; WCCO, Minneapolis; KVOO, Tulsa; KMBC, Kansas City; WOAI, San Antonio; WNAX, Yankton, S. Dak.; and WOC, Davenport, were among the early birds. So were WBAP, Fort Worth; WSM, Nashville; WKY, Oklahoma City; WEAF (now WRCA) New York; WCAU, Philadelphia; WGN, Chicago; WOW, Omaha; WWL, New Orleans; KNBC, San Francisco; KFI, Los Angeles; KJR, Seattle; WTAM, Cleveland; and others.

Now, in 1960, easily a thousand stations have some regular farm programs. In 1958, 1,472 radio stations and 165 television stations were carrying market news information regularly, mostly on a daily basis or oftener.

Some who listen to these broadcasts may not realize that the information they receive was collected by Federal or Federal-State Market News services.

Nearly always are the radio market news reports adapted to the specific needs of the listeners. A city station may broadcast a report of local wholesale prices and prices received by shippers for nearby products. A station serving a producing area may report on local prices, prices paid in city markets, and shipments currently moving from the area.

These reports sometimes are written by a market news reporter or an employee of an area office of the Agricultural Marketing Service. Usually the reports are written by employees of the station on the basis of items furnished by the market wire service through one of the news services. Some radio stations have lines into the market news offices for direct on-the-air reports by market reporters of the Department.

Weather information comes principally from the United States Weather Bureau, although some stations employ their own meteorologists, who supplement Weather Bureau data with their own analyses. Many stations use private weather services.

The United States Weather Bureau,

with its forecasting and reporting services, was a part of the Department of Agriculture from 1891 until June 1940. It is now an agency of the Department of Commerce.

Farm broadcasters take a keen interest in the weather reports. Partly because of their urging, the Weather Bureau offered special agricultural weather forecasts, geared to seasonal activity on farms, and inaugurated a 30-day forecast. It also began studies of longer-range trends.

It was not always thus. In the early 1920's, when radio stations were less numerous, some landsmen learned to make their own predictions from more or less sketchy reports they picked up on distant stations.

I once got a letter from an old rancher in southern Texas telling of an experience in which he saved his herd because over a Kansas City station he heard a mass of cold air was moving down from Canada. In his Model-T and with the help of an ancient slab-sided steer, whose lofty horns he could see at the front of the herd when lightning flashed, he maneuvered his cattle to safety just in time.

ADVANCES in rural electrification and increased programing of farmer-interest material have put radio receivers in more than 98 percent of the Nation's farm homes. One big reason for the rise in the amount of farm broadcasting and the number of stations is the profit afforded by commercial broadcasting.

Manufacturers and sellers of equipment and goods bought by farm and ranch people found that radio offered an effective advertising channel. That made possible more broadcasting of all kinds than a tax-supported broadcasting system, without commercial participation could do.

Requests from radio stations to the Department for material to use in farm broadcasts led to the establishment of a radio service in the Office of Information in 1926. The National Broadcasting Company in cooperation with the Department in 1928 inaugurated the daily National Farm and Home Hour on the network, with regular originations in Chicago and Washington and live features from other places. The Hour later became a weekly program and since 1945 has been sponsored by a manufacturer of farm equipment. The Department has cooperated with the American Broadcasting Company since 1945 in presenting a weekly network program, the American Farmer.

For several years, the Columbia Broadcasting System radio network carried the Columbia Country Journal on a weekly basis. More recently, CBS has covered agricultural news along with general news. The Mutual Broadcasting System radio network inaugurated a daily 10-minute program of farm news.

Meanwhile, more and more stations added specialists in farm broadcasting to their staffs.

Several of the farm broadcasters met in Columbus, Ohio, in 1943, and formed a professional organization, which shortly became national in membership and took the name of National Association of Radio Farm Directors. These men and women have become widely known as "RFD's," thus capitalizing on the happy coincidence of initials that already were identified with rural communication.

When farm programs became popular in television, the organization renamed itself National Association of Television and Radio Farm Directors. The Department cooperates with NATRFD and its members and all broadcasters of farm programs. Membership in NATRFD in 1960 included more than 200 active and 160 associate members in the United States and Canada.

THE FARM BROADCASTER on both radio and television has become a new, refreshing character on the American scene—with some latter day counterparts abroad, especially since our technical assistance program began.

Usually he is a young man, who enjoys seeing and talking with people and talking about them. He is known personally by many of his listeners.

His services include more than regular programs. He may give special broadcasts from field events and special short courses on the air (on such subjects as livestock feeding). He may have organized tours of farmers to points of interest in North America and overseas. He may sponsor agricultural field events, such as land judging contests, usually in cooperation with the experiment stations or extension services.

Some stations offer scholarships in farm broadcasting to promising college students. A dozen or more farm broadcasters at one time were winners of scholarships offered by Ed Mason, John Merrifield, and their successors at WLW, Cincinnati, and Chuck Worcester and his successors at WMT, Cedar Rapids. Other young broadcasters got a start working with such pioneers as Art Page at WLS, Chicago; Herb Plambeck, WHO, Des Moines; Emerson Markham, WGY, Schenectady; and Sam Schneider, KVOO, Tulsa.

Several farm broadcasters were launched by George C. Biggar when he held administrative posts at WLS and WLW. Later Mr. Biggar became president and owner of WLBK, De Kalb, Ill., and producer of his own farm programs.

Some farm broadcasters have moved on to other posts of honor. Phil Alampi, once a poultry farmer and farm broadcaster over WABC and WRCA, New York, became Secretary of Agriculture of New Jersey. Two high officials in the National Grange once were presidents (as was Mr. Alampi) of the NATRFD. They are Roy Battles and C. W. (Jack) Jackson, who left WLW, Cincinnati, and KCMO, Kansas City, respectively, to serve the Grange in Washington. Jack Angell was a newscaster for NBC before he became director of radio and TV activities for the American Farm Bureau Federation.

LITTLE TELECASTING was done in the United States before the end of the Second World War, but the following decade saw forests of TV antennas grow on rooftops as new stations went on the air and cheaper receivers became available. In some American cities the number of television receivers exceeded the number of bathtubs.

Television, already well advanced technically, came to the broadcast-conscious public when restrictions on manufacture were relaxed after the war. At first programs were given only a few hours a day. Before long, the broadcast day of most stations extended from early morning until midnight seven days a week.

By January of 1959, there were 564 television stations on the air and 49 million receiving sets in 45 million homes. Among farm homes, 73 percent had television receivers.

Television made good use of weather maps for explaining weather forecasts—probably a reason for a new public understanding of meteorological terms and the eccentricities of weather. Even to a greater degree than radio, television stations employ meteorologists for this service. Others often present weather information by farm directors or other staff members. Like the radio stations, all draw upon the services of the Weather Bureau for data, although some supplement this with information from private forecasting agencies and their own observations.

Telecasting of farm programs on stations operated in conjunction with radio stations has been done mostly by the radio farm director.

Television is universally popular, but it seems to have a special appeal for persons on farms and in small communities.

Most stations provide news about livestock and produce markets and varying amounts of other kinds of information for farmers.

Farm telecasters make extensive use of the motion picture camera to bring outside scenes into the studio, although studio presentations of interviews, how-to-do-it demonstrations, and studies of livestock, poultry, and plants, have been popular.

The use of the video-tape process for delayed telecast of programs has become popular since 1958.

A growing number of stations have been equipped to originate programs in color—a promising development for agricultural programs because the natural color of pastures, fields, crops, and animals adds a useful dimension in telecasting.

The Radio and Television Service participated in early color television research with the National Broadcasting Company.

Most of the early "farm" television programs dealt heavily with vegetable and flower gardening for the logical reason that most of the television receivers at the time were in urban homes. The earliest farm programs in color followed that pattern. One garden program in Washington switched to color in 1959, with enthusiastic approval by the sponsor, a commercial nurseryman. Video-tape in color was used by some stations in 1959.

An example of the value to farmers of television: A hog raiser in Arkansas saw a picture of a hog suffering from vesicular exanthema, a serious disease of swine. This picture had been sent out as a part of the Department's television package feature service for farm telecasters.

No case of vesicular exanthema was known to exist in Arkansas at that time, but the farmer recognized on the TV screen some of the symptoms he had noticed earlier in his own herd. He quickly called his veterinarian, who confirmed the symptoms, treated the hogs, and stopped what might have been a costly outbreak of the disease in Arkansas.

Many television programs showing "how-to-do-it" techniques are telecast, but the full potential has not been realized. Several telecasters originate live programs or filmed programs on farms. Live pickups pose production problems, but authenticity compen-

sates for the difficulties. Some of the most effective farm programs originate in studios, however; they present live animals, plants, and so on and such features as interviews with farmers and specialists who have something useful to say to farmers.

RADIO AND TELEVISION are important aids of field workers of the Department of Agriculture.

Many stations, whether they employ full-time farm program directors or not, make broadcasting facilities available to extension workers and to field representatives of agencies like the Forest Service, Farmers Home Administration, Soil Conservation Service, and Commodity Stabilization Service, who are frequent guests on programs and are consistent sources of information of significance to farmers and other people.

Federal, State, and county agricultural agents in 2,415 counties made 288,408 radio broadcasts in 1958. In 1,441 counties they made 18,584 telecasts. County home demonstration agents in 1,813 counties made 81,076 radio broadcasts and in 917 counties made 6,490 appearances on television.

These agricultural workers believe the effectiveness of their efforts is extended to more people than is possible on a person-to-person basis. Some of these agents broadcast "live" from their offices over facilities placed there by the radio station.

Every State agricultural service has its staff of information specialists, some of whom help extension specialists and county agents manage their broadcasts and often do radio or TV broadcasting over a station operated by a land-grant college.

Another outstanding development has been the rapid growth of educational television. The 44 educational TV stations on the air in 1960 mostly were on college and university campuses.

The first use of educational TV facilities was to extend classroom instruction, but most stations began to offer evening programs for adults. Directors of ETV stations have indicated an interest in more service to agriculture by broadcasting to rural people or by broadcasting more information useful to consumers. Because ETV lacks the commercial obligations of other stations and offers longer features into which a subject can be probed to a greater depth, ETV may become an important factor in public understanding of agriculture.

The use of broadcasting by agricultural workers and by guest appearances of farmers has done much to increase the public knowledge of farm life, production of our food and fiber, marketing, and processing.

Many stations make direct inquiry to the Department for information of specific nature. Practically all are served by the wire services, which maintain representatives at the Department.

Regional, State, and national officials of the Department are interviewed frequently in Washington and during their travels through the country.

The Department's Office of Information prepares a weekly package—"Agri-Tape"—of recorded features, which are duplicated regionally and redistributed by land-grant colleges and farm organizations. About 350 stations used the recordings in 1960.

Other radio services of the Department reach other millions.

Three television feature packages are issued by the Radio and Television Service in cooperation with various agencies. They reach 10 million viewers each week. The services included still pictures with suggested scripts for the convenience of TV performers.

One service is for farm programs, one for consumer information programs, and one, Research Roundup, for general news programs. More than 200 stations used the services in 1960.

Most broadcasters receive Department news releases in the field of their special interest and daily summaries of all releases.

Farm broadcasters receive the weekly RFD Letter from the Radio and Television Service, which alerts them to agricultural news and events and the services available to them. Many women broadcasters receive the weekly "Food and Home Notes," issued by the Press Service. Other Department publications—new bulletins, pamphlets, and books—are sent them on request.

Motion pictures are made by the Department especially for television use. They are notable experiments in low-cost filming. Most of the motion pictures on file have been cleared for television use and are available. Catalogs of the films are issued by the Motion Picture Service.

THE EFFECTIVENESS of radio broadcasting by professional farm broadcasters and agricultural workers has been enhanced by the use of the magnetic tape recorder.

Recordings of various kinds, especially the electrically transcribed disk, or platter, have been in use by radio stations almost since the beginning of commercial broadcasting. Farm broadcasters have utilized this facility for delayed broadcasts when duty or convenience required them or their broadcast guests to be away from the studios at the time of broadcast. The thrill, or disillusionment, at hearing one's own voice for the first time as others hear it is an experience never forgotten by thousands of broadcast guests.

Because the early equipment for making transcriptions away from the studio was not easily portable, recordings from farms and laboratories were not widely used until small, light recorders were developed about 1947. Every farm broadcaster now uses them for bringing the voices and sounds that otherwise are not conveniently transported physically to the studios. Many county agents and other agricultural workers who broadcast regularly use portable recorders in their offices and on field trips. Many recorders are battery operated and can be used far from electric lines.

Short-wave radio as a means of two-way communication on some large farms and ranches adds to the efficiency of operations. Telephones in automobiles, used in many professions, serve farm broadcasters as well as operators of large landholdings as a means of staying in touch with headquarters and with the outside world while moving from place to place. An adaptation of the walkie-talkie has been used to direct the activities of work crews.

When sight is added to this use of sound, foremen and managers will be able to direct the work of employees by means of the television screen, just as closed-circuit television devices are used to check on the numbers of boxcars in freight yards, in banks to verify signatures, in railway ticket offices to confirm space reservations, and in hospitals to keep an eye on patients. It takes no strenuous exercise of imagination to predict the use of color television in various types of inspection in processing plants. Such activities were technically possible in 1960, as was two-way telephone vision.

# The Role of a Free Press

**L. E. Childers**

MUCH of the credit for the transformation of agriculture from a horse- and hand-labor occupation into a dynamic mechanized and scientific business must go to the vigorous support of our newspapers and magazines, including a strong and enterprising farm press. Recognition of the right of the people to know, written into our Constitution by the Founding Fathers, has served agriculture well.

More newspapers and periodicals are published in the United States than in any other country of the world. A listing of daily papers in 1958 showed a total of 1,969, whose aggregate circulation was almost 57 million. In addition, almost 600 Sunday newspapers have a circulation of nearly 50 million. The United States, with 7 percent of the world's population, absorbs nearly 60 percent of the world output of newsprint. We have a highly developed system of news transmission, including two world news agencies—the Associated Press and United Press International.

Nearly 10 thousand weekly papers with circulation totaling many millions also help to keep people informed. Hundreds of trade publications have a special readership. More than 400 publications devoted primarily to agriculture have a circulation of more than 30 million.

About 85 percent of our total adult population read one or more newspapers, and 65 percent read one or more magazines more or less regularly. More than 80 percent of our rural farm families take a daily or weekly newspaper, and 70 percent receive at least one magazine. Farm people spend an average of 30 to 60 minutes daily in reading magazines and newspapers.

ALL THIS provides a favorable climate for the diffusion of useful and up-to-date information on developments relating to agriculture. The press is an important channel for the diffusion of new ideas and the findings of agricultural research among farmers.

Much of the agricultural research in the United States is done by Federal and State experiment stations. These agencies take the position that research is not completed until it has been fully reported to the people who need it and can use it.

The basis for this view is found in the Organic Act of the Department of Agriculture, which provided that one of its duties is "to acquire and diffuse among the people of the United

States useful information on subjects connected with agriculture in the most general and comprehensive sense of the word."

Secretary of Agriculture J. M. Rusk in 1889 set up a Division of Records and Editing as one of 10 divisions in the Department. Two years later the Congressional Directory noted that the division was issuing press notices that gave official information of interest to agriculturists.

The basis for the Office of Information in the Department was laid in 1913 with a redefining of functions to make possible the wider use of the daily, weekly, and periodical press. It was pointed out then that the Department "could reach 3 million people every week through the agricultural press by means of short, crisp items dealing with facts."

The objective of furnishing facts and information on agricultural research findings, program developments, and other activities and actions has not changed much since then.

Similar services to newspapers and magazines are provided by the land-grant colleges and experiment stations. Many of these had become active in supplying factual information on agriculture to various press outlets by the time the work was formally initiated in the Department. By 1913 also the first conference of State agricultural college editors that formed the nucleus of what later became the American Association of Agricultural College Editors was conducted at the University of Illinois.

Much of the news of progress in agricultural technology reaches press outlets through the extension system, of which the State extension editors are a part, and through announcements issued by editors of the State agricultural experiment stations. Extension information channels reach to the community through county and home demonstration agents or advisors, who conduct their work largely through local leaders.

Newspapers and magazines publish information on new agricultural technology only because it is of interest to their readers. That is why many local newspapers open their columns freely to use by county and home demonstration agents.

American farmers have always welcomed new ideas. Often they originate them, and so they also make news of significance to others. An example is the successful application of some scientific advance on their farms.

Science has become news and farming has become a science. Progress in laboratories and in research stations in field and forest and factory has become exciting news for the farm press and for metropolitan newspapers because the developments touch the lives of everyone everywhere.

Information about the new products of industry and laboratory reaches farmers through various channels besides the news columns. Advertising in newspapers, trade and farm publications, and general magazines gives industry a way to reach the minds and pocketbooks of farmers with a new idea or product.

Competition for the farm market is intense. The market itself is tremendous; supplies and expenses of production have been estimated at some 20 billion dollars annually. To reach farmers who make up this market, millions are expended annually for advertising in newspapers, the farm press, and magazines. This revenue enables the publications to be of service through their news columns in supporting progressive developments of many kinds.

THE COMMUNICATIONS process may involve many channels besides the press.

Dissemination of information on new developments may begin with a technical paper presented before a professional society or published in a technical journal. This may be followed by interpretations for nonscientific readers in the form of daily news stories, magazine articles, and presentations on radio and television programs. More detailed information may be published as features in farm papers and trade or commodity publications.

Precise information, including instructions on how best to apply it, may appear in a bulletin or leaflet from the originating institution.

Farm people get their information from these and other sources. Some may hear about a practice first through conversation with their county agent, at a meeting, or on a tour, or possibly through a demonstration conducted on a neighboring farm. Many get their first information through a farm magazine. Motion pictures, exhibits, and other visual devices may attract attention to an idea. Circular letters, telephone conversations, and various other means of communication may exert their influence.

Information may come from several sources before a new practice is adopted. A study at North Carolina State College showed that nine exposures to new information were required before farm people put a new recommendation into practice.

Studies by the Extension Service credited the adoption of 1 in 10 new farm practices to news stories. Other surveys have continued to emphasize the importance of the press—particularly the farm press—as a source of information on new practices.

Changes in patterns of rural living have had important effects on newspapers and magazines themselves. One of the changes is that farm people have more time for reading.

One of the results is a recognition of the importance of valid interpretation of agricultural news for the producer and the general reader. The farm editor and reporter and the science writer have gained status. Farm programs have become so complex that intimate understanding and competence in agriculture are an essential part of the equipment of the reporter or editor whose business it is to interpret them.

An increasing degree of specialization and localization has occurred in reading material carried by all types of publications.

Metropolitan dailies, particularly those in areas where farming is a dominant enterprise, give improved coverage to agricultural problems and developments that may affect the local economy as well as farm items of national interest. Many such papers publish widely read farm pages.

Greater efforts toward localization of news are seen in the development of regional editions of some national farm magazines. Regional placement and localization of advertisements by large industrial enterprises are commonplace. Increasing also is the number of industry and trade publications carrying agricultural and other business news directed to special-interest groups. The rural weekly continues to find its field of greatest service in covering the news of its community, including the farms.

TECHNOLOGICAL changes in publishing also have paralleled those in agriculture and the rural community. Publishing has always been a highly competitive enterprise. This has stimulated development of new production and distribution techniques that contribute to the more rapid flow of up-to-the-minute information.

New methods of photoengraving, facsimile transmission of pictures and even the entire content of a publication, four-color reproduction, automatic telegraphic typesetting, bulk transportation by air to central distribution points, and similar advances have given to news distribution the wings of Mercury. Magazines and newspapers are in rural mail boxes a few hours after they are printed.

Many editors see in the constantly changing pattern of our agriculture a continuing challenge for greater service. One of the big challenges is the development of better understanding of agriculture and its problems generally for the mutual benefit of farmers and consumers.

528981°—60——8

# The Place of Publications

Lyman J. Noordhoff

PUBLICATIONS long have been a basic method of reporting information from the Department of Agriculture and land-grant colleges to all people.

J. M. Rusk, Secretary of Agriculture, wrote in 1889: "Results shall be promptly made available to the public by a comprehensive scheme of publications. Time and expense, ability and experience lavished on the work of the Department can have no practical results unless we can lay their conclusions promptly before the people who need them."

Millions of copies of more than 10 thousand titles were issued by State land-grant colleges, the Department of Agriculture, and agricultural industries in the fiscal year 1958–1959. State extension services and experiment stations published about 8,500 titles (new, revised, and reprinted); the Department, 725; and industry at least a thousand titles. The 11,100 county extension agents distributed more than 33 million copies of these booklets, brochures, leaflets, folders, and pamphlets in 1960.

Scientists in agricultural colleges wrote 5,500 technical articles for scientific journals and 1,150 articles for magazines in 1958–1959.

Publications are only one of many methods of communication. Others are personal letters, conversations, speeches, reports in magazines and newspapers, demonstrations, tours, meetings, slides, movies, TV, exhibits, and books.

Like any method of communication, publications accomplish their purpose best when they are used with other methods that are suited to the particular situation.

Publications are permanent, relatively inexpensive, and versatile in terms of size, color, and illustrations. They offer enough space, relatively, to tell the whole story. Their distribution can be controlled.

Publications, however, sometimes are impersonal. They rely basically on the reading of words, which some persons consider a hard way to learn. They compete with work, recreation, family, and other activities for a reader's time.

Skills in publication have improved, just as skills in production and marketing have made great strides.

Two consultants, retained by the National Project in Agricultural Communications, analyzed 171 State booklets and recommended improvements. They ranked 3 percent of the booklets excellent or very good in 1954; but 25 percent were ranked excellent or very good in 1956. Thirty percent scored poor in 1954, but none in 1956. Entries rated average or poor dropped from 60 percent in 1954 to 30 percent in 1956. The changes make the booklets easier to read and more useful.

A project was set up in the Department of Agriculture to determine what information people want in which form. The study compared six methods of discovering people's publications needs. Five States—Massachusetts, Mississippi, Oklahoma, Michigan, and Washington—cooperated in comparing the method of recording the questions asked by farmers and others with five other methods. The county agents in 27 selected counties recorded 38 thousand questions during 13 weeks in 1958. The questions were classified by a standard system. Examples of the findings: Questions on vegetables, fruit, and ornamentals comprised 60 percent of all questions in the category of crops in all five States. Twenty percent of all questions on livestock and 10 percent of all questions on crops dealt with marketing.

Recording people's questions plus judgment of professional agricultural workers was found to be the most practical and valid combination of methods for learning the need of people for information.

Another plan, used at Mississippi State University for about 10 years, is to have a committee of authors, editors, administrators, and county agents review all proposals for publications in the light of costs, relative importance and need for each booklet, and similar points. Other States follow a similar plan.

The careful planning of each publication before writing by author, editor, and artist cuts costs, speeds up the work, and produces a more attractive and effective booklet. A booklet on farmhouses had 12 pages and mediocre drawings and cover. It was cut to eight pages, printed in black and a second color, and given good drawings and a cover in color. The revision was highly successful.

Publications have been made easier to read through clearer writing—shorter sentences, more definitions, brevity, more precise terms, shorter overall length, and so on.

Despite the perennial remarks in public about "governmentese" and "bureaucratic gobbledygook," publications of the Department of Agriculture reach high standards of writing, presentation, and printing—all the more if one remembers that appropriations for them are limited and that their function is to inform, not to amuse or sell.

The estimated average length of farmers' bulletins prepared in the Department of Agriculture was 32 pages in 1954 and 24 pages in 1959. Some think many of them could be cut to 16 pages.

A trend at State colleges has been toward one-sheet leaflets and folders or booklets of eight pages or fewer. The author of a thesis at the University of Wisconsin said there is a place for both long and short (four-page) publications, and emphasized that even the long ones should not be any longer than is absolutely necessary to tell the story.

Great progress has been made in printing—more, say authorities on printing, during the 1940's and 1950's than in the whole 500-year history of the industry.

Among the advances are faster typesetting by camera instead of hot metal, faster and more reliable methods of making engravings from artwork, many new kinds and grades of paper and ink, fast-expanding interest in offset printing, speedier presses that are easier to operate, printing on aluminum foil and plastics, color printing, and automation in the bindery and throughout printing.

Another development is the use of joint publications. In Pennsylvania, Delaware, and New Jersey, the horticulture, editorial, and 4-H staff people planned and produced 14 booklets in the 4-H Plan and Plant for Beauty project. Each State did one-third of the writing and printing but received all the booklets in the series.

Even with highly developed tools and methods, the channels of communication are not always clear.

An example—and a symptom—is the findings of two students in the Department of Agricultural Journalism in the University of Wisconsin. Only one-fourth of a group of farmers understood the correct meaning of the basic term, pH. The study stated: "Among the least known [concepts of soils knowledge] are some of the very important, very simple, and very widely used concepts."

A second study showed that among 25 words that scientists claimed they had to use in writing about dairying, each of 10 terms was misunderstood by 30 percent or more of the farmers—fetus, agglutination, virus, lactation, antibody, feces, infestation, lesion, succulent, and pulmonary.

Dr. Glenn Frank, while president of the University of Wisconsin, said:

"The future of America is in the hands of two men—the investigator and the interpreter. We shall never lack for the administrator, the third man needed to complete this trinity of social servants. And we have an ample supply of investigators. But there is a shortage of readable and responsible interpreters; men who can effectively play mediator between specialists and laymen.

"A dozen fields of thought today are congested with knowledge that the physical and social scientists have unearthed, and the whole tone and temper of American life can be lifted by putting this knowledge into general circulation. But where are the interpreters with the training and willingness to think their way through this knowledge and translate it into the language of the street?

"I raise the recruiting trumpet for the interpreter."

Largely through the National Project in Agricultural Communication (NPAC) at Michigan State University, three communication training units have been developed and conducted. These were the basic and oral unit, the written unit, and the visual unit.

Groups of two to four persons from each State had 2 weeks of instruction and then trained their own personnel at State agricultural colleges and county extension offices. The Kellogg Foundation supported this and other NPAC activities with a grant of nearly 725 thousand dollars in 1953–1960. A total of 233 persons from 43 States and the Department of Agriculture and 23 others from other governmental and international agencies attended the six basic training sessions. They in turn trained several thousand coworkers.

In the NPAC written unit, about 125 persons from some 40 States and the Department attended the four scheduled "train-the-trainer" sessions. At least one training session on the visual unit was conducted before Kellogg support of NPAC ended in February 1960.

Federal Extension Service workers helped plan and conduct about 85 publication and communications workshops, mostly 3-day sessions, in 1955–1959. An estimated 5 thousand persons from nearly all States attended.

Land-grant college editors since 1955 have trained several thousand staff members in intensive workshops of their own.

The Department of Agriculture also has conducted its own followup training in clear writing.

# Power

## on

## the Land

## Remaking the Land

G. E. Ryerson

THE ABUNDANCE produced by the American farmer and the resulting economic competition forces farmers to work with greater and greater efficiency. Availability of good land, skill in the art of husbandry, and hard work are no longer enough to assure success.

The present productive capacity of American farmers is the result of many developments in the entire field of agriculture. None of the developments or advances of the past 50 years could have taken place without corresponding improvements in equipment, despite the farmer's skill and aggressiveness in applying new knowledge.

Equipment adapted to the new and changing needs of agriculture has made it possible and profitable to put to use new skills, new techniques, and new knowledge by a spectacular reduction in the labor requirements of agriculture.

The capacity to perform useful work built into today's farm equipment places an additional premium on the managerial skills of American farmers. The full usefulness of any precision or special-purpose tool can be realized only if it is used skillfully for the purpose to which it is adapted.

In this section we review the developments that are significant to the agricultural revolution. We start with the tractor.

Today's tractor is a specialized, highly developed machine. It supplies specialized power to do specialized jobs. It is more than a machine that pulls an implement. It operates tools through power takeoff shafts and belts. It supplies power to regulate, manipulate, and adjust tools through application of hydraulic power. It is designed to operate at the precise speeds needed to perform its function most efficiently and to perform maximum work in the shortest time.

Tillage tools have been developed to do precise and controlled manipulation of the soil in whatever way needed to prepare optimum seedbeds. The requirement that tillage tools produce the desired degree of aeration, compaction, and elimination of weed competition has been far exceeded by modern tillage equipment. Not only are these functions performed far better than ever before; a surface condition is produced that is both resistant to the erosive forces of wind and water and receptive to the infiltration of water. It is possible to work soil when desired to a far greater depth than was possible before.

Today's tools, furthermore, manipulate soils in such a way that it is no longer necessary to destroy crop residues. Residues from almost any crop can be incorporated into the seedbed at almost any desired location and mechanically conditioned in such a way as to provide the maximum beneficial effect on soil structure and the best protection from erosion.

Seeding and planting equipment has been improved by making it possible to place seeds at precisely the right depth with the proper degree of compaction, almost regardless of the amount of crop residue present on the surface. It has been widened from a former standard of two-row to as much as eight-row equipment. The speed of operation has been increased from 2 or 4 miles an hour to speeds as high as 10 miles or more. Even greater precision in spacing seed is possible. It is now possible to produce a stand of almost any desired plant population with precise spacing between seeds even at high operating speeds.

Corresponding improvements have been made in harvesting equipment.

Machines are available that can harvest all or any part of any plant at any stage of its development. The harvested crop is conditioned in such a way that its storage is simpler and easier and its feed value maintained at the highest possible level throughout its storage period. Crops also are processed during harvest to reduce costs of handling and feeding.

In order to utilize the full efficiency incorporated into modern farm machinery, consideration must be given to the conditions under which equipment will be used as well as to the selection of equipment.

Precision tools of any kind perform at their best when used under as nearly optimum conditions as possible. Farm machinery must work in the fields, not in the shop or laboratories. Many things can be done on farms to improve the efficiency of farm tools, which at the same time can increase the productiveness of the soil itself.

We now have the power and the equipment to adapt farmland to the equipment we expect to use as well as to correct many of the scars left by improper use and erosion. Farm and field layouts that were suitable to the use of animal-drawn implements and even to the relatively low-speed and low-powered tractor of a decade ago are usually poorly adapted to the full use of present-day equipment.

The power available on American farms, coupled with adapted earth-moving attachments or equipment borrowed from the construction industry, makes it possible to remove old field boundaries to level the fence rows, remove the frequent rows of trees and brush (or whatever may have accumulated in these rows) efficiently, economically, and profitably.

Field boundaries and land surfaces can be reshaped to meet the needs of modern conservation farming by permitting contour layouts rather than rectangular fields to make possible the most efficient control and disposal of runoff water. They also can be adjusted to meet the needs of the kind of equipment which will be most readily adapted to the kind of farm operations to be carried on on each individual farm.

Terraces to control the runoff water can be built much more economically than formerly. They are spaced and shaped to fit the machines likely to be used. Spacing is adjusted to a multiple of the width of the machine to be used. Terrace alinement is adjusted to produce parallel spacings to eliminate point rows and the difficulties in farming them.

Until recently land leveling and land smoothing were mostly confined to the irrigated areas of the West. Even before there was much irrigation in the humid areas of the East, farmers and research personnel were finding that leveling rough fields improved the surface drainage characteristics of many fields sufficiently to more than pay the cost of the operation.

The efficient use of farm earthmoving equipment made it possible for farmers to reshape their fields to provide for not only more efficient application of irrigation water, but to make it possible for excess water to drain more rapidly from flat areas.

As tractor speeds increased beyond the 5- or 6-mile level, even small gullies became a problem to the operator. The speeds possible in modern machines could not be utilized simply because it was impossible to control machines on such fields at practical operating speeds. Wide equipment also did not work satisfactorily on rough ground. It was either a matter of planting too deep on the high spots or not planting at all in the low spots.

The landplane, which was a common tool in the irrigated areas for smoothing and leveling fields, began to be used to provide improved drainage and to make possible more efficient utilization of today's equipment. This tool, coupled with controlled and planned use of carryall scrapers, makes it possible to reshape completely the surface profile of farmland so that the best possible erosion and water control

system can be established. The farmer thereby can plan a fertility and soil management program that will continuously improve his level of production. It also makes it possible to develop fields so that farm machinery can be used with a highest possible level of efficiency, precision, and speed.

Once field surfaces are shaped for most effective water management, water control, and erosion control, it is possible to start a planned program of soil manipulation to improve soil structure. This may take the form of subsoiling or incorporation of crop residues or it may take the form of precision tillage operations.

Controlled reshaping of fields and land surfaces can be both the first step in building soil to its highest possible level of productiveness and assurance that the maximum benefits can be obtained from the equipment and agricultural knowledge available to the farmer of today and the future.

# Machines for Clearing Land

T. W. Edminster and G. E. Ryerson

MANY EARLY American farms were hewn from forests with an ax, mattock, wedge, or crowbar in a man's hands. As land clearing and field improvement assume renewed importance today, handtools give way to machines that do in a day what our forefathers took months to do.

Changes in patterns of land utilization, the wish to have uniform, large fields to facilitate high-speed mechanization, and the importance of maintaining and developing potentially productive land near markets and population centers place a new importance on the conditioning of agricultural sections through clearing, smoothing, and forming productive farm fields.

The hazards of flooding and overflow meant that much of our early agriculture was established on the steeper ground above the flood plains. Many potentially productive river bottoms were left uncleared or only partly developed for intermittent use. Intensive production of cultivated crops on the steeper lands brought problems of erosion and runoff.

Work under the small watershed protection program of the Department of Agriculture has reduced or eliminated the overflow hazards on many potentially productive river bottoms. Rapid advances in drainage techniques have further facilitated the use of these areas for intensive production. These developments in time permit the use of susceptible to erosion or damaged by erosion cultivated upland areas for hay, pasture, and forest. Thus areas are conserved for the future.

Modern machines need a smooth, uniform surface that will permit precision tillage, planting, and harvest operations. Fields cleared of stumps, stones, and fence rows can be made into large, easily farmed tracts suitable for machine operations.

A smooth, uniformly drained field often permits the operation of tractors at speeds one or two gears higher than on fields crisscrossed with ridges, dead furrows, gullies, stump holes, wet and depressed areas, or exposed rocks. Rock fences, minor drainageways, and rough, brushy areas make for small, irregularly shaped fields that limit the use of machines and cause excessive loss of time because of frequent turning and short rows.

The elimination of such obstructions with modern clearing and earthmoving equipment can be accomplished readily because the rapid development of specialized heavy-duty equipment permits economical and effective clearing and earthmoving

operations of a type and magnitude that would have been impractical a few years ago.

Each land clearing or improvement project has its own characteristics. No single method or piece of equipment is economically or structurally suited to all jobs. Analysis of the existing conditions is essential. Four major factors must be considered: The intended use of the land, the physical characteristics of the tract, the characteristics of the material to be removed, and the economic factors.

Rough, undeveloped rangeland or reservoir sites (where simple cutting and brush removal may be enough) require less thorough clearing than areas intended for improved pasture or cultivation. On areas that are to be intensively farmed, removal of stumps, roots, and rocks and smoothing will be required. Gullied areas would require equipment suited to land grading and smoothing. Wet, swampy areas would need equipment for drain construction and land-forming operations.

Characteristics of plant growth also guide the selection of equipment. Some types of brush may be cut with heavy-duty mowers or choppers, but other types may require root undercutting to remove the bud ring. Large stumps, particularly those with deep taproots, require heavy tractors with dozer blades or stumpers. Stumps with shallow root systems can be handled with root rakes and plows. Light, fibrous materials or brush may be crushed and disked into the soil to decompose. Mature trees and stumps must be piled with equipment that will provide high, dense piles, free from soil, to permit effective burning.

Each of these conditions must be considered when one analyzes the economics of clearing and improving land.

Other considerations include the size of the areas, number and proximity of other jobs, weather conditions, and the experience of the operator.

Intended use of the land and the

proposed time sequence for the intended use also have an important influence on the economics of a land clearing and conditioning program. Land that can be roughly cleared and pastured until roots and small stumps have decomposed can then be prepared for limited cultivation and finally for intensive cultivation through subsequent heavy diskings and plowing. When immediate intensive use is proposed, however, all roots must be removed completely by machines.

Clearing operations include light clearing and intermediate and heavy clearing.

Light clearing operations can be accomplished by surface cutting, undercutting, heavy disking, chemical sprays, and controlled burning. For the other, heavy crawler tractors, equipped with special stumper blades, root and rock rakes, and stump pullers, are needed. Explosives are sometimes used in these operations.

CUTTING EQUIPMENT for removing light brush includes heavy-duty sickle mowers, which can clip stems up to 1.5 inches in diameter. The cutterbar type of mower consists of a short, heavy bar with heavy stub guards and extra hold-down clips. The rate of blade travel often is increased through special gearing to provide a higher cutting rate in relation to the forward speed of the tractor. An important safety feature is an automatic breakaway device that permits the cutterbar to swing back through a 90° arc if an obstruction is hit. On most equipment the bar, when freed, will swing back into position and relock automatically. Hydraulic sickle drives permit the cutting of heavier growths.

Larger rotary brush cutters cut and shred brush up to 4 inches in diameter. These consist of sets of high-strength steel blades revolving at high speed in a horizontal plane. The basic design is similar to that of a conventional rotary lawnmower. Newer types have blades designed to provide a fanning action that facilitates shredding the trash.

Brushbeaters, which have a series of weighted chains revolving about a horizontal shaft, have a shredding action that eliminates the need for piling, although decomposition will be hastened when a heavy disking follows.

Stalk cutters—weighted rollers to which blades of various types have been attached—crush and break up brush and small trees that have been killed with chemicals. Stalk cutters of this type may weigh up to 10 tons and require the large crawler tractors to handle them.

Where large volumes of cut brush interfere with the subsequent land use, tractor-mounted brush rakes can be used to remove and pile the cuttings in windrows for burning.

UNDERCUTTING, to loosen and remove roots, bud rings, and rhizomes to plow depth, is particularly valuable when the ground is to be cultivated immediately. Various types of straight and V-shaped blades have been mounted on tractors or carriers to travel 10 to 18 inches below the soil surface to cut loose these portions of the vegetation. In land free of large stumps or rocks, undercutters of this type can be operated at speeds up to 5 miles an hour, thus permitting undercutting of 25 to 30 acres a day.

Heavy disks or root rakes are used to chop or remove the material to prepare the land for cultivation. Such equipment removes roots well and disturbs the soil profile only a little. In rough rangeland, it is necessary only to cut loose and lift the bud zones to the surface to assure an effective kill. Bush and bog harrows, having disk diameters of 26 to 34 inches and weighing up to 5 thousand pounds, are used sometimes to clear brushy areas, since their deep penetration accomplishes the same cutting action.

Spraying with herbicides of the selective hormone type or the contact type is effective when the standing dead brush will not interfere with initial land use. Sprayers mounted on trucks or tractors are used in open brush. Application from airplanes or helicopters is preferred on large areas or under dense cover and rough terrain. Controlled burning may be used effectively if adequate fire control lanes have been established with conventional clearing equipment.

The selection of the power unit is of primary importance in heavy clearing. Clearing contractors generally believe that "the larger the tractor, the cheaper the job." Full operating efficiency depends on having horsepower available. In a comparative cost study using tractors of 260-, 155-, and 102-drawbar horsepower ratings and equipped with heavy-duty rakes for felling, raking, and windrowing extremely heavy material having stem diameters up to 72 inches, the relative production in acres per hour was 1.3, 0.76, and 0.5, respectively.

On medium-sized equipment, hydraulic implement control has been found preferable to cable control, as it permits more exact positioning of the blade and permits adding additional downward pressure to the blade. Cable controls are satisfactory on the heavier units.

Mountings that permit both angling and tilting are preferred, as they allow greater flexibility in cutting tree roots, rooting out boulders, and carrying out supporting earthmoving—that is, filling stump holes and constructing temporary ditching. Mountings that permit quick interchange between various implements such as stumpers, root and rock rakes, and dozer blades are essential in all instances.

Stumping blades may be equipped with a wedge, or stinger, to split stumps and root crowns, thus facilitating their removal, or they may consist of heavy, narrow-toothed "dozer" mounted at the center of the dozer frame. The latter type is used to advantage on low-cut stumps when a minimum of soil disturbance is required.

Large trees can best be handled by use of treedozers that have a knock-down beam to apply thrust 8 to 10 feet above the ground, while the curved V-blade mounted behind it moves under the stump with a lifting and side-thrust action. Angle dozers equipped with serrated blades slice through trees and stumps 15 inches or more in diameter at ground level.

For large stumps, from which the tree has already been removed, the pull type of stumper, which attaches to the drawbar of the tractor, is effective. Consisting of a single heavy tooth, similar to a subsoiler, it is first used to cut the lateral roots of large stumps by making a pass on each side. The stumper is then lowered behind the stump, and a combined forward and lifting motion is applied to roll the stump out of the ground.

Heavy-duty rake equipment, operating 10 to 12 inches deep, can remove roots, rocks, and other debris with a minimum of destruction of the soil profile. Little soil is left in the piles and windrows to retard burning. Spacing of the rake teeth may be varied to suit the conditions of brush and soil. Replaceable wear caps and special root-cutting shoes may be attached to the rakes. "Shaking" the rake as it mows with a load will remove most of the soil on the roots, and the brush pile that is left will burn more quickly and thoroughly.

In the use of all heavy-duty clearing equipment, the tractor operator should be fully protected from falling limbs and tree trunks by equipping the tractor with a heavy-duty cab guard. Guards have been designed that will withstand high-impact loads.

Maintenance is an important phase of any clearing operation. On range and pasture, use of selective herbicides for controlling shoot regrowth is effective. Annual mowing with rotary mowers also will keep down the regrowth and discourage annual weeds. Normal tillage operations generally will provide the necessary follow-up to prevent regrowth on cultivated fields.

Clearing operations and advances in mechanized farming parallel one another. As new heavy-duty clearing equipment is developed, it makes feasible the clearing and conditioning of land areas to meet the exacting needs of high-speed, precision farm equipment. Increased land values and new concepts in patterns of land utilization will emphasize further the importance of selected land clearing operations.

# Machines for Conservation

Dwight D. Smith and James J. Coyle

SHARP CURVES in the rows did not bother the farmer who used a single-row, horse-drawn cultivator. He took as a grin-and-bear-it matter the turns he had to make in the middle of a field to work the rows that pinched out before they reached the boundary.

But he had to make a choice when he began to use a tractor instead of horses and double-row or four-row equipment instead of single-row cultivators.

He could reshape the surface of his fields to eliminate the irregularities that caused contour lines to twist across his field. Or he could abandon thoughts of conservation and run the rows parallel to a field boundary without regard for possible loss of soil.

Not many farmers had to choose the second course. Machines became available to them that would move great volumes of earth at a unit cost they could afford.

Thus a farmer could have his fields reshaped so he could perform his farming operations on the contour without undue difficulty. He could

have the natural contours of his land altered by cutting the high spots and filling the low spots and so eliminate the twists and turns.

Developments in field machinery and earthmoving equipment have permitted the farmer on irregularly sloping land to remain competitive in overall agricultural production. His fields can be reshaped to work surfaces required for precise placement of seeds, fertilizers, and other chemicals and precise cultivation and harvesting by high-speed, multiple-row equipment. He thus gets the benefits of lower production costs and reduced probability of crop failure.

The transformation of gullies to grass waterways is another way in which conservation work has benefited from the improvements in earthmoving machinery. Gullies that once were a threat to land and property can be sloped and shaped economically with modern equipment. Often the reworked gullies can be fertilized and seeded or sodded to form a waterway for the safe transport of surface runoff. Often they are filled so that terraces and rows can be extended across them. Such work rarely was feasible with horse-drawn equipment.

The demands for water are many times greater on the modern farm than they were a few years ago. They must be met by building impounding reservoirs in sections where supplies of underground water are not plentiful. Such reservoirs of the needed depth and size would have been almost impossible without modern construction equipment.

Reshaping sloping land so that subsoil is exposed or mixed with surface soil may seem counter to good soil conservation. On soils shallow to rock, shale, or other restricted layers, it is. But the result is worth the cost of the added treatments on deeply permeable and some slowly permeable subsoils.

The principal differences between surface and subsoil horizons of these soils is the lower fertility level and organic content and poorer physical condition of the subsoil. Modern soil tests, the availability of low-cost fertilizers, particularly nitrogen, and the management of crop residues have done much to speed the recovery on many soil profiles that have been changed by reshaping field surfaces.

In northwestern Georgia, for example, some road cuts that exposed B and C horizons of Cecil soils produced no cover in 12 years. On others, good covers of grasses and legumes were established quickly, after the soil had been fertilized properly. High-yielding corn has been produced in Missouri on exposed subsoil of Mexico silt loam soil, a Midwest claypan soil of medium to low natural fertility, by special fertility treatments. Knowledge of the soil profile to several feet below the deepest cut, however, is necessary in selecting fields where rapid recovery can be expected. Research on the fertility requirement of exposed subsoil has been started on several major soil areas by the Department of Agriculture and experiment stations.

THE WHEEL SCRAPER, or carryall, a rugged machine carried on two to four rubber-tired wheels, cuts, loads, transports, and spreads earth. It is pulled by tractors—farm tractors of three-plow size or larger crawler tractors of more than 100 horsepower. It has a cutting blade, earth bowl, ejector and sometimes loading mechanisms, and a power-control system. The front wheels on smaller models are omitted, and the tractor drawbar serves as the front support. The cutting blade is on the bottom about midway between the front and back wheels.

The machine in loading moves forward. The blade is lowered, and it cuts a slice of soil, which is forced upward into the bowl. The ejector mechanisms force the soil out in a uniform layer when unloading. The power-control mechanism consists of hydraulic cylinders or steel cables and sheaves and operates the cutting blade and ejection mechanism.

Scrapers used for land reshaping have bowl capacities generally less than 15 cubic yards. The 8-cubic-yard size is the upper limit for construction of terrace ridges and channels. Machine weight varies from less than 1 ton for the 1.5-cubic-yard size to 12 tons for a 14-cubic-yard size. The larger sizes usually have rear push bars for bulldozer assistance to speed loading.

Some of the larger wheel scrapers have integral power units with two or four rubber-tired drive wheels. These are used less to grade land than to construct dams where the haul distance is large. They can operate at 30 miles an hour loaded.

A BULLDOZER is a tractor with a front-mounted blade for pushing earth, rocks, and other materials. The blade is curved in a vertical direction and mounted parallel to the front of a crawler or large four-wheel-drive tractor. The blades generally are 8 to 12 feet long and 2.5 to 4 feet high. The blade may be lifted 3 feet or more by cables from a power-driven winch on the front or back of the tractor or raised and lowered by hydraulic cylinders. Smaller blades fit practically all sizes of farm tractors. The largest bulldozers used in land reshaping require a tractor of about 150-drawbar horsepower with a combined weight of more than 20 tons.

The angle dozer is a modification of the straight blade bulldozer. Either end of the blade may be set at an angle of less than 90 degrees with the direction of travel.

In the U-dozer, another adaptation, the outer ends of the right and left one-third of the blade are set forward in a cup shape to increase the amount of loose material that can be moved in a single pass of the machine.

LANDPLANES, or levelers, also are used for reshaping sloping land. They may be 20 to 60 feet long and 8 to 14 feet wide. They usually are rigid throughout their length, but some of the larger machines are hinged at one or two points to allow horizontal movement to facilitate turning.

The front generally is attached to the tractor drawbar, and the rear is supported by wheels and a curved leveling bar. The larger machines may use a front truck or shoe arrangement with a tongue, which attaches to the tractor drawbar; the front support of the leveler is attached toward the center of the tongue.

A wheel scraper for moving earth is suspended in the center. It shaves off high spots and spreads the cut material in low places. The capacity is 1 to 4 cubic yards.

Hydraulic cylinders control the scraper operation and raise or lower the rear smoothing bar from operating to transporting positions.

Tractors—three-plow conventional farm tractors to 75-horsepower or larger crawler tractors—pull the landplanes.

The larger planes, if they have adequate power, generally are more desirable for fine grading (after reshaping with scrapers and bulldozers) than the small machines.

TERRACING, an old practice, has progressed in America in various stages— from the hillside ditch to narrow-base, bench, broad-base, semiridgeless drainage, parallel system, conservation bench, and basin terraces. The last three are the new models.

Improvement of terrace alinement to reduce the time and difficulty of farming received consideration by engineers and conservationists by 1940. E. L. Arnold, of the Soil Conservation Service, in 1941 suggested a series of alternate ridge and channel types as a means of improving alinement. Topographic maps were used in planning terrace systems before laying out fields so some of the terraces would be parallel to each other. This work began on the Texas Plains, where four-row equipment was already in use.

The construction of parallel terrace systems had started by 1946 in the Midwest. Paul Jacobson, an engineer of the Department of Agriculture in Iowa, developed a method for laying out parallel systems. He used natural drainageways as outlets; the terraces drained to the waterway at each end from the ridge between. Channel grades were varied from 0 to 1 percent to make the ridges as nearly parallel as possible.

Research workers of the Department in 1951 began studies of parallel terrace systems at the Midwest Claypan Experiment Farm in central Missouri. They discarded conventional terrace systems and built parallel systems on three 10-acre fields. They used an alternate ridge and channel terrace with a uniform grade. They made cuts and fills up to 30 inches to make the lines parallel. They eliminated 70 percent of point row areas by the parallel systems. Farming time was reduced 24 percent.

R. P. Beasley and L. D. Meyer, then of the Missouri Agricultural Experiment Station, started a study of parallel terrace layout and construction in 1954. They developed a system for layout, construction, and checking in which the tractor operator could build and check a terrace without other help.

F. A. Kummer, of the Alabama Agricultural Experiment Station, developed a parallel system in which grass waterways in natural depressions were used as outlets. Old terraces were smoothed, ditches filled, and stumps and rocks were removed before the parallel system was constructed.

Intensive programs of building parallel terraces in which grassed waterways are used in natural depressions as outlets have been underway in Alabama, Georgia, Iowa, South Carolina, and other States, where heavy rainfall causes erosion in grainfields.

MORE AND MORE farmers are building parallel terraces and reshaping land before they build the terraces. They generally are assisted by experienced field engineers in determining need for the work, suitability of the field for cut and fill operations, and the surveying, planning, and staking of the terrace lines so the machine operators can proceed in an orderly manner with the reshaping and construction operations. The engineers frequently are employed by Federal or State agencies that work directly with farmers on conservation problems. They also may be employees of the relatively new commercial firms doing farm management, engineering, or construction work.

They first consider the suitability of the soil for the cut and fill operations of reshaping. Information from soil surveys generally provides a good basis for a decision by an engineer. Surveying, planning, staking, rough grading, and fine grading follow. The engineer may vary the order somewhat and may carry out the first three steps simultaneously in the field. A topographic map is needed for some of the more complex situations.

The field engineer can readily determine the desirable locations of waterways and of a key terrace, to which lines above and below may be made parallel. The key terrace is generally near the upper end of natural depressions that will be used as outlets and either the second or third line from the top of the field. It is then staked within allowable grade limitation for the soil. Lines at equal distance are next staked above and below, and the ground surface elevation is determined at each stake.

It may become necessary to adjust the key terrace line to keep cuts and fills on the above and below lines within practical limits. Stakes on the final lines may then be marked for cuts and fills as when grading for irrigation. The difference here is that the lines are curves and not straight, as in reshaping most fields for surface irrigation. Generally three or more lines may be made parallel without excessive cutting and filling. When irregularity of slope precludes sufficient parallel lines in the first set, the procedure is repeated below; a correction area is left between the two sets of lines.

The most effective tool for rough grading in reshaping is the wheel, or carryall, type of scraper with power controls. Operation is parallel to the stake lines and between them. Stakes in cut areas remain in place on a narrow band of soil until final cuts have been made.

Fine grading is usually done with a land leveler or plane after terraces have been completed. Fine grading by landplanes is sometimes omitted, but that is questionable economy. Poor control of planting depth may reduce stand and yield. Small rills and microslope variations will cause contour rows to break during runoff. This increased movement of soil is deposited as silt fans in the terrace channels. Fine grading can be done more effectively and cheaper with the landplanes than with the wheel scrapers or improvised farm tools.

The wheel-type scraper is highly satisfactory for constructing parallel terrace ridges and channels. Channels can be cut to an accurate grade and the soil moved parallel with the terrace line to fill areas. Sizes may range from the 1.5-cubic-yard scraper, pulled by a farm tractor, to the 8-cubic-yard size, pulled by a large crawler tractor, such as used in land reshaping.

Bulldozers also are satisfactory for building parallel terraces if soil does not have to be moved very far. Contractors often use bulldozers with graders and wheel scrapers.

Construction costs in the Midwest for parallel terraces, including land reshaping, have been one-fourth to one-third greater than for the conventional type. The comparison may be misleading, however, as it represents the limited degree of smoothing practiced in 1954–1959 and not the high degree of smoothing that could be done on irregular topography. Layout or engineering costs are also increased probably by about 50 percent or more because of the greater time and skill required than for conventional terrace planning and staking.

The Zingg conservation bench terrace was developed for moisture-deficient areas of deep soils with gentle slopes. It is a terrace system that utilizes contour benches and ridges to retain surface runoff until absorbed.

A level contour bench 80 to 150 feet wide is formed in the lower one-third of a contour interval by cutting along the upper half and filling along the lower half. A terrace ridge is constructed at the lower edge of the bench. Ridges lower in height are constructed at each end of the bench to impound and spread the runoff from the upper part of the interval, called the runoff-contributing area. Slope irregularities are within the contributing area and leave the bench area free of point rows. Since length of slope is controlled, the practice controls erosion and conserves moisture.

Large graders pulled by crawler tractors generally are used to construct the benches. Wheel-type scrapers are used to smooth contours on the lower parts of the slopes before the benches are made.

Basin terraces, used in the areas of deep loess soil of western Iowa, are crescent-shaped impounding structures. They protect the flatter and lower areas from damage by runoff from the pasture areas above, so that the lower areas may be safely used for row crop production. The length of individual terraces is seldom more than 500 feet, although several may be in series. The closed-end channels have a storage capacity of 2 inches of runoff for the area above. All of the disturbed area is reseeded immediately after construction.

Any large earthmoving equipment, such as bulldozers, graders, and wheel scrapers, may be used to build basin terraces. Bulldozers have been used a lot because the distance the earth is moved is short. They operate perpendicular to the line of the terrace, pushing earth downslope to form the ridge and channel.

STRIPCROPPING can be improved as an erosion-control practice by land re-shaping to allow precision control of row grades.

Experiments at the Upper Mississippi Valley Soil and Water Conservation Experiment Station in Wisconsin have shown there is less total erosion in controlled row grades than with level contour rows, because of the reduction of cross-row rilling. Runoff, however, is increased slightly. Equipment and methods for reshaping land for uniform-width stripcropping is the same as for parallel terraces, except that the lines are used for strip boundaries without construction of the terraces.

GULLY CONTROL has been a costly and troublesome problem. With slip scrapers, fresnos, and walking plows as the earthmoving equipment of the 1930's, the removal of clogging trees, brush, and other debris and filling with properly compacted soil were a major problem. Modern bulldozers, treedozers, root plows, and pneumatic-tired rollers make the work easier and less costly.

After debris is removed by treedozers or root plows, gully filling by sloping of banks begins. Removal of debris usually scarifies the bottom and sides enough for the filling operation to begin. Compaction of fill soil, as in making an earth dam, is essential.

Sloping, filling, and compaction continue until a predetermined cross section of desired hydraulic characteristics is obtained. Other steps may include diversion of runoff and installation of seepage drains and grade-control structures.

The final step is to establish sod according to procedures that fit the soil and climate of the section.

Advances in the hydraulics of grass waterways, low-cost drainage techniques, management methods for establishing and maintaining sod, and designs for grade-control structures provide technical tools for use with mechanical tools to transform gullies into grass waterways.

Charts have been published by the

Department of Agriculture based on studies of vegetation-lined channels at the Outdoor Hydraulics Laboratory, Stillwater, Okla., and other locations, by which the engineer can determine the size of a stable channel required for almost any combination of field conditions. The upper limit for stable vegetation-lined channels also can be determined from the charts. Grade-control structures can be designed for more severe conditions from charts based on structure research by Department of Agriculture engineers at the St. Anthony Falls Hydraulic Laboratory, Minneapolis, Minn., and other locations.

IMPROVEMENTS in equipment for constructing ponds began in the 1930's, when cable-control bulldozers became available for crawler-type tractors. They did all the necessary earthmoving work for building ponds where soils at the site were suitable for the fill.

The development of modern cable- and hydraulic-control wheel scrapers for crawler tractors and high-speed two- and four-wheel drive rubber-tired tractors have facilitated the work. This equipment has been used to build the larger farm reservoirs and flood-detention dams where the distance earth has to be hauled is much greater than for dams with ponded areas of less than 2 acres.

Construction operations for an earth fill start with clearing debris and vegetation from the site and cutting a core trench.

The next operation is to place fill material in successive layers 6 to 8 inches thick. Each layer is compacted to desired density. Dry soils frequently do not pack to form stable structures. When moisture tests indicate a lack of moisture, it is added generally by sprinkling as necessary to give optimum compaction.

This process is simple enough when wheel scrapers are used to cut, haul, and spread the fill material in uniform layers.

It can be done also by bulldozers, but two operations are required then. The fill material is first pushed up on the dam base from the pond site by operating back and forth perpendicularly to the line of the dam. When sufficient material is on the fill for a layer, the bulldozer works back and forth parallel with the line of the dam spreading and compacting the material.

Additional compaction by rollers may be required with fill that has been placed by either the bulldozer or wheel scraper.

CONTRACTING TO DO land improvement and conservation work is a new field of endeavor that has grown out of the application of conservation practices and the developments in land reshaping.

Efficient equipment is large and expensive and requires skilled operators and specialized management. Commercial farmers have said the services of the contracting firms are satisfactory and economical. The contractors have formed State associations, which are part of a national organization.

RESHAPING LAND to control and conserve runoff and prevent erosion very likely will continue along present patterns but at an accelerated rate.

We believe the limit has been reached in the number of rows one machine can work effectively on sloping land, because a man's and a machine's efficiency does not increase in direct proportion to the number of rows covered by one pass of the machine, and the limit is lower on sloping than on flat lands.

Rather, any change may be to increase precision and speed of machines used on the altered surface of fields for planting, cultivating, and harvest.

We expect that future reshaping operations will be extended to lands of steeper slopes where soil is high in productive capacity and well located for markets and transportation. That would mean an increase in parallel terracing and—on the steeper slopes—

a new and different kind of terrace still to be perfected.

Bench terraces probably will come back into use on the steeper slopes. The downhill side of these terraces may be stabilized by perennial sods or soil stabilents—materials somewhat like the asphalts or portland cement but more suitable for this type of use— if and when they are ready for field use. These stabilents could be useful in waterways. Channels of stabilized soil would offer less resistance to flow than those lined with vegetation. Higher permissible velocities would make it possible to reduce greatly the size of the channels.

# Engineering for Drainage

William W. Donnan and John Sutton

SOME LAND must be drained because of unfavorable soil conditions and to allow modern equipment to be used efficiently on it.

The character of the soil, depth to water table, position on the landscape, and other related factors must be considered in determining the need and requirements.

Soil surveys and investigations help establish the need. New methods, tools, and techniques also have been developed. Some of them a farmer uses, and some he contracts for. Most of the techniques of investigation and diagnosis, however, are available to him through soil conservation and drainage districts.

An estimated 30 million acres were drained before 1905; more than 102 million acres were in organized drainage enterprises in 1960.

Most drainage has been done by the

group enterprises organized under State laws. There were more than 40 thousand of them in 1960. They averaged some 2,200 acres.

The group enterprises drained the land mostly by open ditch systems. Some constructed levees and dikes, tile drains, and pumping plants. Some of the works were simple, but in other sections expensive and complex works, such as levees and pumping plants, were undertaken.

Surveying techniques to determine the topography of the area to be drained have been improved. Air photographs have speeded the making of topographic maps, and a stereoptical analysis of aerial photographs can be used to determine the topographic feasibility of the drainage plan. Aerial maps give a true picture of a problem area. Maps, mapping details, and getting overall knowledge of topographic features used to be prohibitive in cost but are now widely used. Soil surveys are an important phase of all drainage investigations.

Hole boring was a hand operation in the early days. The ordinary hand auger method of soil study was limited to depths of 5 to 6 feet. Power-operated devices gradually have replaced handpower for drilling to 10 and 15 feet with augers.

One type of portable power auger folds into the bed of a pickup truck. Its drill shaft can be extended to 10 feet. Additional shafts can be coupled on, and drilling can be extended to a depth of 40 feet, although the best operating depths are 8 to 16 feet, depending on the kind of soil and the moisture conditions. Drill bits are 2 to 10 inches in diameter. Six 10-foot holes can be bored in an hour under average soil conditions.

A second type of auger uses a hydraulic motor, which furnishes the power for both the rotation and the vertical travel of the auger. The hydraulic pump is operated from a power takeoff on the vehicle on which the auger is mounted. Forty 10-foot holes can be bored in 8 hours.

The jetting rig is good for logging sands and clays to depths of 20 to 100 feet. It has a small tube, .25 inch to 1 inch in diameter, which is forced into the ground. Water is pumped into it. The ease with which the tube passes through successive segments of the soil and the nature of the soil that bubbles out around the outside of the tube indicate the location of sand or clay in the profile. The texture of the subsurface materials also is indicated by the jetting pressure and rate of boring.

The Veihmeyer type of soil sampling tube was one of the first to be used to obtain small cores in all but extremely coarse soils. In the 1930's, a sliding hammer was hand operated to drive the tube, and the tube was jacked out of the soil with a handpuller. Then came the airhammer, which speeded up the work. New motor-driven devices raise the hammer, let it fall, and then pull the tube out of the ground.

Other coring tubes have been developed for obtaining in-place cores of various types. A power-driven machine designed to get 2-inch, 3-inch, or 4-inch cores up to 30 or 40 feet in depth and in most types of soils was in commercial production in 1959.

Modified geophysical methods also are used to learn the character of the subsurface strata. The electrical resistivity method has been used with considerable success as a cheap, fast technique. It involves the introduction of an electric current into the soil at one electrode and picking up that current at a known distance from its entry into the soil. Intervening electrodes measure the equipotential and indicate the depth and location of sand and clay strata.

RATES OF WATER transmission should be determined in quantitative terms to be of practical use in drainage. Coefficient of permeability of the soil may be defined as the rate of flow of water through a unit cross-sectional area under a unit head during a unit period of time. For convenience in making comparisons, coefficient values are stated in terms of flows of water through saturated soil.

Methods of determining the coefficient of permeability are of three broad classes—field measurements, laboratory measurements, and indirect evaluations.

For field measurements, direct measurement of the permeability of an entire soil profile, based on pumped-well data, drawdown curve, and data on quantity of water pumped are used to compute the coefficient. Other types of direct measurements of the permeability of individual strata are made by means of small tubes, piezometers, or auger holes.

Laboratory measurements utilize samples of packed soil or in-place cores of soil. These techniques seldom give true values of hydraulic conductivity, but under controlled conditions one can rely on them for some fixed relative coefficients.

Indirect evaluations of hydraulic conductivity have been perfected to the point where they hold some promise of being a fast, efficient integer for use in drainage design.

Some of the soil characteristics that control the movement of water through the soil are type of structure, arrangement of aggregate, grain size, texture, pore space, dispersion, swelling, and type of clay mineral.

In many sections of the country, including the Western States, visible soil characteristics have been correlated with measured percolation rates, and the soil permeability is graded in accordance with a classification which has been used extensively by the Soil Conservation Service in describing mapping units of soil surveys.

THE WATER TABLE survey is the most important single factor in the design of any drainage system. It is made usually by utilizing some type of observation well.

The kind, size, and depth of well and

the type of casing depend largely on the type of the investigation. For a reconnaissance of a small plot, auger holes usually suffice. For a valley-wide investigation, observation wells of a semipermanent type are used.

Observation wells generally are installed by placing the pipe or casing in an auger hole dug to the desired depth. Casing pipes are .25 inch to 6 inches in diameter. Pipes open only at the ends should be set on a small amount of gravel at the bottom of the hole. Gravel is then back-filled around the pipe to a point above the ground water table.

A useful drainage-investigation tool is the ground water piezometer, an unperforated, small-diameter pipe so designed and installed that after it has been driven into the soil the underground water can enter it only at the bottom end. The device registers the hydrostatic pressure of the underground water at the bottom of the pipe.

The piezometer can be used to ascertain the hydrostatic pressure at any level in the soil profile. This opens up a wide range of possibilities in drainage investigations. Since underground water moves from a point of high hydrostatic pressure to one of low pressure, the movement of water can be charted if the hydrostatic pressures are measured.

Both piezometers and wells have been installed successfully in certain areas to depths of 100 feet or more by jetting. Much greater depths can be attained by jetting than by driving—the depth of installation is limited mainly by the size of the aggregate encountered.

In large-diameter wells into which a float can be suspended, recorders of water level may be installed. They are activated by clocks and describe continuous records of water table fluctuation on a chart. The records often help to determine the source of water, as they can be checked against records of rainfall, irrigation, rise in elevation of nearby bodies of water, and so on.

Trace materials often are used to outline the sources and movement of water. Some detectable mineral element—such as a fluorescent dye—is put into the soil water at one point in the hope of picking it up at another point downslope. Extremely small amounts of fluorescence can be detected by using an ultraviolet light. Radioactive tracers—low concentrations of radioactive sulfur and radioactive chlorine—have come into use to trace movement of water.

A useful technique in the Western States, where the ground water often is salty, is to analyze completely for all mineral elements the ground water sections where the water table is high. The elements include sodium sulfate, sodium chloride, sodium nitrate, potassium sulfate, potassium chloride, and potassium nitrate. The suspected sources of water are sampled and given complete analysis. A comparison of the analyses reveals which one is the source, since its analysis will more nearly match that of the high water-table waters.

SURFACE DRAINAGE systems are designed to eliminate surface flooding. Ponds 1 or 2 inches deep, which form after heavy rains, often cause wet spots that interfere with timely cultivation and harvesting.

Modern agriculture requires well-drained fields on which high-speed four-row and larger equipment can operate efficiently. A primary requirement is that the field dry out uniformly. A well-designed surface or subsurface drainage system or a combination system suited to the farm is best.

Land grading and smoothing of fields allow excess runoff to flow down a row or over a field without ponding in shallow depressions. Technicians have worked out standards for required slope, row lengths, and maximum depth of cut in many places, but more work needs to be done to firm up recommendations.

Large scrapers, drawn by big tractors, usually are used to move most of the dirt in land leveling. The cut may be only a few inches deep. On many fields the cuts and fills may be 1 to 4 feet deep if the subsoil has good texture and the productivity may be restored by soil amendments. The final smoothing operation is usually done by a land leveler.

The modern system of surface drainage emphasizes ditches of adequate capacity and depth. They are well located and easily constructed and maintained with modern equipment.

A system of parallel ditches often is used on large, flat fields. Rows are then run down the small prevailing slope to provide good row drainage. Shallow drains are installed across these rows to collect the water and transport it to laterals, which convey it to a larger ditch.

A random system of ditches is installed where the topography is more irregular and the ditches need to follow natural swales and draws.

DRAINAGE GUIDES have been developed for many States or problem areas. Drainage engineers, soils technicians, agronomists, geologists, and other technicians may participate in preparing a guide. A typical guide covers the depth and spacing, side slopes, width of bottom, type of layout, coefficients to establish required capacity, and other design requirements. Such guides need revision as additional information and experience are gained.

The proper spacing and depth of tile and open drains used to be determined by rules of thumb or previous experience. Today the design engineer also has tested formulas.

Theoretical concepts of how drainage devices actually work have been developed and proved by using models or electrical analog techniques.

Research in hydraulic laboratories with sand tanks and dye have traced the movement and paths of water from the source to the drainage device.

Model sand tanks have been used to develop and prove theoretical formulas of spacing drains.

Technicians have learned that the flow of water to a drain device in the saturated zone of the soil is comparable to the flow of electricity from one electrode to another. The same analogy holds true for the phenomenon of heat flow.

Thus small models using electricity—electrical analogs—help to solve complex research problems. For example, a sheet of blotting paper is saturated with a graphite solution to simulate a cross section of soil. Then a copper strip is placed along the top to simulate a water table and a copper button is located on the sheet as the tile drain. These two electrodes are hooked up, and electrical current passes from the copper strip to the copper button through the graphite paper. The equipotential of current at any point on the graphite sheet can be measured, and it is analogous to the hydraulic equipotential in soil.

EQUIPMENT and machines of many kinds are used in the work of improving farm drainage systems. High-powered, modern, earthmoving machines work well for making flat, side-slope ditches, which are easy to maintain with the farm tractor.

Some special equipment has been developed. The backhoe is used for digging in hard materials where a dragline bucket would tend to slide over the material. It is used in installing tile lines that are excessively deep and in places where large rocks prevent the efficient utilization of tile-trenching machines.

Tile drains for agricultural purposes in the early days were installed by hand-digging the trench, laying each segment of tile in place, and then backfilling the trench—a laborious job. With gasoline engines and tractors have come the wheel- and the ladder-type trenching machines.

These machines consist of a wheel- or crawler-type tractor, on which is mounted a wheel- or ladder-type trench-digging device. The device usually is powered from the motor that propels the tractor. Behind the trenching device are various attachments. Among them are a metal shoe, which holds the trench open and in which the tile setter rides; hopper chutes for placing gravel below and around the tile line; sliding inclined chutes for delivery of tile segments; a hydraulic ram for holding installed tile in place; and belt-conveyor devices, which carry the excavated earth to one side or to the point of backfill over the installed tile line.

Wheel-type machines can install tile 3 to 10 feet deep. Ladder-type machines can lay it 20 feet deep. They can lay 4-inch to 20-inch tile, with gravel or other filter materials. They install the tile at a controlled grade in one continuous operation at speeds up to 300 feet an hour.

IMPROVED MATERIALS have increased the life of drainage structures and brought down their cost. Advances in manufacturing and improvements in tile specifications and inspection procedures have contributed to improved quality of tile. The American Society of Testing Materials has set specifications for clay and concrete pipe.

Common problems in the past included failures of drain tile due to heavy loads in deep trenches, freezing and thawing of clay tile, and effects of acids and sulfates on concrete tiles. New and stronger tiles now are made to meet such conditions.

New materials include bituminized fiber drainpipe, which is manufactured from wood fibers impregnated with coal tar pitch. It has a high melting point and is chemically inert. One such pipe contains about 25 percent of fiber and 75 percent of pitch. It comes in 8-foot lengths and is joined by couplings. Water enters through perforations. Less skill is needed to lay it in trenches than jointed pipe. Once placed, it remains in line.

Corrugated metal pipe often is used when running sands are encountered. It is strong enough to resist underground forces that would displace jointed pipe. It also is used to protect ends of tile lines.

Plastic and asbestos pipe have been used on a trial basis. Plastic pipe has been used more extensively to conduct irrigation water; it would have the advantages of a lightweight pipe with long sections. Its cost may determine its future use in subsurface drainage.

The design and installation of filters for tile drains on a scientific basis has added much to the life of drain tile. In the past many tiles soon filled with sediment, and blowouts often occurred. Impermeable soils around the tile often kept water out of the tile. The remedy is to surround the tile with a graded gravel filter, which screens out fine sediment and prevents it from entering and clogging the drain. In fine-textured, impermeable soils, the filter layer provides an opportunity for all the soil pores to become drained along the entire length of the drain instead of immediately adjacent to the joint crack in the tile.

Covering tile joints with tar-impregnated roofing paper or such was a common practice to keep sediment from entering the joints. A new material made of Fiberglas has come into use. Research workers have a simple method of determining whether a particular soil will enter the tile through the filter. It should be covered with 2 inches of hand-placed topsoil to insure against damage during backfilling.

By making a mechanical analysis of the soil and determining the particle size and distribution, one can plot these data into a distribution curve. If the curve falls in the safe zone, as determined by research tests, the fiberglass filter will provide adequate filter protection. If the curve falls in the non-safe zone, the Fiberglas filter will not function properly.

MOLE DRAINS are formed by pulling a bullet-shaped or round mole through the soil at a depth of about 20 inches. Ground water collects in the channels and flows into outlets, which generally consist of open ditches or drain tile.

The method is used to drain some of the organic soils of Florida. The mole drains remain effective for 3 to 5 years. Mole drains would fill with sediment within a year in other places. The practice has not been widely adopted.

Research workers have developed a method of pulling moles and lining the channels during the same operation with a U-shaped or round plastic lining. This practice has created wide interest. Field trials have been undertaken to test the practice under a wide range of conditions, varying from the fine-textured soils of the humid areas to the saline and alkali soils of the Western States.

If the practice proves economically feasible, it will open tremendous areas of clay soils to moling and to obtaining the benefits of subsurface drainage.

PUMPING for drainage has increased greatly. Among the advances is the development of drainage pumping installations to reclaim and improve lowland.

Pumping installations have reclaimed some half million acres of fertile bottom land soils near the Upper Mississippi and Illinois Rivers. These districts cover 3 thousand to 15 thousand acres, and are surrounded by dikes to prevent overflow. The drainage pumps lift the water usually 10 to 25 feet from the drainage ditches to the river level.

This type of installation may be adopted readily to reclamation of coastal marsh areas.

The development of small, efficient pumping units and the widespread installation of electric powerlines have made it feasible to install small units to drain low fields frequently less than a hundred acres in size. Such installations may be used instead of lowering outlet drainage ditches. Small pumping installations may lift water from an open farm ditch or a tile line into an outlet ditch or from a deep tile drain into a tile at higher elevation.

In areas where artesian pressures cause an upward movement of the ground water, deep-well pumps, 60 to more than 100 feet deep, are installed to drain the land by pumping from deep subsoil layers. Such installations are most economical where the pumped water is needed for irrigation.

Submerged propeller-type pumps, developed since 1940, are adapted easily to automatic operation. Floats or electrodes, which do not require constant attention of an operator, control them. When the water level rises to a predetermined level, a float activates an electric switch, and the pump operates until the water is lowered in the ditch or tile to a lower level also adjustable to site requirements. These installations provide controlled drainage where the ground water level is raised or lowered to meet needs of the growing plant.

Drainage pump systems in the West are most feasible where the pumped water can be used for irrigation.

More advances in drainage activities can be expected. Our increasing demand for water has led people to think of finding new uses for drainage water.

We have been engaged in developing ways to get rid of excess water. The development of techniques for the full utilization of these excess waters will come in the next decades.

# Aids for Irrigation

Tyler H. Quackenbush and Marvin E. Jensen

FROM MODEST beginnings, irrigation agriculture has spread to nearly 35 million acres in the United States and has involved a capital investment of about 13.5 billion dollars.

Irrigation was practiced as early as 700 A.D., when Indians along the banks of the Gila River in Arizona dug canals to convey irrigation water.

While some irrigation systems were installed in Texas and California in the 17th century, modern irrigation was started by the Mormon pioneers who arrived in the Salt Lake Valley in Utah in 1847 and plowed a furrow from City Creek to a small tract of sagebrush land in order to moisten the soil and grow grain and potatoes.

Our great expansion in irrigated agriculture has been brought about by economics and scientific advances.

The development of water supplies under the multiple-purpose concept began in 1931, when the Hoover Dam, which towers 726 feet above its foundation, was built on the Colorado River. This multiple use of water opened the way for the large-scale development of water resources in the West.

The first irrigation projects usually comprised only a diversion dam, headworks, canals, and suitable turnouts. As the readily accessible land was developed and the simpler storage sites were utilized, projects of greater scope and complexity were required in order to make the best use of water.

Multiple-purpose projects, such as the Columbia Basin project, which supplies irrigation water to a million acres in Washington and includes the largest pumping plant in the world, provide for the production of power, control of floods and silt, navigation improvement, regulation of rivers, municipal water supplies, fish and wildlife, and recreation.

These additional benefits are becoming more and more important. Their addition to project plans has made possible the development of large areas of irrigated land that could not have been economically feasible as single-purpose projects. An example of these less tangible benefits is that in 1959 recreational use amounting to 19.5 million visitor-days was made of 163 irrigation storage reservoirs administered by the Bureau of Reclamation. The value of this use has been put at 31 million dollars.

The scope and complexity of these multiple-purpose projects have increased the engineering problems in their design and construction. Without the advances that have been made in the development and use of such basic construction materials as soil and concrete, many of them could not have been built.

The increased knowledge of the behavior of construction materials has reduced construction costs. An example is the discovery that the addition of air-entraining admixtures to concrete increases its durability and the workability of the mix and allows a reduction in cement and water content.

The knowledge that the introduction of fly ash, a finely divided residue resulting from the combustion of coal, makes possible the use of leaner concrete mixes and lowers the heat of hydration has been a major factor in the design of concrete dams for storing irrigation water. The Hungry Horse Dam in northwestern Montana, which contains 2.9 million cubic yards of concrete, was among the first major structures in which fly ash was used.

Standard laboratory tests for determining the physical and chemical properties of soils to be used as construction materials or in foundations have permitted an expansion in the use of soil as a construction material. New construction control techniques make it possible to build structures of materials and on foundations that formerly were considered inadequate. This increased knowledge of the behavior of soils has made it easier to build irrigation canals and storage reservoirs in places formerly considered unsuitable.

The development of earthmoving machinery, such as carryalls, bulldozers, and draglines, which have been designed to do specific jobs more efficiently, have made it economically feasible to move millions of yards of earth at costs that have increased very little during the recent period of rising installation costs for other construction materials.

Irrigation development by its very nature requires the movement of large quantities of earth in order to store, transport, and use water efficiently on the land. Land leveling on individual farms accounted for the movement of about 500 million cubic yards of earth on 2.5 million acres in 1953–1958.

Modern equipment also enabled us to construct many miles of canals and ditches to transport irrigation water long distances from the source of supply.

A problem in the use of canals is seepage losses, which often amount to more than half of the water diverted into them. As a result, the waterlogging of lower lands has created drainage problems, and accumulations of salt and alkali have made it necessary to abandon some formerly good agricultural land. To overcome this hazard, low-cost canal linings have been developed. They reduce greatly and often practically eliminate the seepage losses.

Control of seepage has been made economically feasible by the development of subgrade-guided slipforms to line small canals and laterals with portland cement concrete or asphaltic concrete, which previously had been prohibitive in cost. The development of ready-mix concrete and the perfection of the equipment used for transporting it has been a big factor in adapting the use of slipforms to the small ditches on the farm.

Shotcrete—pneumatically applied cement mortar—also has been used successfully for many miles of canal linings. It is particularly well adapted to the Southwest, where variations in temperature are not extreme. Other good lining materials are asphalt, bentonite, compacted earth, soil cement, plastic membranes, and butyl rubber membranes.

The manufacture of concrete pipe and installation techniques have developed to the point where it is generally feasible to transport irrigation water in buried pipelines. Concrete pipelines also are cast in place by the use of removable inner forms and slipform techniques. Other widely used types of pipelines are of steel, aluminum, asbestos cement, and plastics.

The use of plastics as plastic pipes and as protective coatings for steel lines has helped solve severe corrosion problems that once limited installations of pipelines in many places.

Aluminum pipe, light in weight and strong enough to withstand high pressures, has sparked a phenomenal growth of sprinkler irrigation.

WATER CONTROL structures are required in irrigation systems.

As irrigation water becomes more valuable and the labor needed to operate and maintain the irrigation systems becomes more critical, more efficient and more fully automatic gates, diversions, and head control structures are required.

An example of this type of structure is a gate, developed in France and widely used in this country, which can control automatically the discharge with a varying water level either above or below the structure. The gate rotates around a central pivot with radial arms and counterweights. It opens or closes as the water surface rises or drops. Gates of this type are expensive to install, but usually they pay for themselves in savings in water and labor.

Other types of water-control structures, which have automatic controls and use power to raise or lower the gates, provide higher operating efficiencies with less labor.

More pumps and wells have come into use. For example, the number of acres irrigated from wells in Nebraska increased 290 percent in 1955–1960; a total of 22 thousand wells were pumped. The number of irrigation wells in the High Plains of Texas increased from 8 thousand in 1948 to more than 45 thousand in 1958.

The Geological Survey estimated that approximately 33 million acre-feet of water was pumped for irrigation in the United States in 1955. That is more than the maximum capacity of Lake Mead above Hoover Dam in Arizona and Nevada or three times the capacity of Lake Roosevelt above Grand Coulee Dam in Washington.

This great increase in the use of ground water for irrigation is due largely to improvements in well drilling techniques, more efficient pumps and power units, and the general availability of power on the farm.

Diesel engines furnish cheap power for lifting large amounts of water great distances. More electricity on farms has eliminated many maintenance problems that were encountered when internal combustion engines were used. The irrigation farmer therefore has a more dependable source of power, which has increased his dividends from his investment in irrigation equipment.

New devices accurately measure water without changing greatly the cross section of canals. Water must be metered accurately when water from a project is distributed to many farmers and when specific amounts of water are applied to fields.

One method of water measurement consists of placing a wall across the ditch or canal with a notch for water to flow through. These notches are called weirs. Rectangular and trapezoidal weirs that use equations for converting the depth of flow to cubic feet per second were developed in the 19th century; they are still being used on many projects in 1960, but they are being replaced with measuring flumes because silt, sand, and gravel collecting above weirs cause inaccurate measurements. One such flume was developed in the early 1920's by R. L. Parshall in Colorado. This flume causes water to flow through a restricted opening in the channel.

Weirs also require more drop in the water level than Parshall flumes. A recent development is a trapezoidal flume whose sidewalls slope to correspond to the usual canal cross sections. It also has a flat bottom that is level with the canal bed. Other new measuring devices are flow meters installed in pipe-lines or pipe outlets. They permit direct reading in acre-feet or cubic feet of the amount of water that has passed through.

Many devices rely on the principles of submerged orifices, pipe orifices, weirs, reduced cross sections (as used by the venturi meter), and velocity meters. A pivoting flow vane can be installed in a channel with a uniform cross section. As the depth of flow and velocity increase, the vane is deflected more so that a direct indication of the rate of flow is obtained.

EQUIPMENT for regulating the flow of water from irrigation ditches to individual furrows or borders have improved the uniformity with which water is distributed and reduced the labor requirement.

Early irrigators cut ditch banks and then used a hand shovel to dig small channels to individual furrows—a laborious job that often did not apply water uniformly. Men have tried to improve the procedure. In Wisconsin in 1900, for example, a 36-inch strip of canvas was formed into a pipe with canvas outlets for individual furrows.

Similar devices used now have been improved considerably. Lightweight aluminum pipe, which has valves or other types of openings such as sliding stainless steel gates, commonly known as gated pipe, has come into use. Gated pipe is used to convey water along the upper end of the field and deliver it to individual furrows with a minimum of manual labor.

Other materials—improved canvas, butyl rubber, and nylon-reinforced neoprene—also are used to make gated pipe. Plastic, aluminum, and rubber siphons are used to distribute water from field ditches to furrows and border strips. Plastic, metal, and canvas dams in field ditches have reduced the labor once required when hand shoveled earth and sod dams were used.

Irrigation water is distributed in the field by surface or sprinkler methods. Early surface irrigation was done with furrows, corrugations, and contour ditches, because little leveling was required. Because the furrows sometimes ran down steep slopes, erosion was caused from irrigation water and runoff from rainfall.

Greater costs and more accurate leveling was required for surface systems that used border irrigation because uniform grade and minimum side slopes were required. Early irrigators often felt the cost was too great to justify extensive leveling with existing equipment. Also, with abundant water supplies, they felt that they did not need such systems for satisfactory irrigation. When water is allocated more sparingly, many irrigation farmers now spend 100 dollars an acre or more to modify surface irrigation systems for more efficient use of water.

Soil-moving equipment, such as rubber-tired scrapers that hold 5 to 11 cubic yards of soil and have chain and paddle loaders, allows the use of tractors for moving soil economically and rapidly from high places to low places. Large scrapers, drawn by crawler tractors, are used extensively. Land-planes up to 80 feet long and land levelers, which have automatic cut and fill devices, are used to finish the land smoothing, often to an inch of the desired grade.

Electronic grade control devices for trenching machines have been adapted for land leveling equipment.

Other equipment constructs and shapes border dikes without the use of hand labor. Fields can be made completely level in both directions. Sloping lands are shaped into level benches. Level irrigation systems provide efficient distribution of water, especially in places where large streams are available for irrigation. Rainfall is also held in level irrigation systems; that reduces the amount of irrigation water that is needed.

Techniques for stockpiling topsoil for replacement over areas that have deep cuts are used when benches are constructed on steeper slopes and topsoil is required to maintain yields.

Subirrigation, usually used in places where subsoils are permeable, permits water from parallel ditches to move laterally as crops use water. New porous pipes can be put close together in the soil for this purpose.

Among the many laborsaving devices are semiautomatic check gates, which open by various timing mechanisms, and are used when water is applied by surface systems.

The designing of modern, efficient irrigation systems requires experienced technicians and involves the consideration of the size of the available stream, intake rates of the soils, crops, water-holding capacities of the soils, and the peak and seasonal water requirements of the crop.

Irrigation guides have been developed to assist technicians in designing irrigation systems. Soil surveys also have provided information.

Reversible two-way plows mounted on tractors or tractor drawn have been developed for plowing surface-irrigated fields. The plows do not leave furrows in the middle of leveled fields. Tractor-mounted ditchers with hydraulic controls build field ditches with a minimum of labor.

SPRINKLER SYSTEMS have been improved greatly. They permit the irrigation of many fields unsuited for land leveling and also are used on soil that could be irrigated equally as well by surface methods.

Sprinkler systems have made possible the expansion of irrigation into areas that ordinarily require only one or two light irrigations to supplement rainfall. They are used also to protect orchards and vegetable crops against frost damage. Many types of quick couplers are used with lightweight aluminum pipe for rapid movement of laterals by hand.

Many types of sprinkler equipment are such that tractors can be used to move completely assembled lateral lines in one operation. Supplemental engines are mounted on some laterals for moving; the complete line is rolled on wheels.

Other self-propelled systems rely on water-actuated cylinders to propel a single pipe with sprinklers attached, mounted on wheels, and pivoted at one end in the center of the field. One such system can irrigate 40 acres to 160 acres in one revolution without the use of hand labor, except for servicing and adjustments.

Some systems use large booms; the sprinkler heads are mounted on movable trailers. Each setting of the boom will sprinkle 2 to 4 acres.

Another system uses a complete coverage of small-diameter aluminum pipe in the field. When the pump is started, only the first sprinkler on each lateral operates. When the pressure is reduced for a few minutes and increased again, the second sprinkler on each line begins to operate. Automatic valves at each sprinkler regulate the flow to individual sprinklers. Automatic controls start and operate the pump for given periods.

Pressure regulating devices permit more uniform distribution of water on sloping ground.

Instruments and equipment turn sprinklers on and off when the moisture in the soil reaches a predetermined level. A clock mechanism turns it on at specified times during the day. Automatic devices turn the sprinkler off when winds are too high for the uniform distribution of water.

Training and experience are needed to determine the best size of pipe and nozzles and the other factors.

Devices to measure soil moisture enable irrigators to determine when to irrigate for optimum yields. An example is the various types of blocks that are sensitive to changes in moisture and are buried in the soil. Wires leading from electrodes in the blocks to the surface are attached to a small meter, which indicates changes in resistance between electrodes. An indirect measure of soil moisture thus can be had.

In coarse-textured soils, such as sands and sandy loams, other instruments measure the suction force at which the soil holds water. The instruments consist of a porous cup at the end of a tube, which is placed in the soil to the desired depth. The tube, which may be of transparent plastic, is filled with water. A vacuum gage is attached to the upper end. The gage indicates the suction exerted by the soil.

The use of these and other instruments has provided valuable information on the water-holding capacities of soils, rates of water use by various crops during various stages of growth, the effective root zone of various crops, and the amount of leaching required to maintain a desirable salt balance in the soil. Continual use of water that contains some salts for irrigation requires occasional leaching to leach salts downward. Evaporation from the soil surface and transpiration of water by plants results in an increase in salt content unless leaching is provided.

# Modifying Soil Profiles

R. M. Marshall and W. A. Raney

MAN CHANGES many things to suit his needs and wishes. He sometimes changes soils when he determines that such modification will enhance his use of the land. He often modifies the soil when natural forces—floods and erosion—and his use have produced a soil with undesirable properties.

Soil often is modified to improve the soil-water-plant relationships. This means improved infiltration, transmission, and retention of water for use by plants.

The anticipated increase in population and nonagricultural demand for land and water resources necessitates much more efficient use of those resources than currently exists.

A major part of the effort expended in producing a crop is associated with the control of soil moisture. That usually is done on the soil surface.

Modifying the soil profile then offers possibilities for positive control of the accretion and depletion of soil moisture.

We discuss here several ways whereby the intake, retention, and transmission of soil moisture may be modified and controlled by modifying the soil profile.

INFILTRATION is the process of downward entry of water into the soil. Whenever rainfall exceeds the maximum rate of entry or infiltration, runoff or impounding of water occurs. The amount of moisture entering the soil therefore is controlled by the infiltration rate and the retardance to runoff.

The infiltration rate of a given soil depends on many factors, including texture and structure of soil, kind of clay minerals, plant cover, tillage practices, surface litter, and the moisture content of the soil profile. Retardance to runoff is dependent on slope gradient, slope length, slope shape—concave or convex—and cover.

It is not always possible or desirable to absorb all of the rain that falls. It is imperative therefore that we know how to modify or control infiltration and internal drainage. Leveling and grading of land, tillage, and cultural practices offer means of modifying the soil profile that will change the rate of infiltration and improve internal drainage in the soil.

TRANSMISSION or permeability is the ability of the soil to transmit air and water. The increase of soil permeability with depth results in downward movement of water under considerable tension. Such movement is called unsaturated flow. This is a condition commonly found in well-drained, productive soils. When permeability decreases with soil depth, perched water tables develop during rains or when water is applied in irrigation.

Retention of moisture is a function of both soil pore size distribution and internal surface area of the soil. Pore sizes may be altered by man's activities. Such alteration often upsets the internal movement of water through the large pores and retention of the water in the fine pores.

COMPACT ZONES and soil crusting often are the result of the deterioration of soil structure.

The deterioration of soil structure in the plowed zone may result in surface soil crusting, reduction of soil porosity, and the development of compact layers (plowpans) just below plow depth.

Compaction of soil may cause the soil to act quite differently than the normal soil in good condition. Since soil density is increased, water intake is slow, root development is hindered, soil oxygen is reduced, and the amount of moisture available to plants is decreased.

Soils low in organic matter and poor or weak in structure are most susceptible to compaction by the traffic of implements used for land preparation, cultivation, spraying, and so on. Compaction is greatest from equipment that exerts greatest pressure on the soil, either because of excess weight or because of low contact areas between implement and soil. Rubber-tired tractors, for example, which have much less contact area than track-type equipment, cause more severe compaction. Such conditions are further aggravated when these soils are tilled when the moisture content is optimum for soil compaction. Unfortunately, more compaction from a given compactive effort usually occurs at the same moisture content that is optimum for operation of most tillage equipment. This is especially true for fine sandy loam and loamy topsoils because they work better at this moisture content.

Conditions of crusting and compact zones are reduced by incorporating organic materials in the surface soil and growing deep and fibrous-rooted crops, which improve the soil structure and make it more stable in water.

The process of shattering compact zones permits ready entry of the first rains and provides an opportunity for deep-rooted crops to grow and distribute their roots deeply in the soil. These compact zones should be shattered when the soil is dry and must be followed with a good cropping system to provide the most effective improvement in compact soil zones. The shattered soil will run back together unless organic materials, added through good cropping systems, follow the shattering process.

Natural pans, weakly or strongly cemented, may occur in some soils, especially those influenced by permanently high water tables. These limit the transmission of water and air and often are strongly developed and relatively impermeable. These pans usually occur at depths not easily influenced by man. Some strongly cemented pans have been broken with dynamite and the soils successfully used for orchards. In other soils, weakly cemented fragipans occur at depths of 20 to 24 inches and are thick and difficult to alter. Fragipans appear to have low structural stability and, if merely shattered with chisels or other ripping types of equipment, will run back together again when wetted. Opportunities exist for growing plants adapted to soils of this character that have seasonal water tables.

DEEP PLOWING offers an excellent method of profile modification on loose sandy soils in areas of low rainfall and high winds. These soils blow when not protected by vegetative cover.

Deep plowing of sandy surface soils with clayey horizons at 14 to 18 inches has been effective as a temporary measure to reduce soil blowing. The clayey materials, when mixed with the loose sandy surface soils, bind the loose particles together and make the soil more resistant to wind erosion.

Fields that have low dunes and hummocks where deep plowing is to be done must be smoothed first in order to get an even distribution of fine-textured soil from the B horizon or subsoil. This practice, using large turning and disk plows (2–5 feet high), must be restricted to soils that have a sandy clay loam or sandy clay horizon that can be brought to the surface in deep plowing. One-fourth to one-third of the furrow slice must be of fine-textured soil, which, when brought to the surface, will reduce the susceptibility of the soil to blowing.

Big plows pulled with large track tractors are used for this job. The surface soil after deep plowing should contain at least 10 to 15 percent of clay so that a cloddy surface condition can be developed for wind erosion control. Soils with heavy clay subsoils should not be deep plowed.

The subsoils that are turned up and mixed with the sandy surface soils should be crumbly and granular, and not high in lime or dispersed. High-lime and dispersed soils break down into powdery, easily eroded soil material when exposed on the soil surface.

Deep plowing for wind erosion control, even on soils where the practice is adapted, is not a cure-all. It will provide temporary wind erosion control and increase crop yields, at least the first year.

Deep plowing in subhumid sections of the United States brings to the surface fine-textured soil materials that contain plant nutrients which have leached to the subsoil and also provides a soil surface with more clay that has a higher nutrient holding capacity.

Conservation cropping systems with adequate fertilization that provide for adequate residue to be returned to the soil surface and cover crops on the surface during the blow season are necessary requirements for longtime use of such soils in cultivated crops. Deep plowing has been a useful measure on some soils in getting cropland areas seeded to perennial grasses.

Deep plowing that brings too much

clay to the surface, especially on sloping soils (1 to 3 percent or more), often creates problems of runoff and water erosion as well as a crusty surface soil that interferes with seedling emergence. Terracing of these deep-plowed soils on sloping land appears impractical because the terrace fills contain too much sand and the winds will blow out spots in the terraces.

The same practice of deep plowing to transfer good soil to the surface after it has been covered by flood-deposited sand and gravel has been common on some of the bottom lands in the United States. Here flood waters have covered large areas of highly productive soils with sand and gravel from the stream channels. Deep plowing greatly enhances the value of the soil that has had its value lowered by flood deposition.

Deep plowing, especially with the large turning plow, leaves the soil in a rough and loose condition. Cross cultivation and packing are necessary to develop a smooth, firm seedbed. Heavy track tractors in tandem are often necessary to provide adequate power to turn a 3-foot furrow slice.

Emergency tillage may be employed during the blow season when plant residues are inadequate to control soil blowing on erodible soils.

Farm equipment, listers, chisels, shovel cultivators, and disk plows operated at right angles to the prevailing winds are effective in roughing the soil surface to provide emergency wind erosion control. Emergency tillage is a stopgap method to control wind erosion and is used only when growing crops or crop residues are inadequate to control erosion.

When residues are light, many farmers list the fields in advance of the blow season to insure holding the rain that may fall and to provide erosion control against both wind and water.

These treatments are applied mostly on the sandy and loamy soils in the subhumid zones. The kind of equipment used is generally related to the texture of the surface soil.

TERRACE SYSTEMS (terraces with protected outlets) are built to conserve moisture, control soil and water losses, and increase the opportunity for additional moisture to soak into the soil. On nearly level moderately permeable soils, this provides an opportunity to impound water behind the terrace ridge and permit the water to percolate into the soil. This method of moisture conservation permits holding all or most of the water that falls.

Crop residues left on the soil surface or worked into the upper part of the plow layer protect the soil against raindrop splash and keep the soil open so that water can percolate into the soil consistent with the natural ability of the soil to take water. In areas of high-intensity rainfall, it often is necessary to provide outlets to handle excess rainfall from the terraces.

In areas where terrace systems are used to assist in the control of runoff water and soil erosion, the terraces are built with a grade.

The terrace system modifies soil profiles by breaking slope length, increasing slope gradient, and reducing the time of concentration of runoff water. In addition, in the construction of the terrace ridge, the soil is scraped from either side of the terrace center line which usually is the loamy surface soil. This exposes clayey materials that are more erodible and have lower intake rates. In other words, excess rainfall is taken off fields in an orderly manner thereby preventing concentration of water and soil erosion.

Measured runoff water from terraced and unterraced land shows only a slight reduction of total runoff in favor of the terraced fields. Where good soil structure and protective vegetative cover are maintained, however, the runoff is reduced and the total water entering the soil is greater.

ROUGH PLOWING, which leaves the soil surface in an uneven condition, may be used to modify soil profiles in areas where rainfall is low in amount but high in intensity to assure the absorption of a major portion of the rain.

Rough plowing has been successfully used to trap rainfall that would normally be lost as runoff whenever rainfall exceeds the infiltration rate. Such practices have also been used successfully in the Northwest to reduce runoff from spring snowmelt.

Rough plowing is used for seedbed preparation in the Pacific Northwest to assure maximum absorption of rainfall that normally comes after the grain has been planted in the fall. In the area, wheat-peas has become a popular rotation. After the canning peas are harvested, a rough-plowed seedbed is prepared for the wheat that is to follow. Soil moisture, from rains, seldom comes until after the wheat has been planted in the rough, cloddy seedbed, and this method traps a maximum amount of rainfall for the wheat crop.

When rough plowing is used as a means of altering the surface of the soil profile, the total capacity of the soil profile to hold water is not affected—only the infiltration rate and total water available to the soil.

Row grades may be established during the course of seedbed preparation. This represents one of the simplest means of reducing the rate of runoff of surface water in rows.

Row grade control is usually obtained by running rows on the contour where the land is sloping. A minimum of earth removing is required. With mechanization, rows must be straight enough to allow tractors and cultivators to follow the rows. On nearly level soils, row grade control is equally as important in assuring drainage as in assuring a low runoff velocity. Considerable earthmoving is required on soils with depressions and mounds to fill in depressional areas, remove mounds, and allow row grades to be carefully controlled.

Surface mulches of dusts are effective in reducing evaporation losses in areas where there is a water table within 3 or 4 feet of the soil surface.

In drier climates where no such water table exists, dust mulches are ineffective in evaporation suppression and are no longer recommended. When a water table is present, the supply of water generally is adequate for crop production, and procedures other than dust mulches at the soil surface are more efficient.

Residue mulches are widely used in the subhumid region of the United States to control soil blowing. Special equipment has been designed and built within recent years to permit leaving crop residues on and near the soil surface.

Stubble-mulch farming systems have developed with machinery designed to plant in residues. The use of residues for water erosion control is being more widely adopted in the more humid parts of the United States.

Research and experience have pointed to the need for judicious use of nitrogen fertilizers where large amounts of crop residues are left on the soil surface following stubble-mulch tillage.

Land leveling, grading, and smoothing are important methods of altering the soil to improve efficiencies in water management.

Soils that have deep, uniform profiles are suitable for this kind of operation. Leveling for dryland farming holds the rain that falls and provides an even distribution of water on the soil surface of the area bordered and thereby makes more efficient use of the rainfall.

Land grading is usually associated with moving soil to provide a grade sufficient to remove surplus water in a specified time.

In coastal areas in the South farmed to rice, many of the soils, such as Crowley silt loam, mound phase, have circular mounds 18 to 24 inches high and 15 to 30 feet across. These mounds make it difficult to apply irrigation water efficiently and cause uneven ripening of the rice. In the leveling and smoothing operations, the plow layer of the soil (which contains most of the organic matter in the profile) is stockpiled, and the mound is leveled with bulldozers. Then the fields are graded according to engineering design, and the stockpiled soil is spread over the area. The final grading is done with large landplanes.

Other soils with uneven surfaces that permit water to pond can be improved for agricultural use by smoothing the soil surface. Filling of the low areas and smoothing permit better utilization for crop use and facilitate harvesting and land preparation. In vegetable-growing areas, crops are often lost because it is impossible to harvest with machines when low wet areas occur over the fields. Such soil modification does not change the profile much, especially when the surface and subsoil horizons are not highly contrasting.

On many soils with claypan subsoils and thin surfaces, soils shallow to bedrock, shallow to gravel, and shallow to calcareous earths, it is not practical to do land leveling or grading.

Earthmoving work must be based on the characteristics of the soil and the problems associated with the individual soils. A detailed soil survey provides basic information for designing engineering works of improvement.

RADIOACTIVE FALLOUT materials have contaminated some farmlands in varying degrees. Ground covers of vegetative mulches and growing vegetation limit the fallout materials reaching the soil. The extent of protection of the soil by this method is limited to the effectiveness of the vegetative cover. The removal of the growing crop or raking up the mulch that is contaminated removes much of the danger of contaminating the soil.

Preliminary research shows that contamination in the soil requires removal of the first inch or two in sandy and silt loam soils. Such modification of the soil profile may affect crop production following this removal of the surface few inches.

The chemistry of the soil, particularly the calcium content and the ion exchange capacity, is important here.

Research and experience are being called on to give us the answers by kinds of soils to the many questions that have arisen and those that will come up in the future. There will be questions about the soils and their use that may be answered only by making minor or major changes in the soil profile or by altering the chemistry of the soil. Each soil or group of similar soils will have problems.

Knowledge and techniques of soils, nutrition, agronomy, chemistry, physics, bacteriology, physiology, plant breeding, and other disciplines and their interrelationships will provide answers to the problems associated with fallout.

# Remaking
# Our Watersheds

Howard Matson and L. L. Kelly

THE HUSBANDRY of our creek watersheds has become a key to the development of our resources of land and water. Those upstream watersheds produce crops, timber, and water, but damage from floods and sediment in them has cost us an average of a half billion dollars a year.

Farmers, communities, and State and Federal Governments have joined in a program to develop, improve, and protect the watersheds.

The farmers and ranchers carry out their own conservation plans, the first step. Then communities and Government join to make detailed plans, move vast amounts of earth, and build structures of concrete and steel to complete the program—tasks that are too big for individual landowners to tackle and cannot be done with ordinary farm equipment.

New equipment and techniques have reduced greatly the time and cost of developing a plan for remaking a watershed.

Air photographs show the physical features of a watershed—the extent and severity of erosion, the use of the land, and the plants that cover it. Study of the photographs in the office saves days of field work. Possible sites for dams can be located, drainage areas can be measured, and an idea of the character of the flood plains can be formed.

An instrument known as the Kelsh plotter helps the technician plot contour maps directly from low-altitude air photographs. If he must go out to survey damsites and pool areas, he finds such improvement as self-leveling levels to be great timesavers.

Flood routing takes time. The technician first determines the area of flood plain that would be covered by the runoff from each flood-producing storm that occurred during a period of, say, 20 years.

Then, after a tentative watershed plan has been developed, he must determine the area of flood plain that would be covered (if any) by the runoff from each storm in the flood series after needed land treatment and proposed flood prevention structures are completed. Electronic computers can calculate in minutes water surface profiles for the 20-year flood series, a job that formerly required several man-weeks. The computers can be used also in designing improved channels and drainage ditches.

New types of equipment for drilling and soil sampling have speeded the geologic investigation of damsites.

Hydraulically controlled power augers can drill to depths of 15 to 20 feet without adding sections of tubing. Power-controlled rotary drills can be operated much faster and can be equipped with tools and fittings to permit use of many different methods of drilling and sampling. Such devices as driving points, piston samplers, and penetration and vane shear testers sometimes can be used to sample and measure the physical characteristics of soils.

Advances in the technology of soil mechanics have been matched by improvements in soil testing equipment. One is a device that uses infrared rays to measure the moisture in a sample of soil in 15 minutes, compared to the 24 hours required to ovendry a sample.

The work of designing structures and preparing construction specifications has been put on an assembly line basis. Not enough engineers could be found to prepare individual designs for each element of each of the hundreds of structures that are designed and built each year. Graphical reservoir flood-routing aids have been devised to speed the hydraulic design of structures. The many sheets of standard detail drawings that have been developed cover many types and sizes of structural elements, so that the appropriate sheets for any particular structure can be selected for inclusion in the set of plans. Structures can be designed in this way for as little as 2 percent of the construction cost.

MANY TYPES and kinds of measures that require earthmoving are involved in an upstream watershed program. The major ones, in point of individual size, are upstream floodwater-retarding structures, structures to stabilize gullies and control sediment, and improvement of stream channels.

An upstream floodwater-retarding structure is a relatively small earth dam, with an average capacity of perhaps a thousand acre-feet, that traps floodwater near its source and then releases it at a rate that the channel below can comfortably carry.

A structure for stabilization and sediment control, another type of earth dam, is used for stopping the great gullies that work up the stream channels and into farmlands and for trapping sediment.

The enlargement and straightening

of a stream channel so that it can carry greater volumes of floodwater within its banks is called stream channel improvement.

By September of 1959, 202 watersheds had been authorized under the Watershed Protection and Flood Prevention Act, popularly known as Public Law 566. Operation, planning, or construction was going forward on the watersheds with 1,339 floodwater-retarding structures, 288 stabilization and sediment control structures, and 2,479 miles of stream channel improvement. That meant moving about 140 million yards of earth.

(The largest earth fill dam in the world, the Fort Peck Dam on the Missouri River in Montana, contains 128 million cubic yards.)

These are the major structures in point of individual size. In point of total volume of earth to be moved, however, they about equal the minor structures to be built by farmers in the same 202 watersheds. They will move another 140 million yards of earth to complete the 36,700 miles of terraces, 14,400 ponds, and other small works on their individual farms.

The 202 authorized watersheds may be only a start. The National Association of Soil Conservation Districts reported that 16 thousand watersheds have flood prevention or water conservation problems, which may be handled on a watershed project basis.

Let us assume that 10 thousand of these may be economically feasible and that the work underway represents a realistic sample of amounts of earthmoving. That would mean men and equipment must move about 7 billion cubic yards of earth into earth dams and out of stream channels and push and pull another 7 billion cubic yards into terraces, fills for farm ponds, and other small works.

The art of moving earth has come a long way since Abijah McCall and James Porteus of Fresno, Calif., patented their dirt scraper in 1885—the scraper that became known as the "fresno" and found its way to all

parts of the globe. It was an improvement. With half the mule power once needed, the fresno moved twice the yardage that clumsy wheel scrapers could.

On a very short haul and with four good mules, a skilled fresnoman could pile up 225 cubic yards in a day. On a longer haul (a quarter mile per round trip, say) he would do well to move 60 yards a day. This outfit would have taken more than 4 years to move the required 70 thousand cubic yards of fill for a retarding dam of average size. A rubber-tired carryall of a capacity of 25 cubic yards can now do this job in about 30 days.

The difference between the two types of outfits is not in the operators' skill. Maybe the difference is not wholly in the general design of the equipment; we recognize elements of present-day design in early sketches of scrapers, elevating graders, dredges, and shovels.

The difference is in power. A skilled man with four mules simply cannot compete with an equally skilled man commanding 350 horsepower.

The invention and development of the internal-combustion engine, improvements in metals, and the application of electrically and hydraulically powered controls made great earthmoving projects physically possible and economically feasible. The cost of moving the earth into our 70,000-cubic-yard dam with mules might be around 45 thousand dollars—if the mules could be found today.

The job could be done for 25 thousand dollars with the carryall scraper.

The costs of moving earth have remained relatively stable. The average bid price for common excavation on Federal-aid highway construction was 26 cents a cubic yard in 1933. It was 39 cents in 1958. The cost of moving a cubic yard of earth in 1933 was equal to the cost of 6.8 pounds of reinforcing steel—in 1958, to 3 pounds. And in 1958 the operator of heavy equipment got about 2.5 times as much for a day's work as he did in 1933. In fact, the costs of moving earth, relative to some of the other elements of construction, have decreased substantially.

Besides the carryall scraper, progress has been made in all types of earth-moving equipment. Draglines, bull-dozers, dump trucks, graders, back hoes, shovels, and trenchers move earth in the jobs for which they are suited. Contractors have a choice of either track or rubber-tired machines in much of the equipment. They base their choice on the conditions and jobs they handle.

Special equipment does much more. The sheep's foot roller, which packs the earth as would the hoofs of a flock of sheep, is used to make earth fills compact. Large tractors equipped with tree dozers or saws clear and grub the rights-of-way for dams, reservoirs, and channel improvements.

Great progress has been made in equipment for establishing vegetation on spillways, disturbed areas, and slopes of dams. Seed and fertilizer, and a followup mulch treated with a bind-er, can be blown onto slopes from above or below. A machine can even plant grass sprigs—a hand job a few years ago.

IMPROVEMENTS in concrete and con-crete products, too, have contributed to the economy with which conserva-tion structures are built.

A retarding dam operates on the principle of temporarily storing flood-water behind the earth fill and then releasing it through a pipe passing through the dam. The water is re-leased continuously but slowly until the flood storage is exhausted. This pipe and its inlets and energy-dissi-pating device at the downstream end of the pipe comprise the principal spillway of the dam. Next to the earth fill, this spillway is usually the most costly single item of construction.

The development of reinforced con-crete pipe with rubber gasket joints has simplified and reduced the costs of the principal spillway. The pipes, in 12- to 16-foot lengths, are manu-factured by several companies. They make possible a strong and relatively light pipe with dense concrete walls and ample steel reinforcing. The water seal between the sections is a rubber gasket, which provides flexibility after installation to allow for the movement caused by the settling of earth and changes in temperature. The weight of the pipe is much less than that of a concrete conduit poured in place around reinforcing steel. Savings thus are made in materials and expensive form work.

The inlets to the concrete pipe, the energy-dissipating device at the down-stream end of the pipe, and the cradles and antiseep collars normally are built of reinforced concrete, formed and poured in place.

The availability of ready-mix con-crete provides an economical and highly convenient service. Mixing in a central plant makes it easier to get the proper proportions of cement, sand, gravel, and water in the mix. Produc-tion of good concrete in small amounts with on-the-job mixing can be difficult.

The gunite method of construction has cut the costs of some concrete work. A machine sprays the concrete through a tube and onto the floor and sides of canals. The process requires no form work and a minimum of hand finishing.

SINCE THE START of the watershed program in 1948, a total of 1,192 applications for planning assistance had been received by the Soil Con-servation Service on July 1, 1959. Of these, 469 have been authorized for planning assistance, and 202 were authorized for operations.

Local initiative and action are prime requisites to the planning, construc-tion, and maintenance of a project. Projects cannot be installed without approval of the community and the State. The National Association of Soil Conservation Districts has recom-mended that work on 2 thousand of these projects be undertaken by 1968.

Preventing damage to crops and property in the upstream flood plains is foremost in the minds of the members of most communities who have begun watershed projects.

The Chigley-Sandy Creek watershed in south-central Oklahoma is typical. Damage to crops and improvements in the flood plain of this watershed, which covers 29 thousand acres, averaged about 41 thousand dollars a year. Most of the damage was to the crops and pasture on the flood plain. Installation of the dams and other parts of the watershed program was expected to reduce the average damage to about 9 thousand dollars each year. The unusual floods of 1957 caused damage of about 4.5 thousand dollars. Without the 14 small dams and other watershed measures, the damage would have been about 105 thousand dollars.

Under the terms of the law in which the Federal Government furnishes much of the earthmoving and structural costs, farmers in the watershed bind themselves in agreements with the local soil conservation district to enter wholeheartedly into conservation programs covering their entire farms.

When help is given farmers to develop their conservation plans, a problem is to help them find ways to retire steep and eroding cropland to sod-forming grasses or woodland. The increased production on the protected bottom lands allows them to make this shift without reducing their income or upsetting the balance of their farming operations.

Prevention of damage is a dominating feature of the upstream programs. But individuals in many localities have become aware of the possibilities of storing water in upstream areas for use in irrigation, homes, and industry, and for boating, swimming, and fishing. Such storage upstream would aid in stabilizing the economy of farmers and communities by supplying irrigation water for suitable lands. Each year, as municipalities grow larger, the need for dependable supplies becomes more apparent.

MACHINES and power have truly made giants of men. But we must not forget that men made the machines. The names of Diesel, Holt, and LeTourneau are synonymous with our engines and power equipment. Men still control the machines. Only the skill of the operators, the expertness of the engineers, and the initiative of community leaders can remake a watershed.

# Plowman's Progress

M. L. Nichols and A. W. Cooper

THE PLOW that broke the plains and conquered the rich valleys of the United States was almost a direct copy of the European plow, which had been developed through the centuries in Asia and Europe. It was made of wood; iron covered the places where the wear was greatest.

In the United States, the plow was modified to meet the new conditions the settlers encountered as they trekked westward. The development of the country followed the development of the plow.

The significance of the plow in national development was recognized in colonial times by men like Thomas Jefferson and Daniel Webster, who personally studied the implement and made proposals for improving it. Jefferson designed a moldboard plow from mathematical computation in 1798. He hoped to get an ideal shape that would work in all soils. Webster built a cumbersome plow in 1836.

The first letter of patent for a plow in the United States Patent Record was to Charles Newbold in 1797 for a cast-iron plow to use in sand or gravelly soil. It proved to be unsatisfactory because the whole bottom had to be discarded when one section wore out.

The most practical improvement of this period was made in 1813 by R. B. Chenaworth of Baltimore. He patented a cast-iron plow with share, moldboard, and landside in separate pieces so that worn parts could be replaced.

Jethro Wood, who took out patents in 1813 and 1819 on improvements in cast-iron plows, gave his entire life to the promotion of the use of the cast-iron plow.

About 25 years elapsed between the invention of the practical cast-iron plow and its use: Many people thought the plows poisoned the ground and caused weeds to grow.

As immigration moved westward into the fertile valleys of the Mississippi and the prairies, the plows could not turn the heavy soil the second year after the virgin sod was broken. The soil would stick to the plow after the sod had decayed, and the plowman had to stop every few feet to clean it with the paddle he carried. Some people thought the rich prairie land of the Midwest would have to be abandoned because it was so sticky.

Many blacksmiths by trial and error developed shapes that would scour and turn certain soils.

John Deere, a blacksmith in Illinois, about 1837 built a steel plow from a piece of heavy circular saw carefully shaped over a log pattern. This plow turned the sticky soils better than other plows then available. John Deere—and other companies—soon started manufacturing steel plows.

The moldboard plow breaks and pulverizes the soil to open it for infiltration of water and aeration. It cuts the furrow slice from the land and buries the crop residue in the turned furrow slice. It leaves the plowed land relatively smooth and in condition for further tilling or planting.

The modern plow functions mechanically as a wedge driven into the soil. The furrow slice is cut from the lower soil by the share and from the side by the shin or a colter. As the plow is pulled forward, the pressure builds up between the moldboard and soil until the slice breaks out forward and toward the wall of the previous furrow. This breaking occurs on primary areas of shear and accounts for much of the pulverizing of the soil. The pressure of the curved surface of the moldboard develops a secondary set of pulverizing shear areas in the soil, which tend to be at right angles to the primary planes. The top of the moldboard pushes the soil away from the new furrow wall, giving it a spiral turning action. Gravity causes the slice to fall in the open furrow to complete the inversion and placement of the slice. The amount of pulverization and turning depends on the steepness of the moldboard and the soil properties. The path of the soil on the moldboard depends on the speed of plowing and the stiffness or friability of the soil.

The early moldboard plows were designed to operate at the speed of a walking horse. They did not function properly at faster speeds, as with tractors. Plows designed to operate at fast speeds did not work well at lower speeds. The most satisfactory way to increase the plowman's output therefore was to use several bottoms attached in a gang. Large steam tractors or multiple-horse units were used in the West with gangs of 12 or 14 plow bottoms. Plow bottoms have been designed to work satisfactorily at speeds up to 5 miles an hour.

ATTACHMENTS have improved the functioning of the plow. Rolling colters help cut the furrow slice and keep trash from collecting on the shin. Stationary jointers—miniature plow bottoms that cut a narrow, shallow furrow ahead of the shin to move the trash and a small amount of soil towards the furrow—were developed to insure clean plowing. Weed hooks or wires, which hold loose trash under the turning furrow until covered, assist in clean plowing. Clean plowing makes it easier to plant, cultivate, and control insects, diseases, and weeds.

Devices for attaching tools to the tractor, like the three-point hitch developed by Harry Ferguson, have made it much easier to attach a plow (and other implements) to a tractor. More than half of the plows now used are mounted on frames carried by the tractor and have one to five bottoms.

A new type of plow has both right- and left-hand bottoms so mounted that it can throw soil to the right or left as desired. This two-way plow is especially desirable for irrigated lands and sloping land because it eliminates dead furrows, which cause difficulty in handling surface water and using large cultivating implements.

Subsurface sweeps also are used for the primary breaking of land. They differ from the moldboard plow in that they have a horizontal blade, which is pulled through the soil and acts as a plowshare. Since there is no moldboard to turn the soil, they leave crop residue at the surface.

Subsurface sweeps are used extensively to break the soil in places where surface erosion by wind or water is a major problem. They and chisels are used widely in the wheat stubble lands of the Northwest, where they open the soil for infiltration, leave the stubble on the surface, and avoid complete exposure of the soil surface to erosion and drying out.

The disk plow was first built and used in this country in the latter part of the 19th century. The disk blade for tillage probably was invented in Japan. Americans have added precision roller bearings, improved steels, notched disks for better penetration, and improvements in the operating mechanisms.

Part of the friction of turning the soil is carried on the disk bearings. When weight is added, the disk can be operated on hard, dry soils that a moldboard plow will not penetrate. On sticky soils, where a moldboard will not scour, the soil can be scraped from the disk surface as it turns.

The disk is better adapted to stony or stumpy fields than the moldboard plow because it rolls over them. The disk plow requires about 10 percent more draft per square inch of cross section of soil turned than the moldboard plow.

The disks on a common disk plow are tilted backwards at an angle of 15 to 25 degrees, but they may be mounted vertically on a central shaft and used for primary tillage. The latter is called a cylinder plow, disk tiller, one-way, or wheatland plow. It is particularly adapted to high-speed, extensive production with minimum manpower.

THE DEVELOPMENT of the tractor and power takeoff made possible the more direct application of engine power to pulverize the soil by means of different spading and chopping devices.

Rotary tillers became widely used after the Second World War. They are self-propelled, garden-type units, 18 to 30 inches in width of cut; trailed or tractor-mounted units, with power takeoff drives, which cut 4 to 7 feet; and self-propelled, field-type machines, which cut 6 to 8 feet.

The usual arrangement of the rotor consists of a power-driven transverse shaft, on which knives, hoes, or tines are mounted to cut the trash and soil. The usual rotor peripheral speeds are 400 to 1,000 feet a minute. Tines are used on relatively clean ground.

Heavier L-shaped knives generally are better for trashy conditions.

Various systems of springs, couplings, and clutches are designed to reduce shock and protect against overloads that may cause breakage or bending on hard or stony ground. The tines are staggered around the periphery and spaced along the axis of the rotor so as to distribute the load on the machine uniformly. The rate of forward travel of the tiller and the speed of rotation affect the degree of pulverization. The rotary tiller does an excellent job of distributing organic matter, fertilizers, or other materials through the soil profile.

Some use is made in European countries of plows pulled across fields by cable. They were tried in the United States but never had wide application. The cable system theoretically is an efficient way to conserve engine power in plowing, since it avoids all unnecessary haulage and minimizes soil compaction. In practice, however, the high capital cost of equipment and difficulty of operation offset the advantages.

The change from horse power to tractor power from 1920 to 1960 brought about a number of research projects dealing with the physical factors that apply to the design and use of tillage implements. R. W. Trullinger, of the Office of Experiment Stations, Department of Agriculture, contributed materially to the development of the program, which included specialized projects at the Alabama, California, Iowa, and Pennsylvania agricultural experiment stations. The National Tillage Machinery Laboratory was established at Auburn, Ala., by the Department in 1935 to study factors applicable to the design of tillage implements and tractive devices, such as tire and crawler track.

THE INCREASED USE of power equipment has brought problems that call for material changes in soil management. The use of heavy tractors and other power equipment, for example, under many conditions, produce soil compaction which materially affects plant production.

A joint committee of the American Society of Agricultural Engineers and the Soil Science Society of America inaugurated a joint program of research in 1954 to gather the information necessary to solve this problem.

The old art of tillage does not provide the experience or knowledge to meet this situation, and research on the basic reactions of surface soils to force applications is underway by the Department of Agriculture and several State experiment stations.

The research seeks methods of appraisal of the strength of soil in resisting changes in its structure or arrangement of particles as this arrangement affects the environment of roots, including the infiltration of water and air and other ecological factors. This information is necessary as a basis for practical soil management and the development of farm equipment.

Present knowledge of the conditions affecting the shattering or pulverization of various soils or their compaction is inadequate to determine power requirements or safe limits of loading over the usual range of field conditions.

Research workers at several locations began a study of the findings that vibration of tillage tools reduces the draft requirement.

Plastic coatings for tillage tools look promising to turn sticky soils, and attention has been given to such practical problems.

More attention will be given in the future to the efficiency of tillage operations to determine the work done on the soil per unit of energy input.

The question of economics in soil management for cropping depends on how much work in preparation should be done by power and how much can be safely left to the forces of weather that cause the crumbling of the furrow slice. Better methods of soil characterization may give us a better understanding of the minimum amount of tillage needed on each particular type of soil.

WITH KNOWLEDGE gained in recent years, we still have conflicting opinions on questions such as why we plow, the degree of pulverization needed, and the depth of plowing needed.

We feel that the research work in progress and the research that should be done will help us make progress in changing tillage from an art to a science.

The knowledge scientists and farmers are looking for involves the basic relationship between climate and soil physical conditions for optimum plant growth and how to apply force to soil to produce various physical conditions. Many specific problems are included in these broad needs.

One example is the problem of plowing each spring or fall. For row crops the farmer usually plows every year. He has a fair idea where he wishes to place the crop residue, such as cornstalks and wheat stubble, but does not have a satisfactory way to determine whether or not the soil needs pulverization nor the best degree of pulverization for the particular plant he is growing. If he guesses the degree of pulverization needed, he does not know how to obtain it economically. Work on root ecology and soil mechanics will help answer these questions.

Another example of a specific problem, which needs coordinated research by the soil physicist, the soil chemist, the plant physiologist, the microbiologist, the plant pathologist, and the agricultural engineer, is a way to get plants to root deeper in certain areas.

Subsoiling has been done in an attempt to increase water intake into the soil and to make plants root deeper to take advantage of a greater root feeding area and soil-water reservoir. Much good has been done, but much power has also been wasted in this operation, and results have been disappointing in many instances. So, while we have come a long way, we still have a long way to go in tillage.

The world-wide recognition of the importance of economical, efficient tillage is indicated by new research at the National Institute of Agricul-

tural Engineering at Silsoe, England; the Agricultural Research Center at Braunschweig, Germany, and several places in the Soviet Union. The Japanese have an active program of research in tillage machinery and have completed a new tillage machinery laboratory like the one at Auburn.

This extensive development of interest in research in tillage apparently reflects world conditions: The rapid increase in population and the need for a larger food supply; the need to use power and machinery instead of hand labor to raise standards of living through industrialization; and international competition in the implement industry to supply the machines.

# Preparing the Seedbed

W. G. Lovely, G. R. Free, and W. E. Larson

MERELY placing some seed in the soil is not enough.

Seeds need a physical and biological environment in which efficient use is made of soil, water, and nutrients. Different crops require different soil conditions and climates.

Growers, farmers, scientists, and agricultural engineers have worked for a long time to determine the soil conditions plants need and to design and develop equipment and practices to create those conditions.

One approach has been to isolate physical and biological factors of soil to determine their separate and combined effects on plant growth and the physical condition of soil and then develop equipment and practices that will achieve the desired condition.

The physical conditions are described in terms of the status of gaseous, liquid, and solid phases and the stability of the soil framework or structure. Cropping and weather changes the physical condition from year to year—even from day to day.

The soil is manipulated to promote the movement of air, water, and roots through the soil for the better growth of plants and to control runoff and erosion.

The movement of air, water, and roots is related primarily to the size and continuity of the soil pores.

Bulk density of soil is a measurement of space available in the soil for air and water. It measures the denseness of the soil but not the size and distribution of its pores. Soils of different textures can have the same bulk density and total air and water space but a different size and arrangement of soil pores. Soil bulk density thus is only a rough—but practical—measure of the general physical condition of the soil mass.

A specific soil density is hard to get and may be unnecessary. For medium-textured soils for corn and small grain, as in Iowa, a bulk density range of 0.9 to 1.4 grams per cubic centimeter seems to have little effect on crop growth. The soils at time of preparation and throughout the season were well within that range for most methods of seedbed preparation.

Crops do not grow well when seedbeds are too loose. Neither do they do well in high densities, as in some natural subsoils or in places where heavy loads drawn over wet fields have compacted the soil. The intake of water from rain or irrigation generally increases as the density decreases.

Soil temperature affects plant growth and can be modified by tillage practices. Tillage affects soil temperature through its effect on compaction, moisture, surface roughness, configuration, and shading and reflection by plant residues or other materials on the surface. They make it hard to separate the effects of temperature.

The early growth of corn increases with soil temperatures from a mini-mum of about 50° to 80–90° F. Then it drops. For many warm-season crops like corn, differences in soil temperature early in the growing season due to tillage methods become progressively more pronounced from south to north because temperatures in the north are oftener near the minimum level for growth.

Methods of seedbed preparation that leave plant residues on the surface usually cause reductions in soil temperature. Soil temperatures are lower in the crop row when seed is planted in furrows. They are higher in the crop row when planted on ridges. Rough surfaces also may raise the temperature of the soil.

Under normal growing conditions, most locally adapted crops tolerate greater changes in soil temperature than can be brought about by the manipulation of the soil during preparation of the seedbed. These differences in temperature may be critical only during abnormally cold and wet springs.

A major function of seedbed preparation systems is to control the soil moisture.

The problems in humid areas are concerned mostly with excesses at planting time, deficiencies later in the season, and adequate control of runoff and erosion at all times. The problem in the drier areas is largely one of conservation of needed moisture by preventing losses from evaporation and runoff.

Tillage systems that help get rid of excess water in the spring without erosion but retain sufficient moisture for full-season growth of crops are desirable in the humid areas. Seedbeds that absorb and retain maximum amounts of water without runoff and wind erosion are needed in the drier areas.

The microbial activity in the soil influences the availability of nutrients and soil structure. Tillage can affect markedly the microbial activity through its effect on the interrelationships of soil moisture, soil temperature, and aeration and also through placement of plant residues. The requirements for high microbial activity are similar to those of growing plants. This means that the systems of seedbed preparation that create warm, moist conditions early in the season usually are best suited for both microbial activity and for growth of higher plants.

The properties in soils that influence conditions of plant growth determine the methods and equipment used for preparing the seedbed. Their interrelationships and relative importance depend on the conditions of crops, soils, and climate.

A LARGE NUMBER of tools are used to prepare seedbeds.

Seedbed preparation can be broken down generally into primary and secondary tillage.

The moldboard plow is the tool most commonly used for primary tillage. It cuts the soil loose from the furrow. Then it shatters and inverts the furrow slice. Highly polished steel plow bottoms are used in places where scouring is a problem. Chilled cast-iron bottoms are more abrasion-resistant than steel bottoms and are used on gravelly or stony soils.

The shape of the moldboard determines the degree of soil pulverization and inversion that occurs during plowing. The shapes vary from a long, gradual curve, which gently inverts the furrow slice, to the short, abruptly curved moldboard, which shatters the furrow slice as it is being inverted. The general-purpose plow bottom falls about halfway between these extremes and does satisfactory work in many situations.

Many shapes of moldboards have been developed for specific needs. For example, the blackland plow with its small moldboard area improves scouring. The slatted moldboard is used for the same purpose.

Disk plows also cut, shatter, and invert the furrow slice. The inversion of the furrow slice is not so uniform or complete as with the moldboard plow. Disk plows leave plowed fields in a rough, cloddy condition. They operate well in hard, dry soils, in stony and stumpy fields, and in push-type soils, such as peat lands.

For shallow plowing, smaller disks, 20 to 24 inches in diameter, are uniformly spaced 8 to 10 inches apart along a common axle so that a gang of disks rotates as a unit. It is commonly called a vertical-disk plow or a one-way disk plow. It is used for shallow plowing and mixing crop residues with 3 or 4 inches of soil.

Tillage tools that cut and shatter the soil without inverting it are referred to as field tillers, field cultivators, subsurface tillers, and now and then as plows. They very often consist of a framework (pull-type or tractor-mounted) and standards to which are attached various soil-working implements, such as spring-tooth points, shovels, sweeps, and chisels. The standards may be ridged or made of heavy coil springs. The depth of operation, spacing of the shanks, and the soil-working tools that are used depend on the soil condition desired. Most of these implements are operated at plow depth. Where it is desirable to leave most of the trash on the surface, a few shanks with wide sweeps work best. Where there is less trash and some mixing is desirable, smaller soil-working tools placed close together are better and pulverize the soil more.

The secondary tillage operations are performed to pulverize the soil more, kill weeds, level the surface, and pack the soil into a firm seedbed. Of the several types of harrows, the most popular is the disk harrow. Heavy-duty disk harrows frequently are used as primary tillage tools to cut up and mix soil with crop residues and to control weeds. The lighter units are used to cut up crop residues before plowing and pulverize and pack the seedbed. Spring-tooth harrows and field cultivators are used for this same purpose.

The final field operation before planting usually is done to pulverize, level, and pack the soil surface. Spike-tooth and spring-tooth harrows, treaders, and rollers are some of the tools.

Special equipment is required for some tillage systems. Furrow planting requires listers, middlebusters, or disk furrow openers. These may or may not be attached directly to the planter. Bed or ridge planting requires tools to construct ridges. Plows, lister bottoms, disk hillers, and bedding tools are commonly used.

For loose, finely divided seedbeds for gardens, the rotary tiller, which cuts the soil into small clods and thoroughly mixes residues, has become popular.

NEARLY every farmer has worked out his own special technique for preparing seedbeds.

In general, crop residues are cut up or removed, and the land is plowed. Occasionally sod crops are plowed under without cutting or removing. This is followed by harrowing or rolling operations, or both; they make a firm, finely pulverized seedbed.

We can call this the conventional way. It works well over a wide range of soils and climates for many crops. Crop residues are turned under for rapid decomposition. The numerous field operations are rather expensive, but many of them can be accomplished during the off season—late fall or early spring. With no surface residues and a finely pulverized seedbed, the conventional system makes for efficient and effective planting.

It leaves the soil susceptible to runoff and erosion, though. It is costly, and often the many trips over the field destroy tilth, produce compact seedbeds, and tend to seal the surface and reduce water intake. This type of seedbed is ideal for weed growth.

Excessive manipulation of soil became common when tractors became available to most farmers. The attitude was, "if a little is good, then a lot should be better." Seedbeds were prepared by working the soil until a finely divided, packed condition existed at planting time.

The weight and movement of heavy equipment on soil at a moisture level suitable for compaction and even puddling and the excessive working of soil at the dry end of the moisture scale were the extremes of practices that prevailed. Sometimes soil was worked too much as a rather futile attempt to correct damage done by plowing when the soil was too wet. People soon learned that a lot of this working of the soil was unnecessary for good crop production and led to excessive runoff and erosion. The general trend now is toward less soil manipulation during preparation of seedbeds.

NEW TILLAGE systems have been developed to aid in creating the desired seedbeds.

Three general methods are used to utilize available moisture more efficiently: Surface roughness—rough, cloddy seedbeds erode less easily, have a more rapid rate of water infiltration, and tend to have less surface sealing than finely pulverized seedbeds; surface configuration—listing, ridging, and bed planting are examples of this type of seedbed that utilizes a surface shape to control water; surface mulching—to increase intake of water and prevent runoff and erosion.

Minimum tillage generally refers to a method that requires fewer field operations than the conventional practice. Plowing usually is delayed until planting time. The result is a rough, cloddy condition between the rows and a firm, finely pulverized seedbed in the row. On coarse or medium-textured soils at the proper moisture content, it is possible often to pull a planter directly behind a plow, thereby reducing seedbed preparation and planting to one field operation. Plowing at planting time and planting in the tracks of the tractor wheel or packing wheel is another form of minimum tillage. Various other schemes have been tried. Clodbusters, rotary hoes, treaders, or other similar tools are pulled directly behind the plow to break up the larger clods; planting is in the conventional manner or in wheel tracks.

The minimum-tillage systems that utilize surface roughness lower the costs of seedbed preparation by eliminating some of the field operations entirely and by combining others. Aeration and intake of water are increased. Weed growth is less in the loose, cloddy area between the rows.

These systems also have some disadvantages. Getting crop stands may be a problem. Excessively cloddy conditions, from plowing too wet, make it difficult to obtain good seed contact with the soil. The planting operation is slowed down to plow speed. Many farmers planting large areas cannot afford to prepare seedbeds during this critical planting time and prefer to plow in the fall or early spring. Control of weeds in the row frequently is a problem. Early cultivation with the rough, cloddy condition between the rows is sometimes difficult.

Listing, middlebusting, ridge planting, and bed planting can be classified as seedbed preparation systems that utilize surface configurations. With them the surface is manipulated so that a corrugated or ridge-furrow surface profile is obtained. With listing and middlebusting, crops are planted in the furrows; with ridging and bed planting, the crops are planted on top of the ridges. These systems were developed mainly to control runoff and erosion or to improve wet conditions. Some of them require fewer field operations than the conventional practice. Each has many variations in terms of practices and tools used.

Middlebusting and listing are similar in that the crop is planted in the furrow. When done on the contour, they hold the water well until it can soak in. Weed control by subsequent cultivations is made easier by having large amounts of loose soil to throw into the row to cover weeds. Often the temperature in the furrow is low, and the moisture is too high. This leads to poor emergence and slow early growth of crops. Sometimes the soil erodes into the furrow and forms a crust that reduces stands.

Ridge and bed planting have the same conservation features as listing. In addition, the soil temperature early in the season usually is higher on the ridges. Because of the ridged configuration, the soil tends to dry out more rapidly. This usually makes for more rapid emergence and faster earlier growth. Subsequent weed control is more of a problem with these two systems than it is with listing or conventional methods. Where beds or ridges are maintained for several seasons, plant residues may become a problem both with the planting and the cultivating operations.

The number of field operations required for the configuration systems varies considerably. Under some conditions only one field operation, such as disking, is required before planting. At the other extreme, more operations are needed than for the usual way.

Mulch tillage utilizes a surface mulch for soil protection. The kind and amount of mulch varies according to the crop to be grown, the previous crop, the availability of mulch material, and other factors. Straw, wood chips, sawdust, paper, and plastic sheets are some of the materials that have been used as carried-in mulches for special situations, such as nursery plantings. Interseedings and finely pulverized surface soil have also been used as mulches. Some mulches protect the soil and suppress weeds. The commonest type is the residue from the previous crop.

Tilling or loosening the soil while leaving the previous residue on the surface can be accomplished with field cultivators, one-way disks, double-cut plows, and subsurface sweeps. This system has been most widely accepted and has frequently become the normal seedbed preparation practice for small grains in the regions where moisture conservation is essential and wind erosion is likely. The mulches reduce erosion and increase the rate of water intake. Often the number of field operations equals or exceeds that of the conventional practice.

This system has been used for corn with varying degrees of success in the more humid areas. Planting and cultivating operations are somewhat impeded because of the large amount of residue on the surface. The amount of soil moisture sometimes is excessive under these mulches early in the season, and temperatures tend to be reduced. Emergence and crop growth early in the season often are slowed down. Shallow-cultivating tools (such as weeders, rotary hoes, and drag harrows) and sweep-type cultivators work less well in mulches.

Some form of mulch tillage is rather widely used for seeding or renovating pastures. Grassland drills are used in the South to seed cereal crops in pasture. At the time such seedings are made, the erosion control resulting from residue mulch protection is highly desirable, and any depression of soil temperatures may be beneficial. The mulch is the growing, undisturbed sod between the drilled rows.

MOST OF THE tillage methods we have discussed use the plow or cultivator as the basic or primary tool. Various forms of rotary implements have been used for preparing seedbeds. Early forms of this type of equipment damaged the structure of the surface soil, but newer tools leave the soil in a less finely pulverized state.

Much conflicting evidence is at hand as to the crop yields obtained with different methods of preparing seedbeds. With high levels of fertility, uniform stands, adequate moisture, and uniform control of weeds, yields of corn obtained with the various systems in Iowa have not been materially different. When those factors were not constant, the differences in the yield often were substantial. That also is true for other crops in other areas.

Most of the available data, however, do not include the long-term cumulative effects of less runoff, better erosion control, less field traffic, better drainage, and general improvement of soil structure that can be obtained with some of the methods we have discussed.

Under extreme conditions of moisture or temperature, yields from some of the systems are greater than from others. For example, listed corn, which starts slowly, has far outyielded conventionally planted corn when a critical shortage of moisture occurred during the pollination period of the conventionally planted corn but not during the pollination period of the listed corn. Similarly, ridge- or bed-planted corn has yielded 50 or 60 bushels per acre, compared to 5 or 10 bushels for listing or conventional tillage when flooding occurred shortly after the corn emerged.

Under normal conditions, the crop yields can be maintained at a high level with any of the systems discussed.

It is difficult to generalize on the relative costs of the various practices. Preparation of the seedbed is only part of the whole farming operation. Tillage costs vary from farm to farm. Cost analyses of the various practices, however, indicate that the conventional practice is more costly than the others, particularly when charges are made for soil loss. With minimum-tillage systems, it is usually necessary to prepare the seedbed and plant at the same time. Where the planting seasons are short and acreages are large, speed of planting becomes critical. When a reasonable charge is assigned to these systems for this factor of timeliness, their costs approach that of conventional practices.

A farmer should choose his method of seedbed preparation on the basis of efficient and effective use of power and labor available as well as on soil conservation and crop yield.

How WILL seedbeds be prepared in the future? Engineers and crop and soil scientists generally concede that we have been doing too much rather than too little tillage. The soil should be worked only enough to insure satisfactory stands and to control weeds. Many of our field operations in seedbed preparation have been aimed at weed control only. The recent and future developments in herbicides indicate that it may be possible to control weeds without tillage. This should lead to further reductions in field operations.

This type of approach has been successful to a limited extent in corn production. Where the soil factors of soil density, moisture, and temperature were not critical, it was possible to control weeds with chemicals and prepare seedbeds by attaching a cultivator sweep or a similar tool in front of the planter furrow opener. This system takes advantage of the conservation features of mulch tillage and provides a finely pulverized firm area in which to plant the seed with practically no tillage. Planter attachments for applying insecticides and herbicides in either the spray or granular form make it possible to control subsequent infestations of weeds or insects without additional field operations.

On steeper slopes where erosion is a problem, a surface configuration technique will probably be used. Contour ridging or contour listing could very well be the answer. Replanting in last year's crop rows not only looks feasible but in some instances very desirable.

SOURCES of power are changing rapidly. Some day it may be economically feasible to utilize atomic or other similar power for farming operations. Unlimited power may make it feasible to mix soil to obtain a uniform mass ideally suited for a particular crop as well and to level and smooth large areas for more efficient use of large equipment.

The development of new methods and materials, particularly agricultural chemicals, along with this large source of power may make it possible to control soil temperature, soil moisture, biological activity, weed growth, soil insects, and nutrient supply.

For the immediate future, engineers and scientists will continue to study what is needed for a seedbed and how to prepare it. Advances in tillage techniques, fertilizers and their application, and pesticides and their application may make it possible to prepare a seedbed, plant, and control weeds and insects in one field operation.

# Management of Fallow

J. S. Robins and B. D. Blakely

SUMMER FALLOWING is a land management system in which crops are produced every other year or two years in three rather than annually. The extended time between crops is designed primarily to store moisture for use by the succeeding crop. Buildup of nutrients in the soil is a second beneficial result.

Research and experience have led to general use of the system in the 10- to 20-inch rainfall areas of the Great Plains States, in the Pacific Northwest wheat area where rainfall is less than about 16 inches, and on extensive acreages in California. Even with summer fallowing, however, crop production throughout these areas is limited by insufficient moisture and recurring drought.

To store maximum moisture, the land must be kept relatively free of weeds and volunteer crop growth during the moisture-storage period. This usually means periodic tillage in excess of that necessary for normal seedbed preparation. This can be done in several ways. However, each tillage operation breaks up and covers crop residues and tends to destroy the cloddy structure of the surface soil. Severe wind and water erosion consequently are frequent byproducts of excessive tillage during the long cropless periods of summer-fallow systems.

Proper fallow management, therefore, must be directed toward both moisture storage and protection of the land against erosion. Stubble-mulch farming is the principal land management practice to meet these requirements.

STUBBLE-MULCH FARMING is a year-round way of managing plant residues on cropland. Harvesting, seedbed preparation, planting, and cultivating all are done so as to leave a protective covering of crop residues on top of the soil until after the next crop is seeded.

Crop residues on the soil surface afford protection similar to that of growing vegetation. Such residues, whether standing or lying flat and anchored in the surface soil, keep the force of the wind from acting directly on the soil and therefore are particularly effective in preventing wind erosion. They also reduce the impact of raindrops on the soil surface and impede the flow of water down the slope, thereby helping to control water erosion. Therefore, if weeds can be controlled, the fewer number of tillage operations (with the right kind of implements), the more effective stubble mulching will be.

Research results and the experience of farmers indicate that about 1,750 pounds of small-grain residue per acre is needed on sandy soils at planting time for good protection against wind erosion. About 750 pounds is usually enough on loams and silt loams.

While stubble-mulch farming is generally thought to be adapted only to small grains, it also can be practiced on row-crop residues such as corn or sorghum, although the amount of residue from these crops necessary to protect the soil is about twice the amount of grain stubble needed.

Stubble-mulch farming is particularly effective in combination with stripcropping. Stripcropping is the practice of growing erosion-resisting crops in strips alternating with strips of row crop or fallow. The strips are placed either across the direction of prevailing winds to control soil blowing, or on the contour to reduce run-off and water erosion. Width of strips for wind stripcropping may vary from about 2 or 3 to 10 rods or more and for contour stripcropping from 100 to 200 feet, depending on the soil and slope of the land. Some multiple of the width of tillage and planting equipment is most convenient.

EXTENSIVE RESEARCH, development, and testing of equipment have resulted in a workable stubble-mulch farming system. Since the objective of the system is to retain a protective amount of crop residues on the surface rather than plow them under, it was necessary to deviate radically from use of the moldboard plow.

The stubble-mulch system uses the principle of pulling a blade, sweep, rod or other tillage tool through the soil beneath the surface. Major stirring action, therefore, occurs with only minor covering of plant residues.

A WIDE VARIETY OF subsurface tillage implements have been developed to meet the specific needs of the stubble-mulch system.

One of the basic implements is the subsurface sweep plow. It consists of a heavy V-shaped or straight metal blade 6 to 10 feet or more wide and mounted on a toolbar or carrier. It is used primarily for the initial tillage operation following harvest, either in the fall or in the spring, but it can be used for subsequent operations also. The blade cuts off plant roots and, if the soil is reasonably dry, breaks it up to the depth of tillage, normally 4 to 6 inches. Since only one or two shanks penetrate the soil for each section of the blade, there is minimum covering of residues. This implement usually covers no more than 10 to 15 percent of the original plant residues.

Several other implements often are used for the first operation. The chisel is a tongue-shaped attachment 1.5 to

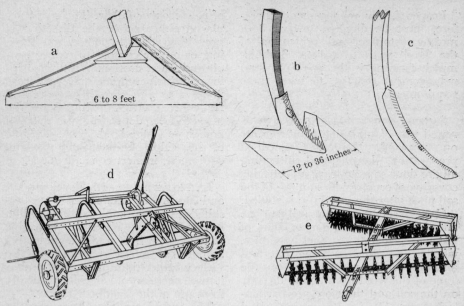

*Maintaining crop residues on or near the soil surface to protect land from wind or water erosion in summer fallow systems requires tillage tools different from those that are ordinarily used to prepare land for planting crops. The wide-sweep or blade (a) is extensively used for initial tillage operations in the fallow season. Narrower sweeps, 12 to 36 inches wide, (b) work successfully for either initial or subsequent tillage operations if residues are not too heavy. Chisel points (c) successfully loosen the surface soil layers without covering vegetative residues and are frequently used for initial tillage operations. Rod weeders (d) are one of the most successful implements for tillages later in the fallow period. Special implements have been developed or adapted to surface residue management systems to overcome special problems. The skew treader (e) successfully breaks up and distributes residues which have been bunched by previous tillage operations and breaks up long-stemmed straw or stalky residues.*

2.5 inches wide, 4 to 10 inches long, and about 0.5 inch thick on toolbar-mounted shanks. The narrow sweep, or field cultivator, is a V-shaped sweep 12 to 42 inches wide and mounted on a toolbar or wheel-frame carrier. The one-way disk is a wheel-mounted single disk with the gang operated at an angle of 40 to 60 degrees.

Chisels and sweeps do not turn the surface layer of the soil. Since chisels or narrow sweeps of a field cultivator are mounted at 12- to 30-inch spacing on the toolbar, they disturb the surface soil and residue more than the wide sweeps and ordinarily cover 15 to 20 percent of the residues. Sweeps 30 inches or more in width have about the same covering action as the wide sweeps.

The one-way causes major stirring

and partial turning of the surface soil and usually covers 40 to 60 percent of the residues. This implement, properly adjusted, does considerable stirring without completely covering much of the crop residue. It can be used for initial and for subsequent tillages where residues are heavy (4 thousand pounds per acre or more). Three or four operations sometimes can be performed on loams and silt loams and still leave enough trash for good protection.

This tillage implement should not be used during periods when very little residue is produced.

SUBSEQUENT TILLAGE operations in the fallow season are performed successfully with a variety of tillage implements. Toolbar-mounted narrow sweeps (24 to 42 inches wide) do an excellent job, as does the field cultivator with narrow sweeps (12 to 30 inches wide). The blades pass beneath the surface and cut off weed roots with a minimum of surface disturbance. These implements normally cover no more than 10 to 20 percent of the initial surface residues.

Another common implement is the rod weeder. It consists of a rod—square, oblong, or round—that operates beneath the soil surface. The rod turns slowly, revolving upward as it advances and depositing coarser materials on the surface. The rod is driven by a gear or chain mechanism from the wheels of the implement. This implement usually covers about 10 percent of the original residues.

Several useful modifications of rod weeders have been developed. One is the attachment of narrow (3- to 6-inch) chisel points ahead of the rod weeder bar. These aid in penetration of hard soils. Curved metal rods attached at intervals behind the rod weeder tend to stir the soil, shake soil from weed roots, and assist in keeping residues at the surface.

No LESS IMPORTANT THAN PROPER tillage devices in the fallow system is suitable planting equipment. It must be designed to operate through the residues on the surface without clogging and without bunching or unduly covering them. It also must place the seed at the proper depth.

Particularly successful are deep-furrow drills equipped with shovel- or hoe-type furrow openers. Such drills push aside surface residues and the dry surface soil and deposit the seed in moist soil to promote rapid germination. Packing wheels are the most satisfactory method for covering the seed or compacting the soil over the seed. This drill leaves a ridged surface with most of the residues concentrated between the rows. Spacing of rows is usually 10 to 14 inches.

Drills with closely spaced single- or double-disk openers are usually less successful in stubble-mulch farming. The main difficulty is in getting uniform depth of planting, because the residues prevent even penetration of the disk openers and clogging is a problem with heavy residues.

A WIDE VARIETY OF SPECIAL implements are used in the stubble-mulch fallow system to overcome specific problems. Where excessive amounts of residue (5 thousand to 8 thousand pounds per acre) are encountered (as frequently occurs in the Pacific Northwest and occasionally in the Great Plains area), straw or stalk shredders are used to break up the straw before the initial tillage. This implement is essentially a rotobeater with a series of hard metal rods or cutting blades attached to a revolving horizontal shaft.

Where excessive residues remain or where bunching of residues has occurred during tillage, a skew treader can be used to distribute and break up long plant stems. This implement is essentially a tandem rotary hoe with the two sections operated at an angle to each other. The angle can be adjusted to obtain the action required.

A troublesome problem sometimes arises when spring tillage is delayed by inclement weather or for other reasons. Under these conditions, cheatgrass, wild oats, volunteer grain, and other weeds may infest the fallowed land. Such plants are often difficult to eradicate with subsurface tillage implements if they make considerable growth. Many of the weeds may not be killed if rains occur soon after tillage. When excessive weeds are present because of such conditions, it is advisable to sacrifice some residues by utilizing a one-way disk, which will eradicate them in one operation.

One of the keys to successful stubble-mulch farming is uniform distribution of residues before tillage. This eliminates bunching of residues and clogging of equipment during tillage. A straw spreader on the combine is helpful.

With coarse residues, such as corn and grain sorghums, clogging of equipment is sometimes a major problem. When that occurs, a stalk chopper or shredder can be used ahead of initial tillage to reduce the length of the stalks.

DURING PERIODS OF DROUGHT, it often is impossible to produce and maintain enough residues to protect the land against wind erosion. Emergency tillage may be necessary then.

The purpose of emergency tillage is to create a roughened, ridged, or cloddy surface to protect the land against soil blowing. Implements used for this operation should bring large clods to the surface if possible. Chisel implements operated at a 5- to 8-inch depth normally do a successful job. Toolbar-mounted furrow openers or narrow sweeps can be used effectively if the surface soil is crusted and will produce clods. Even a spring-tooth harrow is successful under some conditions.

Since emergency tillage sometimes is needed on fields of winter wheat, wider spaced implements such as the chisel or furrow opener, which disturb only a part of the soil surface yet produce a rough condition, are required. Emergency tillage can be done in strips when erosion hazards are not too severe and lasting protection is not required. One-fourth to one-half of the surface is usually tilled at each operation. Such practices may allow salvaging at least a part of the crop.

In severe situations, the common lister is the most successful implement for emergency tillage. Spacing of the furrows over the land can be varied, depending on severity of conditions and the length of time protection may be required. Solid listing is often needed on sandy soils.

"CHEMICAL" summer fallow is a new practice which has been studied somewhat since about 1950. With the development of new herbicides to control weeds, complete or partial substitution of chemicals for mechanical tillage seems to hold promise. Elimination of tillage in this system permits retention of more crop residue and thus gives more protection to the land. As a substitute for some of the tillage operations, 2,4-D can now be recommended to control broadleaf weeds. Chemicals for consistent control of grassy weeds, however, were not available or too costly for use in 1959. In addition, residual effects from these chemicals on the succeeding crop have been noted. Complete chemical fallow, therefore, is not yet feasible.

The second new innovation in fallow management is so-called rough tillage. In this system, land is moldboard- or disk-plowed once during the fallow season at a time when the surface soil is relatively dry. This operation produces large clods, which persist through the planting and cropping season and afford protection against wind and water erosion. The system appears to be adaptable to the Pacific Northwest wheat area, where winter precipitation dominates in contrast to the summer rainfall in the Great Plains. The single tillage operation is delayed until after the first winter rainy season following harvest. Because summer precipitation is negligible, there is usually little weed growth. The second winter precipitation is readily absorbed by the open, cloddy surface. Total moisture storage and yields are equivalent to those on conventional fallowing.

The place of rough tillage in fallow management has not been completely assessed, but the apparent water erosion control benefits make it particularly appealing. Tillage costs are reduced since only one operation is performed.

OTHER PRACTICES and improvement of present equipment and methods for better fallow land management will doubtless be developed. Ultimately, summer fallow with its attendant erosion problems may be eliminated by better methods of conserving and utilizing moisture. Until that time, however, stubble-mulch farming has proved itself as a way to protect and preserve land resources on semiarid fallow lands. Investigation has begun of its possible adaptation to more humid areas or other cropping systems to control erosion.

# Planting
# and Fertilizing

Elmer B. Hudspeth, Jr., Richard F. Dudley, and Henry J. Retzer

FAST, MULTIROW machines are used to make timely plantings of today's large acreages possible. The single-row planters that once were used are giving way to six-row and eight-row units. Seven-opener grain drills have been replaced by 16-opener and larger drills which sometimes operate in gangs.

An average of 7 acres could be planted in a 10-hour day with the one-row, one-horse planter when the rows were 3.5 feet apart. With the same width between rows, a six-row tractor planter can cover 80 to 100 acres in a day.

One of the farmer's biggest problems is how to get a uniform stand of plants at a desirable spacing. There is an old saying that once the crop is up to a stand it is half made.

Some factors that must be considered in planting are type of seedbed, soil moisture, temperature, and weather conditions. Firmness of soil in the immediate vicinity of the seed is of importance in securing good germination and in promoting early plant growth.

In broad terms, the seedbed should be firm enough in the seed row to give good seed-to-soil contact, supply a solid base for the pressure needed for emergence of seeds, and reduce losses of moisture. It must be loose enough for aeration, root penetration, and water infiltration.

Adequate moisture in the seed zone is mandatory. This moisture must be maintained around the seed until it germinates and the root system begins to spread.

The method and equipment used in planting seed can make the difference in getting or not getting a stand.

Planting may be done on the flat surface of a field, in furrows, or on ridges and beds. Flat planting generally is practiced where natural moisture conditions are favorable. Much of the corn and soybeans are flat planted in the North Central and Eastern States.

Furrow planting (or lister planting) is common in sections of limited rainfall for such row crops as sorghum, corn, and cotton, and in the western part of the North Central States. Grain drills, equipped with special openers to place the seed into moist soil, permit furrow planting in regions where protection from wind and winterkilling is needed. Furrow planting, however, may retard germination when the soil is cold or may subject the crop to water erosion or restrict aeration of the soil.

Bed planting is common for many row crops in the more humid areas where surface drainage is a problem. It also is used in furrow-irrigated sections. The beds may take the form of simple rows or ridges. With closely spaced row crops, such as sugar beets, lettuce, and certain other vegetable crops, two rows or more sometimes are planted close together on a single bed.

Research has enabled the implement industry to provide better planters and attachments for different conditions of soil, tillage, and climate. Band seeding and side fertilizer placement equipment, for example, is available for drills.

Band seeding is an improved way to place seed and fertilizer. Grass and legume seeds are placed at precise depths directly above a concentrated band of fertilizer. The nutrients are readily available to the young plants; they thus are able better to withstand droughts and low temperatures.

Band-seeding experiments with tall fescue and ladino clover, conducted by R. E. Wagner and W. C. Hulburt, of the Department of Agriculture, showed the most effective method of establishment was the combination of drilling fertilizer one and one-fourth inches deep and seeds one-fourth inch deep.

The tests showed that band-seeded plots yielded 130 percent more forage than plots on which the same amounts of fertilizer and seed were broadcast. When only one-half as much seed and one-third as much fertilizer were banded as were broadcast, forage yields were 29 percent greater. Weed growth was light on band-seeded plots but was heavy on broadcast plots. Plants in the band-seeded plots got off to a more vigorous start and had a higher survival rate when weather conditions were unfavorable. Costs of planting with fertilizer were lower on the band-seeded plots since fertilizer and seed were applied in one operation.

When the band seeding is practiced, press wheels for firming the soil over the seed help to insure good stands. The press-wheel action conserves moisture around the seed and increases germination, especially in dry weather. When a land roller is used for compacting the entire field, the weed seeds between the rows also will germinate and offer more competition to the young plants than where narrow press wheels are used only over seed. Press wheels are available for many commercial drills.

When large quantities of fertilizer are drilled with the seed of wheat and other cereal crops, the percentage of germination often is lower. It is recommended for them that the fertilizer be placed 1 inch to the side and 1 inch below the seed. Experimental openers for grain drills are being developed to obtain this placement.

We cite some examples of improvements in planting methods and equipment to illustrate the type of progress that can result from a coordinated research program on crops.

In the Piedmont areas in the Southeast, between the coastal plains and mountains, when winter cover crops are planted on terraced fields to control erosion or to condition the soil, planting the cotton may be difficult because of undecomposed litter on or in the soil. F. G. Futral and J. L. Butler, in Georgia, found that the use of double-disk openers with depth bands solved many problems of planting in trashy soil.

O. B. Wooten, E. B. Williamson, and F. E. Fulgham at Stoneville, Miss., compared double-disk seed furrow openers to sword openers on heavy clay soils. The disk openers required less power and equipment for seedbed preparation, scoured better in moist soil, and conserved moisture because only a narrow furrow was opened. Better stands of soybeans were produced with the double-disk openers than with sword openers when dry weather followed planting.

H. P. Smith of Texas reported that a narrow shovel furrow opener, with shields to hold the loose soil out of the furrow until the seed reached the bottom of the furrow, gave better results than a shovel 4 inches wide. With the trend toward the use of delinted cottonseed for planting, the shielded opener can now be narrowed to three-fourths inch.

A farm implement company in 1950 furnished a 1 x 8-inch hollow rubber-tired press wheel for experimental use at Lubbock, Tex. The size of the wheel was changed to 1 x 10 inches in 1951. The flexing action of the hollow rubber tire prevented it from picking up moist soil under most conditions. Thus the ideas of a narrow shielded furrow opener and of pressing the seed into the soil before it was covered were adapted to the lister planter.

E. B. Hudspeth found in 1952 that two to six times better early emergence was obtained with this unit than with conventional equipment. Implement companies have since made these modifications available for planters as well as for drills.

J. G. Porterfield and E. M. Smith in 1954 in Oklahoma designed a planter that produces a wide furrow with a raised center section by using a modified lister bottom, two bed-shaping disks, a narrow seed press wheel, and drag coverers. This seedbed has improved emergence by furnishing a firm, moist seed environment, while giving protection from silting and washing in. The seedbed was said to have the advantages inherent in both planting on the bed and in the furrow. It is called plateau planting.

SEVERAL NEW methods for preparing seedbeds and planting have been developed. One is to prepare only the narrow strip of soil that immediately serves the seed row. Another is to arrange the timing of various operations to reduce field work in seedbed preparation.

The term "minimum tillage" is used often for some of the methods, which include principally plow-plant, wheel-track planting, and mulch-till planting. Other methods include interplanting grasses (in row crops) and seeding in sod (sometimes termed sod seeding).

In wheel-track planting, the fields are plowed at planting time as a regular plowing operation and are planted immediately in the tracks of the tractor pulling the planter.

R. L. Cook and his associates at Michigan State University have used wheel-track planting since 1946. The tractor wheels are spaced to match a two- or four-row planter so that the tractor wheels firm only the soil where the rows are planted. The rest of the soil between rows is left undisturbed; that is favorable for development of roots and intake of water but is unfavorable for germination of weed seeds.

Plow-plant of row crops and grain crops is similar to wheel-track planting, except that the plowing and planting are combined as one operation. The planter or drill may be attached to the plow or to one side of the tractor, and planting may be done directly on the freshly plowed soil. It is said to reduce costs and cause less packing of soil by removing tractor wheel pressures from the plowed land.

Till planting is a method devised to place seed without previous seedbed preparation in sod or stubble ground. Crop residues left on the soil surface between the processed areas prevent wind and water erosion.

The till planter consists of two tillage units, one mounted on each side of the tractor. Each unit consists of an upper 36-inch sweep and a lower 18-inch sweep followed by a rotary hoe section. A rolling colter operates ahead of the sweeps. A two-row planter is mounted on the rear of the tractor. This unit has also been used as a rangeland seeder.

The heavy-duty grassland drill has become important in the grassland farming program for the improvement of rangeland and pastures. It is basically a fertilizer drill on a heavy frame, with openers that can cut through tough sods to place fertilizer below the seed. The uses and advantages of the machine vary.

Early fall seedings of 60 pounds per acre of rye in Bermuda-grass pasture in Maryland extend the fall season from September into November and make possible early spring grazing. This made possible beef gains of 410 pounds an acre, compared to 300 pounds for three other single species of grass. It is possible farther south to graze through the winter, remove the livestock in March, and still have the cereal mature and yield satisfactorily.

The pasturing season in the Northeast can be extended by seeding winter cereals in the pastures. The danger of soil erosion on a prepared seedbed is overcome.

This heavy-duty drill can be used on

croplands to seed such crops as rye and vetch into row crops in one operation after harvesting.

An opener for the establishment of small-seeded legumes, such as ladino clover and birdsfoot, in the faster growing pasture grasses is being developed.

Orientation planting of corn is an experimental method. The seed is placed in the ground so that upon germinating the leaves grow out perpendicular to the row. Increases in yields are due to the extra moisture for the plant from the shaded ground between rows and to the greater amount of sunlight that strikes the leaf surfaces. Equipment for placing the kernels point down with flat sides parallel to the row still has to be developed.

Planting to a stand is now possible with precision planters. It is no longer necessary to seed twice the desired rate and then thin out half the plants. Various systems, using celled wheels, disks, or belts (sometimes with vacuum or compressed air) have been developed to place seed at the best spacing and depth in the soil. High manufacturing costs have limited their use, however.

Precision planting also has been achieved by coating the seed with an inert material to enlarge it for accurate planting.

A national organization was formed by research workers and commercial men in 1924 to study the problem of fertilizer application. This National Joint Committee on Fertilizer Application is comprised of appointed representatives of three national professional societies (agronomists, engineers, and horticulturists) and three commercial associations (fertilizer, farm equipment, and food processing groups).

The committee meets annually with one of the professional societies (in rotation) and conducts a formal program. Proceedings are published annually. Bulletins and visual aids concerning field equipment and research equipment for experiments are pre-

pared. The name of the organization was changed in 1960 to the American Council on Fertilizer Application.

BETTER FORMS and more concentrated fertilizers have made it possible to produce larger crops at relatively low costs.

The use of fertilizer more than doubled between 1942 and 1951. Since 1951 more than 22 million tons of fertilizer have been used annually.

American farmers invested more than a billion dollars annually in fertilizer in the 1950's. That was about one-tenth of the cost of annual crop production. The investment has been responsible for one-fifth of our net agricultural income. On the average, 3 dollars have been returned to the farmer for every dollar invested in fertilizer.

Commercial fertilizers comprise mainly one or more of the three primary elements—nitrogen, phosphorus, and potassium—in suitable chemical form.

Other nutrients added to the soil in large quantities are calcium, magnesium, and sulfur, the secondary nutrients. They act mainly as soil amendments to permit release of plant nutrients that may otherwise be unavailable to crops.

Trace elements include boron, copper, manganese, and zinc. In an increasing number of areas and circumstances the application of these micronutrients give beneficial results. Depending on the element, the crop, and other factors, deficiencies of these nutrients can be remedied by applying them directly or including them in foliage sprays or mixed fertilizers.

Chemical fertilizers are marketed in dry and liquid forms.

Dry fertilizers are available in powdered, granulated, or pelleted forms. Their physical properties have been improved as a result of studies of caking conditions, particle size distribution, and drillability. Granulation or pelleting of mixed fertilizer is used extensively in the manufacture of dry fertilizers. The physical condition of fertilizers is also improved by reduction of the moisture content and by better packaging.

Prescription mixing of the primary nutrient materials is done in many farming areas by local blenders. Savings accrue because no bag or bagging expense is involved; few if any additional conditioners are required because the mixed fertilizers are seldom stored; and less manual labor is needed to move and handle the material. Disadvantages may be lack of uniformity because of poor mixing or subsequent segregation, difficulty of regulating standards, and the possible difficulty in getting ample supplies.

Liquid fertilizers are obtainable in high- and low-pressure and nonpressure forms. Mixed fertilizer solutions are nonpressure liquids.

Nonpressure liquid fertilizers and most dry fertilizers are applied by banding below or below and to the side of the seed or plant at time of planting; broadcasting on the surface (by airplanes, trucks, and field machines) and plowing under before planting; topdressing of established crops, such as grasses and hay by the broadcast method; sidedressing of field crops and booster solutions for vegetable and small fruit crops; transplanting solutions, primarily for use with vegetable crops, tobacco, and sod sprigs; applying solutions for lawns and house plants; using hydroponics, or soilless culture; including foliar nutrients with spray materials, as in orchards; and using them in irrigation water.

Farm manures, which contain some plant nutrients and are high in organic matter, generally are broadcast on the surface and plowed under.

Changes in fertilizing practices reflect new types of materials, higher analyses and rates, improved equipment, and methods of application of fertilizers.

The metering mechanism is the key part of most field fertilizing machines. With the exception of broadcasters, the mechanisms usually are attachments to preplanting equipment, such as subsoilers, plows, harrows, and chisels.

Drills (grain, vegetable, and heavy-duty grassland drills), planters, and transplanters usually have fertilizer attachments. Sidedressing and topdressing attachments usually are mounted in conjunction with cultivating and spraying equipment. Applicators (if not a part of the base machine) usually consist of shovels or rolling disks or colters to make adequate placement.

Dry fertilizer broadcasters employ a regulated gate opening over rotating vanes or an agitating mechanism over an orifice of regulated size. Examples of the former are truck spreaders and endgate broadcasters, which have effective width of application from a few feet up to 20 feet or more. Some truck spreaders use augers in long distributor tubes and often carry 8 or 10 tons of fertilizer.

The other broadcasters are tractor mounted or pull machines, 10 or 12 feet wide. For many years the metering device for these distributors was a rotating bar reel over a series of outlets of adjustable size. A later development is a metering notched disk, mounted vertically over each outlet, usually spaced 6 or 8 inches apart. Their metering accuracy is considerably superior to the older type of mechanism, particularly when the fertilizer is in poor condition. Auger agitators also are used.

The star-wheel dispensing unit is used commonly on drills. It operates horizontally and has fingers that carry the fertilizer under a shield, which is adjustable in height. It is used on some row-crop fertilizer hoppers, although such machines are generally fitted with a revolving bottom distributor, which meters fertilizer through an adjustable or a fixed side gate. To change the rate of application on the fixed side-gate type, the outside of the hopper is raised or lowered in relation to the revolving bottom.

Some distributors have reciprocating plates on the bottom of the hopper, which oscillate slowly or are driven by tractor power takeoff at high speeds. Newer mechanisms on some equipment frequently combine older metering principles or possess some special fluidizing action to make the fertilizer flow uniformly.

HIGH PRESSURE liquid fertilizer (anhydrous ammonia) is regulated mainly by a valve or a positive displacement pump. The opening may be controlled manually or by a pressure regulating valve. Special depositors that place the liquid in the soil are used to prevent loss of nitrogen gas in the form of ammonia. Placement at a 6-inch depth is usually adequate.

FERTILIZING solutions (low-pressure or nonpressure) are usually metered by gravity dribble tubes, gear pumps, roller pumps, metering piston pumps, metering hose pumps, or compressed gas systems. All systems require constant ground speed to insure uniform application rate except for ground-driven metering piston pumps and the metering hose pumps.

In the gravity system, four to six sizes of openings are provided to meet the various rates of application requirements. Often by means of an inverted siphon tube in the supply tank (to minimize change of hydraulic head) a fairly steady flow of liquid can be maintained.

The compression gas method uses a small compressor with a pressure relief valve to maintain constant pressure in the tank regardless of volume or temperature changes that may occur to the solution. This method is especially good for low-pressure solutions, as their pressure may vary up to 15 pounds per square inch. The main feature is the constant discharge pressure.

Gear and roller pumps meter nonpressure solutions quite well when the speed of equipment is kept uniform.

The metering piston pumps and metering hose pumps are driven by a ground wheel or comparable drive and deliver a constant rate of application regardless of throttle or gear changes. This is desirable on irregular fields or when operators are unskilled.

Proper application of fertilizers is the key to efficient fertilizer use. Banded fertilizer close to the developing root system gives quick growth response to small plants. Too heavy an application may injure the plant. Phosphate, if banded, remains available to the plant longer than if it is broadcast. Banding generally is more efficient for row crops than broadcast applications.

The use of radioactive phosphorus in studies of fertilizer placement is helping to solve some of the problems in the application of fertilizer. The fertilizer, labeled as to content of radioactive isotope, is supplied to the plant in various placement positions.

In a given experiment with fertilizer placement, at any time during the growth of the plant, at least three questions can be answered: Has the plant root system reached the point of fertilizer application? Which fertilizer placement has resulted in the greatest uptake of phosphorus? How much better in crop production is one placement than another? The response of a crop to placement, as in the third question, may be obtained by ordinary phosphate fertilizers without the aid of radioactive phosphorus.

The uptake of the "tagged" fertilizer can be measured by tissue tests of parts of the growing plant.

FARMERS and manufacturers of farm implements have been slow to accept new planting and fertilizing practices for economic reasons. Rising costs and prices will make it necessary for farmers to get more from their seed and fertilizer. That is possible only with up-to-date equipment.

We should see more devices to create ideal conditions for establishment of seedlings. Seed and fertilizer might be embedded at the proper spacing in a single water-soluble tape. This tape could then be placed in the soil and covered, perhaps with a moisture-controlling sheet of plastic on top.

Fertilizers will become more and more concentrated with plant food percentages of 80 or more as we learn how and where to apply it.

Quantities of fertilizers used undoubtedly will increase. Only 11 percent of American farmers used the recommended rates, and 37 percent used none on their cash crops in 1959. Labor requirements for the handling of fertilizer will continue to go down as new laborsaving devices are designed.

More liquid and high-pressure fertilizers will be used, since they may be handled with little labor and are the cheapest source of material.

# Engineering for Crop Protection

Orve K. Hedden and Ross D. Brazee

PEOPLE and other living creatures often like the same things—the flesh of fresh, juicy peaches, for example.

Foods are only part of the crops insects and other pests destroy. Many of them feed on juices, fibers, and other parts of plants and animals that people use for clothing or other purposes.

Try to name a fruit, vegetable, tree, or other plant grown for food, clothing, or beauty or for building homes that insects or nematodes will not feed on or that fungi, bacteria, or virus will not destroy if it is left unprotected. Domestic animals, poultry, fish, and animal products, like wool and meat, are food for many organisms. Other pests thrive on trees, shrubs, flowers, and lawns.

Plants that escape infestation or infection must compete with weeds—

plants that are out of place. Weeds use soil nutrients. They eventually become unsightly trash. They clog machinery and prevent a clean harvest.

Isaac Newton, the first United States Commissioner of Agriculture, in his annual report in 1864 made many references to crop destruction by pests. Among the pests mentioned were the now extinct passenger pigeon and the wild turkey. Suggested pest controls included improved cultural practices and application of lime, soot, ashes, elder leaves, plaster, charcoal, and ordinary dust. The equipment and methods to apply them were crude.

This early reference indicates that people had begun to study and inquire more closely into the nature, habits, and responses of pests. Thus began the development of a technology that cleared away the idea that the visitations of pests were supernatural acts, from which there was no escape.

CONTROL METHODS and machines evolved slowly from the use of hand-operated tools to animal-powered equipment. Both are still used—plows, cultivators, mowers, sprayers, dusters, and the dependable hoe. There are cultivators with sweeps, disks, and special accessories to destroy weeds and insect habitats. Mowers are effective against some weeds; other weeds may simply mature multiple seedstalks if their tops are removed. Weed populations seldom can be reduced permanently by mowing after the seed matures.

Sprayers and dusters may be carried in the hands or on one's back. They also are pulled or carried by animals. They are effective for applying chemicals to small plantings or to rough areas where heavy, motor-driven equipment cannot be used satisfactorily.

Sprayers, dusters, mowers, and cultivators fit the power and speed available in tractor equipment and can treat large acreages quickly and economically.

Airblast or mist-concentrate sprayers are a late development for spraying orchards and row crops. The use of a well-designed machine of this type enables one man to make a satisfactory concentrated pesticide application. The low-gallonage spray requires less pumping and hauling of water. Refilling time is reduced. This changed technique and equipment provides a substantial economy in labor and other costs without any sacrifice of effectiveness.

Baits and granular pesticides also are distributed by tractor-drawn equipment. Some soil-working implements combine operations and place fertilizer and pesticide simultaneously. The result is more timely application of materials with less work.

Application of pestkillers from airplanes is suited to the treatment of large or inaccessible areas and to situations in which timeliness of application is of special importance. Its use is seldom desirable in thickly populated areas where small fields contain a variety of crops. The complete coverage of surfaces of plants, necessary for effective use of some materials, is difficult to obtain by aerial distribution.

When the use of airplanes is feasible, areas that formerly required hours or days for treatment are covered in minutes.

Insects, nematodes, soil fungi, and weed seeds may be safely destroyed by soil treatment before some crops are planted.

Damage by nematodes is responsible for the failure of many crops to respond to the application of fertilizers. Several crops believed to be growing at a normal level have made extra growth when seeded in nematode-free soil. Poor crop growth formerly attributed to "sick soil" may disappear after proper application of appropriate nematode killers.

Soil treatments should never be applied recklessly. The application of chemicals to soil may kill useful organisms or reduce nitrogen available for plant growth. Chemicals can be toxic to the crop itself. Proper knowledge and guidance can be obtained from publications and from research or extension personnel of various agricultural and industrial institutions.

Soil treatment materials in liquid or granular form may be mixed into the soil by plowing or by the use of a pulverizing tool. Liquid or granular materials may be injected and sealed at the desired depth back of the teeth of a field cultivator. Sealing may be accomplished by compacting the soil, by sprinkling or flooding with water, or by laying a covering material, such as polyethylene film, over the treated area.

Aerosol generators produce a very fine spray, usually by thermal or centrifugal action. This equipment is useful if residual chemical deposits must be kept to a minimum. It produces good results when treating a pest susceptible to a very small dose of the lethal agent.

CULTURAL METHODS of pest control are effective under some circumstances. Rotating the planting of one crop with that of another that is not attacked by the same pests can prevent the multiplication or development of certain organisms, such as potato scab.

Some infestations may be controlled by selecting crop-planting dates that produce growth unsuitable for the deposition of insect eggs. Disease-resistant varieties of crops, such as rust-resistant wheat, can be used as controls.

Effective use of these methods requires drills and planters of large capacity engineered to operate accurately at high tractor speeds. This equipment enables the farmer to plant a greater acreage of pest-resistant crop on selected dates than he and a neighbor or two could have planted in their entire farming operation using older types of hand- or animal-operated machines.

Mowers, rakes, and sprayers have important use in clearing weed growth from ditch banks, fence rows, and wasteland. This eliminates the debris in which many eggs and adults of harmful insects or host plants of disease-producing fungi may over-winter. Clean plowing eliminates debris that might shelter larvae or adult pests coming to the surface. Thus exposed, they may be eaten by birds or destroyed by the sun and lack of moisture. Many kinds of tillage and planting equipment are available to do this work at high speeds.

CHEMICAL METHODS of pest control utilize a staggering variety of inorganic manufactured compounds, as well as suitably processed natural organic and inorganic chemicals. Their popularity results from convenience in use, great effectiveness, and economy in application. Spray applications of these chemicals by modern, well-designed, and well-engineered ground and air equipment get rapid and thorough results.

A tabulation of organic and inorganic chemicals available for spray application lists several thousand trade formulations. Some may be applied as solutions and some as suspensions of wettable powders. Others are oils or emulsions.

The list also contains numerous organic or inorganic compounds for application by dusting machinery. They are usually diluted with clay, talc, lime, gypsum, pyrophyllite, or other inert materials. Dusts are convenient to apply and are less apt to injure foliage than spray. Their poor adhesion, lack of coverage and effectiveness against many pests, and high cost are disadvantages.

A recent development in dry materials is a compound that desiccates some insects. The material, dusted on plants, absorbs the body fluids of insects and destroys them.

Closely related to the dust materials are those that are impregnated on granular forms of clay or other inert carriers. Each tiny grain then carries its load of pesticide. These can be readily distributed from air or ground applicators if the carrier consists of small particles of generally cubical or spherical shape. These preparations may produce a long-lasting action.

Baits and repellents usually are placed on or in a carrier material before distribution. Equipment must make a uniform and thorough distribution so the bait will be found by a hungry insect or rodent. Rats, mice, and rabbits often cause extensive damage to orchards and other crops, and well-distributed baits may be of great help in their control. Repellents, too, may be useful in this respect, as well as in the more familiar aerosol applications to rid us of mosquitoes.

Fumigants may be sprayed or dusted on foliage. They usually are highly volatile and produce a highly toxic concentration and quick kill. Their cost and the need to use them safely require precision application, which is possible through the use of proper equipment.

Several types of machines have been developed for the application of indirect chemical action to achieve pest control.

Burners using petroleum products as fuel are used for cleaning roadsides and ditch banks of certain weeds and for flaming the young, tender weed growth in some hard-stemmed crops, such as cotton. Brief heat exposure kills sprouting weeds without injury to the crop. Greenhouse and potting soils are sterilized by treating with steam or heating in ovens.

The growth of many pests can be stopped by preventing access to sunlight or oxygen. Mulching with the required thickness of straw, paper, plastic film, or other opaque materials can do that. Machines can be used to assist or perform most of these operations quickly. Water flooding a soil plot to a depth at least 6 inches will exclude air and kill some species of perennial weeds, insect eggs, and larvae. Flooding for at least 3 weeks is usually required.

OTHER PEST-CONTROL methods are not so widely adaptable as chemical controls but have been successful in some instances.

Fungi and bacteria that attack some

insects or their larvae and antibiotics that counteract virus or fungus disease can be passed through sprayers and applied to control crop pests.

Insects that feed on insects we want to get rid of can be propagated and released in infested areas. Airplanes have been used to release male screwworm flies that have been made sterile by exposing them to gamma rays. They mate with female flies; without fertile eggs, the species dies out.

Electrical equipment in the form of lamps is available to lure insects into traps or electric grids, where they are destroyed.

Electricity has been used to heat and sterilize soil.

Crops in storage after harvest may be attacked by various pests. Reduction of the moisture content of soybeans by preharvest defoliation lessens the danger of damage by mold or other decay-producing fungi after storage.

The use of defoliant chemical sprays or dusts that cause plants to die or quickly drop their leaves can facilitate potato harvesting or reduce the moisture and trash gathered by the mechanical cottonpicker.

Thorough grading removes damaged or diseased portions of the crop and so eliminates many sources of infection. Spoilage is minimized when the harvest is placed in a rodent-proof storage, which may include temperature and moisture control.

Forage, fiber, lumber, food, and grain crops in storage are susceptible to attack by weevils, rots, molds, and other pests. Such loss can be prevented or reduced by the use of suitable fumigation equipment for the application of chemicals or by the use of heating devices.

INDIVIDUAL productivity and efficiency have greatly improved since the first Zulu rubbed his head with rotenone-bearing plant leaves to rid his scalp of the head lice on it. Labor and pesticide materials have become more costly. Crude equipment for applying pesticides can no longer be economically tolerated. Engineers are designing this machinery for long life, labor reduction, and for precision application of minimum amounts of materials. Timely application is essential because many pests are vulnerable for only short periods. Versatile, easily operated, and reliable equipment with adequate capacity for timely covering of the treated area even under adverse conditions therefore has become more necessary than ever.

The combined use of plastics, synthetic rubber, and corrosion-resistant metals of the latest types in the manufacture of sprayers, dusters, and other pest control equipment is necessary to assure uninterrupted field performance.

THE INCREASED USE of chemicals has brought an intensification of other problems. Beneficial insects, nematodes, fungi, domestic fowl, animals, and people are susceptible to many of these pesticides.

Man has characteristics, other than appetite, in common with the pests he would eliminate. His cells contain some of the same enzymes as those of insect cells. Insecticides that destroy these enzymes are toxic to both man and insects. This is only one example of the many pesticides which are poisonous to both.

Properly used sprayers and other pesticidal applicators leave a uniform pesticidal deposit on fruit or foliage of the treated crop. Some pesticides are taken in by the plant leaves, roots, or stems and will be within the plant tissues. These residues in or on the crop made necessary the adoption of State and Federal laws to regulate the sale and use of pesticide materials. The regulations are for human safety. They are intended to prevent the appearance of dangerous quantities of a pesticide in or on raw agricultural commodities, including uncooked meat and poultry.

A tolerance must be established by the United States Department of Agriculture for each economic poison before it can be sold in interstate commerce. Tolerances are stated in parts per million in or on the marketed product. Most tolerances are included within the range of 0 to 10 parts per million. Some have been set as high as 200 or more. It is illegal to sell raw agricultural products containing more than prescribed tolerances of economic poisons.

Pesticide residues can be mechanically removed by washing, brushing, or husking. They can be reduced or eliminated by control of the final pesticide application date. Users of pesticides should adhere strictly to the application of amounts recommended in the directions for use of the product. Residue removal is necessary for the safety of the consumer, unless its presence is otherwise prevented. This operation usually improves the looks of the product, but effective cleaning equipment is required to prevent damage to soft or delicate fruit and vegetables.

# Aircraft in Agriculture

David A. Isler

AIRCRAFT were first used in agriculture more than 40 years ago. Military planes of the First World War were used to patrol for forest fire detection in 1919 and for air photography and reconnaissance.

An important new use was opened in 1921 when lead arsenate dust was applied from a wartime Curtis JN6H trainer on a catalpa grove near Dayton, Ohio, to control the larvae of the catalpa sphinx, which were defoliating the trees.

The Department of Agriculture at the Delta Laboratory, Tallulah, La., at the same time was developing ground equipment for applying calcium arsenate to combat the cotton boll weevil. After the work in Ohio, B. R. Coad, an entomologist who was in charge of the laboratory, became interested in the use of planes for dusting cotton. He arranged for the beginning of test and development work at Tallulah in 1922. Planes and pilots were provided through cooperation of the Air Service of the War Department.

The first dust hopper used in Ohio was constructed to hang over the righthand side of the plane so that it could be operated by handcrank from the observer's cockpit. The hoppers built at Tallulah were mounted inside the planes. The first model occupied the front half of the rear cockpit and required an operator to stand behind it and turn the feeder crank. Dust discharge was arranged through the bottom of the fuselage. Flow of air across the bottom of the discharge tube interfered with dust delivery. Then a funnel was made and attached to direct air into a slot cut in the front side of the discharge tube. This was the first attempt to use the venturi, or spreader, principle for breaking up the dust and mixing it with air to improve distribution.

Many ideas such as air suction, ram air, and conducting the engine exhaust across the dust outlet for better dispersal of dust from the hopper were tried and discarded.

Improvements made then, and still in use, included wind-driven mechanical agitators to prevent bridging of dust in the hopper; full fuselage-width feed gates; and funnels or spreaders beneath the fuselage to mix the dust with air and improve uniformity of distribution of the materials. These developments at the Tallulah laboratory established the practicability of applying materials from the air.

THE FIRST PLANES designed especially for dusting operations were produced in 1924 by the Huff-Daland Co., of Ogdensburg, N. Y. They were used in the Mississippi Delta in the first cotton dusting under contract on a commercial basis. This company, which later joined Keystone Aircraft Corp., Ogdensburg, N. Y., and Bristol, Pa., about 1925 built a fleet of 14 cotton-dusting planes, which were operated by Huff-Daland Dusters, Inc., of Monroe, La. They carried about 800 pounds of dust, had a cruising speed of 90 miles an hour, and were nicknamed "Puffers."

The present Delta Air Lines, Agricultural Division, Monroe, La., acquired the Huff-Daland planes and continued to build and use them for a quarter of a century.

Aerial dusting to control insect pests in cotton became an established practice during the late 1920's. That, more than any other use, established the airplane as a tool of agriculture.

Trial flights were being made at the same time to test the effectiveness of applications of insecticides to control mosquitoes, crop and orchard insects, and forest insects.

The airplane seemed particularly suited to applying materials to forests because of the difficulty of getting ground equipment into them. Officials in charge of gypsy moth control set up some trials as early as 1922. An airship was tried in a dusting experiment in New Hampshire in 1923. Heavy applications of as much as 40 to 50 pounds of lead arsenate to the acre were used. Because the dust did not adhere well to the foliage and rain washed it off, retreatments were necessary.

Other early uses of aircraft in agriculture included flights to spread grasshopper bait and to seed and fertilize rice. An airplane was first used to distribute wet bran mash grasshopper bait in 1930. The material was fed into the airstream by hand from sacks.

The first liquid larvicides were applied for mosquito control in New Jersey and California and oils were sprayed on orchards about 1930.

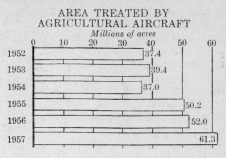

AREA TREATED BY
AGRICULTURAL AIRCRAFT
*Millions of acres*

| | | |
|---|---|---|
| 1952 | 37.4 | |
| 1953 | 39.4 | |
| 1954 | 37.0 | |
| 1955 | 50.2 | |
| 1956 | 52.0 | |
| 1957 | 61.3 | |

The autogiro was used against the gypsy moth in 1936. Special equipment permitted applying thick spray mixtures from rotating disks or screens. Another method released liquids, such as water or adhesives, separately but simultaneously with the dust materials. The spinner disks were adapted later for use on fixed-wing aircraft in the application of thick slurries of cryolite to control the gypsy moth.

Despite all the various uses developed for aircraft in agriculture, only about 200 planes in this country were equipped for application of materials by 1939. Probably the low prices for crops during the depression years caused a general lack of interest in pest control. Aerial application of insecticides was not always economical, partly because chemicals then in use had to be applied in heavy dosages.

SEVERAL developments during the Second World War accelerated the use of aircraft in agriculture.

Most important was the discovery of DDT and its effectiveness in protecting people from disease vectors and insect pests. At the request of the War Department, workers at the Orlando Laboratory of the Department of Agriculture developed equipment for spraying DDT from military planes.

Many military planes were declared surplus at the close of the war. Among them were the $N_3N$'s and the Stearmans. Both were biplane trainers with 220- to 235-horsepower engines and were converted easily for dusting or spraying. Many pilots and mechanics released by the Armed Forces were anxious to continue in aviation. The per acre value of crops was higher than prewar values.

The effectiveness of DDT was considered to be so spectacular that it was tested against a great number of insects of economic importance as soon as it was available generally in 1944 and 1945. DDT was so potent that only a small amount per acre was required to control most species of pests. Aerial applications once considered uneconomical became practical.

Soon other new, effective insecticides were discovered. They could be used efficiently in the form of concentrated sprays. One planeload of the new compounds would cover up to 10 times as much acreage as a load of the older prewar materials. The use by civilians of such concentrated materials, however, required carefully controlled applications to insure economical and safe distribution over the area being treated.

EFFORTS to develop more efficient equipment and operational procedures were expanded about 1945 by the Department of Agriculture primarily at the Forest Insect Laboratory of the Forest Service at Beltsville, Md., and at Agricultural Research Service laboratories at Toledo (now at Wooster), Ohio; Forest Grove, Oreg.; and Stoneville, Miss.

The aerial application phases of the gypsy moth, grasshopper, and other plant pest control programs of the Agricultural Research Service were consolidated into the Aircraft and Special Equipment Center in 1951. State experiment stations or agricultural colleges with agricultural aviation research programs included Ohio, Texas, and California. Nebraska and Mississippi later initiated studies of aerial application equipment. Commercial concerns engaged in the manufacture and sale of aerial application equipment have made many valuable contributions toward simpli-

fying and improving such equipment.

Dual spray apparatus—two complete spray systems on one plane—was developed to aid research on forest insect control at the Beltsville laboratory. It permits the release of spray simultaneously from both systems.

The result is that the effect on distribution of spray of any two degrees of atomization, and different nozzle arrangements, spray formulations, et cetera, can be compared under identical meteorological conditions. The use of different dyes in the spray liquid of the two systems makes it possible to determine the quantity of spray deposited from each system at any point in the spray swath. A spectrophotometer, which measures the intensity of each color separately in samples of the spray, is used.

The boom and nozzle type of spray release is more commonly used for general-purpose spraying than other types, such as small venturi tubes, or rotating disks, brushes, or screens.

Standard commercial nozzles are comparatively low in price and permit easy variation in flow rate by varying the number of nozzles used. Atomization can also be changed by using different types and sizes of nozzles as well as by changing the direction of the nozzle orifice in relation to the thrust line of the plane.

The efficiency of aerial spray equipment has been improved by the use of corrosion-resistant materials, such as Fiberglas reinforced plastics in tanks. Pumps have been improved by making them of aluminum to reduce weight and providing better seals and bearings. Spray pumps are mounted in some planes inside the fuselage to reduce external resistance. They may be driven by hydraulic motors, which permit fine adjustments in pump speeds.

THE EQUIPMENT for dispersing dry materials was not changed very much in the earlier years, but many improvements have been made since the war. For example, the design of combination dust and spray equipment permitted changing from dust to spray application, or vice versa, with only minor alterations in the apparatus. Feed gates also were improved to provide easier operation and more positive shutoff. A sawtooth baffle just above the hopper gate provided for fine adjustment in feed rates for small seeds and granular materials. Fluted rolls driven by a hydraulic motor also have been devised for metering out granular materials.

Spreaders have been widened or flared out toward the exit end and provided with vanes curved outward to provide lateral thrust for wider and more uniform distribution of the material. These spreaders are about 6 feet wide for such planes as the 450-horsepower Stearman. The Forest Grove laboratory designed and used experimentally a streamlined distributor that is only 1 inch thick at the rear end but is 14 feet, 8 inches wide.

The process of dust fluidization, or forcing air through dry material until it becomes like a liquid, has been experimentally developed for metering, conveying, and distributing pesticides from a small, high-wing monoplane. This work was done at the Toledo laboratory. Further study of this principle will be necessary, however, before it can be applied generally to agricultural aircraft.

THE MOST important commercial use for aircraft in agriculture is aerial application of materials. Aerial applicator aircraft in use in 1957 totaled 5,100, compared to only about 200 in 1939. These aircraft treated more than 61 million acres in 1957. About 75 percent of the acreage was treated for insect control; 12 percent for weed and brush control; 5 percent for fertilization; 3.5 for defoliation; 2.5 for seeding; and 2 percent for control of plant diseases. The acreage treated in 1957 represents an increase of 63 percent from the 37.5 million acres treated in 1952.

DRY MATERIAL APPLIED FROM THE AIR FOR INSECT, PLANT DISEASE, WEED AND BRUSH CONTROL AND FOR DEFOLIATION

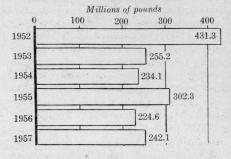

There was a decline in the use of dry materials and an increase in use of liquid materials from 1952 to 1957 for the control of insects, plant diseases, weeds, and brush and for defoliation (removal of foliage to hasten drying or maturity).

The tonnage of dry fertilizer, however, increased more than 50 percent during this period and liquid fertilizer 10 times as much.

The amount of seed sown from the air has varied considerably from year to year, but no significant trend has been apparent.

THE FIRE CONTROL program of the Forest Service used aircraft for patrol work in the early 1920's. The dropping of water or chemical bombs to extinguish fires was tried in 1936 and again in 1946 and 1947.

The bombing idea was discarded because of the danger to persons on the ground. The idea of discharging a tankful of water over the fire was tried in 1953. This developed into the use of aerial tankers for spreading fire-retardant chemicals. Agricultural spray planes with extra large discharge gates on the bottom of the tank are used. The Forest Service in 1959 spread 3.4 million gallons of fire retardants from the air. They also carried 908 thousand pounds of freight and dropped 390 thousand pounds of cargo in fire control work.

Aircraft, including helicopters, were used by the Forest Service in 1959 for a total of 32,700 hours of flight time for fire control activities. This includes reconnaissance, smoke jumping, and transportation of firefighting personnel. Nearly 85 percent of the total flying was by private planes under contract or charter.

Numerous State forestry departments and timber companies also operated aircraft for an unknown number of hours.

The use of aircraft by public and private forestry agencies for spotting and appraising insect infestations has increased materially in the past few years. Both visual and photographic methods are used.

Direct seeding of forest areas by aircraft is increasing rapidly since the discovery of repellents to prevent birds and rodents from eating the seeds. More than 108 thousand acres were direct seeded in 1959, as compared to 4.7 thousand in 1955. The ability to cover a large area in one season is the big advantage over tree planting.

MOST COMMONLY used for application of materials to crops are biplane trainers, such as the Stearman and N3N, and small monoplanes, such as the Piper and Aeronca.

Large planes are replacing the smaller ones for application of materials to large areas, such as forests and range, and also for forest fire control work. Among the large planes there are probably more Grumman Avenger TBM dive bombers in use than any other make. They haul about 700 gallons. Other large planes that have been used include the C–47 and B–18, B–17 Superfortress, C–97 Stratocruiser, the Trimotor Ford, and C–82 Packet. The Fords carry 400 gallons, and the others 1 thousand to 3 thousand gallons. A number of other surplus military planes have been used.

Helicopters have been used to apply liquids and solids to field crops, orchards, and forests. They can operate from small landing fields close to the

LIQUID MATERIAL APPLIED FROM THE AIR FOR INSECT, PLANT DISEASE, WEED AND BRUSH CONTROL AND FOR DEFOLIATION

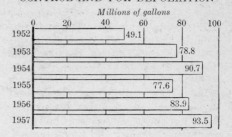

*Millions of gallons*

| Year | Millions of gallons |
|---|---|
| 1952 | 49.1 |
| 1953 | 78.8 |
| 1954 | 90.7 |
| 1955 | 77.6 |
| 1956 | 83.9 |
| 1957 | 93.5 |

area being treated. They can work small areas easily because of their maneuverability and slow speed. Materials can be distributed from a helicopter as uniformly as from a fixed-wing aircraft, and some tests have shown more uniform spray distribution from the helicopter. Operation at slow speed creates maximum downdraft to carry the material down through vegetation.

The initial cost of helicopters has been high, compared to that of the war-surplus biplane trainers and small high-wing monoplanes. Costs of operation and small payload also make it difficult for helicopters to compete with fixed-wing aircraft in large-scale contract spraying operations.

New aircraft are being designed specifically for aerial application of materials. The Ag–1 low-wing monoplane, designed in 1950 under the direction of Fred Weick, then of the Texas Agricultural and Mechanical College, stimulated the design and construction of the Ag–2 by Transland Aircraft, Torrance, Calif. This all-metal, low-wing monoplane has a 600-horsepower engine and a payload of 2 thousand pounds. Then Mr. Weick designed the Ag–3, a low-wing monoplane with a 135-horsepower engine and a payload of 800 pounds. It was the forerunner of the new Piper Pawnee PA–25, with practically the same performance as their PA–18A agricultural model.

Grumman Aircraft, Bethpage, N.Y.,

placed the Ag–cat on the market in 1959. It is a biplane with 220-horse-power engine and a payload of 1.2 thousand pounds. Other special agricultural airplanes available commercially are the Fletcher "Utility," the Callair 150 A–5 and 180 A–6, the Snow, and the Rawdon. Kellett Aircraft Corp., Willow Grove, Pa., revived production of their KD–1A autogiro.

Commercial applicators do practically all of the aerial application work. Very little is done by individual farmers. According to a survey by National Aviation Trades Association, the average applicator in 1956 had a capital investment of 48 thousand dollars. The companies used an average of four or five planes. The list prices of small monoplanes equipped for spraying and dusting were 7,500 to 10,500 dollars in 1960. The biplanes and helicopters cost more. Most of the farmer-owned aircraft, used almost entirely for private transportation, listed at 5,000 dollars or more in 1960.

One of the advantages of aerial over ground applications is that large areas can be covered quickly to insure prompt application at the proper time. Aerial operations are also advantageous when mechanical damage to the crop by wheeled machines cannot be tolerated or when soil conditions would not permit heavy machines to pass over it. Application of materials is feasible only from the air in some circumstances—the treatment of large, inaccessible forest areas, for example, and crops, such as rice, under flooded soil conditions.

Aerial applications may not be most efficient when the area to be treated is small. Because of drift, aerial applications afford more chance for damage to adjacent crops than ground applications. Material released from an airplane cannot be placed on the target as precisely as material released from a ground machine. It is also harder to cover the lower side of leaves by air application than by ground machine application.

### DRY FERTILIZER APPLIED FROM THE AIR

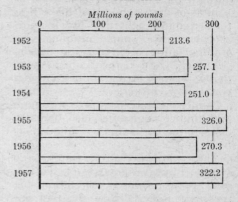

*Millions of pounds*

| Year | Value |
|------|-------|
| 1952 | 213.6 |
| 1953 | 257.1 |
| 1954 | 251.0 |
| 1955 | 326.0 |
| 1956 | 270.3 |
| 1957 | 322.2 |

NOT ALL problems have been solved. Even with all of the recent developments and increase in use of agricultural aircraft, many improvements remained to be made in 1960.

It is characteristic for spray and dust deposits to be heaviest near the flight line of the plane and gradually become lighter toward the edges of a swath. The overall application rate undoubtedly could be reduced if the material could be more uniformly distributed.

The controllable factors that affect distribution include performance of the dispersal equipment, physical characteristics of the material, and operation of the aircraft.

The uncontrollable factors, which affect the material from the time of its discharge from the plane until its deposition on the target, include the aerodynamic forces created by the aircraft and the meteorological conditions. Maximum advantage should be taken of all these factors, and more efficient distribution equipment should be developed.

Faster, more accurate methods for determining the uniformity of distribution of materials would speed up the work on improvement of equipment. Methods for assessing the quantity of spray deposited at various points across the swath and measurement of spray atomization have been developed for oil sprays. Further simplification of these methods is under way at the Beltsville Forest Insect Laboratory.

There is a definite need for the development of procedures for assessing water sprays and dry materials. Accurate methods for use in research and rapid methods for field use are necessary. Research must determine the most effective degree of spray atomization for pesticide applications.

The lines of flight can be marked for the pilot when he is applying materials to farm crops but not when he is treating large inaccessible forest areas. There is urgent need for development of a satisfactory pilot guidance system to insure more uniform swath spacing. Several electronic systems have been suggested and evaluated but had not proved to be practical in 1960.

THE FUTURE for agricultural aviation will be closely allied with the development and formulation of pesticide materials, fertilizers, chemicals to control forest fires, and so on.

Effective disease control requires fairly complete coverage of plant surfaces, and aerial applications generally are not so satisfactory as ground applications. Development of more efficient aircraft dispersal equipment or more effective fungicides could open another field of work for aircraft.

It may turn out that virus materials will be effective for control of several forest insect defoliators. Water suspensions of virus have been effectively used for controlling some sawfly infestations. Experimental applications have also been made for control of the Great Basin tent caterpillar. Aerial applications have not been effective in control of bark beetles in forests because it has not been possible to

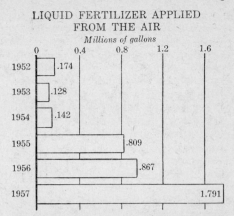

LIQUID FERTILIZER APPLIED
FROM THE AIR
*Millions of gallons*

apply insecticides to the trunks of trees by this method.

If a control method (such as through the use of systemics—an insecticide that would be absorbed and translocated to various parts of the host in amounts lethal to certain insects) could be developed, the destructiveness of these insects over large areas might be halted.

The application of fertilizers is another use of aircraft in forestry that may be expected to develop in the future.

It is certain that we will see increased use of aircraft in the agriculture of the future not only for application of materials but for personal transport. On many ranches in the Western States, small planes have replaced the horse and saddle for inspecting fence lines, pastures, and water supply and for checking livestock.

The legal aspects of aerial application work should be checked with the Federal Aviation Agency and State Aeronautics Commissions. Information on the use of various pest control materials may be obtained from local county agents, State experiment stations and agricultural colleges, and the United States Department of Agriculture, Washington 25, D.C.

# Power

# in

# the Harvest

## Swift, Untiring Harvest Help

Herbert F. Miller, Jr.

THE PROGRESS men have made during the past century in methods of harvesting crops is the progress from flail to freedom.

The flail, which was little more than a stick or whip, was all men had for centuries for separating grain from the straw. The sickle, a simple curved blade, was an improvement for cutting grain. It dates from 3000 B.C. or earlier. Otherwise, about the only significant advances during the next 4,800 years were the scythe and the cradle.

Then came the reaper in the 1830's to open the way to complete mecha-

nization of the harvest—to savings in hours and money and food; to a previously unknown freedom from uncertainty in harvesting.

The grain reaper of the 1830's was a one-horse machine made mostly of wood. Its few metal parts included a ground wheel used to drive gears, which transmitted power to a sickle-type cutting mechanism. The grain was cut near the ground. A revolving reel gently pushed the grain to the rear onto a small platform, where it was raked off onto the ground in small bundles, which were later bound with pieces of straw. The bundles were picked up and placed in shocks in the field for drying before threshing.

The reaper cut in half the labor required to harvest grain and permitted a more timely harvest.

Inventors soon saw ways to improve it. Progress continued step by step and almost year by year, until the first patent was issued on the self-binder in

164

1850. Both the wire and twine self-tying binders were common by the middle 1870's, but before long the wire binders, self-rake reapers, and the combination reapers and mowers were obsolete.

Farmers almost everywhere were excited over the twine binders and many bought them. They were improved greatly through the years and were the first equipment to be adapted—in 1919—to power takeoff from tractors. An estimated 1,250,000 binders were in use in the United States in 1938. That year the actual production of another machine, the combine, overtook production of the binder and within a decade replaced it completely.

During the days of the reaper and binder there was still another operation in the harvesting of grain—threshing. The grain had to be separated from the straw. The flail was used for separating the grain from the heads. Sometimes the grain was tread out by the feet of oxen or by sleds and wheels run over the grain on a flat floor or ground. Then the grain was winnowed—the grain was separated from the chaff. A man with a flail could thresh 7 or 8 bushels of wheat in a 10-hour day.

Early stationary threshing machines, known as groundhogs, were operated by tread or sweep horsepower. Some were turned by hand.

A patent was issued in 1837 on a machine known as the combination thresher that used the idea of the groundhog thresher and the ordinary fanning mill. This portable machine was operated at first by animal power and later by steam engines or gasoline tractors. Models made in 1850 could thresh several bushels of wheat an hour with a four-man crew and six to eight horses on the sweep power—that is, horses hitched to a pivoted pole walked in a circle to furnish power. A larger model 10 years later was operated by eight horses and had a capacity of 300 bushels a day.

A major improvement was a device that vibrated and shook the grain from the straw. Others included steel teeth, elevators, stackers, grain weighers, self-feeders, bandcutters, wind stackers, and all-steel construction.

Steam engines soon replaced the horse and other types of power. The early steam engines, which developed 6 to 8 horsepower, were transported by animal power. Later the horsepower was increased, and the steam tractor furnished beltpower to the thresher.

The gasoline engine began replacing the steam engine not long after 1900, and the steam-powered thresher soon became a curiosity. The thresher itself is rarely seen today. Only a few threshers, but more than 50 thousand combines, were manufactured in 1959. Thus ended a symbol of the earlier days of farm mechanization—the threshing crew. The thresher was put on wheels and coupled with the cutting mechanism of the binder to form the combine.

THE STORY of the grain combine is almost as old as the story of the reaper. The first successful grain combine, it is said, was built in Michigan in 1836, 10 years before the reaper went into commercial production.

It is supposedly the result of a dream of the wife of one of its inventors. The machine had all the major features of the present-day combine, but the idea was almost a century ahead of the technological progress that was necessary to make the machine a success. The machine was used for 10 years and would cut and thresh up to 25 acres a day, but its inventors gave up. The lack of a suitable power unit, such as is used on self-propelled combines today, and excessive moisture, which caused spoilage of the threshed grain, were two of the major difficulties they encountered. It is said that California took up where Michigan left off.

The Michigan combine was shipped around Cape Horn to San Francisco and harvested several hundred acres during the 1854 season. A more favorable climate, larger acreages, and

Californians' love for big machinery started this type of harvester on its way to general use. California-made versions of the combine began to appear in a few years. As many as 40 horses were used to pull the large 15-ton machines, which cut swaths up to 35 feet. Factory production began in California about 1880, when the twine binder was coming into general use in the Midwest.

The first hillside combine was built in the late 1880's and the first self-leveling model about 10 years later. Steam engines then were being mounted on the combine to supply a more constant power than could be provided from the ground wheels. Steam tractors began to replace horses as the propelling unit for the entire machine.

The gasoline engine began to replace steam for pulling the combine and operating its mechanism about 1912. Big combines were coming into their own during the 1920's and 1930's.

The design was being improved. Makers adopted the steel frame and body, antifriction bearings, V-belt drives, and rubber tires, and made the machines lighter.

Another major advancement before 1949 helped to reduce manpower requirements: Bulk handling of threshed grain eliminated the sack sewer and sack jigger. For the hillside combines, several ingenious automatic leveling-control devices were developed so that a two-man crew could take the place of the original five-man crew.

A milestone in 1935 was the development of the one-man combine powered by a two-plow tractor. More than a million grain combines were in use on American farms in 1956, and 1.5 million grain binders that had been in use in 1930–1940 virtually had disappeared.

The pull-type combines, generally in sizes of 6 to 12 feet, have gained wide popularity, particularly for the family-sized farms. They have power take-offs, or power is furnished by an auxiliary engine mounted on the combine.

Self-propelled grain combines have appeared on American farms in increasing numbers since 1938. About 20 percent of the combines in 1960 were self-propelled, and the trend to them seemed to be increasing.

The self-propelled combines are more maneuverable, they save more grain in opening up fields, and the driver has better visibility and control of his machine.

Self-propelled combines were produced in 1960 with cutterbars up to 18 feet wide, lifetime lubricating bearings, improved V-belt and pulley drives, and mechanisms for easy adjustments or change in speed. Windrow pickup attachments for combining grain and other crops from the windrow were available.

Several companies offered attachments for combines that make it a dual machine for harvesting either grain or corn—a development that has increased the utility of the self-propelled combine so that it may replace many of the present corn-harvesting machines.

Air-conditioned cabs are available for self-propelled combines. The compressor for cooling is belt driven from the combine engine. Full-view windows of safety glass give greater visibility and comfort to the operator.

Several makes of hillside combines were available in 1954, but the first hillside combine, with factory-installed automatic leveling controls, was introduced that year.

Hillside combines differ from conventional combines in that the separator body is kept level regardless of the ground slope. The separator body is kept level in the lateral direction.

In some combines a part of the separator (or all of it) is kept level to some degree in the longitudinal direction.

The two main types of sensing devices for automatic controls have the force of gravity acting either on a solid mass or on a liquid. The first uses a pendulum, which controls hydraulic valves directly and also controls electric switches, which energize hydraulic-valve solenoids. The second uses the force of gravity acting upon a liquid similar to a mercury-type switch.

Safety precautions are particularly important when using hillside combines. They have a wide wheelbase, so that the center of gravity falls well within the wheelbase in extremely hilly areas. Each individual wheel has its own brake and power steering. Automatic controls make it impossible for the operator to level in the wrong way.

Almost all combines used for grain employ the direct-cut method on the standing grain. In fields badly infested with weeds and crops that do not ripen uniformly, however, the crop may be cut and laid in a windrow and harvested with the combine using a pickup attachment.

Windrower machines are generally made in sizes from 9 to 16 feet and may be either a pull-type unit for attaching behind a tractor or self-propelled. Self-propelled windrowers can cut and windrow 75 acres a day. They are generally powered by small gasoline engines of 20 to 25 horse-power.

Besides wheat, oats, and barley, combines are used for harvesting soybeans, grain sorghums, rye, oats, flax, peas, dry beans, rice, clovers, alfalfa, lespedeza, timothy, millet, lupines, and safflower.

More details about combine adjustments for harvesting such crops are given in Farmers' Bulletin No. 1761, "Harvesting with Combines," by R. B. Gray. Copies can be had by writing to the Office of Information, U.S. Department of Agriculture, Washington 25, D.C.

EQUIPMENT for harvesting beans and peas is used on 1.5 million acres each year, mostly in Michigan, California, Idaho, Nebraska, New York, and Wyoming.

The older method of cutting, windrowing, stacking or baling, and stationary threshing of beans is giving way to the use of threshing machines that have been converted to a combine harvester-thresher (either pull-type or self-propelled) fitted with a special pickup device.

A pickup combine, which works from windrows, has come into common use with navy beans in Michigan. Some growers have special bean combines with two cylinders designed especially for the crop, but the trend in harvesting edible beans has been to use the grain combine.

Attachments for harvesting edible beans with a grain combine include cylinder speed reduction drives and screens. Some machines have rubber-covered bars that replace grain threshing bars on the cylinder and special bean grates that can be placed under or back of the cylinder.

A torsion spring-tooth cylinder and concaves for combines help eliminate cracking of beans and reduce the time one must wait for the heavy bean roots to dry before being combined. This spring-tooth equipment is less effective in threshing small grain than regular types of cylinders and concaves.

A common machine used to push dry beans from the soil and form them into windrows is known as a blade-type bean harvesting cultivator. It is fitted with vine turners, row dividers, and windrowing rods.

A rotary crop cutter has been successfully used in harvesting tests. It consists of hydraulic, motor-driven, notched disks horizontally rotating toward each other so that each, in cutting a row, forms a windrow from two rows.

Farmers would prefer to combine beans directly in order to avoid the possible loss in the windrowing due to inclement weather. Scientists therefore have been working on a new variety of navy bean that grows as an upright plant rather than a vine.

In direct combining, a power-driven, six-batt, finger-type reel is used with an eccentric mechanism to vary the pitch of the tines (fingers) during reel rotation. This reel is more efficient than the standard batt-type reel because the tines can be adjusted to lift the bean plant toward the cutterbar, thereby saving many pods from being cut by the sickle. The shatter loss at the cutterbar is reduced as much as 50 percent.

When a grain combine is used for cutting beans, the cylinder speed should be reduced to about one-half to one-third that required for threshing wheat. For best results, defoliation of the crop (when the beans are harvested standing) is necessary to help reduce the moisture content of the bean.

Harvesting efficiency depends largely upon correct combine adjustment. Many machines are not designed so that these adjustments can be made easily and in a reasonable time. Improvement in the design of combines is needed to rectify this deficiency.

To HARVEST our large acreage of corn (of the total annual production of 3.5 million bushels, 70 to 80 percent comes from the 12 North Central States) about 750 thousand cornpickers were used in 1960, an increase of about 42 percent since 1950. More than half of the pickers were in the Corn Belt, but their use has increased rapidly in the South, Northeast, and West.

The first machines for harvesting corn were known as row-crop binders and were used on farms around 1893. They cut the entire stalk, bound them with twine or wire, and placed the bundles in neat rows on the ground as the machine traveled through the field. The bundles were generally shocked or put in small stacks in the fields—a sight familiar to many of us today only in pictures in books that show the pumpkins at the foot of corn shocks in the field about Thanksgiving-time.

Row-crop binders also cut the corn and sorghum that was harvested for silage, not for grain. In 1942 there were 609 thousand row-crop binders on farms; by 1952, one-half of them had disappeared. Today row-crop

binders have been replaced almost entirely by field-type mechanical corn-pickers, which came into general use soon after the First World War. Farmers had about 10 thousand corn-pickers in 1920; by 1952 the number of pickers increased to 588 thousand.

Cornpickers are of two types.

A snapper-type corn harvester is much the same as a picker-husker, but the snapper does not remove the husks. Snapped ears are removed directly into a wagon or a trailer. The snapping rolls, which operate at about 500 to 600 feet per minute peripheral speed, are made of cast iron or cast steel with spiral ribs or lugs on their surfaces.

On a picker-husker, the husking rolls may be on a separate bed, incorporated in the snapping roll elevator, or may be a direct extension of the snapping rolls. Most husking units have at least one roll of each set made of rubber. Other rolls may be made of steel, wood, rubber, or cast iron.

Field losses with these machines generally range from 5 to 10 percent. Proper adjusting of the machine, careful driving, and avoidance of high speeds generally will keep field losses to a minimum. The speed of the machine, under most operating conditions, should not exceed 3.5 miles an hour.

Cornpickers started out as one-row units, but two-row pickers have become more popular. That is not the end of the story, though. As with most other farm machines, further advances were to be made. One was the picker-sheller.

Picker-sheller corn harvesters are of the same general design as the picker-huskers. Manufacturers have added the shelling unit and a bin or elevator for conveying the shelled corn into a trailer.

Picker-shellers were introduced in the middle 1930's, but field shelling of corn made slow progress until 1954, when corn header attachments for the grain combines were produced commercially. A further advancement was made in 1958, when sheller attachments for the standard cornpicker were first put into production.

The corn header attachments for grain combines first proved most successful in California, possibly because the drier climate made high moisture in grain less of a problem and because of a fast increase in corn acreage in an area where the combine was already in use on most farms.

When picker-shellers first appeared, commercial drying facilities were too costly and inconvenient for most farmers. About 1949, however, portable driers appeared with capacities to match that of the field machine, and commercial drying became increasingly available. Harvesting corn with field picker-shellers and combine attachments was an established method of harvesting corn in 1960.

Slightly more than 5 thousand picker-sheller units and 9 thousand grain combine header attachments were in use for picking and field shelling of corn in 1957. The use of field shelling equipment no doubt is destined to increase fast, and someday may replace entirely the cornpickers. Corn is now being grown and harvested mechanically in some areas with fewer than 4 man-hours an acre. This is less time than it takes for one man to hand-husk an acre of corn.

Safety is important. Since most of the accidents with cornpickers are due to carelessness, operators must be trained properly.

The Farm Division of the National Safety Council has listed rules for normal and safe operation of cornpickers. They include safety suggestions: Keep all shields in place. Stop the machine when you oil and adjust it. When the mechanism becomes clogged, disconnect the power before cleaning. Keep hands, feet, and clothing away from power-driven parts. Wear tight-fitting gloves and clothing. Keep other persons off.

FOR 5 THOUSAND years or so forage for hay was cut with a sickle or scythe. Harvesting hay generally remained a hand operation until the middle of the past century. It has progressed from the various hand- and horse-powered methods to the tractor-powered mower, side-delivery rake, and field baler. Perhaps next will come a machine that forms hay into wafers or pellets in the field.

Haying used to be a hot and heavy job. It consists generally of three operations—mowing, raking, and stacking or storing.

More than 100 million tons of hay are produced each year in the United States. Hay accounts for about 20 percent of all harvested crop acreage.

About 25 percent of all hay was baled at the time of the Second World War. More than 75 percent of the crop was put up in bales in 1960. Primarily responsible for the change is the automatic-tie, pickup balers. Baled hay needs less storage space and is easier to handle than loose hay. Less than 20 percent of the total crop now is loose hay, and the percentage of chopped hay for curing and dehydration increased from about 2 to 10 since the war.

Much progress has been made in improving equipment for mechanizing the harvest, although hay generally has a relatively low cash value per acre.

Early cutting devices paralleled those used on reapers and binders for cutting grain. Cutterbars were rigid at first. Then came two-wheeled mowers with flexible or hinged bars. These changes occurred about 1860. It was reported that by 1865 nearly all hay in this country was cut mechanically except on the roughest ground. Tractor-drawn mowers gradually replaced horse-drawn ones after the turn of the century. Today the 5-foot cutterbar on two-wheeled, horse-drawn mowers is a thing of the past.

Cutterbars on tractor mowers usually are 6 or 7 feet long. Modern tractor mowers may cut as much as 30 or more acres a day.

An advertisement of such mowers might very well read as follows: "Featuring a slip-clutch-protected roller-chain drive assembly, fully enclosed and running in an oil bath; tapered roller bearings; a heavy-duty 28-pound flywheel to provide smooth practically vibrationless operation; a safety release spring, which permits the cutterbar to swing back should it hit an obstruction; high, easy lift of the cutterbar; full vision cutting; excellent maneuverability; and ease of handling in the field and on roadside work."

Tractor mowers may be of several types, such as trail-behind, with either traction or power takeoff drive; direct-connected, trail-behind; integral rear-mounted mowers; and integral side or central-mounted mowers. Almost all mowers by 1958 were power-driven instead of having a ground drive.

Newer developments in mower design consist of high-speed operation, with a reduced stroke length and a dynamically counter-balanced reciprocating blade so designed that its operation is not affected by the raising and lowering of the bar. Many are also equipped with special antifriction bearings throughout.

The number of hay crushers, a machine long established but little used, increased from a few hundred to several thousand during the decade before 1960. "Hay in a day" is often promised with the use of hay crushers along with the mowing operation. Consisting of a pair of steel rollers held together under pressure by adjustable springs, the crusher is driven by the tractor power takeoff. The rollers may be attached directly to a mower, or a pickup may lift the hay from the swath and feed it between the rolls. The crushed hay is dropped back onto the stubble, where later it may be further conditioned with a tedder or raked into a windrow.

Many reports indicate that crushed hay generally dries to a moisture content safe for storage in one-third to two-thirds of the time required for uncrushed hay. The drying time is seldom reduced enough to allow cutting and storing in the same day. Crushing, however, often allows the hay to be picked up on the second day in some climates when normally it would take 3 or 4 days for it to reach a safe moisture content. Some crushers have smooth rolls. Others are equipped with fluted rolls, which tend to crimp the hay.

Hay tedders sometimes are used by farmers to turn and fluff up windrows or swaths of hay that become wet to help speed drying. Although this machine has never really been used to any great extent, the tedding process may often be helpful in connection with hay crushing and the general need to dry hay as quickly as possible.

Spring-tooth sulky rakes were used for many years for windrowing or bunching hay. They have been replaced largely by side-delivery rakes, known as cylindrical reel, oblique reel-head, or finger wheel rakes.

The development of side-delivery rakes made the old hay tedder much too slow and tedious.

Side-delivery rakes move hay in a gentle yet rapid pace into a well-formed, fluffy windrow. If the windrow becomes wet on the bottom or needs to be turned, the side-delivery rake can be used to move the windrow over a few more feet, thus aerating and further helping to dry the hay. Early models of such rakes were used soon after 1900, but not until 1940 did the tractor-operated, power takeoff, side-delivery rake appear.

Many stages have come and gone in hay handling. The familiar pitchfork and the portable hay stacker, which reached the market about 1882, are examples. The stacker and similar types of equipment were powered first by horses and later by tractors. Now we have mechanical hay balers.

THE FIELD PICKUP baler, which began to attract attention about 1932, was a spectacular development. Baling machines saved at least two handlings of the crop—in itself an important contribution. Self-tying balers came along in 1940. Self-propelled machines came in 1958.

The number of automatic pickup balers increased more than threefold between 1950 and 1960. An outstanding change was the use of twine for tying. Of approximately 600 thousand baling machines in the United States in 1958, about 80 percent used twine.

There has been a noticeable trend toward the use of smaller bales, which are easier to handle. With a baler equipped with the bale ejector, one man can operate his machine and unload his hay into the mow with a barn bale conveyor.

The two main types of balers are the plunger-type, which makes a rectangular bale, and the roll-type, which turns out a round bale. Rectangular bales are more popular, although some say the round bales absorb less water when rained on in the field.

Twine used for baling hay, somewhat heavier than binder twine, has a tensile strength of about 275 pounds. The normal rectangular bales use slightly more than 3 pounds of twine per ton. Round bales require slightly more than 2.5 pounds.

Automatic twine tying devices have been refined and improved until they give little trouble. Important features on modern balers include safety clutches or shear pins to prevent overloading in various places —between the flywheel and the plunger; in the needle drive, should it strike an obstruction; in the drive ahead of the baler flywheel on balers driven by power takeoff; in the pickup and conveying drive; in the drive to the tying mechanism; and in the feed mechanism drive.

THE DEVELOPMENT of the field forage harvester marked another milestone in harvesting silage crops. Forage used for silage was cut in the field with row-crop binders during the early days of mechanization and was chopped with ensilage cutters before being placed into a silo. Direct-cutter attachments later enabled these machines to cut and chop silage in a single operation. Special attachments were developed to handle corn and other row crops. Simplified rotary or flail-type forage harvesters became popular in the 1950's, primarily among farmers who chopped forage for immediate drylot feeding.

The number of field forage harvesters on farms increased from about 80 thousand in 1950 to 240 thousand in 1957. They took the place of the row-crop binder. They are of two major types; their cutting knives are placed in a flywheel or in a cylindrical arrangement. A third, the so-called flail-type forage harvester, developed out of the swinging blade stalk cutter-shredders, has gained in importance.

In the flywheel, or cylinder-type, forage harvesters, a separate blower (or blades) is attached to the flywheel for blowing the chopped material into the wagon. The flail-type machine uses the air movement from the swinging blades to carry the material into the wagon. The flail-type machine, of simple design, has relatively few working parts. It can be utilized to harvest ensilage, chop hay and straw, shred stalks, cut weeds, and top beets, among others.

Perhaps machines for pelleting or wafering hay in the field may come into general use someday for harvesting forage. The cost of handling from field to storage and from storage to feeding would be greatly reduced with hay in pellets. Experimental field machines for making wafers or pellets have the capacity of about one-half that of a conventional baler and make wafers best from hay that has a moisture content of 12 to 16 percent.

No doubt ingenious inventors and engineers will continue to improve such machines until they will be satisfactory and perhaps will replace or at least compete with the now popular, powerful, and efficient hay baler.

MECHANICAL COTTON harvesters available in 1960 were of two basic types—strippers and pickers.

Stripper-type harvesters strip the entire plant of both open and unopened bolls and many leaves and stems.

Picking machines remove the seed cotton from open bolls and leave the burs on the plant.

Mechanical picking of cotton has been a great challenge to the imagination of cottongrowers and agricultural scientists and engineers. A cotton-picking device was patented in 1850. A stripper-type harvester was patented in 1871.

Such problems as uneven opening of the bolls and keeping the cotton lint free of leaves and trash remain. On few farm machines has as much money been invested in engineering development as cotton harvesters.

Several hundred patents have been issued on cotton harvesting machines since 1850. Many of those machines no doubt would have done the job just as well as some that are now in use if they had been put into production.

Many factors hindered the early acceptance and use of machines before the Second World War, however. One was that the gins were not equipped with devices to handle and clean the machine-harvested cotton with all the extraneous material it contained. Farmers in general had an ample supply of relatively cheap labor. They wanted machines that would harvest cotton comparable in cleanliness to that of hand-harvested cotton and leave little cotton in the field. The farmer was satisfied with hand-harvesting his crop and was not particularly ready for any great change.

The scarcity and high cost of labor during and after the war and new developments in harvesting and ginning equipment were primarily responsible for changing the cotton farmers' viewpoint about harvesting cotton with machines.

Great strides have been made in mechanizing the cotton crop in places in the Cotton Belt. Reducing costs through mechanization has helped to keep cotton on a more competitive basis with foreign competition and syn-

thetic fibers. The costs were still too high in 1960, however, and considerable effort was still being placed on mechanization of all phases of production and harvesting. In fact, many disciplines of science and engineering have been involved in this overall mechanization endeavor—plant breeding, to produce varieties adaptable to machine picking; chemistry, to develop defoliants to take the leaves off before picking and chemicals for weed control; soil science, to determine the best method of land preparation and irrigation practices; and engineering, to furnish the right kind of machine for each operation.

Mechanization has reduced the labor to grow an acre of cotton from 150 hours with one-row, horse-drawn equipment to about 30 hours with tractor equipment and machine picking. In the Texas High Plains, where stripper-type harvesting is practiced, labor requirements are as low as 6.5 man-hours an acre for all the work of production and harvesting.

Stripper harvesting, simpler than picking, was first referred to as sledding. Homemade horse-drawn sleds were used in Texas as early as 1914. A few tractor-mounted strippers were built in 1930, but there was little interest in them then.

Stripping machines pull entire bolls from the plant as in hand stripping, which has been done in West Texas and Oklahoma. Gins were improved for handling this type of cotton in the early 1940's. About 30 thousand stripper-type machines were used on farms in 1959 to harvest approximately 14 percent of the United States crop.

Stripper harvesters were used first on low-yielding dryland cotton. They are now used in High Plains irrigated cotton yielding up to a bale or more and in central Texas, Oklahoma, and New Mexico. Stripper use is limited primarily to cotton of a stormproof nature and work most satisfactorily after frost has killed the green leaves and vegetative growth.

The two-row, tractor-mounted stripper will harvest a bale of cotton in about 30 minutes when operating in cotton yielding three-fourths of a bale an acre—one man stripping cotton by hand does that in a 10-hour day.

Cotton-stripping machines include single-steel roller, double-steel roller, and finger types.

The inclined rollers first approach the cotton plant at the base of the stalk. As the harvester moves forward, the bolls and many of the leaves and stems are stripped from the central stalk. The cotton falls into a conveyor on either side of the roller and is conveyed to the rear of the tractor and into a trailer.

The conveying systems for taking the cotton from the stripping rolls to the trailer are mostly of three types—finger-beater, auger, and air. Generally an auxiliary air blower on the loading elevator assists in uniform loading of the trailer.

The best type of plant for mechanical stripping has relatively short-noded fruiting branches 8 to 10 inches long and is less than 3 feet high. Closely spaced plants in the row have shorter limbs, and the main stalk is smaller in diameter. Plant populations of 30 to 50 thousand per acre in 40-inch rows are commonly recommended for stripper harvesting.

In cultivation, sweeps are set flat, so that little or no soil is thrown around the base of the plant. Therefore more clearance is left between the ground at the base of the plants and the lowest limb or boll of cotton, so that the fingers of the stripper can slide easily under the open cotton bolls and strip the plant.

Double-brush nylon rollers used in place of steel rollers gave good efficiency for gathering most varieties of cotton (including open-boll types), but they allowed too much soil and trash to be mixed with the lint. Many trials were made of rubber paddles in place of stripping rolls, but neither they nor the brush rollers had come into wide use in 1960.

A development in the stripper-type harvester is the use of long, brush-type stripping rolls with a combination stick and bur remover. Mechanical conveyors are used between the stripping unit and the basket. The long brush rollers permit the harvesting of taller, higher-yielding cotton of the open-boll type. The combination stick and bur remover takes most of the bur and sticks out of the cotton before putting the partly cleaned seed cotton into the basket.

Further improvements may make this type of harvester economically feasible if the quality of the lint can be maintained. No doubt it can be used successfully for the second picking in many cases. Its obvious advantage is that it deposits the burs and most of the trash in the field rather than carrying them to the gin.

We expect that the stripper-type machines of conventional or improved models will be used more and more as cotton is further mechanized, primarily because of their low cost and the speed at which they can operate, as compared with picking machines.

Approximately 24 thousand picker-type harvesters were used to harvest 22 percent of the crop in the United States in 1959. That and the 14 percent harvested by strippers meant that about one-third or more of the total United States crop was machine harvested.

Less than 5 percent of the cotton in the Southeast is harvested by machine. More than 80 percent of the irrigated crop in the West is mechanically harvested.

Cotton production has been moving west. We think it will continue to do so because of the larger fields, higher yields, fewer insect problems, and more uniform and better weather conditions during the harvesting period.

Picking machines are used primarily in the large fields that often yield as much as 3 bales an acre under irrigation in the West.

Mechanical cottonpickers are of two general types because of their spindles—tapered-tooth and straight-smooth. Pickers are single-row machines, which may be tractor-mounted, or two-row machines, which generally are self-propelled.

The tapered-tooth pickers generally have what is known as a spindle drum arrangement. The spindles are mounted on vertical bars arranged in a cylindrical manner somewhat like a drum set on its end. The spindles are mounted 1.5 inches apart on the bars, which are connected to a crank arm at the top.

The spindle drums are operated with one on each side of the row, but are not directly opposite. As the slightly offset drums of spindles rotate with the forward movement of the picker, the spindles enter the slightly compressed cotton plant on either side. The rotating spindles remove the lint from the burs.

After the revolving spindles and rotating drum reach a position just opposite that of the cotton stalk, the cotton is doffed off the spindle by a rotating mechanism turning in the same direction as the spindles but somewhat faster. This action unwinds the cotton from the spindle. The seed cotton is then picked up by means of air suction and blown or mechanically conveyed into the large picker basket.

The tapered-tooth spindle pickers are available in a low-drum size (14 spindles high) or high-drum (20 spindles high). The low-drum pickers are somewhat less expensive and work satisfactorily in cotton up to 3 feet high. The low drum is also offered as an attachment to tractors, and no major conversion of the tractor is necessary. The small pickers replace 25 men or more and can be considered economically feasible on as few as 40 acres of cotton.

The straight-smooth spindle-type machine may have the spindles slightly roughened, or they may have light knurled surfaces. Such pickers are generally referred to as having the chain-belt arrangement, since the spindle bars are attached to an endless chain belt. The belt has 80 spindle bars or slats, each of which has 16 spindles, or a total of 1,280. The spindles project into the row of plants from one side only. On some models, however, it is possible to place a belt on each side of the row similar to the drums of the tapered-tooth spindle picker. The straight spindle is friction driven. The tapered-tooth spindle-type pickers use gear drives for each spindle.

Both types of spindle pickers have moistened pads, over which the spindles pass during each revolution of the drum or belt. The moisture helps the lint adhere to the spindles and keeps them clean of plant juices and other sticky material. Wetting agents are sometimes used to reduce the amount of water necessary and still do an acceptable job of picking.

Cottonpicking machines perform best when the cotton plants are of medium size and the lowest limbs are at least 4 inches above the ground. The machines require a well-opened boll, locks that are fluffy, and fiber that is long enough to afford good contact with the spindles but set deeply enough into the burs to provide reasonable storm resistance. Fairly thick and uniformly spaced plants (20 thousand to 30 thousand plants per acre) aid in the performance of mechanical cottonpickers. Picker performance depends almost entirely on proper adjustment and operation. A well-trained and careful operator is essential.

A 500-pound bale of lint cotton requires approximately 1,400 pounds of clean hand- or machine-picked seed cotton. The price for handpicking cotton varies from 1.50 to 4.00 dollars a hundredweight. When this cost reaches 2.50 dollars or more, it is generally considered profitable to use machine pickers. That shows how easily the availability of labor and wages for handpicking determine when machine harvesters are used.

ROOT CROPS are grown on about 5 million acres in this country. They include potatoes, peanuts, sugar beets, sweetpotatoes, onions, carrots, and radishes.

The harvesting of sugar beets has been mechanized completely. Some edible crops, such as sweetpotatoes, are dug by machines, but the entire crop is picked up by hand.

THE FIRST POTATO harvesters, used in the 1940's, had attachments for putting the potatoes in sacks. Most of the machines have been converted to load directly into a truck with bulk body. Conveying or dumping attachments on the truck are used for unloading at the storage or processing warehouse. Nearly all the harvesters built after 1950 used the direct-loading method. Approximately 5 thousand potato harvesters were used on farms in 1958.

Production areas with good soil suitable for mechanical harvesting, such as Idaho, the Pacific Northwest, and the Red River Valley in North Dakota and Minnesota, were the first to make good use of mechanical harvesting methods. Modern equipment was used first in Florida in 1953.

Stones in the soil in Maine have limited the use of harvesters there. However, in 1955 many growers started using them as fast as they could adapt their farming operations to the bulk handling methods. Mechanization of potato production in the San Joaquin Valley in California has been deterred primarily because of the difficulty of clod separation.

The two main types of potato harvesters are diggers and the combination digger-pickers—often referred to as a potato combine.

The diggers handle one or two rows and generally are power operated from the tractor power takeoff. Several types of blades or shovels are used for digging or scooping up the potatoes and surrounding soil. One-row diggers are usually equipped with pointed blades. Two-row diggers may have a pointed blade for each row or a continuous straight blade across both rows.

The digger blade delivers potatoes and some soil onto a rod-chain type of elevating conveyor. Oval-shaped idler sprockets support the elevator chain and give it an up-and-down motion to aid in sifting out the soil. Most diggers have adjustments to control the speed of the elevator and sprocket for the different operating conditions. Higher speeds give a better cleaning action, but the potatoes are more apt to be bruised. The potatoes are deposited back onto the ground behind the digger, where they are picked up by hand or by a combine-type machine.

A potato combine may be operated in one of two ways—as a once-over harvester or as an indirect harvester by picking the potatoes off the ground following a digger. The combine may be a one- or two-row machine. An auxiliary motor or power takeoff operates the conveying chains and the separating and loading devices. Potatoes pass from the elevating chain to a sorting conveyor.

Workers stand on a platform near the sorting conveyor and assist in removing vines, stones, clods, and other foreign material that is not separated mechanically. The potatoes are then discharged from the sorting conveyor into an elevator, which carries them into the truck. The number of handpickers required depends on the amount of foreign material to be removed and the forward speed of the machine.

The free-fall distance between conveyors or from the conveyors into the containers should not be more than 6 inches. Rubber-covered links are used on elevator chains to lessen damage to the tubers. The floor and sides of trucks for bulk handling usually are padded.

Sweetpotatoes are harder to harvest mechanically than white potatoes because they bruise more easily. Several types of plows or digging blades may be used to lift them from the ground, but the digging is followed by handpicking. The lack of a completely successful mechanical harvester is one reason for a drop in sweetpotato acreage in the United States. An average of 600 thousand acres were grown in the 1945–1947 period, compared with approximately 300 thousand acres in 1957–1959.

HARVESTING OF PEANUTS is becoming increasingly mechanized.

Harvesting involves digging and shaking to remove nuts from the soil, windrowing or stacking, and picking to remove the peanuts from the vines.

The roots are cut just below the nut zone with a half sweep or blade, which also lifts them from the ground. Side-delivery rakes or shaker-windrowers then place the peanuts in windrows, where they can dry somewhat before harvesting.

Before combines were used, the nuts were shaken by hand and stacked in the field, where they were allowed to dry before picking with stationary threshers.

Mechanization of harvesting the Spanish-type peanuts grown in the Southwest was practically complete in 1960. One reason was that weather is apt to be good during the harvest period. After 5 or 6 days, windrowed peanuts in the Southwest often are dry enough to be picked up and threshed. Converted peanut threshers or modified grain combines generally are used.

About one-half of the peanut crop in Alabama, Georgia, and Florida was harvested by machines in 1959.

Machines using the carding principle have been most popular. It has seemed, however, that a combination cylinder and carding principle may be used successfully on the same machine to increase capacity and efficiency. Both the Spanish and the larger runner or bunch varieties of peanuts are grown in the Southeast. Combination equipment, which incorporated tractor-mounted digger blades and a pull-behind, shaker-windrower, was developed before 1958. This equipment began to replace the side-delivery rakes.

The old method of hand stacking and picking peanuts with stationary threshers was used altogether in the Virginia-Carolina area up until 1957.

The Virginia-type peanuts grown there are the large nuts like those sold in the hull at baseball and football games. Mechanical harvesting was begun by several growers before 1959. The development of special digger-shaker-windrowers, improvements in combines for the larger peanuts, and better techniques for artificial drying may make complete mechanization possible in Virginia-Carolina.

The windrow harvesting methods mean that peanut growers would not have to keep a large labor force for peak harvest seasons. Only one-sixth the man-hours of labor per acre is needed with the windrow method, as compared with the stack-pole method of harvesting. This saving in labor costs alone can justify the cost of equipment needed for the windrow method if more than 30 acres of peanuts are grown.

Although techniques for mechanical drying of combined peanuts have been worked out in general for the Virginia-North Carolina area, increased mechanical harvesting will depend on the speed with which suitable drying equipment can be provided.

MECHANICAL HARVESTERS for sugar beets were used somewhat in the 1930's. The shortage of workers after the war brought about the extensive use of machines. About 4 thousand harvesters were used in 1947 for 30 percent of the United States crop. Twenty thousand harvesters gathered 100 percent of the crop in 1958.

Modern harvesters do the work of topping, gaging, cutting, lifting, and loading sugar beets into trailers.

Two common harvesting principles have been in use.

One is in-place topping, followed by two rotating converging wheels that loosen the beets and lift them from the ground. Kicker wheels are used for cleaning, and a rod-chain type elevator carries the beets to the trailing container.

In the other, a spiked wheel lifts

Farmers, engineers, and conservationists change the American landscape to make the land fit changed ways of farming. They use huge tractors with heavy clearing blades to remove brush and trees. Bulldozers remove obstructions.

Land is leveled and graded. The purpose is to transform small, inefficient fields into large, smooth-graded, and contoured fields that provide effective worksites for farm machinery; to make uniformly alined terrace systems; to correct poorly drained depressions; to restore to usefulness land damaged by carelessness or misuse.

On the Nebraska farm pictured above, about 20 acres on a 5-percent slope were bench leveled, and water is delivered to each end of the field. On the California farm pictured below, checks for border irrigation are being made.

Slip-form concrete linings in irrigation ditches reduce seepage losses, save water, and reduce damage to land. In the picture below, a field of a grower of seed corn near Johnson, Iowa, is irrigated by sprinkling.

Plows are basic in a productive agriculture. Men since antiquity have used plows. The first ones were crooked sticks. Then came simple plows of wood, sometimes tipped with a piece of iron. One, now at the Farmers' Museum in Cooperstown, N.Y., is shown above. The vast areas of new land in America to be settled and tilled challenged men to design and manufacture better plows. The two-way mounted moldboard plow shown below works well on contour strips.

The reversible disk plow also is well adapted to two-way operation on contoured fields. On wheatland near Garryowen, Mont., (below) nine 16-inch moldboard bottoms, pulled by a large tractor, can plow 6 acres an hour.

Compacted zones—"plowsole pans"—limit the depth of rooting of taprooted plants, such as cotton, which normally go down more than 2 feet for water and nutrients but here penetrate only 4 inches and spread out above the plowpan. Deep tillage is done to correct the fault. On a farm near Twin Valley, Minn., deep tillage with heavy-duty subsoil chisels is done after leveling with a landplane and harrowing.

In San Diego County, Calif., contour subsoiling is performed on seeded pasture. In the photograph below, of a farm in Hockley County, Tex., plowing to a depth of 24 inches or more brings clayey layers to the surface and helps stabilize loose, sandy soils.

Good soils covered with sterile sand (as in the picture above of a tract near Manhattan, Kans., which was covered by sand during a flood of the Kansas River) can be rehabilitated by deep plowing. A 4-foot moldboard plow is used here. Minimum tillage, a new practice, is accomplished with a plow-press drill operating directly behind a plow.

Emergency tillage in a direction perpendicular to the prevailing winds reduces soil blowing when vegetative cover is lacking or is too sparse. A rod weeder (below) is effective for tillage in the stubble-mulch farming system on summer fallow. A rotary revolving rod passes under the surface and kills weeds and volunteer grain, but keeps vegetative residues on the surface to protect the land against wind and water erosion.

The blades of a rotary tiller slice, loosen, and mix the soil. The machine is used to mix crop residues and green crops into the soil, prepare seedbeds, reclaim abandoned land, and cultivate orchards. Below, near Walla Walla, Wash., a stubble cutter operates on heavy winter wheat stubble. The following fall the ground was subsurface tilled.

Dramatic strides have been made in improving methods of planting, fertilizing, and protecting crops by the use of fast, efficient, and precise power machinery.

With a six-row cotton and corn planter equipped with a liquid fertilizer attachment, fertilizer is placed to one side and below the seed. Fertilizer openers operate ahead of seed runners. In Hidalgo County, N. Mex., (below) seedbed is prepared and rangeland is reseeded.

This is an all-crop fertilizer drill with grass seeder and press wheel attachment. The photograph below of a farm near Tennille, Ga., demonstrates a major result—timeliness of operations—of new machines and practices. Soybeans are being mulch planted in grain stubble directly after the combining of the crop. There is a saving in cost and moisture. Soybeans can be planted 7 or 10 days earlier than with other methods.

A lister planter is used here to plant corn in an untilled field. Contoured lister furrows help in the control of runoff and erosion. A commoner way (below) is to plant corn in a seedbed prepared by plowing, disking, and harrowing.

For ridge, or bed, planting disk hillers mounted on toolbars are used to make the ridges in previously plowed soil. Two trips over the field were necessary to build the ridges shown in the photograph above. Illustrated below is a two-row potato planter.

On a 2,900-acre wheat farm 18 miles west of Pendleton, Oreg., winter wheat is fall seeded in stubble mulch with a full-furrow press wheel drill. Below, a strip tiller is combined with a rear-mounted planter that has attachments for applying fertilizers, herbicides, and pesticides.

By removing the tractor fenders and using 2.5-inch spools inside the drum, the farmer in the picture above could set the rear wheels on 45-inch centers and so plant in wheel tracks of the tractor on freshly plowed ground. On depleted rangeland near Guymon, Okla., a one-way plow was used to kill sagebrush. Enough residue was left to protect the soil against blowing. The seedbed was firm enough for seeding grasses.

Mr. and Mrs. Bethel Jackson use a grassland drill to plant vetch in African weeping lovegrass and apply fertilizer on their farm in Garvin County, Okla. Two shovel drills in multiple hitch (below) seed wheat in McKenzie County, N. Dak., in the 12–14-inch rainfall belt. About 50 pounds of 0–45–0 fertilizer is applied per acre. These drills are designed to operate in trashy seedbeds.

Farmers always have fought, as best they could, pests that threatened their crops. Some times the insects and plant diseases have won. The fight will continue, shifting in intensity and location, but technologic advances have given powerful new weapons. One, shown above, is a row crop sprayer-duster, designed by research men in the Department of Agriculture. Airblast sprayers can shoot a spray many feet.

Aircraft are being put to many uses in agriculture and forestry. The specially equipped plane in the picture above is one of many under contract to spray areas with high populations of grasshoppers. For gardeners in the country and cities, countless dusters, sprayers, and other items are available.

This four-row cultivator is used on a broad terrace laid out so machines could be used effectively on it. The line in the foreground indicates a cross section of the terrace channel. The equipment shown below accomplishes three operations in one trip of the tractor—it cultivates cotton, sprays insecticides, and controls weeds with flames.

A rotary cutter (above) shreds cornstalks into mulch. The old picture below shows how grain was harvested years ago.

The great changes in methods of power harvesting that have been introduced for crop after crop have cut costs, improved the product, and made weather a less vital factor. A two-row combine in the picture above digs potatoes and dumps them into a truck on a Florida farm. A conveyor machine speeds up the picking and packing of sweet corn.

This celery harvester travels 5 or 6 feet a minute and covers 24 rows. The celery is cut, trimmed, washed, sorted, and crated before it leaves the field harvester. Rice from the combine harvester flows into a waiting hopper.

A machine that digs and trims five rows of radishes at a time takes the place of a one-row walking type. With a catcher-conveyor unit on each side of the tree, 3 men can harvest fruit from 30 to 40 trees in an hour. The fruit is shaken from the tree by a tractor-mounted hydraulic shaker.

Rubber-covered fingers on an electric-powered vibrator, which is held by the worker, shake blueberries from the stems. Two persons using the collecting unit can pick 6 tons of berries in 30 days. The pull-type combine may be equipped with a pickup attachment or cutterbar for use in standing grain.

A sugar beet harvester of the in-place topping type has two rotating converging wheels that loosen the beets and lift them from the ground. Kicker wheels clean the beets. A rod-chain elevator carries them to the conveyor. A self-propelled hay baler (below) picks the hay up from the windrow and presses it firmly into a neatly formed bale.

In northwestern Texas, sesame is harvested from shocks by means of a modified combine with a special platform. A two-row tractor-mounted harvester is used in Texas to harvest a dwarf type of castorbean.

A development in corn harvesting is the use of picker attachments on the commonly used self-propelled grain combine. The combine operator can use a helmet with a filter to avoid breathing in dust, pollen, chaff, and insects.

Equipment mounted without supporting wheels is referred to as integral mounted. The mounting on this tractor mower is on the three-point hitch of the tractor. Hay crimper, or crusher, machines are used to condition hay for faster drying.

This self-propelled unit mows, windrows, and crushes hay in one operation. A field forage harvester (below) with direct-cut attachment cuts and chops the forage and places it in a trailer. Such harvesters can be had with a pickup attachment, which picks up partly cured hay from the windrows.

The cottonpicker in the Southwest (above) replaces 30 or 40 handpickers in removing cotton from high-yielding plants that have been defoliated with chemicals. A two-row, stripper-type harvester (below) removes bolls, stems, and leaves from thickly spaced plants. It has been used chiefly in the Texas High Plains on stormproof cotton.

the untopped beets from the ground. Inclined steel stripper bars raise the beets off the spikes far enough to permit topping at the proper level with a pair of rotating disks. The beets are then deposited in the trailer.

HARVESTERS for carrots, beets, turnips, radishes, and onions were in various stages of development in 1960 and were used for harvesting vegetables grown primarily for commercial processing and canning. Bruising and cutting is not nearly so serious when vegetables are to be processed as when they go to the fresh market.

Root-crop harvesting machines dig, top, and load in one operation. Special plow points lift the ground around the carrots or beets as guide rods lift the plant, which is firmly held by the leafy portion between two rubber belts. A device removes the tops, which fall to the ground. Then the vegetables are conveyed into a side-delivery elevator and into a truck or trailer. Not many of the harvesters have been sold. Generally they are manufactured by smaller companies that may specialize in this type of equipment.

Small one-row, as well as three- and five-row harvesters, were manufactured and used in several areas for harvesting radishes in 1957–1959. Multiple-row harvesters, at a speed of about 3 miles an hour, can pull and top 10 acres of radishes in a 10-hour day. They are adjusted to harvest 5 rows planted 9 inches apart, but they can be adjusted to several different bed widths and numbers of rows per bed.

RADISHES are pulled from the soil by the tops between pairs of inclined moving V-belts and are carried to revolving knives for topping. Conveyors take them to a trailer or truck, which moves beside the harvester. Small, one-row harvesters are available for use in small fields. The operator walks behind the machine.

A small gasoline motor powers the unit. A platform is built on the machine for boxes or crates to receive the harvested radishes.

Coby Lorenzen, of the California Agricultural Experiment Station, in 1950 developed an experimental mechanical onion harvester that could dig, lift, top, and sack onions in one operation. It handled about 2 acres of onions in a 10-hour day under normal field operations. This development stimulated further work by manufacturers, who have since developed onion harvesters.

Onions are harvested by cutting underneath the bulbs with a blade or knife, so that the tops will dry. The harvester picks the onions up later. A fan blows the tops up while a cutterbar clips them from the bulbs. An airblast blows the cut tops onto the field while the bulbs are conveyed into a box. Hand labor for harvesting onions often accounts for as much as 50 percent of the total production cost. We believe developments in harvesting equipment will make it possible to harvest a large percentage of the commercial crop in a few years.

MANY PEOPLE have seen how fruit and nuts are gathered by hand from trees. Migrant workers start on the harvesting in the South and work northward with the harvest season. They hurry to get the fruit out of the orchards so they can return to the South before cold weather comes.

The scarcity and high cost of labor and management problems have caused growers to consider what might be done to mechanize the harvest.

Various mechanical shaking methods to remove fruit and nuts have been tested and put into use. Sometimes the product is allowed to fall onto the ground, where it is picked up by machines or by hand. Catching frames sometimes are provided for receiving the product and conveying it into some type of box or container.

The harvest of walnuts is more completely mechanized than is that of other tree nuts. Mechanical shakers remove the nuts from the trees. Tractor-mounted machines, which have closely spaced steel fingers that act as a brush, windrow and pick up the walnuts and rake and throw them onto a drag-type elevator, which dumps the nuts into a screen conveyor. Soil falls through the screen. Leaves and trash are blown out by a fan. The nuts are dumped into a trailer behind the harvester.

Management of the orchard is doubly important when harvesting is mechanical. Trees must be planted suitable distances apart and properly trimmed and pruned. The ground under and between the trees must be kept fairly level. The surface has to be smoothed before the harvest. Operators of mechanical shaking equipment must not damage the limbs when trees are shaken. Workers must be trained to do a particular job efficiently.

Mechanical shaking of pecans has increased. Various devices have been developed to catch the nuts as they are shaken off the trees, but none has proved to be entirely satisfactory. Most of the pecan crop was still picked up by hand in 1960.

About 35 percent of the filbert crop was harvested with mechanical equipment in 1959. Filberts are allowed to fall to the ground when ripe, and so they are left free of the husks. They are swept or brushed with a rake into piles and scooped into a cleaning or sacking machine, which is pulled through the orchard.

Fifty percent of the almond crop in 1959 was gathered with harvesters like those used for picking up walnuts. Mechanical shakers have not been used widely for almonds because they do not clean the tree without additional poling or knocking by hand.

Engineers of the California Agricultural Experiment Station developed an experimental machine for harvesting grapes. It reduces hand labor and approaches handpicking in efficiency. To use the machine, the vines must be trained so that the clusters of grapes

hang uniformly under the wires holding them.

Mounted on a four-wheeled tractor, the machine clips the bunches of grapes with a moving knife and loads them into a trailer pulled by another tractor between adjoining grape rows. Because of the difficulty of training the vines just right, it is expected that several years may elapse before vineyards can be grown with properly trained vines.

PRUNES also have long been harvested by hand. Some varieties are picked from the trees. Others are left to fall on the ground and be picked and marketed mostly as dried fruit.

Paul A. Adrian and R. B. Fridley, agricultural engineers of the Department of Agriculture and the California Agricultural Experiment Station, respectively, developed a machine in 1958 that picks prunes from the ground.

The prune pickup machine is 20 inches wide and is self-propelled. It is operated by one man walking behind. It can pick up 1 thousand pounds of prunes an hour. Two rollers rotate to pass fruit between them as the machine moves over the ground. The fruit is pulled into the space between the two rollers and passed up between two conveyor belts, which carry the prunes to a box mounted on the rear of the machine. The ground must be level and free of stones, broken branches, and other debris for efficient operation. Commercial manufacturers made several machines based on this principle in 1959.

Picking figs from the ground with the same type of machine as I described for prunes may be possible. Different adaptations and adjustments may be necessary for figs and other crops.

A self-propelled catching conveyor was developed in 1958 for harvesting such small-tree fruit as plums and apricots. It was an improvement over frames previously used. Three men can operate a pair of the catcher-conveyors. With a tractor-mounted tree shaker, the fruit of 30 to 40 trees can be harvested in an hour.

Each catcher-conveyor is about 18 feet long. A conveyor belt, 6 feet wide, runs the length of the machine. On one side of the conveyor is a 4-foot flexible flap, tilted upward. On the other side is a flap, 1.5 feet wide, tilted upward and split in the center so as to fit around a tree trunk. Two catcher-conveyors, with the short tree-side flaps adjusted so as to lap over each other and around the trunk, form a complete seal. As the fruit is shaken from the tree and falls on the conveyor, the belt carries it to the rear of the machine, where it is dumped into bulk boxes.

Engineers at the California Agricultural Experiment Station studied the feasibility of shaking peaches and Bartlett pears onto a catching frame. More than 75 percent of the peaches shaken onto the frame and an average of 68 percent of the mechanically harvested pears were free from visible injury. More fruit was damaged in the fall through the tree than was injured in falling onto and over the catching-handling device. The taller the trees, the more injury is to be expected.

Mechanical lift machines for use in orchards may be of considerable help also in harvesting fruit. One, developed about 1955, enables one man to do about twice as much of the work that used to require ladders. The machines have air-cooled gasoline engines, which also operate an air compressor for pneumatic tools. A hydraulic cylinder raises and lowers a platform on which a man can stand. The operator runs the machine by foot-operated controls, and both hands are free to perform work.

Similar machines have been used more and more for pruning and thinning work but have not been used to any large extent for picking fruit. The cost of such a machine has been too high for the use of one person in a picking operation. Also, it is hard to maneuver such machines in orchards where props are used to hold up the limbs.

J. H. Levin and S. L. Hedden, of the Department of Agriculture, and H. P. Gaston, of the Michigan Agricultural Experiment Station, have studied many aspects of fruit harvesting. They investigated mobile ladders, mobile platforms, hydraulic booms, picking tubes, and other picking aids. They concluded that complete mechanization of apple picking is not promising for the near future. Apples can be picked faster by hand, however, when equipment is used to carry the weight of the harvested fruit.

It is hard to visualize a picking device that can select apples among the leaves and limbs and twist them quickly from the tree faster than a man can with his hands.

The investigators found that bulk boxes can be used for handling apples, peaches, and pears with no more bruising during filling than when field crates are used.

The amount of fruit for processing—harvested directly in bulk boxes and transported to packing or storage houses—has increased from practically none in 1953 to several million bushels in 1960. Each year there was a big increase in the use of bulk bins.

Bulk boxes have been used in increasing numbers since 1957 for bulk harvesting and handling of apples in the Pacific Northwest for the fresh-fruit market. The development of hydraulic lifts and loaders on farm tractors and the change to bulk boxes have saved money over operations that use the smaller boxes. The size of box, details of fabrication, and materials of construction are subjects of continuing study by public and private researchers.

A ventilated picking lug for strawberries was developed in 1957. It is used for picking and transporting the fruit to the processing plant. It is referred to as "ventilated" because the sides, slightly lower than the ends, permit free movement of air through the stacks of lugs after they have been placed on the transport vehicle. The container has an easily removed metal handle.

Also developed was a detachable lug carrier for harvesting raspberries, like the one for strawberries. It has a metal frame made from one-fourth-inch iron rod that will hold the lug approximately 10 inches off the ground and provides a means of carrying it.

Further progress has been made in harvesting blueberries by the development of a catching frame and a specially designed shaking device.

The shaker consists of an electric drill motor. It has a rubber-finger attachment used in place of the drill bit. The berries fall onto the catching frame before being further delivered into the boxes. This development is possibly only a transition between hand harvesting and a completely self-propelled harvesting machine. The researchers envision a machine that will travel through the field, straddling a row of blueberries, and harvest and place them in containers as it travels along.

MECHANIZING the harvest of vegetable crops has become more and more necessary because of the high cost of hand harvesting and the lack of workers when they are needed. Vegetable growers find it difficult to pay high wages for harvesting such crops as asparagus, celery, and cauliflower. Two to eight times more man-hours are required for hand harvesting them than for all other growing operations.

The generally small acreages per farm of vegetable crops, compared with field crops, does not encourage large manufacturers to develop expensive harvesting equipment for vegetables. Further, the number of machines needed is too small for mass production. As the demand for such equipment grows, however, work on harvesting equipment is started in one way or another. Individual growers,

manufacturers of small equipment, and research workers tackle the problems. Several breakthroughs were made in the decade before 1960.

Spinach and green peas for commercial processing were among the first major vegetable crops to be mechanized successfully. Machines cut the entire plants near the ground with a sickle-bar cutting device and load them into trailers or trucks pulled behind or beside the harvesters. The crop is hauled to a processing or shelling plant.

Machines for harvesting green beans baffled engineers for many years. It was not until plant scientists produced a bean which would lend itself to mechanical harvesting that the problem began to be solved. Present varieties used for mechanical harvesting mature a large percentage of the beans at one time so that the harvesting may be accomplished in one complete operation. Several hundred mechanical snap bean harvesters were in use by 1960. The two-row machines grasp the leaves and stems between rollers, pull the beans from the plant, and drop the refuse on the ground.

Since snap beans can be harvested by machine only once, some growers pick their beans first by hand and then follow with machines for the second and final harvest.

Plant breeders are continuing to work on varieties of beans that will be even better adapted for machine harvesting. The stage of maturity, shapes of the plant, and other factors make a difference in the efficiency of machine harvest. Growers often sacrifice total yield in favor of low harvesting cost when it is economical for them to do so, or the lack of available labor dictates that this method of harvest must be used.

Mechanical harvesting of sweet corn for processing came into widespread use during the 1950's. Two-row, tractor-mounted harvesters strip the ears from the stalks and convey them into trucks or trailers. The harvesters reduce the cost about 60 percent. Each replaces 10 to 15 handpickers.

A type of harvester has been developed for such crops as celery, cabbage, and lettuce. It usually is mounted on a large trailer or tractor chassis. It moves slowly through the field as the vegetables are cut by hand and placed onto conveyor belts. The belts extend out on either side of the machine to bring the hand-cut vegetables to a central location. There they are either loaded in bulk on trailers and trucks or fed into a packing line. If the packing lines are on the machine, several workers handle the vegetables through their various cleaning and sorting stages and place them in boxes ready for shipment.

Several attempts have been made to develop a mechanical harvester for celery. None has been used to a great extent, primarily because of the difficulty of gaging properly the cutting device for removing the roots from the stalk.

The same difficulty has been encountered with experimental machines for harvesting lettuce and cabbage. If precision planting and cultivating equipment is developed for these crops, perhaps they will be grown with such uniformity in the row that a machine can be made to do a satisfactory job of cutting them at the proper position.

Growers of asparagus have watched with interest the engineering developments made by Robert Kepner, of the California Agricultural Experiment Station, on a machine that may some day be used successfully in harvesting asparagus. Several prototypes of the machine have been made, each one better than the previous model.

The Kepner machine has a bandsaw type of blade, which cuts the asparagus spears just below the ground surface immediately after they have been caught by a gripping unit. The spears grow in level beds 30 to 36 inches wide. Only one bandsaw covers the entire bed, but several of the gripping units operate across the width of the bed. They look like small wheels placed close together rolling down the row. They are made so the gripping units open up while rolling over the asparagus. They close at the ground level, gripping the spears about 3.5 inches above the ground.

The machine cuts all spears regardless of their length. Many of the spears therefore are not long enough to be saved. In tests in 1957, the machine-harvested yield was considered to be 55 percent of the hand-cut, because of the loss of the short spears.

Under certain assumed conditions and estimated costs, mechanical harvesting and hand cutting would yield about the same net return on a per acre basis if the machine-harvested yields were 65 percent of the hand-cut yield. Thus, by further modification of management and cultural practices, it may be possible to increase the percentage of harvested yield so that this method of harvesting asparagus will be practicable. It may also be possible to develop new varieties that would fit into this pattern of harvesting more successfully.

The harvesting of cucumbers was speeded up by machines that had platforms, on which pickers were carried. Conveyor belts also increased picking speed by taking cucumbers from the hand to containers at a central place.

Mechanical cucumber harvesters by 1957 were capable of harvesting 1 to 1.5 acres an hour. One machine did the work of 40 harvest hands. The machine gathers the cucumbers from the vine and leaves the vine practically undamaged. Certain varieties are harvested more easily than others. Care must be taken in planting and cultivating the crop so that the vines are in a condition to be harvested with machines.

The mechanical harvesting of tomatoes can be expedited through the use of self-propelled field conveyors, which speed up the harvest as much as 100 percent. During the decade before 1960, there were reports of partial success in the development of mechanical tomato harvesters. A successful harvester depends largely on the existence of a variety that is adaptable to mechanical separation of the fruit from the vine; the fruit must ripen rather uniformly so that a once-over harvest method may be used.

For other crops, such as melons, broccoli, and cauliflower, field conveyors and mechanical aids make for more efficient harvest. Many of these conveyors have belts as long as 70 feet, which bring the fruit from hand cutters to a central location for loading or packing. It can be expected that this type of equipment will continue to assist in the harvesting of many vegetable crops until satisfactory mechanical harvesters can be developed.

Sugarcane has its share of harvesting problems. Present methods of harvest in Louisiana are mechanized, although harvesting is not accomplished in a once-over cutting and loading operation. The harvesters cut the cane at the ground, remove the tops, and lay the cane back on the ground in windrows. After burning the dry leaves from the cane, it is picked up by tractor-mounted grab forks and loaded on trailers for delivery to the mill or a central loading point.

Experimental machines for gathering, cutting, topping, stripping, and loading the straight variety of cane grown in Louisiana work fairly well. Remaining problems are those of gathering the cane when it is blown down by strong winds and increasing the efficiency and economy of the stripping device.

Sugarcane in Florida is burned while still standing, cut by hand, and placed in windrows. Pickup machines load it into wagons or trucks and transport it to the mill.

The scarcity of labor in Puerto Rico has heightened the interest of commercial and public research workers in harvesting equipment for use there. Problems are even greater there than in Louisiana because of the higher yield, difference in growing characteristics, and irregular terrain. Most of the cane in Puerto Rico is cut by hand

and hand loaded into various types of trailers and trucks for transport to the mill.

Machinery for harvesting the high-yielding sugarcane in Hawaii consists primarily of bulldozers. The mass of tangled cane is pushed up in bunches and loaded with grab forks. The mass of cane, leaves, and soil is carried to a mill, where it is washed.

THE HARVESTING of tobacco appears to be yielding to mechanized methods.

Approximately 1 million acres of flue-cured tobacco are grown in the United States. Mechanical aids for harvesting vary from small to large machines that carry several workers. Tobacco is primed—harvested—by workers who ride on the lower platform of such machines. The leaves are elevated by endless conveyors to the upper part of the carrier, where they are tied and placed in racks until unloaded at the end of the row.

In tobacco, as with many other crops, the small acreage on each farm precludes the introduction and use of costly machines. The use of a machine is based on its weekly capacity in acres, as each acre of tobacco must be harvested weekly for up to 6 weeks. A machine capable of harvesting 3 acres a day therefore could handle approximately 18 acres a year. Most growers do not have as much as 18 acres of tobacco, but perhaps a machine of this capacity could be used cooperatively by several.

W. A. Splinter, of the University of North Carolina, has developed a mechanical tobacco harvester for removing the leaves from the stalk. High original cost, bruising of leaves, and accurate selection of mature leaves are some of the problems still being studied.

SOME OF THE common problems in harvesting all crops includes usually fragile or unstable type of material, limitations and uncertainties of the weather, and large tonnages, which need to be handled in a short time.

These and economic problems relating to the size of farm and the need of heavy-duty equipment for some jobs confront the engineer in his attempts to develop machines for completely mechanizing harvesting.

It appears there will be an ever increasing and almost unending demand for modification and improvement of present harvesting machines to perform more efficiently at less cost. Likewise, new machines for crops not yet mechanized will continue to demand more attention, depending on the economic necessity.

# Outrunning Time; Combating Weather

W. V. Hukill, Robert A. Saul, and Daniel W. Teare

TECHNOLOGY in agriculture is largely control of change.

Change is characteristic of all living things. Our purpose in agriculture is to stimulate, direct, or retard the changes that Nature wants to accomplish.

A growing blade of grass may continue to grow. It may be eaten by an insect or animal. It may be consumed by disease or other organisms. It may be separated from the rest of the plant and wither to become relatively dormant. In any case, change will continue. Even the dormant dry grass will change slowly.

If we happen to be interested in this blade of grass, we will do what we can to control the changes. In a pasture, we hope it will grow without interruption until an animal eats it. In a cover crop, we intend it to be consumed by micro-organisms. In a hayfield, we stimulate its growth to a point and then at harvesttime attempt to hold it

without further change until an animal eats it months later.

To grow old is as natural and inevitable as to grow. Plants and animals and plant and animal products continue to change even though from our point of view it would be desirable sometimes to keep them exactly as they are. How many times have you wished in April that you could have an apple or a peach that tasted like the one you had last fall?

It is seldom possible to prevent all change in product quality, but by knowing some of the rules we do slow down some of the aging processes at will. This is not new. Men have made hay and stored crops for a long time. It is relatively new, however, to choose practices on a basis of knowledge rather than on a basis of tradition. It is also relatively new to have available mechanical power and mechanical devices other than very simple tools and implements. The combination of a high degree of rational management and unreserved acceptance of mechanization accounts for the revolution in agricultural performance now underway.

The job of making crops and farm products available when they are wanted, as contrasted with the job of producing them, is largely a matter of retarding change. Success in this depends on knowing how the changes occur and having appropriate equipment to modify them.

What do we know and what do we have to learn about these changes?

What equipment do we have and what new equipment and methods are emerging?

In this discussion, we concern ourselves mostly with practices that may be applied on the farm, even though with many products the techniques of preservation have only begun when they leave the farm.

The changes we are combating in preserving farm products are mostly biological—that is, they are the consequence of living. Most of the products themselves are alive or are still responding to chemical changes set up while they were living. In addition, they are subject to invasion by living molds, yeasts, and bacteria.

All these biological processes are regulated by temperature and moisture content. The processes are fast when the products are hot and slow when they are cold. They are fast in the presence of adequate moisture and slow when moisture is limited. Cooling and drying are two basic control processes in preserving farm products. There are others, of course. In canning, for example, the products are sterilized by high temperature and sealed. In ensiling feed, the products are sealed to prevent the entry of oxygen, thus limiting the biological activity. The availability of gases, particularly oxygen, may influence the character as well as the speed of the changes.

Equipment and methods for cooling, drying, and controlling the composition of the atmosphere are a part of farming. It is convenient to think of this equipment and these methods as separate and apart from other activities in farming. But their use and development influence and are influenced in turn by the use and development of all the other practices on the farm.

For example, equipment for drying hay and grain could not develop very far until demands for light and power for other purposes had brought highline electric power into being. Field shellers for corn were designed and manufactured and available to farmers for a number of years before they came into much use. A farmer has to know that he can hold his harvested crop without spoilage. Before drying equipment was available, he had to harvest his corn on the ear and let the wind dry it in a corncrib.

All the technological changes in farming are related to each other. Some are less dependent on others and can be accomplished quickly. Some are necessarily slow. Substituting a light aluminum scoop shovel for a heavy steel one is relatively simple; such changes have a large part in our changing ways. But eliminating the scoop shovel as a farm implement, as is being done, is a long-time procedure. It requires appropriate power, equipment, buildings, feeding methods, and even modification of the form of materials that are to be handled.

Changes in methods that depend on changes in buildings may be expected to be slower than most other developments in farming methods. Even the simplest building has a relatively long life, and changes in existing buildings or replacement require substantial investment. Emotional attachment to conventional types of buildings tends to stand in the way of technological change. Changing ways of protecting, holding, and handling farm products include changing building types. The conventional type of corncrib gradually is disappearing from the farmstead.

The changes underway in handling farm products include cooling and protecting milk and other dairy products, cooling and storing fruits and vegetables, drying and storing grains, and drying and preserving forage.

Of these, the revolution in hay and grain handling we discuss in some detail.

VERY LITTLE GRAIN was dried mechanically on the farm before the Second World War. Seed corn was then and still is harvested with high moisture content and dried with heated air. The high per bushel value of hybrid seed made it economical to use mechanical drying equipment. This experience demonstrated that seed drying was practical and could be depended on. The only reason it was not practiced with other grains was its cost and availability.

Obviously mechanical drying could take its place among routine farming operations only if its costs were returned by increasing the quantity or quality of grain or by reducing costs somewhere else. The increased mechanization and the decrease in the supply of farm labor since the war have resulted in the general acceptance of mechanical grain drying, although in 1960 it is not yet as generally used as, say, mechanical grain harvesting. Many of its advantages are obvious.

Grain that is to be kept for any substantial period must be dried in one way or another. Sunshine and wind will do the drying. But sometimes they are not dependable. Sometimes after grain is harvested rains make it difficult if not impossible to salvage the crop. While corn is standing in the field waiting for the elements to dry it, storms may break the stalks or knock the ears to the ground. The moisture content of ripened wheat standing in the field fluctuates from hour to hour. Wheat that is dry enough to harvest and store in late afternoon one day may be too wet the next morning to be harvested safely. It is not unusual for combine harvesters to be unable to operate before noon because the wheat is too damp.

In any of these instances, if mechanical drying equipment is available, the grain can be harvested when it is convenient without waiting for natural drying. With corn particularly, if the crop is not harvested until it is dry, some of the grain will shatter from the ears and be lost. Shattering loss can be avoided almost completely by picking early before drying is completed. This can be done only if drying equipment is available. Not only is the grain lost when shattering occurs; the seeds germinate and become a nuisance the following year. Sometimes volunteer corn is the weed most in evidence in soybean fields. Sometimes waiting for the corn to dry naturally before harvest interferes with crop rotations or delays the harvest until cold weather when neither the men nor the machines operate at good efficiency. Every farmer has experienced the situation in which grain was harvested too wet for storage in spite of his best efforts to avoid it. He is likely then to lose some grain unless he can dry it.

MANY WAYS OF DRYING grains have been proposed and used experimentally.

Vacuum drying, drying with infrared radiation, use of the heat pump, capturing the sun's energy and concentrating it on the grain, absorption of moisture by chemical or hygroscopic materials—each of these (and others) has been studied and applied in some degree to the drying of grain.

Without attempting to forecast what methods may emerge for the future, we can say that current practices in mechanical grain drying are limited to forcing air through layers of grain. The air may be either at atmospheric temperature or heated before passing through the grain. All present farm grain driers may be classed as either heated-air or unheated-air driers.

It would be interesting to review the apparent possibilities and limitations of various drying processes other than passing air through the grain. Some of these will undoubtedly be of practical importance in the future. But it is of more immediate interest to consider the principles utilized by present equipment.

Grain is hygroscopic—that is, it will exchange moisture with the air surrounding it; whether the transfer of moisture is from the grain to the air or from the air to the grain depends on which is relatively drier. This exchange takes place inevitably as long as the air in contact with the grain is drier or wetter than the grain. Grain having more than 25 to 30 percent moisture will lose moisture to any air that is not saturated. If we wish to dry the grain, it is necessary only to surround each kernel with air that is relatively dry. The dryness of the grain having a given percentage of moisture depends on its properties. Studies of "equilibrium moisture" that have been made on grains permit us to anticipate the conditions under which the moisture exchange will result in drying the grain.

Drying of the grain is necessarily accompanied by wetting of the air. If drying is to continue, the wet air will have to be replaced by dry air. This is what any farm grain drier does. It passes air continuously through a bed of grain, the air being relatively dry when it enters and relatively wet when it leaves.

The quantity of air required, the rate at which it will pick up moisture, and the effect of the grain and air conditions on these quantities and rates are governed partly by the rules of psychrometry. Psychrometry is the study of the behavior of mixtures of air and water vapor and is used also in refrigeration, air conditioning, and climatology. For example, it may be computed that to dry a bushel of corn from 25 percent to 12 percent moisture content, using air at 70° F. and having a relative humidity of 65 percent, would require not less than 55 thousand cubic feet of air.

The grain in a typical drier does not all dry uniformly. When the air enters, the first kernels it touches give up moisture. As the air moves on to the next layer, it becomes wetter and can take up less moisture. Continually becoming wetter as it progresses through the grain, the air will reach saturation and may pass through the last layers without doing any drying at all.

Later, after drying has continued for some time, the first kernels will have become so dry they can no longer add much if any water vapor to the air and the other layers will dry. This sets up what may be described as a wave, or front, of drying, which proceeds through the bed of grain in the direction of airflow. At any time during the drying process, there is grain nearest the air entrance that is already dry and there is a relatively thin layer that is being dried; the rest of the grain has lost none of its moisture.

The existence of the drying front, which is the junction between the wet and the dry grain and which continually moves forward during drying, is characteristic of current drying processes. The sharpness of the drying front or the thickness of the layer in which drying takes place is modified by the temperature, moisture content

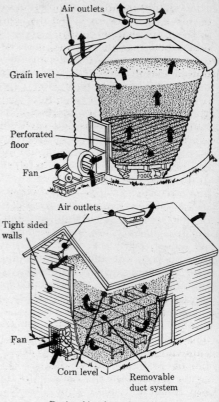

*Drying bins for unheated air.*

of the grain, rate of airflow, and other factors.

Control of the rate of progress of the drying front and the thickness of the drying zone are two principal factors in the design of grain driers.

Each cubic foot of air passed through the grain has a capacity for removing just so much moisture. If the air leaves the grain before it has picked up its limit of moisture, the process will be inefficient in that respect. When the drying zone is very thin relative to the depth of grain, the air will carry out a full load of moisture practically all the time the drier is operating. On the other hand, if the drying zone occupies most of the full depth of grain in the drier, then the air will pass through the grain without becoming as fully saturated as possible.

We should mention one other aspect of this drying process. When the water in the grain changes to water vapor, it uses up heat. In driers such as we are discussing, practically all this heat must come from the air. This means that for every particle of water vapor picked up on its way through the grain the air must surrender a corresponding quantity of heat. When it leaves the grain it therefore is colder than when it entered. The amount of temperature drop in the air as it passes through the grain is directly proportional to the amount of water vapor it has picked up. A cooling front accompanies the drying front as they both move through the grain in the direction of airflow.

UNHEATED-AIR DRYING as practiced on farms is accomplished by putting the grain in a storage bin and blowing air through it.

Usually the bin has a false floor a foot or so above the bottom of the bin. The false floor is perforated or of such construction that air may penetrate it but the grain cannot fall through. The space between the bin bottom and the false floor is used as a chamber into which air is driven by a fan and from which the air moves upward through the grain. The rate of airflow is such that the drying front moves upward and completely through all the grain, usually in a period of from 1 to 4 weeks. For corn that is harvested in the fall, a longer drying period may be permitted than for small grains that are harvested in midsummer.

The operating cost for such a drier consists mainly of the power cost for driving the fan. A typical drier might require 1 to 10 horsepower, depending on the quantity of grain in the bin and a number of other factors. In the design of such a drier, the rate of airflow is adjusted to the lowest rate that can confidently be expected to dry all the grain before any of it spoils. The use of a greater rate of airflow is expensive, because the total power required to supply a given total quantity of air is greater if the air is moved

at a fast rate than if it is moved more slowly. A rate of airflow less than that required to prevent spoilage obviously is unsatisfactory.

The most economical unheated-air drier is one in which the drying is completed—that is, the drying front has moved through all the grain, just before the biological changes in the grain have reached the point of damaging the grain. A margin of safety must be allowed, of course, because it is impossible to anticipate the weather and just how suitable the air will be for drying. Weather records for specific areas where drying is used are helpful in this.

The time that may be permitted to elapse before drying is completed is decided largely on observation and experience. It is influenced by the temperature, the moisture content, the types of molds present, and the initial condition of the grain. Kernels that have been torn or broken during harvesting or handling will mold much more quickly than whole, sound kernels. This last effect illustrates how the performance in one farming operation may influence the opportunity for improved techniques in another. The difference between a corn sheller that cracks the kernels badly and one that shells the grain without damage might be the margin between economical and uneconomical operation of unheated-air drying equipment.

During the drying, the undried grain in the upper part of the bin continues its biological activity. This generates heat and consumes a small part of the solid material in the grain. As long as air is continually forced through the grain, the heat generated is carried away by the air. Usually the loss in dry material on account of the continued respiration is relatively small. The undried grain remains cooler than the atmospheric temperature because of the cooling that accompanies the evaporation.

Forcing the air through the grain requires pressure. The deeper the grain layer and the more air moved, the more the pressure must be. Electric fans usually are used. The type of fan, whether centrifugal or of the propeller type, is of less importance than selecting the proper size and speed. Practically all fans manufactured before 1940 were for industrial purposes. They could be adapted for agricultural use, but the difference in operating ranges made it difficult to get suitable fans. Now manufacturers are making fans for farm drying, and the availability of suitable equipment is much less of a problem.

The drying bin with a false floor has some disadvantages, and some farmers prefer to use a system of ducts or tunnels on the floor of the bin instead of the perforated false floor. The duct system has the advantage that it is cheaper, and the ducts may be readily removable for cleaning or for easier grain handling during unloading. The duct system usually consists of one main duct extending the length of the bin and lateral ducts extending sideways from it to the sidewalls. Air is delivered through the main duct to the laterals, from where it moves upward through the grain. With a duct system, the air distribution is less uniform than with a false floor, and it is necessary to use a greater volume of air to get equally effective drying.

With unheated-air drying, the operation depends completely on the weather. Humid weather will slow the drying. Long periods of unseasonably humid weather may make it difficult to complete drying quickly enough. Many farmers are using supplemental heating equipment to avoid this possibility. For this purpose, a small gas burner is installed in the airstream leading to the bin. It generates enough heat to raise the air temperature by 10° to 15° F. This will reduce the relative humidity of the drying air so that even when the atmosphere is saturated the slightly warmed air will continue to remove moisture. This permits the farmer to use his drying system with complete confidence that no combination of weather will prevent the suc-

cessful drying of his crop. The use of supplemental heat with appropriate humidity control equipment is one of the practical alternatives among the various ways of drying grain, and the development of controls is keeping up with the increasing use of such equipment.

The power requirement for supplying the air for drying becomes prohibitive when the grain is too deep in the bin. For practical purposes, the depth of high-moisture grain to be dried in a bin is limited to 6 or 8 feet. Deeper layers could be dried if the air supply were increased proportionately, but under most existing conditions the cost of power would be too great.

One way of utilizing a deeper bin to good advantage is to practice layer drying. The bin is first filled with, say, 4 to 6 feet of grain. The fan is operated until the drying front has reached the top of the grain—that is, all the grain is dry. Then a second layer of 2 to 4 feet or so is put on top of the first; again the fan is operated until the drying front has reached the top of the second layer. A third, thinner layer may then be added. Each successive layer needs to be thinner than previous ones, because with the increasing thickness of dry grain below, the resistance to airflow cuts down the rate of ventilation. This procedure is particularly suitable for shelled corn. With the small grains harvested in midsummer, the harvest season might be too short for this practice to offer much advantage.

IN DRYING WITH HEATED AIR, as contrasted with unheated-air drying or the use of supplemental heat, much higher temperatures are used, and sufficient artificial heat is supplied that the drying capacity of the atmospheric air is not depended upon at all. Air temperatures from 100° to 200° commonly are used.

This type of drying is seldom done in a storage bin but usually in a separate drying compartment designed for the purpose. Natural or bottled gas or fuel oil are used to heat the air. The drying compartments take a variety of forms but usually are so constructed that when filled with grain the heated air will pass through grain layers from 12 to 24 inches thick. The air in some will move vertically, much like in a wagon bed having a perforated floor. In others, the air passes horizontally through columns of grain held in place between screen or perforated walls 12 to 24 inches apart. Still others contain the grain in what amounts to a large box, with air ducts extending through the box from one side to the other in a symmetrical pattern. Some of the ducts supply air, and the rest provide an air escape. The air moves through the grain from one duct to another.

In any of these driers, the grain may be stationary, or it may move slowly through the drier, a supply of wet grain continually entering and a stream of dried grain continually leaving. In some, the grain is continually recirculated within the drier to prevent excessive variation in the final moisture content. Each of these and other variations is used, and each has its advantages and disadvantages.

We pointed out that drying with unheated air is a race against the development of damage from mold. This is not true when drying with heated air. The race in this instance is to get the grain through the drier at a rate that will not hold up other operations.

In heated-air drying, practically all the heat for driving off the moisture is supplied from fuel. The drying capacity of the natural air is of little importance. At the temperatures used, the grain, once it is in the drier, will be dried within a few hours.

The capacity of a heated-air drier in bushels per hour or bushels per day is one important measure of its suitability. Its capacity depends directly on the rate at which heat may be supplied to the drying air. For example, in summer operation each gallon of fuel oil burned in a drier may be expected to evaporate about 80 pounds of water from wet grain. No drier will perform much better than this, and none of good design falls far short.

Improvements in design that are underway and that may be expected look to reducing the cost, simplifying the operation, reducing fire hazard, fitting the equipment to conform better with handling and storing operations in harvest, and improving the quality of the dried grain. No great improvement of the efficiency of use of fuel may be expected.

A drying front moves through the thin column of grain in a heated-air drier just as in an unheated-air drier. Because of the thinner layer of grain and the higher volume of air used, it is not so sharply defined. The drying zone may include the full thickness of grain, in which case the air is still capable of doing some drying when it leaves the grain. If the air leaves without picking up all the moisture it has capacity for, the drier is wasteful of heat. On the other hand, if all the grain is drying from the start, then the final moisture content will be more uniform. With this type of drier, uniformity of final moisture content is not consistent with economical use of the heat.

AIR HEATED to a high temperature tends to dry the grain excessively. The drying in heated-air driers will be continued until the average grain moisture content has been reduced to the desired level. Some of the grain will usually be considerably drier and some considerably wetter than this average. If the grain is well mixed upon removal from the drier, it will all tend to equalize within a few hours. Grain coming from a continuous-flow drier may be mixed well enough without further attention.

The dried grain will be hot when drying is completed. Before it is put in storage, it will have to be cooled. That is done in many driers by continuing to operate the fan after the heat is shut off. The grain thereby is brought quickly to atmospheric temperature. The grain itself seldom gets as hot as

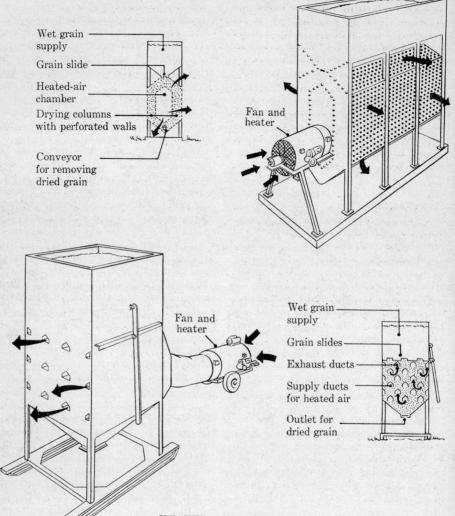

Wet grain supply

Grain slide

Heated-air chamber

Drying columns with perforated walls

Conveyor for removing dried grain

Fan and heater

Fan and heater

Wet grain supply

Grain slides

Exhaust ducts

Supply ducts for heated air

Outlet for dried grain

HEATED-AIR DRIERS

the drying air because of the absorption of heat for evaporation.

When fuel is burned to heat the drying air, the heat is all contained at first in the products of combustion or smoke. When these hot products are mixed with other air, the mixture contains the heat, the carbon dioxide, and the moisture resulting from the burning. By mixing the right proportion of air with the products of combustion,

any desired degree of heating may be added to the air. In many driers, such mixing is accomplished and the heated air is blown through the grain. This is called direct heating.

In indirect-heated driers, the products of combustion are not mixed with the drying air but are passed through a heat exchanger. The heat exchanger, like an automobile radiator, has a large amount of metal surface. The air on the way to the drying grain is heated by passing over the exchanger. The products of combustion are exhausted from a chimney and do not enter the grain. The cost of an indirect drier obviously is greater, and some of the heat does not get into the drying air. The advantage of indirect heating is reduction of fire hazard.

For feeding or most other purposes, the quality of the grain is not impaired by direct heating unless the burner operates badly and fails to burn all of the fuel. In this case, unburned fuel carried in the airstream may be deposited on the grain and make it unpalatable.

Since the rate of carrying off moisture depends on the amount of heat carried by the air, a drier of a given size has more capacity at a higher temperature. This would suggest that extremely high temperatures be used. From the viewpoint of the drying process only, it is economical to use very high temperatures. Because high temperatures affect the quality of the dried grain adversely, however, actual operating temperatures are limited by what is known about the effect of temperature on quality. The temperature and duration of exposure both influence these effects.

We still have much to learn about the effects of heating and rapid drying. It is not possible at present to weigh the advantage of high temperature in drying capacity against its disadvantage in damage to the grain and arrive at a most economical temperature for drier operation.

The loss in quality from excessive temperature depends on the use to be made of the grain. If the grain is to be used for seed, air temperatures above 110° to 120° are found to be too high. If the germination is unimportant, as with grain to be fed to animals, temperatures up to 200° are used. Some feeding studies show little reduction in protein value at air temperatures even above 200°. Corn that is to be used for the wet milling industry frequently is difficult to process on account of high-temperature treatment. An air temperature limit of 130° to 140° has been suggested for corn destined for this use. Rice, practically all of which is eventually milled for food, may check badly during milling if it has been dried with air hotter than 120° to 130°. All of these limits are poorly defined.

Undoubtedly the losses in quality are influenced by moisture content and the way the drying front moves through the grain as well as by the air temperature. Perhaps the next important modifications in drying equipment will come about from learning just how high capacity and good grain quality may both be accomplished at the same time.

Mechanical grain drying has been gradually taking its place as one of the routine operations in farming. Even if there were no further developments in methods and equipment, it could be expected to continue to improve productivity and efficiency.

Improvements will be made. They will result, as in the past, from three things: First, improved understanding of the drying process and its effect on grain quality. Second, improved coordination of various operations such as feeding, storing, handling, harvesting, and cropping so that all the operations are supplemental to each other. Third, improved drying equipment.

Of these, the first two are most significant. An understanding of the principles and coordination of the operations are difficult to come by, while invention of equipment follows more or less naturally when the principles are known and the need is well defined.

GRAIN IN STORAGE, having been dried either by the sun and wind or by mechanical equipment, needs to be kept dry.

"Dry" is a relative term with hygroscopic materials such as grain. When we say "dry grain," we usually mean grain having a moisture content of not more than 12 to 13 percent.

Seldom, if ever, is grain completely

free from all moisture. It would not be usable for most purposes if it were bone dry. At 12 to 13 percent moisture, the biological changes are very slow. Most grain is stored at about this level of moisture content. In warmer climates where insect infestation is serious, it may be desirable to keep it drier.

Grain stored in tight bins will not pick up much moisture from the atmosphere. It may, however, increase in moisture content in some parts of the bin by migration of moisture from other parts. In colder climates, it is typical of grain stored in bins of more than 1,000 to 1,500 bushels for the upper layers of grain to increase in moisture content during winter.

This moisture does not come from the atmosphere but from grain in the interior of the bin. The grain by the end of summer is warm. Grain is a good heat insulator, and the interior grain stays warm while that near the walls of the bin tends to follow the atmospheric temperature and become cold. The kernels in the bin fit closely together, but even so the space between kernals is filled with air. This space is about 40 percent of the bin volume; the grain actually occupies about 60 percent. Because the air assumes about the same temperature as the grain, the air near the walls is cold while that in the interior is warm. The warm air, being lighter, moves upward and is replaced by the heavier cold air from the walls, which moves down and over to the center. As long as the temperature difference persists, this convection will continue. The air movement is very slow but continues for months. The warm air moving upward in the center of the bin comes out through the surface layer of grain. This surface layer is cold; as the warm air passes through it, moisture is absorbed or condensed out of the air onto the grain in much the same way that the moisture is condensed on the sides of a pitcher of ice water in warm weather.

This condensation takes place slowly but may continue throughout the fall and winter, with the result that the surface grain may become seriously wet. In extreme cases, the surface grain may build up to 25 to 30 percent moisture content and spoil quickly. Such moisture migration always occurs when the grain is warmer than the atmosphere, but it is seldom as severe as the example mentioned.

The absorption of moisture in the upper layers may be prevented by eliminating the convection air currents that cause it. Recognition of just how this increase in surface moisture comes about is relatively new. Since about 1950, aeration has been used to prevent it.

AERATION is the term used to describe forcing low volumes of air through grain for purposes other than drying.

Aeration equipment is used in stored grain that is already dry. It is not to be confused with drying equipment.

Practically all grain stored commercially for more than a few weeks and much farm-stored grain is now aerated with equipment installed specifically for the purpose.

For aeration, the storage bins are equipped by providing a simple duct system on the floor and a fan to discharge air from the ducts. In commercial storages, except very tall elevators, the rate of ventilation is usually about one-tenth of a cubic foot per minute for each bushel stored. The fan is not operated during hot weather. The fan is started in early fall when the average outside temperature has dropped to about 10 degrees below the grain temperature.

Pulling the air downward through the grain sets up a downward moving cooling front similar to the drying front that forms in drying bins. At one-tenth cubic foot per minute per bushel, the cooling front will have moved through all the grain in a week to 10 days of continuous operation and all the grain will be at about the same temperature as the air. The process is repeated later in the fall. Thus the temperature of the grain in the interior of the bin is never permitted to be much higher than that of the outside air.

A different method is sometimes applied in aerating farm bins. If the length and width of the bin are not much greater than the depth of the grain, a vertical pipe extending down through the grain in the center of the bin is substituted for the duct system. The lower part of the pipe is perforated with small holes. A small fan mounted at the top of the pipe draws air out of it and sets up air circulation through the grain. Air enters the grain through the upper surface and moves downward, eventually entering the pipe and being discharged by the fan. In this arrangement, the air volume is even less than usually is used in commercial storage. The cooling front moves very slowly, and the fan is operated continuously from early fall through the winter. A typical fan for this would use about 60 watts of electric power. One advantage of this arrangement is that it takes a minimum of attention. Temperature or humidity controls are used on some aeration systems.

Equipment for grain aeration is useful for other reasons. In fumigating stored grain, for example, the slow, positive circulation of air facilitates the penetration and distribution of fumigants.

Ventilation of stored grain for control of moisture migration is relatively new. Modifications of the foregoing methods to reduce their cost and increase their effectiveness will continue as more is learned.

MORE FARMERS produce hay than any other crop. Hay has been first in acreage and second in value to corn in the United States. At least 80 percent of the tonnage was legume hay and mixtures that have the better feed values. Farmers making high-quality hay by mechanical curing often double the feed value of their hay. When this is generally practiced, hay and corn could be nearly equal in money evaluation.

Mechanical hay-drying installations are increasing in number yearly. Many have been made on dairy farms to reduce feed costs. High-cost protein and grain feed supplements necessary to maintain milk flow can be reduced when high-quality, mechanically cured hay is available.

Many dairymen find it profitable not to feed a protein supplement when they feed high-quality hay. This saves a good deal on their feed bill during hay-feeding months. Dairymen in Tennessee, Virginia, Wisconsin, and Minnesota, among others, have been quick to recognize the necessity of making high-quality hay. Protein up to 22 percent and carotene equivalent up to 75 thousand International Units of vitamin A per pound of hay can be retained.

COLOR AND LEAF CONTENT of legume hays are the chief visible indications of high quality.

Each is reduced or lost by the action of sun, rain, dew, and the passage of time in field curing. The wind and haymaking machinery are also adverse forces that winnow the leaves in gathering operations. Other hidden enemies include oxidation, enzymes within the plants (chemical agents), heat, and mold. All of these remove a large part of the feed value that an animal would obtain if the hay were pastured.

These losses are greater when drying is slow or when the crop is stored with a moisture content of more than 20 percent. Federal hay grading requirements are quite lenient, considering the leaf loss under field curing. The percentage of leaf by weight and the percentage of color content required for U.S. No. 1, U.S. No. 2, U.S. No. 3, and U.S. Sample legume hays permit great losses in feed values. With unassisted sun curing, it is not possible in many sections of the country to have enough color and leaves to meet higher requirements.

Studies made by men of the Tennessee Valley Authority showed that in a large number of hay cuttings, by conventional methods, only 9 percent was U.S. No. 1 hay, 26 percent was No. 2, 35 percent was No. 3, and the remaining 30 percent was U.S. Sample. This is probably a good example of the average farmer's experience in making hay. That means only one very good crop in ten; 65 percent of the total is in No. 3 or Sample grades.

Poor hay makes it necessary to practice heavy feeding of grain, protein, minerals, and vitamins to obtain proper animal growth and production.

In the dairy business, about half the cost of milk production is for feed. High-quality hay can cut feed costs in half. Some farmers have made heavy cuts in the cost of raising feeder calves by putting them on high-quality alfalfa hay when they weigh 300 to 600 pounds and then full-feeding them until they are ready for market.

High losses of leaf reduce yields and rob animals of the most highly digestible nutrients in the hay. The protein in alfalfa helps overcome the deficiencies of the proteins in cereal grains. When crude protein in supplement costs 10 cents a pound, No. 2 hay with 25 percent leaves has lost 20.41 dollars' worth of digestible protein through leaf shattering for every ton gathered. In making 100 tons of No. 2 alfalfa hay a year with a leaf content of 25 percent, the loss is 2,041 dollars' worth of digestible protein. High-quality hay takes that amount off the feed bill and adds it to profit. Besides, animals will have adequate vitamins, especially vitamin A, for health, growth, and production of milk and less breeding and calving difficulties. Other feed elements, including fat, sugar, and minerals, also are more abundant in good hay. Also included are calcium, phosphorus, nitrogen, potassium, and trace minerals.

THE MOISTURE CONTENT of growing plants cut for hay is 65 percent to 95 percent. The maximum moisture content should be down to 15 percent for best storage. But sun drying to that

SYSTEM FOR AERATING FARM BINS

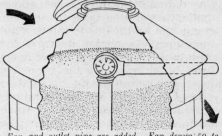

*Fan and outlet pipe are added. Fan draws 50 to 80 watts, moves 50 to 100 cubic feet of air per minute.*

point causes great losses in feed value in the field. When moisture of more than 20 percent is present in hay, there is danger of heating in storage, which may cause fire. There may be large losses of feed value from oxidation and enzymes because of moisture.

In good weather the sun efficiently removes moisture from hay in the field. But farmers seldom are able to select good weather of sufficient duration to cure hay and retain high quality. A hot sun may overdry the leaves, causing fading of color and shattering of leaves when the hay is gathered.

Mechanical drying of hay calls for cutting, raking, and storing in one day's time before moisture falls below 35 percent. Then air is blown through the hay until the moisture is reduced to 15 percent for safe, longtime storage.

As an example of the efficiency of the sun in removing moisture, assume that a given sample of hay contained 80 percent moisture when it was cut. It would require 8,500 pounds of green hay to make 1 ton of dried hay with 15 percent moisture content. Then 6,500 pounds of water would have to be removed to have 1 ton of dried hay. In 4 to 6 hours the sun may remove 5,667 pounds, reducing the hay to 40 percent moisture content. Hay is tough at this stage of drying. The leaves are much less subject to separation from their stems. Gathering operations do not waste them.

By storing hay at 35 to 40 percent moisture, the damages caused by sun, rain, and dew are stopped with minimum losses. Drying must then be completed in storage to prevent heating and spoilage. At 40 percent moisture it requires 2,833 pounds of hay to dry to 1 ton of 15 percent moisture hay. This means that 833 pounds of water must be removed from every ton of cured hay on the drier.

Final drying by the fan requires 3 to 10 days, depending on air conditions during that time. In this example, the sun would remove 83.4 percent of the water, the fan and drier would evaporate 12.2 percent, and only 4.4 percent of the original moisture would be left in the hay dried to 15 percent moisture. Hay with less than 15 percent moisture loses leaves during feeding and handling. At less than 10 percent moisture, hay is brittle and may cause mouths of animals eating it to become sore.

At an air temperature of 60°, some evaporation occurs if relative humidity is below 50 percent. If the relative humidity is high, there will be little drying of hay even though the air is quite warm. Heating does not occur with slow drying. The exchange of air removes the heat that develops from oxidation. There is little point in operating the blower fan to dry hay unless the relative humidity is low enough to cause the air to absorb water from the hay.

The exception to this rule is when poor drying conditions would cause hay to heat with the fan off. The blower fan should then be operated 1 hour out of every 4 hours, to remove any heat that may form in the hay, until drying conditions improve. On a drier, the hay nearest where the air enters dries first. The sides and top dry last. When the outside foot of hay on all surfaces is dry, the operation has been completed.

Full sun curing may require up to 3 weeks. The time depends on the rain, dew, humidity, and air temperature. To obtain high-quality hay, it must be gathered within 6 to 36 hours after cutting. Raking should be started when moisture in the hay has dropped below 45 percent. At this point, leaves are tough and cling tightly to the stems. At 35 percent moisture, the leaves are dry enough to begin shattering. Shattering increases as the hay gets drier. Quick gathering thus greatly reduces losses caused by overdrying, leaf shattering, chemical action, fading, bleaching, and leaching by the sun, dew, and rain.

Every farmer knows that tough hay will heat in storage. But with mechanical drying one may put up much wetter hay than any farmer would consider putting in his barn in the past. The difference is that air is blown through the hay by large fans to remove both heat and moisture. In fact, the mechanical drying process actually reduces both hay and drying air temperatures by the effect of water evaporation. The drying hay and escaping air may be as much as 25° below the temperature of the air blown into the hay to cure it. This drop in temperature in the drying air is determined by the relative humidity and the rate of evaporation. When ingoing and escaping air are of equal temperature, the hay is down to 12 to 15 percent moisture and drying has been completed. Farmers with properly designed and operated hay driers have no fear of haymow fires. The moving air, in large quantities, removes the heat as fast as it forms. The reduced temperature retards the rate of chemical and organic action, which causes deterioration of feed values of the hay.

Enzymes depend on moisture for activation, and as moisture drops they become less active. When poor drying weather slows mechanical drying, the fan can be operated intermittently. Then the heat developing in the hay while the fan is off will assist drying when the fan is again turned on. Actually this heating process is oxidation (a slow burning). Some feed value in the hay is destroyed by the generation of heat. It is an expensive method of heating the drying air but can be justified under adverse drying conditions during barn or stack curing.

A MECHANICAL HAY DRIER completes the drying of hay after partial field curing by conducting large volumes of air at low pressure and distributing it uniformly through the hay placed upon it.

Three general types of systems are in use: Dehydration for almost complete removal of water from the crop (commonly done only in commercial operations); batch drying with either a fixed drying platform or the specially equipped drying wagons; and the mow drier for both finishing and in-place storage. Batch driers generally employ supplemental heat. Most mow driers are of the unheated type because of the fire hazard.

The following comments deal only with the mow drier.

This system consists of a blower fan and main air duct, which releases air uniformly into smaller lateral ducts or under a slightly raised, slatted floor.

The main air duct receives air directly from the drier fan. Recommended air velocities in the ducts are 1,000 to 1,500 feet per minute. Adjustable air doors are sometimes used in the sidewalls and top of main air ducts. They control, direct, and regulate the release of air into laterals or slatted floors. The tops of some main air ducts are also slatted. Main air ducts can be tapered to equalize air pressure and promote uniform air distribution.

Lateral ducts must carry all the air away from the main ducts for uniform distribution into the hay. The total cross sections of all the laterals should be at least as great as the cross section of the main duct at the fan end. When very long laterals are needed, they may be tapered to equalize air release.

Slatted floors can be used in place of lateral ducts. These are generally made in panels so they can be lifted for cleaning underneath. They also must carry and distribute all the air delivered by the main duct. Slatted floor tapering is accomplished in wide barns by reducing the stringer width by 2 inches for each additional row of slatted floor

panels. The open ends of the outside tier of panels are closed. This seals the air from direct escape from the panels and forces it up through the slats into the hay.

The air passing up through hay picks up moisture and must be released from the barn. Thus every drier must have planned exhaust air escape areas to release the air. Four to six times as much area is required for air escape from a barn as for air inlet to the fan. This prevents back pressure from developing on the drier. Back pressure limits the flow of air through the hay.

An important factor in the construction of mow hay driers is to have a tight floor. Knotholes, cracks, openings, or breaks in a floor will permit air to escape downward. Air pressure is reduced thereby, and less air passes through the hay. All such openings under the drier must be closed and sealed to prevent the loss of air pressure. A well-made tongue and grooved floor generally will be all right, or a paper covering over the floor will make it airtight. Hay chutes and stair wells are closed or sealed off to prevent leakage of air and loss of pressure.

Sufficient air must be blown through the hay to carry away the moisture and heat to prevent spoilage. Most hay driers have been designed so that it is necessary to force the air through about 8 feet of undried loose or chopped hay. Baled hay is stacked 10 to 14 layers deep over a slatted floor.

For normal operating conditions, the volume of air required is based on the kind of crop, the moisture content of the crop, and the method of gathering and storing. The volumes of air required are the same for heated- and unheated-air hay drying because the air must remove the moisture. The added heat makes it possible to pick up the moisture continuously. Poor drying weather does not interrupt heated-air drying.

FOR LOOSE, FULL-LENGTH HAY, a minimum of 2 cubic feet of air per minute per cubic foot of the hay being dried is supplied. Additional air will cause faster drying. For chopped and baled hay, a minimum of 2.5 c.f.m. of air per cubic foot of hay is necessary. It is desirable to dry as large a quantity of hay at one time as possible for efficient use of the fan and motor.

All hay resists the flow of air. The fan must provide enough pressure to force the required amount of air through the hay. Hay having a moisture content of 45 percent or more packs too tightly for necessary air penetration at the desired low pressures. Most crop-drier fans available in 1960 would not supply the required air volumes at higher pressures. The hay settles as it dries and so tends to maintain resistance to airflow. The greatest resistance occurs normally when the hay is first put on the drier.

Air pressure for loose, full-length hay of 40 percent moisture and 8 feet deep, ranges from .75 inch to 1 inch of water. Chopped hay with 40 percent moisture, cut 4 to 6 inches long and placed 8 feet deep, requires an air pressure of 1 inch to 1.5 inches of water. Baled hay at 40 percent moisture with twine ties, or loosened compression for metal ties, requires the most air pressure to overcome resistance. Air pressure of 1.5 to 2 inches will be necessary to get air penetration through the bales stacked 10 to 14 layers deep.

Bales should be stacked to break cracks and tie the stack together. This breaks up air channels between bales. It also prevents air pressure leaks as the hay dries and settles. Air penetration through the center of the bales is also assured. When air must penetrate more than 8 feet of hay of 40 percent moisture, higher pressures are necessary. Lower pressures are required for hay less than 8 feet deep. After one 8-foot layer of hay has been dried, a second 8-foot layer can be put on the drier and successfully cured. This does not apply to baled hay.

HEAT IS REQUIRED from some source to evaporate water. The heat for evaporation with unheated-air drying must come from the air and the hay. Thus both hay and air are cooled several degrees in the drying process—in extreme cases, as much as 25 degrees. Normally a 10-degree drop in temperature indicates satisfactory drying progress. The rate of drying with unheated air changes with variations in air temperature and humidity.

As in grain drying, in climates where cool, damp weather retards hay drying, the air can be heated. Adding heat to the air decreases its relative humidity and enables the air to pick up more water. This makes it possible to dry hay mechanically regardless of weather. The air temperature usually is increased by about 20 degrees in heated-air hay drying.

Gas and oil burners are used to heat the air. There may be a fire hazard from sparks unless a heat exchanger is used to avoid mixing burned gases and fumes with the heated air. Temperatures are controlled by thermostats. A fuel cutoff is essential because of the danger if the flame goes out.

In an electrically heated air drier, air is heated with black-heat units, and there is no fire hazard. Humidistats regulate the heat units. When relative humidity is below 55 percent, no heat is used. Heated-air drying normally is about twice the cost of unheated-air drying.

Any farmer who makes hay can use the equipment he has on hand to make high-quality hay with a mechanical hay drier. Regular mowing machines, rakes, loaders, elevators, choppers, and balers can be used successfully with few mechanical adjustments. Since hay of 40 percent moisture is heavy, it is advisable to use as much laborsaving equipment as possible.

Side-delivery rakes, which move the hay a minimum distance to a windrow, are desirable, because they cause less leaf shattering. Field choppers should be set for a cut of 4 to 6 inches. To obtain these cuts, apron speeds can be increased and knives removed if necessary. One cutting knife and counter weights work very well. Hay balers should be set to make 28- to 36-inch bales. When wire or twine ties are used, baler compression should be reduced so air can penetrate the bale. Maximum bale density should be approximately 10 pounds per cubic foot. Round balers should be equipped with a soft center attachment so air can penetrate the bale during the drying period.

HAY CONDITIONERS, such as crushers and crimpers, make it possible for the sun to reduce hay moisture to 40 percent in less time. This reduces field drying time and speeds up haymaking. It results in better hay. Hay conditioners are not essential, but they reduce field drying hazards. Windrowers that deliver freshly cut hay immediately to a windrow slow down field drying. Freshly windrowed hay may not drop to 40 percent moisture for several days. During this time, enzymes, oxidation, and weathering losses are sure to reduce quality too much. Direct windrowing machines therefore are not universally recommended for making hay. Forks, slings, chain elevators, and blowers can be used for putting hay of 40 percent moisture in the barn. Since loose, full-length hay, chopped, or baled hay can be mechanically dried, each farmer can select and use the equipment most suitable for his needs.

HAY OR GRAIN must be dry enough for safe storage in order to sell it through commercial channels. If it is to be used for feed at the place of storage, however, it may be ensiled instead of dried.

Storing forage and grain at high moisture by ensiling is an alternative process. If managed properly, it can insure feeding value of the ensiled crop equal to that obtained by mechanical drying. It generally is superior to field-cured hay or grain.

Ensiling field crops at moisture contents well above those that can be tolerated for safe storage by other methods is perhaps the least expensive method of preserving the high quality of feed from the time it is ready to harvest until it is needed for feed.

While the practice of storing dry grain and hay has been carried on as far back as history is recorded, the practice of ensiling crops is older than mechanical drying. The United States has been called the land of silos. Since about 1876, American farmers have been storing a steadily increasing part of the corn crop as silage. About 36 million tons of corn silage were produced in 1946, and 54 million tons were produced in 1956. Corn silage made from the whole immature corn plant was the main crop ensiled in 1930.

More and more other crops, such as small grains, grasses, and legumes, are being preserved by ensiling. This is done to avoid the large losses of dry matter and nutritive value. In order to reduce the labor involved in loading and unloading and also the initial cost of an upright or tower silo, farmers have started to use other types of storages. Grass silage has been made in stacks, trench silos, and bunker silos. Losses due to excessive fermentation, seepage, and spoilage because of air leaks due to the difficulty of sealing the surface, run quite high but may be as low as in tower silos.

MATURE SHELLED CORN or ground ear corn are stored successfully in the silo. This has become known as wet corn storage, but it is corn stored by the ensiling process. The adaptation of the ensiling process to grass and high-moisture mature grain arose from several factors—a better knowledge of the process and the great improvement in the quality of silo construction.

Silos are being made to hold greater loads of grass silage and wet corn silage. New materials for coating the walls of conventional concrete or tile stave or block silos are available to seal them against air leakage. The development of low-cost plastic sheet material has made it possible to seal trench- and bunker-type silos more effectively. New steel structures are made impervious to the effects of acids by ceramic coatings and are so gastight that gas pressure relief is required and handled in ingenious ways. Finally, there has been developed materials handling equipment, such as loading elevators and mechanical silo unloaders, unloading from either the top or the bottom of the silo, that have reduced the labor of silage making and feeding to almost the pushbutton stage. The tower-type silo properly located in the feedlot lends itself to mechanization very well.

THE PROCESS of silage production in the United States is changing. By tradition, moderately airtight structures are used, making it necessary to ensile the product with high moisture content in order to hasten the development of acids needed to preserve the material. This usually results in the formation of large quantities of heat and excessive consumption of dry matter. Now many silos are virtually airtight. With more nearly complete exclusion of air, lower moistures are used, the temperature does not get so high, and less acid is formed.

A growing practice is a low-temperature fermentation process. Grass that has been partly wilted and reduced in moisture (30 to 60 percent) is placed in an airtight silo. The oxygen of the silo atmosphere is quickly used up by respiration of plant cells and is replaced with carbon dioxide. The carbon dioxide arrests respiration and prevents spoilage caused by oxygen and acts as the preservative. If there are no leaks to allow oxygen to enter the silo, there is no spoilage. The type of silo is not important. It is only necessary to have an airtight silo.

Ensiling crops at lower moisture contents prevents loss of dry matter through drainage of juices pressed out under the pressures developed in the silo. This loss will be as high as 10 percent of the stored dry matter in the better managed tower silos filled with fresh-cut grass. Low-temperature fermentation results in much lower dry matter losses due to gaseous losses of fermentation and respiration.

Conventional silos can be made nearly gastight with proper applications of the new resin-base wall sealers, plastic sheet covering of the silo unloading doors, and plastic silo covers. With grass silage made from low-moisture hay crops, special precautions are needed in the packing during filling, especially around the edges and the top. The truly gastight structures have the advantage of requiring no packing, and the silage can be fed at any desired rate rather than a rate set by the need for keeping ahead of spoilage once the conventional silo is opened. The gastight structure is of higher initial cost than the conventional silo.

Feeding trials of shelled corn, of ground ear corn, and of low-moisture grass stored in gastight silos and well managed conventional silos have been conducted at several experiment stations.

Some of the first feeding trials with grass silage stored under gastight conditions were conducted by the Agricultural Research Service at Beltsville, Md. The results of all of the tests indicate that in general grass silage made under the low-temperature fermentation process, whether in gastight structures or well-sealed conventional silos, is equal to well-made hay from the same crop.

The same generalization seems to be in order concerning the feeding of ensiled shelled corn or ground ear corn. There are indications the cattle produce more efficient gains on ensiled ground ear corn than on dry ground ear corn or shelled corn. Fewer tests have been made with ensiled corn grain than with grass silage.

Many cattle feeders in the Corn Belt are turning to the "wet" storage of shelled and ground ear corn for cattle feed. Some troubles observed indicate a need for the study of the storage of wet corn below 25 percent moisture, particularly in the conventional-type silo.

# Preparation of Product

Arthur E. Browne and William M. Bruce

BEHIND THE thousands of food items and other farm products that are available to consumers every day in the year in towns and cities all over the country is a highly organized system of product preparation.

By product preparation we mean all the operations, procedures, and treatments after harvesting that are necessary to convert the products of the farm into forms acceptable to consumers and to make them available where and when people want them.

Included are processing—preserving or manufacturing treatments—and the cleaning, sorting, sizing, grading, conditioning, curing, refrigerating, storing, and packaging that are required in the marketing of fresh, perishable foods.

Product preparation has advanced a long way from the time when only one or two hand operations—usually performed by the farmer—were all that was necessary to prepare his products for sale to consumers.

Because most fresh fruit and vegetables are highly perishable, much of the preparation has to do with maintaining their freshness and quality. Care to minimize bruising from rough handling must begin with harvesting and go on through every step in marketing until the product reaches the retail store.

Control of temperature and humidity is important. Most fresh vegetables and fruit benefit from having the field heat removed as quickly as possible after harvesting and being held under refrigeration throughout the marketing process.

As most of them contain a large percentage of water, the relative humidity in the atmosphere surrounding them must be kept high to prevent wilting and drying. Waxing such items as cucumbers and oranges also retards wilting during marketing. A few commodities like onions and sweetpotatoes must be cured if they are to be stored for weeks or months during marketing.

The processes of preparation also includes sorting to remove defective specimens, sizing, washing or brushing, storing, and packaging.

Some growers, especially the smaller ones, sort and pack their products into shipping containers in the field, orchard, or vineyard as harvested in order to avoid the extra handling and possible bruising that might occur if they were taken to sheds for sorting and repacking. Packing in the field usually is less expensive because there is no rehandling.

Because of the greater economy of field packing, head lettuce customarily is packed into shipping containers in the field as harvested, although not many years ago all head lettuce was brought to packing sheds to be trimmed, sorted, and packed. The general adoption of fiberboard shipping cartons in place of nailed wooden crates and the development of vacuum cooling made this change feasible.

Another development is large, mobile packing equipment, which can be moved into the fields. In Florida, California, and some other regions where large acreages make it feasible, much of the celery and sweet corn is packed in self-propelled machines, called "mule trains," which move through the fields with the harvesting crews. As the celery is cut, the harvesters place it on long, moving conveyor belts, which extend out from the body of the machine. Inside the "mule trains," the celery is trimmed automatically to uniform length, washed, and then sorted and packed by hand into shipping containers.

The loaded crates are then transferred to trucks that follow at the rear
for movement to centrally located hydrocoolers or vacuum coolers. The
coolers remove the field heat from the
crated celery before it is reloaded into
refrigerated trucks or railway cars for
shipment to market. A similar system
is used for sweet corn.

One way to lessen bruising and other
handling injuries is to use large pallet
boxes in moving fresh produce from
field or orchard to packinghouse and
during the preparation processes. These
large boxes or bins, which are reusable,
hold several hundred pounds to a ton
or more, depending on their dimensions, and are handled with forklift
trucks or tractors with forklift attachments. The use of pallet boxes reduces
the number of handlings required with
field boxes or crates and makes it possible to handle larger volumes of product faster and at less cost.

Pallet boxes, which hold the equivalent of approximately 25 field boxes,
have been used extensively in some
apple-producing areas, and they are
being tried out for other commodities.
Ease of handling and stacking the pallet boxes with forklift trucks has led to
their use also as storage containers,
especially for apples.

Pallet boxes also are being tried for
shipment of such commodities as apples and potatoes from producing areas
to terminal markets, where they are to
be repackaged. They also are used for
shipping raw products to processing
plants, as, for example, shipping potatoes to chipping plants.

ONE OF the first steps usually taken
after harvest is to remove the field
heat as soon as possible. The temperature of fruits and vegetables when harvested usually approximates the temperature of the outside air. Precooling
normally reduces the product temperature to somewhere within the range
of 45° to 65° F., depending on the requirements of the commodity and the
length of the cooling process. This
operation is called precooling because

it takes place before the product is
shipped to market.

Precooling is particularly important
because fresh fruit and vegetables continue the process of respiration, or
"breathing," after they have been harvested.

Most vegetables begin to deteriorate
as soon as they are harvested. Cooling
slows down the respiration process and
thus retards aging. It also inhibits or
retards the development of decay organisms. Most noncitrus fruit continues to ripen after harvest. Cooling
slows or sometimes arrests the ripening
process and retards the development
of mold or decay.

The main purpose in cooling citrus
fruit is to prevent mold and decay,
because citrus fruit does not continue
to ripen after harvest.

A common method of precooling
western deciduous fruit, including
grapes, is to place them as soon as
packed in a refrigerated storage room,
where they are held up to several days
before they are shipped in railway cars
or trucks.

Another of the older methods is to
force refrigerated air through a railway
car or truck immediately after loading.
Stationary equipment or specially designed trucks with refrigerating equipment and blowers are used.

Still another method, possible on
refrigerator cars equipped with special
fans, is to use the fans to circulate air
over the ice in the bunkers of the car
and then through the load. A disadvantage of these methods of car precooling is that cooling takes several
hours; even then, the desired degree of
cooling often is not attained before the
car is shipped.

Hydrocooling and vacuum cooling,
two newer methods, precool produce
faster. Hydrocooling involves subject-
ing the product to a bath of ice water.
Sometimes the product is immersed in
a tank of cooled water until it reaches
the desired temperature, or, more frequently, the cooled water is sprayed
over it. The water may be cooled by
mechanical refrigeration or by ice.

Among the commodities commonly hydrocooled are eastern-grown peaches, sweet corn, celery, green beans, radishes, and some of the salad greens.

Hydrocooling usually is done after the product has been sorted, sized, and packed and just before it is loaded for shipment. The shipping container therefore must be of wood or a type of fiberboard that will not collapse when it is wet.

Because most fiberboard shipping containers do not meet this requirement and because more of these containers are being used each year, new hydrocooling practices have been developed that will still permit their use. One new method, used by some Florida orange shippers, for example, is to hydrocool the fruit in field boxes or sometimes without any containers before it is packed. Then, after the fruit is sized, graded, and packed, it is ready for shipment without further precooling.

Hydrocoolers are large pieces of equipment, often 25 feet long or longer, with motor-driven conveyor belts, or "chains," which carry the product through the cooler, and large-capacity pumps for circulating the cold water.

Ordinarily it takes about 15 minutes to hydrocool peaches in a basket or crate. Sweet corn normally can be cooled in about 25 minutes.

Vacuum cooling is done by evaporating surface moisture from produce when the air pressure is reduced rapidly to a near-vacuum. Cooling takes place inside heavy metal vacuum tubes that usually can hold half a carload of produce at a time. A few vacuum coolers have been built in the West to accommodate a fully loaded railway car. Head lettuce, for example, can be cooled in 20 or 25 minutes.

All of the early vacuum coolers were stationary because the tubes themselves and the pumps used to reduce the air pressure in the tubes are large and heavy. Some vacuum coolers have been designed that can be taken apart and moved on trucks from one producing area to another as the season

progresses. They have been used in the Eastern States, where harvesting seasons generally are shorter than those in the West and the investment in permanent locations may not be justified.

Vacuum cooling is used a great deal for head lettuce. A relatively small volume of celery, escarole, endive, and cabbage is vacuum cooled.

The handling of lettuce at a typical western vacuum-cooling plant exemplifies the extent to which equipment has reduced hand labor. Fiberboard cartons, packed in the field and usually holding 24 heads, are stacked on wooden pallets and trucked to the plant. Each truck usually holds half a carload. At the plant, a large forklift truck unloads the entire truckload— up to 320 cartons—in one bite. The loaded pallets are transferred to a long, narrow dolly, which also accommodates a half carload. The dolly is rolled into the vacuum tube through an opened end by a small tractor. The cooling process begins as soon as the ends of the tube are closed and sealed.

The ends of the tube are opened and the dolly is pushed out when the desired temperature is reached. The cartons then are transferred by hand from the dolly to a conveyor belt, which takes them to a waiting railway refrigerator car or refrigerated truck for shipment to market. This manual operation and stacking of the cartons in the car or truck are the only phases of the entire cooling operation that take hand labor.

OF THE MANY operations necessary with fruit and vegetables—cleaning (usually by washing or brushing), sorting to uniform sizes, sorting to remove defective or damaged specimens, packaging, and storage—most have been highly mechanized.

A packinghouse is a maze of equipment that moves the product from process to process with a minimum of hand labor and as automatically as possible.

Apples are brushed and sized by

automatic equipment, sorted by hand for defects and color, and packed into consumer units or shipping containers by hand or machine. A large proportion of the crop is held in refrigerated storage to make supplies available in winter and spring.

Oranges and grapefruit are treated to make their color more uniform. They are washed, waxed, and sized automatically; sorted by hand for defects; frequently stamped by machine for identification of brand or production area; and packaged by hand or automatically.

Potatoes are cleaned by brushing or washing. Sometimes they are colored or waxed; then they are sized, sorted, and packaged. The fall-harvested crop, about two-thirds of the year's total crop, is stored immediately after harvesting, usually on or near the farms where it is produced, and often no further preparation is done until it is ready to be marketed. The rest of the crop is prepared for market as it is harvested.

Sorting fruit and vegetables for defects always has involved a good deal of manual labor, although the sorting is done from mechanized conveyor belts. The speed of the belts and the way products are presented to the sorters affects the efficiency of the sorting operations.

An automatic sorting device—an electric eye—for separating lemons on the basis of color may well be adapted for use for other fruit and vegetables. It separates lemons into five color groups through the use of a photoelectric cell and operates at a speed much greater than is possible by manual separation. One of the first uses of the electric-eye principle in the food industry was for sorting dry beans for removal of discolored or defective beans. Later it was put into use for sorting coffee beans, almonds, and shelled peanuts.

NEW PACKAGING materials and techniques have been developed and prepackaging—putting goods in packages of sizes consumers find most convenient—has gained in volume.

The need for cheaper containers, greater product protection, and lower cost of filling containers has encouraged extensive experimentation.

Significant changes are an increase in the use of fiberboard and wirebound shipping containers in place of baskets, hampers, and nailed wooden containers; a general reduction in the size or capacity of shipping containers; the development of automatic filling devices; and the adoption of consumer-unit packaging.

Oranges, grapefruit, lemons, apples, and lettuce are now packed extensively in fiberboard containers. Some eastern peaches are packed in wirebound wooden boxes and fiberboard boxes instead of bushel baskets. Some celery, cabbage, and green peppers are shipped in fiberboard containers instead of hampers, mesh bags, or wooden crates.

Half-box fiberboard cartons, holding one-half the volume of the old standard nailed wooden boxes, have been adopted in California and Arizona as the standard shipping containers for oranges, lemons, and grapefruit. This shift has been stimulated by the development and use of automatic volume fillers so that hand packing is not required. The same trend toward use of smaller boxes has become evident in the citrus industries of Texas and Florida.

For western lettuce, the standard nailed wooden crate, which held 36 to 60 heads, has given way to fiberboard cartons that usually hold 24 heads.

Potatoes used to be packed almost entirely in 100-pound bags. The 50-pound bag has become common in some places; considerable quantities are packed in 25-pound, 15-pound, and 10-pound bags.

Nearly one-third of the fresh produce sold in retail stores now is prepackaged; very likely two-thirds of it will be prepacked before long. Some items, such as carrots and radishes, are prepackaged almost entirely. Others, such as sweet corn, asparagus, pears, and peaches, are seldom found ready-packaged in consumer units. A large group of additional items, such as potatoes, citrus fruit, apples, cherries, and lettuce, is consumer packaged in substantial volume and the proportion is increasing.

The rapid increase in prepackaging is due mainly to two factors: Self-service merchandising and a demand for kitchen-ready foods. Prepackaged fresh produce reduces labor costs in the produce department and the checkout counter in supermarkets, speeds up shopping, and—properly handled—may reduce losses from spoilage.

Consumers seem to want more kitchen-ready foods—a reason why an increasing variety of processed foods has become available. Retailers, growers, and shippers realize that fresh fruit and vegetables must be easy to buy and easy to use or consumers will turn to the processed foods even more.

Handy, attractive containers—transparent film bags, film overwrapped cardboard trays, folding cardboard window boxes—make purchasing in the retail store quicker and easier than selecting from bulk displays.

The preparation of products before they go into consumer-unit packages by selection of specimens, trimming, and washing help to make them more nearly kitchen-ready. Lettuce is trimmed and usually washed before prepackaging. Sweet corn is husked and trimmed. Spinach and kale leaves are sorted and washed. Kitchen-readiness even extends to potatoes. Restaurants can buy potatoes already peeled, although there has been relatively little retail distribution of peeled potatoes.

Large-scale prepackaging of fresh fruit and vegetables began in retail stores and much of it still is done there, although specialized prepackaging firms have grown up in terminal markets to service retailers. Some prepackaging is being done in producing areas.

Lower labor costs and the efficiencies that come with large-scale operations favor packaging at the shipping point. Large quantities of potatoes, citrus fruit, apples, and cauliflower, for example, therefore, are consumer packaged where produced. On the other hand, the perishability of many items, such as lettuce, spinach, and most soft fruit, makes it desirable to delay consumer packaging until the products reach the terminal market or the store.

Automatic and semiautomatic machines facilitate consumer-unit packaging. One fully automatic machine forms a plastic bag, fills it, and seals it. It is used for packaging radishes, walnuts, and almonds.

Other machines are semiautomatic bag fillers, automatic bag closers, machines that wrap such items as lettuce or celery in transparent film sheets, machines that form paperboard boxes, and others for overwrapping and sealing these boxes with transparent film.

STORAGE is important for some fresh fruit and vegetables that are marketed long after harvest.

Controlled-atmosphere storage for apples—a relatively recent development—differs from ordinary cold storage in that the amount of oxygen and carbon dioxide in the atmosphere inside the storage room is controlled by use of special equipment and held at levels different from those that would otherwise develop. This process retards the rate of respiration of the fruit, lengthens its storage life, and preserves its quality even better than ordinary cold storage.

Not all varieties of apples respond equally well to controlled-atmosphere storage. The McIntosh, which is well adapted to it, could be held in ordinary cold storage only a few months because its quality and condition deteriorated rapidly after about January. Now it can be held for marketing as late as June without serious loss of quality.

Controlled-atmosphere storage may be suitable for other fruit and vegetables, such as cabbage, and we may expect to see its use extended.

The use of polyethylene film liners inside shipping containers has had a notable effect on the marketing of some fresh fruit and vegetables. These large bags, which just fit the inside of a container, were developed for winter pears. The film modifies the atmosphere inside the box enough to retard respiration and thus prolong the storage life of the winter pears. Before long the liners were found to have a similar effect on Bartlett pears, the main summer variety.

With other fruit, such as Golden Delicious apples and sweet cherries, film liners are of value in marketing, not primarily by retarding ripening but by reducing deterioration due to loss of moisture. Similar results have been reported for cabbage, celery, and lettuce, in which retention of moisture is important in maintaining firmness and crispness.

PROCESSED FRUIT and vegetables, available to consumers in canned, frozen, pickled, dried, and dehydrated forms, are used also as basic ingredients in such products as beverages, jams, and jellies.

Of the 16 million or 17 million tons of fruit produced commercially in the United States annually in recent years, more than half has been utilized in processed form. The remainder has been used in fresh form.

Of approximately 20 million tons of commercial vegetables produced annually, much more than a third has been processed. The proportion of these crops preserved by processing has been increasing over the years—a trend that probably will continue.

To process this large volume, a well organized, highly mechanized industry has developed.

The preparation of canned clingstone peaches is an example of the many operations involved in making a canned product ready for consumers. In the orchard, field boxes or lugs that have been filled by the pickers are stacked on wooden pallets (as many as 48 boxes to a pallet), which are loaded by forklift tractors on trucks or trailers for transport to the cannery. There another forklift unloads the pallets and carries them to the start of the processing line. Single stacks of boxes, usually 6 or 8 high, are moved by hand-trucks to dumping machines, which automatically but gently dump them one at a time. The fruit flows out on to a conveyor belt while the boxes are returned automatically by another conveyor to the loading dock or storage area.

An alternative and newer method of handling from the orchard to the processing plant involves the use of large pallet boxes instead of field boxes or lugs. These pallet boxes are loaded and unloaded from trucks by forklifts and are emptied by automatic dumping machines.

Conveyor belts carry the peaches from one ingenious machine to the next. Careful timing is needed to insure that all phases are coordinated and no bottlenecks develop. Because the average western canning plant is a large-scale enterprise, several "lines" may be running simultaneously, depending on the volume of raw fruit.

As a first step, the whole peaches usually move into a sizing machine, which separates the fruit into two groups. The peaches then move to pitting machines, which cut them in half and remove the pits in a single operation. Peaches are positioned in the pitters by hand because it is desirable to have the peaches cut along the natural suture. From the pitters, the peach halves go to a shaker, which separates the pits from the halves. The next step is a sorting line, where workers remove any peaches with the pit still attached or any loose pits not taken out in the shaker.

After moving past the sorters, the peaches go to another shaker, which turns the halves so that they ride on the conveyor pit side down—the skin side up. As the peach halves pass through a peeler on the conveyor belt, a bath of lye solution is sprayed down on them to loosen the skin. Next they pass through high-pressure sprays of water, which rinse away the remnants of skin and the lye solution.

Then the peach halves move to size graders, which sort them by sizes. Next comes a most important operation. The halves are moved on sorting belts past workers who separate the fruit on the basis of color and remove all that show defects. The peaches that are to be canned as halves then are conveyed to filling tables, where workers direct the halves into a moving line of empty cans so arranged that the tops of the cans are positioned just below a wide slot in the table. The peaches are fed into the cans by the worker as the cans move along under the slot. The cans, filled with halves, then move by conveyor to the siruper, where a predetermined amount of hot sugar sirup is metered into each can.

Peaches that are to be canned as slices rather than halves are conveyed to an automatic slicing machine and then to the filling tables.

The filled cans are conveyed from the siruper to the closing machine, where they are lidded and sealed hermetically at a rate of 125 or more a minute. After closing, they are moved, still by conveyor, to a continuous cooker equipped with automatic temperature controls. Cans are fed in at one end and pass through the cooker on a conveyor set at a speed to give just the prescribed amount of time for the cooking process. From the cooker, the cans are next conveyed through a cooling tank of water, where the temperature is reduced as rapidly as possible.

After cooling, the cans are stacked on pallets and moved by forklift trucks to adjoining warehouses, where they are stored until they are shipped. At that time the cans are run through a machine for applying the paper labels and then through another machine that cases them into fiberboard shipping containers.

There are many variations of this process, depending on the commodity and its requirements, but the basic pattern is the same.

PROCESSING by quick freezing has expanded rapidly. The consumption of frozen fruit and vegetables (on a fresh-equivalent basis) was about 2 pounds per capita annually in the years immediately before the Second World War. It exceeded 50 pounds in 1958.

One example of this growth is frozen concentrated orange juice. From the beginning of commercial production in Florida during the 1945–1946 season, the pack of frozen concentrated orange juice has grown until it amounted to more than 80 million gallons in the 1958–1959 season. That is enough juice, when reconstituted, to supply every person in this country with about 40 average-size servings.

The consumption of frozen vegetables (on a fresh-equivalent basis) has increased more than three times since the war. Packs of the leading commodities, such as frozen peas, lima beans, green beans, corn, and potato products have grown steadily. New frozen vegetable products have been added each year.

Another rapidly expanding group of frozen products is the many prepared foods—partly prepared dishes, such as fruit pies, ready to put into the oven to be baked, and the cooked foods, such as french-fried shrimp or entire dinners, that merely need to be heated before serving.

The appeal and success of frozen foods have been due largely to their convenience and their quality. Frozen vegetables, for example, are washed, trimmed, and selected so that they are ready for cooking.

Processing of frozen peas illustrates the high degree of mechanization and automation that has been developed in the frozen foods industry. Mechanization begins with harvesting. As soon as the peas reach the proper stage of maturity, the vines are cut by a tractor-drawn cutter equipped with an elevator to convey them into high-sided trucks, which move through the fields alongside the cutters. The truck takes the load to a vining station at the processing plant or near the fields. There the peas are separated from the pods and vines in automatic vining machines. Air-cleaners—blasts of air—then remove from the peas any sticks, pieces of pods, and other material.

If the viners are located at some distance from the processing plant, the fresh peas, after air-cleaning, may be hydrocooled to preserve quality by retarding the conversion of the natural sugar in the peas into starch while they are being transported to the plant.

The peas are flumed—carried by a stream of water—into the plant and into a washer. The peas are flumed from the washer to the blancher, where they are exposed to a high temperature for a few seconds. This inactivates enzymes, which otherwise would continue to react with other constituents in the peas—even while frozen—and result in rapid loss of quality and flavor. After coming out of the blancher, the peas are cooled while being flumed to a brine separator, which separates the peas of desirable maturity from those that are more mature and, therefore, less desirable.

The peas next move to a revolving drum, called a squirrel cage, where loose skins, pieces of pod, or other materials are removed. The peas then pass on to a conveyor belt for final inspection by a crew of sorters who pick out any remaining defects.

The actual freezing process may take place before or after the peas have been packaged. The commonest method is freezing after filling, but an increasing volume of peas is being frozen loose in bulk and packaged afterward.

By the former method, peas are automatically filled into paperboard cartons, which are closed and overwrapped by machine with colored, printed labels. Freezing takes place quickly—usually in plate freezers—as the peas are subjected to temperatures well below 0° F. After freezing, the cartons are cased in fiberboard shipping containers, stacked on pallets, and moved by forklift into adjacent warehouses for storage until shipment.

In the second method, peas are individually frozen in loose form as they pass on belts through continuous freezers and are subjected to blasts of air at temperatures as low as —40° F. Since the product is not packaged when frozen by this method, less time is required for the actual freezing. Labor and handling costs may be lower because the freezing process is continuous.

Along with freezing in loose form has come a new packaging method—putting loose frozen products, such as corn, peas, green beans, lima beans, mixed vegetables, french-fried potatoes, and some berries, in polyethylene bags instead of paperboard cartons. Because loose frozen products flow easily, a consumer can open a bag, pour out any desired amount, and return the remainder to the freezer. This method was first developed for institutional users, such as restaurants, but it was soon extended to retail-size packages. Polyethylene bags make the product visible to potential purchasers and are cheaper than paperboard cartons.

DRYING FRUIT is an ancient method of preservation. It has changed little. Grapes have been dried into raisins on trays in the vineyards. Apricots, peaches, pears, and apples have been cut by hand and sun-dried on trays. Dates and figs have been dried on the tree.

Some of those practices still are followed, although new and improved ones are being perfected in an effort to produce dried fruits of higher quality and in forms that are more attractive and more convenient.

The use of dried fruit in the United States on a per capita basis has been declining for many years. Perhaps the development of new processing techniques will reverse the trend. An example is prunes, practically all of which now are dried in dehydration plants instead of being sun-dried. They are stored in this dried state until ready for marketing. The prunes then are washed, sized, sorted, and rehydrated to a uniform higher moisture level just before packaging. Rehydration means that consumers no longer have to soak dried prunes before cooking them.

Dried apples no longer are sun dried; all are artificially dehydrated. Practically all raisins still are sun dried on papers or trays in the vineyards.

A new process for dehydrating fruits—especially the cut fruits—to much lower moisture levels than previously was economically feasible has come into use. The substitution of dehydration for sun-drying permits closer control of quality during drying. Because fruits so prepared have less volume, they can be shipped more economically. The low moisture also permits them to be stored longer without deterioration.

VARIOUS FORMS of instant foods, which require little or no cooking time to prepare the finished dish, have met with enthusiastic response from consumers.

Instant mashed potatoes have been developed more recently and are expected to have considerable effect on potato marketing.

Two basic methods are involved in producing instant mashed potatoes. The older makes use of a spray-drying technique and produces a product called potato granules. The other, more recent, process involves a drum-drying technique and produces a product called potato flakes. Both products combine readily with a mixture of hot water and milk to make good mashed potatoes.

While production of potato granules has been confined to the Western States, potato-flake plants have been built in the East and Midwest as well.

The most widely consumed potato product is potato chips. Production has increased each year. About 7 percent of the crop in 1959 was used to make chips.

A STRIKING change in the pattern of food consumption is the sharp increase in consumption of broilers or fryers, young chickens of either sex, usually 8 to 10 weeks old, and weighing about 3 pounds.

The commercial production of broilers has increased more than 500 percent since the war. The number produced exceeded 1.6 billion birds in 1958. On a per capita basis, broiler consumption was about 20 pounds annually (ready-to-cook equivalent basis). This is roughly one-fourth as much as per capita consumption of beef and nearly one-third as large as per capita consumption of pork. Consumption of broilers in the years just after the Second World War was less than one-tenth as large as the consumption of either beef or pork.

Among the factors responsible for this rapid growth are developments in breeding that led to faster gains in weight, lower prices in relation to other meat, and improvements in methods of preparing broilers for market. When broilers, like other poultry, were retailed in an uneviscerated form, dressed broilers could be held for only limited periods. Consequently birds were shipped to market live, and dressing operations took place mostly in or near terminal markets, the centers of population.

With the almost complete shift to sale of broilers in eviscerated form, a number of significant changes have taken place in the preparation for market. Dressing operations have been moved to the areas of production to take advantage of lower labor costs. The average size of dressing plants has increased, and with this growth has come a high degree of mechanization. Plants that can handle 6 thousand or more birds an hour are not unusual.

Live broilers in crates are trucked to dressing plants. At the unloading dock, the crates are placed on a conveyor line and move along to a station where the birds are taken out of the crates and hung on an overhead conveyor. At plants with Federal inspection, an official inspector next examines the live birds and removes any that show signs of disease. After the birds have been killed and the bleeding completed, they are conveyed through a scalding tank and into a picking machine, where the feathers are removed automatically. Pinfeathers and any feathers missed by the machine are removed by hand. Afterward they are singed.

Next the birds are cut open and pass by a second official inspector, who examines them to determine that none of the internal organs is diseased. Any birds showing disease are removed from the line. After inspection, the birds are eviscerated, and the head and feet are removed.

Plant employees inspect them for eviscerating workmanship. They next pass through a washer, after which the necks are clipped off for packing with the giblets. The broilers are then removed from the overhead conveyor line and placed in chill tanks filled with slush ice to cool the meat as rapidly as possible.

For shipment to market, the eviscerated poultry are packed in crates with crushed ice. Most move to market by refrigerated truck—some over long distances. It is not at all unusual, for example, to ship fresh broilers by truck from Georgia to the west coast.

Most broilers are marketed by dressing plants in whole eviscerated form, but an apparently increasing volume is being marketed as cut-up parts. At meat counters in most supermarkets, consumers are offered a choice of whole eviscerated broilers, cut-up broilers, or broiler parts.

Most of the cutting up and packaging of broilers or broiler parts in 1959 was done in retail stores, but it seems that this operation, too, may be shifting back to the poultry-dressing plant.

The bulk of the broilers is marketed fresh, but a considerable volume is frozen, both as whole eviscerated birds and as cut-up parts. This method of handling offers the operator of a dressing plant a means of evening out his marketing over the year and enables him to process peak supplies whenever they are available. From the consumers' standpoint, it means that supplies of broilers are available always, regardless of seasonal fluctuations.

Preparation of turkeys for market is handled in much the same way as the preparation of broilers, except that a considerably larger proportion of turkeys is marketed in frozen form. Practically all turkeys are marketed in eviscerated form ready for the oven. Some merchandisers offer frozen stuffed turkeys so that all a housewife has to do is put it in the oven. Another innovation has been the sale of half turkeys—cut down the middle to give one leg and half a breast.

The increased convenience of being able to purchase eviscerated turkeys, the availability of frozen turkeys throughout the year, and some decline in prices of turkey meat compared with most other meats have contributed to the near doubling of per capita consumption of turkey in the years since the war.

EGGS, too, pass through a number of processes of preparation on the way to the consumer.

Assembling from producers, cleaning, candling, grading, sizing, packaging into cartons, and refrigeration are essential parts of the job of preparing eggs for market.

Cold storage makes it possible for consumers in all regions to have adequate supplies of eggs every day of the year, even though egg production fluctuates seasonally during the year.

MILK we consume in fluid form as whole milk, skim milk, buttermilk, and cream and in processed form as butter, cheese, ice cream, evaporated or condensed milk, and dry whole milk or nonfat dry milk solids. Many processes are necessary to convert milk into these forms.

At a fluid milk plant, for example, milk is pasteurized, clarified, separated, and standardized in order to provide whole milk, skim milk, buttermilk, half-and-half, coffee cream, and whipping cream. The whole milk is homogenized; to some of it extra Vitamin D is added; to some, chocolate sirup is added to make chocolate milk. Then all these different kinds of milk and cream are filled automatically into a variety of sizes of bottles or cartons for distribution through retail stores or by the home deliveryman.

The preparation processes at milk processing plants differ widely, depending on the product that is being produced. In nearly all such plants, however, except those that manufacture cheese, mechanization and automation have progressed to a high degree. In a plant that produces dry milk, for example, about the only workers one sees are those who check periodically on the equipment to see that it is operating properly.

TOBACCO is an expensive crop in terms of the labor required per acre. Flue-cured tobacco, one of the principal types grown domestically, normally takes more than 400 man-hours per acre to produce. Some of the production and farm preparation operations have been partly mechanized, but much labor is still required.

The leaf is harvested (primed) by hand as it ripens on the stalk. Five to seven primings usually are needed. The leaves are hauled to the barn, usually on a wooden sled that is narrow enough to pass between the rows of planted tobacco and is drawn by a horse or mule.

Some partly mechanized harvesters have been introduced, but no appreciable reduction in labor has been apparent. Much the same is true of the tobacco handling and curing phases.

Flue-cured-type tobacco brought from the field on sleds usually is separated into "hands," consisting of two to four leaves and tied with string on sticks or laths. One stick may contain as many as 100 leaves. Sticks of tobacco are then hung on poles in curing barns. Curing consists of applying heat generated by gas, oil, coal, or wood. The technique requires close control of temperature and relative humidity during the various curing stages. A barn of tobacco can be cured in about 5 days.

After the barn curing has been completed, the tobacco is allowed to hang a few hours at atmospheric temperature and humidity in order to take up moisture from the air and become less brittle. It is then removed to a holding room, where it is packed down and covered to complete the curing process.

Several weeks of storage usually are necessary before the tobacco can be removed to the conditioning room. There the humidity is raised by natural or artificial means, and the leaves are allowed to "come in order" for sorting and grading.

Grading depends largely on small variations in color. Exact lighting is required to bring out the shades of leaf color, which are indications of the desired grades. Other qualities, such as leaf thickness or body and leaf conformation, also are factors to be considered. The graded tobacco is tied into hands by passing a leaf around the butts of 8 or 10 other leaves. Hands of the same grade are packed in a basket and transported to the market for sale.

These conventional methods of preparation are being modified somewhat as a result of research studies. For example, curing in field bundles, shredding and curing, and artificial lighting of grading rooms are some of the practices that are being studied and show promise of coming into use in the industry.

Several other types of tobacco are grown in the United States. Among them are the light air-cured tobaccos, which comprise the burley tobacco grown principally on the limestone soil of Kentucky, North Carolina, Virginia, and Tennessee, and the Maryland tobaccos, grown on the sandy soils of the Chesapeake Bay area. Production practices for these tobaccos are similar to the flue-cured varieties until they reach the harvesting stage. Harvesting is accomplished by cutting the whole stalk and allowing the leaves to remain on the stalk until the barn curing is completed.

The curing barns are much larger than those for flue-cured tobacco and not so tightly constructed, because circulation of air is essential to the curing process. Supplemental heat is used sparingly and only to evaporate the moisture that may collect during periods of high atmospheric humidities. Farm grading, packing, and handling operations are similar to those used for flue-cured tobacco after the leaves have been stripped from the stalk.

Cigar-type tobaccos comprise a large portion of the domestic poundage. The wrapper types, grown in Connecticut and Florida under cloth and commonly referred to as shade grown, demand the highest price and require the most labor and the most skill in producing, harvesting, and curing of any domestic tobaccos. The filler and binder types of cigar tobaccos are stalk cut, while the wrapper type is primed. Curing and handling are similar to those techniques used for the air-cured types.

COTTON is an important crop in farm value and as a source of raw material for clothing and many other products.

Most of us have read about Eli Whitney and his cotton gin. The principle of separating the fiber and seed is the same today as it was in the early Whitney gin, although the heart of this operation, the gin stand, has been improved and added to until it would hardly be recognized as a machine that might perform the same operation.

Most of the handling of cotton in the ginhouse is accomplished pneumatically, and many of the processes are automatically controlled to insure even feeding and prevent overloading or underloading of the various parts of the processing equipment.

Handpicked cotton usually contains some dirt, hulls, leaf fragments, and other foreign material which must be removed if the fiber is to have the highest market value.

Foreign matter in seed cotton has increased with the expansion of machine harvesting practices. Ginning processes gradually have expanded therefore to include drying or conditioning, cleaning, extracting, feeding, ginning, lint cleaning, and packaging as distinct stages of an overall semiautomatic operation.

The sequence of operations at the gin begins with unloading the seed cotton from the farm conveyance by an automatically controlled suction device. The cotton is subsequently removed from the airstream and deposited into an automatic feeder, from where it passes to a drier if moisture reduction is needed. Next, the seed cotton goes through a series of cleaners, which are designed to remove trash, sticks, cotton burrs, and leaves. A second drier may be included in the line for very damp, trashy cotton. The cotton passes from the cleaners to gin stand feeders, where some additional drying and cleaning may be done before ginning.

The actual separation of the lint from the seed is accomplished by the action of high-speed circular saws, which pull the lint through narrow openings, called ribs, from which the seed fall into a conveyor.

The fiber is doffed (removed from the saw teeth) by jets of air, and conveyed directly, or through one or more lint cleaners, to the press. When the ginning of sufficient seed cotton for a 500-pound bale of lint is completed, the bale is covered and compressed and ties are fastened around it. The bale is numbered after it is released from the press and is weighed and put in the yard for transportation to storage.

Gin structures are seldom designed for the storage of either seed cotton or lint cotton in bales, although a seed house to provide temporary storage for the seed until it can be hauled to the oil mill is usually a part of the overall layout. Shelters may be provided at gins in areas of frequent rainfall for temporary storage of bales of cotton. From the gin, the bales may be shipped to spinning mills or to bonded warehouses, where they may be further compressed if the cotton is to be exported. Otherwise, it will be shipped directly to a buyer, usually the firm that will do the spinning.

Cotton farmers in the United States grow principally upland cotton, which is ginned on saw gins. Considerable interest has developed in the Southwest in the growing of the extra-long staple cottons, but even so it represents a small portion of the total crop. Extra-long staple cotton is used for the manufacture of sewing thread and the fancier items of clothing.

Roller gins are used on extra-long staple cotton because gin saws damage the long, silky fibers, but the same or similar equipment is used for handling, cleaning, drying, and pressing the extra-long staple varieties as for upland cotton.

The roller gin has a fixed blade held against a roller covered with material to which the cotton adheres. The space between the blade and the roller is insufficient for the seed to pass; hence, the fibers are pulled from the seed as the roller revolves. A vibrating knife, operating in conjunction with the stationary knife and roller, assists in separating the seed and fiber.

Annual consumption of raw cotton in the United States has been 8 million to 9 million bales of 500 pounds each. The per capita consumption of cotton in the United States is approximately 25 pounds annually. Some fluctuation has occurred, but cotton consumption was substantially the same in 1958 as it was in 1920 despite the development of synthetic fibers.

BOTH FARMERS and consumers benefit from the many processes for preparing agricultural products for market. Product preparation aids the farmer by broadening the market and increasing returns for his crops. It helps him to reach customers who live greater distances from his farm. It lengthens his marketing seasons. It expands his sales by making it possible to offer some crops in both fresh and processed forms.

Consumers benefit from the greater variety of products available at all seasons of the year and from the many forms in which these products are prepared.

Every additional preparation operation adds to the cost of marketing agricultural commodities—but how many consumers would want or could use these commodities if they had to take them without the preparation that has come to be an accepted part of marketing in the mid-20th century? Few of us would willingly return to unpasteurized milk. Not many would agree that we could easily do without commercially canned and frozen fruits and vegetables or prepared baby foods. Many would be the complaints if fresh produce were delivered to retail stores orchard-run or ungraded, direct from the field.

# Harvesting the Woods

Fred C. Simmons

SEVERAL new machines are designed and priced for use by the farmer who works in his woodlot only a few weeks out of the year. Some are logging accessories he can use with his ordinary farm tractor.

Other specialized devices help the custom or commercial logger who spends most of his time logging on his own and his neighbors' properties.

Besides this new equipment, farmers and commercial loggers are working out methods to do their logging with greater efficiency and safety and in ways that will leave the woodlots in good condition for future growth.

Specifications and methods are being developed to enable farmers and loggers to recognize, cut, and market woodlot products, other than logs, that often are overlooked by the small operator. Among these products are such high-priced items as oak stave and birch turning bolts, softwood poles and piling, and hardwood and softwood veneer bolts.

AN EXAMPLE of efficient woodlot logging is the work methods of John Calhoun III, a consulting forester of Keene, N.H. For the owners of small woodlots he estimates and maps the timber stands and recommends the forestry operations that should be carried out to improve them.

If thinning or harvesting operations are needed, he will mark the timber to be cut and do the logging with his own crew. Then he will market the products of the operation among local mills to the best advantage.

The owner is assured of getting a good job of forest management on his lands, with a minimum of damage to reserved trees, and a reasonable return from the sale.

Mr. Calhoun maintains small and mobile crews of experienced woodsmen, equipped to log efficiently most of the nearby small timberlots. Usually each crew is composed of two men— a chopper, who works with a gasoline-powered, one-man chain saw, and a man who drives a small, diesel-powered crawler tractor equipped with a blade, a winch and boom, and a trailing scoot. This scoot, a sturdy sled, brings the logs from the stump to the roadside free from embedded grit and gravel.

On a timberlot of average accessibility (about one-third mile skidding distance from stump to truck road), this two-man crew cuts and delivers to the landing about 4 thousand board-feet of logs a day.

When skidding distances are shorter, another chopper is added to the crew to make logs and help run the tongs in loading the scoot. Under these conditions, the third man increases production by another 2 thousand board-feet a day.

This productivity is being attained in previously unmanaged stands of dense young white pine, where the trees being cut are generally short-bodied, crooked, and limby, and the average log diameter is only about 9 inches. The better, straighter trees are saved for continued growth.

With hand-and-horse methods, production under these conditions would only be about 1 thousand board-feet per man-day.

Mr. Calhoun also has a three-axle, short-bed truck, equipped for self-loading the logs and bolts he selects and sorts to meet the requirements of various local wood-using industries. The loading device is known as a timber tosser. It consists of a pair of swinging arms, hinged to the side of the truck bed, with cradles at their ends. One medium-sized log or several small ones are rolled into the cradles. Then the arms are lifted by a cable attached to a winch under the truck, and the logs are tossed over the side stakes onto the bunks. This truck can pick up logs anywhere along the roadside, without the need for building skidways or any accessory loading device.

Mr. Calhoun believes that the loggers' traditional list of disadvantages pertaining to marked cutting are not valid today with the type of organization and equipment he has:

"As a forester marking timber for others to cut, I can say that if there is material to be cut suited for the market, it can be marked so that a careful operator can remove it and still leave a healthy stand for the next cut. Winches and logging booms have made possible the type of operation that could not have been imagined 15 years ago, except as a showcase example, a real exception."

MISMANAGEMENT on the farm woodlots in many instances has been the result of the owner's ignorance or indifference. Often, when the owner needed money and a timber operator would offer him a lump-sum payment for the salable products on his woodlot, he would accept it with no restrictions on the methods of cutting and no concern for keeping some thrifty young trees or a few seed trees. Such operations very likely are inefficient and wasteful. Trees not taken are knocked down or skinned up, and washouts and gullies follow cuttings. As a result, growing stock has been so depleted on many woodlots that they will produce little valuable material for many years in the future.

The farmer who desires to manage his woodlot more productively and more profitably has many sources of help—Forest Service, State forestry agencies, the extension service, industrial extension foresters, and private forestry consultants. These agencies supply leaflets, bulletins, and sometimes personal visits to the woodlot. Any county agent can direct the woodlot owner to the proper local source for such aid and advice. Few of them, however, provide logging services.

It is usually assumed that farmers will do their own logging. They do in many sections—usually the agricultural areas interspersed with commercial forest lands where many farmers traditionally work in the woods part of the year. Frequently they own such logging equipment as chain saws, log trucks, and skidding tractors. They can do the work they have equipment for and call on neighbors to help out with the rest.

In places away from large timber tracts and commercial logging operations, many farmers hesitate to undertake a woods job. Lacking experience, they feel that such work is dangerous and unprofitable since they do not have the special skills and equipment to handle it properly. These are the types of woodlot owners most apt to deal with unscrupulous or indifferent logging operators.

Even in these more settled areas, some farmers are logging successfully. They have found that equipment is now available to make it easier to do a safe and efficient job in the woods and that the equipment is priced low

enough to justify its purchase even for part-time use.

For example, many woodlot models of power chain saws are now available at prices under 150 dollars. These economy models do not have the high horsepower ratings or the durability of the more expensive industrial saws, but they will work well when used a few weeks out of the year, particularly when the timber being cut is not too large.

Inexpensive saws are available in direct-drive models. The sprocket driving the chain is attached through an automatic clutch directly to the engine crankshaft. There are no speed-reduction belts or gears. This makes for higher chain speeds, so that there is almost complete freedom from any tendency to kick or grab in the cut. With a direct-drive saw, cuts can be safely made out toward the end of the bar, top or bottom, and limbs and even brush can be cut safely and easily. A direct-drive saw with an engine rated at 5 horsepower or less is recommended only for cutting hardwoods less than 15 inches in diameter or softwoods less than about 18 inches in diameter.

For part-time use in larger timber, the woodlot logger ought to buy one of the inexpensive reduction-drive saws. These machines cut more slowly than their direct-drive counterparts; the operator must be careful constantly not to be caught by kicks or grabs.

Learning to use a power chain saw is not hard. Instruction books are available from most manufacturers, and local dealers can provide additional help. Once mastered, the chain saw is a useful tool. It will make logging two or three times faster than with handtools. It can also be used in much construction work around the home place. The modern saws, for example, rip just about as well as they crosscut, so they can be used for squaring up timbers and even for cutting out mortises and flat-bottomed notches.

For transporting logs out of the

woods many accessories are available for the ordinary wheeled farm tractor.

One of the most useful is a set of rear wheel crawler tracks. These rubber and steel track assemblies generally run around the rear tires and a set of small bogie wheels installed in front of the rear wheels. The tracks greatly improve flotation and traction in soft ground and snow. They stand up well in rough going in the woods and across rocky places. They also are useful for such jobs as snowplowing.

Another useful accessory for a tractor used in the woods is a rear-mounted winch. Equipped with wire rope, the winch makes it possible to pull logs out of gullies and rocky places where a tractor could not be driven. When an upgrade or a boggy place is encountered in skidding logs to the truck road, it is possible to drop the load, run the tractor ahead to firm ground, and then reel the load in with the winch, which gives up to twice the power to be had at the drawbar.

Logging arches or lifts of various models are also available. Some are attachments for the hydraulic-lift drawbar with which many tractors are equipped. Others are trailing devices, which run on their own rubber-tired wheels. These raise the front ends of the logs for towing, thus preventing their lodging behind rocks, roots, or other obstructions. They increase the size of the tow load and also deliver cleaner logs.

As an alternative to the arch, many farmers use a trailing sled or a wheeled trailer, on which the logs are carried completely off the ground. These are favored in glaciated areas, like northern New England, where the grit and gravel in the woods are especially abrasive, and where the small mills buying the logs are not equipped with log cleaners or debarkers.

Many farmers who do their own logging find that they can sell their logs at the roadside. This eliminates loading and hauling to the mill, which call for specialized equipment, or else much slow, hard, dangerous work.

If the material logged is to be cut into lumber for home use, the farmer can call in a mobile, truck-mounted sawmill. Such units can be driven to the individual farm and put into operation in a matter of minutes. They will saw the farmer-logger's accumulated logs to his particular orders for a set price per thousand board-feet or for the job. In this way he is relieved of hauling his logs to a permanently located mill and hauling the lumber back home again.

Other pieces of equipment are available on a contract or rental basis in many places. They include heavy crawler tractors equipped with bulldozer blades, which are sometimes needed to make a truck road into his woodlot; mobile debarkers for pulpwood and posts; mechanical splitters, which often are needed to make fuelwood or charcoal wood; and chippers to convert slabs, limbs, and brush into stock bedding or mulch.

A DEPENDABLE commercial logger, equipped to operate efficiently in the local woodlot, will continue to provide the best answer to forest-management problems for many farmers.

His specialized knowledge and equipment enable him to conduct a more efficient logging job than almost any individual farmer and to market the products of such a job to the best possible advantage. This latter task calls for a detailed knowledge of log and bolt grades and specifications and the measurement and payment practices of the wood-using industries in the locality.

Most commercial loggers use industrial-quality chain saws. Payment of the higher price for such saws is justified by their faster cutting rates and greater durability in continuous use. Direct-drive saws of this quality have become available with engines rated at 9 horsepower.

The commercial logger's other equipment will vary, of course, with the particular area and type of woodlots in which he operates. For example,

John Calhoun is equipped to operate efficiently in only the most accessible woodlots (those woodlots that merit the most intensive management). His woods tractor is too slow to operate effectively more than about a half-mile back from an existing truck road, and he is not equipped to build a new truck road.

Construction of truck roads is usually no longer necessary for woodlots a mile or more back from the truck road. Specialized four-wheel drive skidding tractors, with winches and integral arches, can operate efficiently, when the going is reasonably good, over skidding distances up to 3 miles. Special off-the-road tires inflated to 20 to 30 pounds of air pressure give these vehicles good traction through mud and snow, and over rocks, stumps, and other obstacles.

The best skidding tractors are completely articulated, so that all wheels remain in contact with the ground at all times in the roughest going. They are equipped with no-slip differentials, so that they continue to travel when only one wheel is getting traction. The soft tires resist injury for a surprisingly long time.

A manufacturer on the west coast, Garrett Distributors, of Enumclaw, Wash., has introduced a small four-wheel drive skidding machine. It weighs only about 6 thousand pounds unloaded, but 70 percent of this weight in the unloaded machine is on the front wheels. When a load of logs is pulled up into the arch, 9 thousand pounds of weight are available for traction on the wheels. Loads of a thousand board-feet of tree-length logs can be hauled if conditions are favorable.

Larger models of four-wheel drive skidding tractors are to be had. They can handle loads of 10 thousand to 15 thousand pounds. They usually are driven at 12 miles an hour, loaded and unloaded, over the roughest of woods roads. They can maintain speeds of 25 miles an hour on the open highway.

A Canadian manufacturer—Bombardier Ltd., Valcourt, Quebec—has developed specialized skidding machines that have some of the features and advantages both of the wheel tractor and the crawler tractor. They were designed as snowmobiles for use in the bottomless muskeg areas of northern Canada, but they are serviceable and durable for use over swamps in the South and rocky and slippery hillsides in northern woodlands. These muskeg tractors have four sets of rubber-tired wheels on each side to carry a nylon and rubber belt track. Curved spring-steel grousers engage the tire tread. Traction comes from a special nylon and rubber sprocket at the front of the machine. Ground pressure of the unloaded machine is about 1 pound to the square inch.

One model of the muskeg tractor pulls a four-wheeled log trailer, which is also equipped with crawler tracks. A winch and boom is used to assemble loads of logs and to load the trailer. The logs can then be hauled to the landing, up slopes as great as 15 percent, and through mudholes and over rocks.

Another model has a tilting steel platform on the tractor itself. A winch behind the tractor cab, and a fairlead on an upright fence at the front of the platform, enable the machine to haul in its load of either bundled pulpwood bolts or tree-length logs. In this winching job, the trailing rear edge of the platform acts as an anchor for the machine. When the load is assembled, the platform is retracted so that it lays on the frame of the machine, and the products are transported to the landing.

These are just two examples of specialized log-skidding equipment, suitable in price and size for the woodlot logger, now available in various parts of the country.

Similarly there are many models of self-loading trucks, adapted to handling various sizes and types of logs and bolts.

Tubular steel and hardwood pallets are widely used for assembling, loading, and hauling packages of short-length wood, such as pulpwood, mine props, and excelsior and charcoal wood. The trucks that carry pallets are equipped with winches and ramps for loading.

Timber tossers, which enable a log-hauling truck to load itself with small- to medium-sized logs, are available in both mechanically and hydraulically actuated models. For loading themselves with even larger logs, trucks are now being equipped with built-in crosshauls, powered by winches (under the bed) operated from a power take-off on the truck transmission.

Even more versatile and useful in certain areas is the type of truck that has a swinging boom attached to a mast just behind the cab. A winch at the base of the mast, with the cable running up to the base of the boom and then out to a sheave at its tip, provides the means for assembling logs over a considerable area and then lifting and loading them on the truck. They can be operated either mechanically or hydraulically.

Generally the hydraulic machines are more responsive and easier to control, but the mechanical ones can carry longer lengths of cable and so can assemble their loads over a wider area. Some of them make the trucks suitable not only for loading and hauling, but also for skidding-in material over a 200- to 300-foot radius.

A Massachusetts logger, Dick De-Maranville, of Hanover, has carried this idea one step further. He has provided a radio control for the winch on his truck, which can be operated by a pushbutton control attached to a walkie-talkie radio. Consequently, in assembling his load of logs he can put the winch in free-spooling, and then pull the log tongs on the winch cable out into the woods. When the tongs are attached to a log, he pushes the radio control button, the winch starts reeling in the cable, and the log is pulled toward the truck.

Mr. DeMaranville walks along behind. If the log lodges behind a stump or some other obstruction, he punches his pushbutton control again, the winch stops, and he rolls the log clear and starts it on its way again. This is repeated until the truck load of logs is assembled. In his operations the radio-controlled equipment is usually used to load the logs onto another truck to increase overall productivity. But when picking up an isolated load of logs, the radio-controlled truck can do both the bunching and hauling. The entire radio-control device was assembled from surplus Army material for about 200 dollars.

Many other devices have been developed by ingenious loggers and equipment manufacturers throughout the country to solve other specialized problems of the small woodlot loggers.

I hope I have said enough to indicate that these problems are being solved, and that woodlot logging is well on the way to becoming an easier, more profitable, and more effective practice than it has ever been before.

In the years ahead we can expect efforts such as these to result in more of our country's woodlots being left in a productive condition after cutting.

# Power

# and

# Livestock

## New Barns
## for Old

Norman C. Teter and Henry Giese

FARM BUILDINGS develop according to the necessity wrought by economic, sociologic, and technologic changes—the development of markets, communications, power, and construction techniques.

The very nature of a structure makes it a lasting symbol of the genius and folly and needs of the builders. Only a few farm buildings are erected each year in any locality. New barns may be built from obsolete plans. Economic pressure dictates that many buildings continue in service after they have seen their best days. Customary practices that sometimes determine the plans and methods of building retard newer ideas.

All this gains emphasis in a review of building practices in the past 200 years.

The pioneer period was one of self-sufficiency. With a few handtools and native materials, the pioneer built minimum shelter necessary for his isolated family. Survival was his primary objective. He produced what he could to feed, clothe, and house the family and the few animals he needed for power for clearing and tilling the soil.

Earth-floored houses built of logs in timbered areas and sod on the prairies were roofed with shakes rived with a froe or, less commonly, with grass thatch woven onto pole frames or with deerskins. Because he lacked the incentive of monetary gain from production, the pioneer had only the crudest type of lean-to shelter for the animals or no farm service buildings at all.

The pioneer period ended at no precise date: One era blends into the next. When pioneering was dominant west of the Appalachians, the populated areas along the eastern seaboard had markets for wheat, tobacco, cotton, and livestock, and some eastern farmsteads were well developed for salable production. The New England and the Middle Atlantic sections were in heavy production in Revolutionary times.

A. J. Downing, in a book, *The Architecture of Country Houses*, published in 1850, quoted J. W. Turner of Illinois as follows:

"Throughout the vast regions devoted to stock raising in the West, especially in Illinois and Missouri, and all the states south of these, stables are used, not for sheltering common stock or their fodder, but merely for the few horses and milch cows which are kept for family use. Many farmers in these states annually fatten some one or two hundred head of oxen, and some few, even a thousand or more for the market, and still a very moderate sized stable, or rather no stable at all, answers all their purposes. . . .

"The things to be provided for in the stable, are stalls for from one to four horses, and from one to four milch cows, though sheds are generally used for the latter—a place for pigs and fowls—and room for storing, temporarily, hay and provender for their food. I say temporarily, for most of the hay is stacked, and the corn 'cribbed', in the fields, and it is important that the stable should only hold enough of each for present use, as the housing of all the provender of a western farm is, for the present at least, out of the question."

THE PERIOD of expanding markets brought a complex of economic, moral, and technologic ideas that determined the type of farm structures used. More advanced and complicated buildings appeared first in New England, New York, and Pennsylvania, where winters were severe enough to emphasize the need for shelter, the population was sufficiently dense to create competitive pride in ownership, and the cost of marketing was comparatively low.

On the fertile plains of Illinois great acreages of corn were fed to hogs, which were selling for about 2 cents a pound in 1850. In a region where good timber or stone for building had to be shipped by wagon over roads that became almost impassable with mud, prices of produce and costs of building materials prevented any elaborate farm building on the plains.

Mentioned in writings in 1850–1868 were compact barns designed for full use; good arrangements to reduce chore labor and utilize the power of horses, steam, and water; insulated construction to reduce feed costs; and sanitation of buildings and sites.

In the report of the United States Commissioner of Agriculture for 1867, it was said:

". . . Large and excellent barns have greatly multiplied of late, and many of them are planned and built upon principles of sound science and the most rigid business economy. . . .

"One is struck at first sight with the substantial character of the structure, and the more thorough the scrutiny the more will this be seen. From pinnacle to foundation, nothing has been slighted; all the work has been well done; the timber is sound, the framing correct, braced, bolted, and counterbraced; and the same thoroughness is exhibited in every part."

J. Wilkinson, a rural architect of Baltimore, designed a unique barn for Benjamin Hershey, of Muscatine, Iowa. Started in 1875 and completed in 1878, it featured bent, laminated rafters; facilities for handling grain; laborsaving arrangements; and air conditioning. Each hip rafter was made from 24 pieces, 1 by 6 inches, and required a keg of nails. The side rafters, spaced 8 feet on center, used 19 laminations. Elevated roadways from a nearby hill permitted wagons loaded with grain or hay to enter the barn in two places near the roof level. From that point in the 90-foot structure, grain flowed to bins below and hay was tossed over a low rail into mows. Air conditioning, aimed at maintaining 62° F. in the 148-cow milking stalls, utilized steam heat in winter and air from a 500-foot underground passage for cooling in summer. Cows used the underground passage to reach a pasture. The cost was said to be 40 thousand dollars.

Barns of the period of expansion had places for root storage, carriage rooms, harness rooms, steaming rooms, horse stalls, ox stalls, and threshing floors. They were arranged to reduce chore duties, but they are a conglomerate of uselessness to anyone who would try to remodel them for production with modern equipment. Sometimes the old buildings are a liability rather than an asset.

The designer in 1867 did the best he could. He tried to foresee probable changes so his design would not be soon outmoded. But he, like everyone else, could not foretell all the tremendous changes.

Then lumbering burgeoned. Logs from the virgin forests came down the rivers to the lumber mills, where they were sawed into beams, planks, and boards for building barns.

The carpenters who supervised the erection of these mortise-and-tenon barns were skilled men, trained as apprentices for years. The carpenter who directed his apprentices to precut each piece so it fell properly in place at the barn raising was a proud and honored man.

Large timbers used for post-framing of barns became scarce about 1900, and builders had to find other materials. Wood remained the main building material, but a scarcity of heartwood of large sizes led to the use of smaller lumber in trusses and balloon framing.

Gambrel roofs, framed of lighter timber, met the need for a large clear space for storing loose hay. Shawver trusses, Wing joist bracing, and other forms of gambrel roof bracing became popular.

Gothic roofs, using sawed rafters, were put in some barns in Michigan in

EXPERIMENTAL TURKEY SHADE
Plant Industry Station, Beltsville, Md.

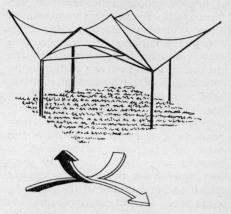

HYPERBOLIC PARABOLOID

*A hyperbolic paraboloid roof shape can accomplish wide spans with less material than some other conventional shapes.*

1885. Short boards were sawed to the arc of a circle, and several were nailed together with staggered joints to form an arched rafter of the desired length.

Concrete began to be used in the early part of the 20th century.

H. E. Cook, in an article in the *Cyclopaedia of American Agriculture* in 1907, showed a picture of a truss steel-frame barn built in Fayetteville, N.Y. He said he thought this was the first barn framed with steel in the United States and predicted that before long builders would be forced to use iron and concrete in farm structures.

THE MODERN PERIOD—a period of assembly-line production, new sources of power, and buildings designed to accommodate the new machinery—may have grown out of the period of market expansion shortly before the First World War.

Some say it was in 1915, but of that we cannot be sure—the farmer who built a gambrel-roofed barn in northern Missouri in 1931 may not have belonged to our modern era. It was a fine example of a general barn. On one side he built individual stalls for eight horses; on the other, three box stalls. A shed of hollow tile in one wing had homemade stanchions for milk cows. A shed at the back accommodated the sheep. He skimmed the milk, hauled cream to town once a week, and fed the skim milk to the hogs and chickens. He bought a hand-powered cream separator in 1935 and considered it a major improvement. It was useful only a year and a half, however, because roads were improved, and farmers then could market whole milk. He certainly lived in the period of expanding markets; maybe his heart was in one era and his business in another.

He was one of those who tempered the speed with which the self-sufficiency of the pioneering era and farming as a way of life of the expanding era moved toward industrialized farming. The depression after 1929 strengthened the belief that the farm is a secure place to live and that farming differs from industry because it is a way of life that involves the whole family.

Something can be said for such a belief, but we might also argue that the family before the Industrial Revolution that maintained a cobbler's shop in one side of their house had a family way of life. Farming and consequently farm buildings will continue to be influenced by two basic facts—that on a farm one can always have something to eat and that farming has been a family unit business. But both are opposed to industrial development of farming. Buildings that serve the old-time family farm rarely are adequate for industrial farming.

BUILDING MATERIALS changed rapidly in the modern era.

John D. Cole, a farmer of Mulliken, Mich., is said to have contracted with a bridge company in 1923 for the first all-steel barn in the United States. Soon after, many manufacturers could furnish steel hay barns, sheds, garages, hoghouses, and brooder and chicken houses. Some of them looked much like grain bins with windows cut in the side.

Wood shingles continued through the 1920's as the primary roofing material. The composition asphalt shingles are among the newer roofing materials.

New methods of wood utilization brought into use plywood, laminated rigid-frame bents, insulating board, and pressed board. Gothic barn rafters made from bent boards laminated and nailed together gave way to the use of glued, laminated rafters and later to rigid frames.

Hollow tile popular in the 1920's was displaced somewhat by properly cured concrete blocks, made by factory-type machines.

Because monolithic concrete construction requires forming and heavy equipment, it has been exceptional rather than popular.

Concrete has been used to make feeding floors, water tanks, walks, floor slabs, and foundations for a half century.

Concrete walls made from panels tilted into position were used in 1925 by J. Leo Ahart of Dow City, Iowa, and possibly by others. Research has led to further development of "tilt-up" monolithic concrete construction. Heavy forming was eliminated by casting wall panels in skeleton forms laid on a flat surface. A tilting frame designed to utilize the drawbar pull of a tractor enabled a farmer to tilt the panels to a vertical position. Rollers equipped with jackscrews can be placed on the bottom of the panel to move the panel into position. This use of concrete has been extended to machine sheds, trench and bunker silos, poultry houses, and dairy buildings.

Research workers have started experiments looking to refinements of casting insulation inside the monolithic concrete. Panel connection is obtained by casting a connecting column in place after the panels are properly alined. Tests have been made of walls of two 3- or 4-inch walls of concrete, separated with an insulated core.

A further development of panels appears promising. Grout can be cast in half-inch thickness or less. When two such thicknesses are reinforced and interconnected with sufficient web to cause the two faces to act as flanges of a beam, the panel can be designed to resist ordinary wall loads.

When the core of the panel contains expanded polystyrene, a semirigid insulation, the panel is insulated and vaporproofed and requires no further treatment for weatherproofing. A panel, 2 by 8 feet, weighs about 200 pounds. A tractor with a front-end loader can swing the panels into place to be fastened to steel, wood, or precast concrete columns. When polyethylene, a slick, water-resistant plastic, is used to surface the bottom of the panel form, the cured surface has a glazed finish that is fine for interior walls of milking plants. Patents were applied for on this panel construction.

Pole construction, used for temporary buildings since pioneer days, has become highly popular. Reasons for the increased popularity are: Good methods were discovered for thoroughly impregnating poles with preservative. Baling of hay and straw made overhead storage less economical. New tractor attachments, such as posthole diggers and lifts, made it possible to erect poles with farm equipment. Less skill and time are generally needed for erection of pole buildings. The cost is low.

Aluminum, a material used only now and then before the war, became a competitive material in farm construction after the war.

Plastics, which had been used in the form of fiber or wire-reinforced cellulose acetate, also may become a major building material. After the Second World War, chemical research developed a host of thermoplastic compounds, which exhibit desirable structural properties for use in buildings.

Panels (and outside paints) of acrylic resin give promise of wide use. Epoxy resin reinforced with fiberglass can be molded or cast into any desired shape for use as framing members of great strength.

Polyethylene sheets form excellent vapor barriers under concrete or near wall surfaces and make good airtight covers for trench or bunker silos, fumigation, and temporary weather coverings. Research workers have designed greenhouses covered with polyethylene and polyethylene lambing sheds. Poultry houses of combination asphalt-impregnated paper, poultry netting, and polyethylene serve as temporary shelters for broiler production.

Polyester and polyvinyl resins may also be used with fiberglass to form strong watertight troughs and other equipment. Their noncorrosive properties, strength, ease of shaping, and durability make them potentially valuable materials in the manufacture of barn equipment.

Tetrafluoroethylene resins are highly resistant to change in temperature, moisture, and chemicals. They also may be reinforced with fiberglass to form high-strength shapes.

Phenolic resins are used as a waterproof glue for exterior plywood and high-pressure laminates formed from woodpulp and as glues for the prefabrication of panels and gusset plates on roof trusses. Casein glues have sufficient moisture resistance for use in protected places, but phenol-resorcinol glues are superior for exposed gluing.

Robert A. Aldrich and James S. Boyd reported work done at Michigan State University on rigid frames formed with fiberglass and a modified epoxy and polyester in 1958. Their work indicated that these laminates have uniform mechanical characteristics that make them adaptable to the formation of structural members.

Plastic coatings and impregnations (elastomers) promise to be increasingly important in farm building construction. Nylon fabric with plastic impregnation and coating is quite flexible, strong, and weatherproof. Nylon coated with neoprene and other chemicals can be used for shades, tarpaulins, "bubble" buildings, and similar uses.

"Bubble" buildings have no structural framing. A flexible cover suitably formed to stretch into a circular or oblong building is sealed tightly into the soil so that air does not leak around the lower edges. A blower inside the building delivers a static air pressure of 5.2 to 20.8 pounds to the square foot, depending on the tautness and stability desired in the building. The high pressure would resist wind and snow loads of about 21 pounds per square foot. Since the actual air delivery of the fan is quite small, unless the air has to be changed for ventilation, the horsepower requirement for keeping the buildings inflated is quite small. A drawback is that the supply of air must be reasonably continuous.

Plastic coating in the form of viscous paints offer promise as roof coatings for plywood or pressed-board roof panels. Synthetic rubbers like neoprene and butyl have been used.

Foamed and foamed-in-place polystyrenes and polyurethanes (isocyanates) make excellent light-weight insulation materials. At best, 1.25 inches of polyurethane expanded with a refrigerant gas is equivalent to 3 inches of conventional mineral wools. They have some structural strength and are rotproof, nonsettling, and vaporproof and resist breakdown from moisture, acids, sunlight, and air. Their main farm use has been in refrigerated fruit and vegetable storage plants and difficult foamed-in-place jobs such as the insulation of exposed water pipes in houses or service buildings. The material meets specifications for insulation of livestock structures.

Hundreds of new materials await study and tests.

THE PURPOSES and shapes of farm buildings have changed completely.

Many buildings have lost their function. General-purpose barns, which once had greatest value of all farm buildings, icehouses, smokehouses, privies, woodsheds, and older carriage houses, steaming rooms, the threshing floors, and springhouses have been disappearing gradually. The conversion from horse power to tractor power, the change in methods of preserving food, new systems of livestock management, and the electrification of farms did it.

The big, general-purpose barn with the large hayloft is giving way to singlestory structures, which can be adapted to many types of activity because its uncluttered interior, without posts, makes it easy to keep and use machinery there. They also meet many needs of modern livestock production. Their exterior shell gives a weatherproof skin, which resists the normal forces of wind and snow but is not designed for any internal loading. Their flexibility allows changes of interior arrangement for different uses.

Large clear-spans require roof trusses. Those developed for other industrial buildings are not always suitable for farms. When theoretically analyzing stresses in trusses, designers assume that joints are pinned or rigidly fixed. Since most joints are actually neither pinned nor fixed, testing of roof truss designs for proof of their ability to resist imposed loads of deadweight, snow, and wind is desirable. Several agricultural engineering research laboratories have testing floors arranged with flexible systems to hydraulically load roof trusses and other structural elements for proof testing. Such research has enabled the design of many economical trusses capable of clear-spans for farm buildings.

Other methods of achieving clearspans work quite as well as roof trussing. Some methods can achieve space bridging with less material than that involved in roof trusses. A popular type of rigid-frame construction, first used in 1925 for Gothic-roof arches, continued the arches through the plate line of the building to form the stud wall. The next rigid frame, employed in singlestory buildings, had glued gusset plates between the stud and the rafter to form a moment-carrying haunch at the eave line. It was in effect a three-hinged arch. Glued, laminated, three-hinged arches of wood have become commercially available.

Steel was adapted readily to rigidframe design. Many of the factory-fabricated buildings are rigid-frame struc-

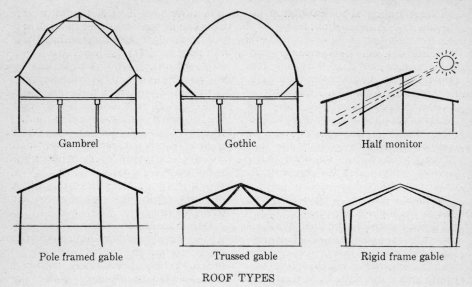

ROOF TYPES

*Typical roof types commonly used on farm buildings.*

tures of the three-hinged or two-hinged type. The clear-span achieved with such construction depends on the use of steel sections, which can be fabricated and erected on the job. Spans from 20 to 180 feet are available. Rigid frames employing either open web or homogeneous beams can be purchased from many steel companies. Columns are anchored into or bolted to concrete foundations designed to resist horizontal thrust.

Another way of achieving large clearspans is to arrange the structural material in a manner to subject the supporting members to compression. This technique is older than written history and is still used in arched and domed buildings in the Near East. Putting aluminum, steel, plywood, and insulation boards into such spherical shapes is new. Small geodesic domes (spherical structures composed of repetitive polyhedrons) built of plywood have been put on the market.

A third technique of building clearspan roofs, the conoid, has been applied to one farm building in England. This roof shape has a double curvature, which has a structural advantage and

can have a pleasing architectural form if it is properly designed. The shape results from the surface generated from a series of straight lines drawn between sloping edge members. Conoids of concrete roof several buildings in Oklahoma.

The surface generated is called anticlastic because it cannot be developed—that is, it cannot be laid out as a flat sheet and warped into the shape of a hyperbolic paraboloid. This property lends structural stability but increases the fabrication problem.

The Agricultural Engineering Research Division of the Department of Agriculture erected a small turkey shade, 16 feet square, that used four hyperbolic paraboloid roof sections of four different materials—aluminum, portland cement plaster, plywood, and waterproofed insulation board. The project permitted engineers to study techniques that could be employed for different materials. The materials can be formed economically into roof coverings, but further study on larger areas and with different shapes was considered necessary before any practical application could be recommended.

Curved shapes offer unlimited opportunity in structural design.

CONSTRUCTION METHODS have become specialized.

Packaged buildings, complete with all of the parts necessary for erection on the proper foundation, can be bought to fill several needs on livestock farms. They include parts or equipment for feeding, watering, ventilating, and removing manure. Packages are designed for milking rooms, milk rooms, broiler houses, layer houses, pork production from farrowing to market, machine sheds, grain and feed plants, and utility buildings. Their variety and completeness have increased year by year.

Contractors, who often work with a building supply dealer, can erect almost any type of building a farmer may want. The farmer may do none of the erection work, a part of it, or all of it. Many farmers elect to do at least part of the construction work, as they have tractor hoists that can be used to swing panels and trusses into position on the building. Earth scoops and blades on tractors can be used for much of the excavation, although extensive trenching may be accomplished more economically by renting a tractor with a backhoe attachment.

Because many farmers live within the economical shipping range of a ready-mix concrete plant, the labor of hauling and mixing cement is eliminated. Most ready-mix plants furnish concrete of the water-cement ratio desired for the strength needed on a particular job. For paving lots or similar exterior work that is subject to heavy freezing and thawing, air-entrained concrete, which withstands temperature changes better than regular concrete, can be bought.

A farmer who elects to buy his own material and erect his own barn has first the problem of obtaining a plan. He can make his layout fit his own situation, but he does not have specialized training in engineering the structure and structural equipment. The new techniques of materials handling and new materials of construction are such that most farmers need professional help in developing building plans.

Extension agricultural engineers in each State are ready to help with building, but such staffs usually comprise no more than two or three men, and they can use their time best by explaining basic principles to groups of county agents and farmers. Many farmers therefore get help from local building dealers and contractors, who may or may not be thoroughly acquainted with the farm needs. Some farmers have time to investigate possible sources of help, but others, hard pressed for time, cannot search for expert advice on construction.

To help solve that problem, the Cooperative Farm Building Exchange was formed in 1929 by the land-grant institutions and the Department of Agriculture. Committees in the South, Northeast, West, and North Central States meet and discuss regional farm building needs and determine the specifications for certain farm buildings that meet the needs of most farmers in the region. The specifications are put into working drawings by a group of architects and engineers. The drawings are printed by a commercial company, which furnishes reproducible transparencies to extension workers in the State colleges. The extension workers can furnish plans to anyone in the State. Many States develop plans of their own to fit specific needs. Expert help is thus available to all farmers.

Anyone wanting a plan for a farm home or service building can obtain construction drawings from the farm building specialist in the agricultural engineering department of the land-grant college in his State.

The Midwest Plan Service, with headquarters in Ames, Iowa, operates in the north-central region as the Cooperative Farm Building Plan Exchange does elsewhere.

Some industrial firms and farm publications have services from which farmers can buy plans for farm buildings at small cost. Dealers in building materials have information on the plans their franchising companies offer.

Such equipment as electric saws, drills, welders, and grinders, which every modern farm shop has, makes it much easier to put up a building of steel or wood.

The larger contractors who specialize in one or a few types of buildings can erect a building quickly. Many of the laborsaving devices they have require a large capital investment that must be used enough to pay the interest, taxes, and depreciation. Since the farmer builds infrequently, it rarely pays him to make a large investment in heavy construction equipment. Sometimes, however, farmers can advantageously rent equipment or have special lifting and earthmoving jobs done on a custom basis.

BECAUSE DAIRY production requires special attention to sanitation and serves specialized markets, dairying has been a special enterprise longer than other types of livestock production. Stanchion-type dairy barns were introduced in the United States early in this century.

The Ney Manufacturing Co., established in Canton, Ohio, in 1879, was one of the early manufacturers of barn equipment. William Louden, who patented an all-steel stanchion about 1900 and displayed it at the National Dairy Show in 1907, was another pioneer. Although gravity-fed individual watering bowls were made by local shops, the first record we have of an automatic bowl for a pressure system is in 1910, when the Rassman Co. of Beaver Dam, Wis., advertised one for sale.

Since provision of a stanchion for each cow can be expensive, some farmers built a few stanchions for use while milking and feeding the cows. The cost of equipment and shelter thus was less than for a barn with regular stanchions.

The next step was loose housing, a system in which cows move anywhere they like within the resting barn, open lot, and feeding barn. The barns are

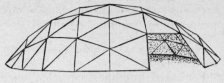

*A geodesic dome.*

low-cost, dirt-floored sheds which usually open on one side for ample ventilation.

The first milking rooms employed a stanchion arrangement like those in stanchion barns. In the 1930's milking rooms were built on two levels so the cow stood at a convenient working height for milking her. Then came various improvements, such as the side-entering tandem (single or double), the walk-through stall in-line, the U-type side-entering, the four-abreast walk-through, and the various combinations of them.

A herringbone arrangement, in which cows stand side-to-side at an angle of 30 degrees from the milking pit, was introduced into the United States from New Zealand in 1957. A large number of herringbone installations have been made—an outstanding example of the speed with which farmers adopt innovations now in contrast to the earlier reluctance to change buildings.

Milk rooms and methods of handling milk changed radically the marketing of milk—from 10-gallon cans to bulk tanks that hold 80 to 1 thousand gallons. That meant changes in the farmers' milk rooms, transportation trucks, and processing plants. Codes, laws, or regulations changed little.

Cow pools, a highly specialized operation in which a thousand cows or more are kept in one place, very likely will increase in popularity. The milking room operates 24 hours a day in three shifts. They are like factories that run continuously to make the most of the capital investment in buildings and equipment. Cow pools bring entirely new problems. Some one-story sheds work well when built to a large scale, but arrangements for the feeding and breeding and care of cows, sanitation, and disposal of manure are details that are harder to cope with.

The milking part of the business has been developed more highly than the engineering of the feedlots.

Research on handling of silage and automatic feeding has produced some satisfactory methods for herds of 50 to 200 cows. The use of gutter cleaners for manure removal has become common. An extension of similar principles to operations ten times larger, however, requires more study.

Artificial insemination, a growing practice, has caused changes also. Bullpens, breeding racks, extra-strong fences, and similar equipment disappear as farmers turn to artificial insemination and keep no bulls on their own farms.

PRODUCTION of beef also has moved toward a factorylike scale. Some producers have found it more economical to haul feeds from centralized processing plants to drylot feeding centers. A common arrangement for finishing beef has been a series of rectangular lots separated by lanes for feed trucks and for the animals when they move from one lot to another. The size of the lots and the shelters in them depends upon the size of the beef enterprise and climate. Cattle in cold sections need a shed-type shelter; in moderately dry areas, a windbreak will serve; in warm localities, sun shades are needed. Fence-line feeders can be filled from a self-unloading wagon or truck.

Some farmers feed as many as 40 thousand head of beef at one location. At the Monfort Feedlots, Inc., near Greeley, Colo., 30 thousand to 35 thousand head receive 500 thousand pounds of feed each day in the form of green chop, silage, and concentrate rations that are proportioned in a feed grinding and mixing plant with a storage capacity of 500 thousand bushels of grain. An elevator on the farm can hold a million bushels more of grain. An alfalfa dehydrating plant furnishes hay. Silage is stored in a 2-acre pit silo about 30 feet deep. Forty trucks operating 24 hours a day for 25 days can deliver the 52 thousand tons of silage the silo can hold. In the growing season, side-dumping trucks deliver green chop to two dump pits, where drag chains and unloading beaters put the green chop on an endless belt. An overhead weighing bin measures the feed into the self-unloading feed trucks.

One type of trench or bunker silo has self-feeding fences. The fences can be moved as the cattle eat the silage. It has worked well for beef producers and is used by more and more dairymen.

Automatic or semiautomatic feed bunks may be built with covered roofs to shelter the animals on both sides. They also may be installed along a barn wall for feeding from one side only. Feed is distributed down the bunk by augers; continuous conveyors, which return under the lower side of the bunk; reciprocating conveyors, like reciprocating gutter cleaners; feed carts, operated on tracks on the upper edge of the bunk; or feed carriers that are operated from tracks supported on the center line above the bunk. Concentrates may be fed through the same system by hand feeding or automatically metering concentrates to the flow of silage, hay, or green chop.

Thus in beef production the system of operation determines the structures. Some of the specialized structures are not adapted readily to other types of production. Such specialization and its reduction in labor costs mean inflexibility. It is hard for a farmer to switch from one type of production to another if he cannot apply his investment as easily in one enterprise as in the other.

Performance testing—the practice of testing of beef animals to prove the value of sire and dam to upgrade a herd—requires changes in layouts so that the animals can be weighed efficiently. Cattle traffic lanes to and from the scale and arrangements for singling out the fattening stock may modify the entire layout of the lot.

Planning of specialized beef production, then, is more than just building shelters for livestock. Storage for feed, silage, and hay, shelter, handling of manure, and equipment for feeding must be arranged so each component of the enterprise fits the overall plan. They must be planned and placed with the same degree of worksaving efficiency that determines the layout of machines in factories.

PORK PRODUCTION systems have been undergoing change. Central farrowing was widely advocated in the 1920's. Half-monitor houses with windows to admit sunlight over a large part of the floor area were recommended. Central farrowing houses had the advantage of concentrated location of feeding, watering, and cleaning chores, but had the disadvantage of greater hazard of disease.

The McLean County system of farrowing advocated isolation and rotation of the farrowing houses to obtain better control of disease. A movable farrowing house for one or two sows would be dragged from one spot to another to keep the house on clean ground. After the pigs were weaned, they usually were fattened on pasture with an unused farrowing house serving as a sleeping shelter.

A later plan was to use individual and isolated farrowing houses, but the pigs were finished in a drylot feeding program. Sometimes, instead of being isolated, the farrowing house was moved into a rather closely placed row and set on concrete.

A newer idea is a system of continuous farrowing and confinement feeding. Each step is planned for: Care of the breeding stock, farrowing, nursery, and fattening. Instead of the rotated pasture plots in the McLean system, the hogs spend their entire lives on concrete. The houses must be cleaned and disinfected carefully.

Continuous production through such a plant begins with controlled breeding, so that the farrowing stalls are occupied always by farrowing sows, except when the building is being disinfected.

Sometimes the pork industry is specialized further. One farm produces weaned shotes for sale to farmers who specialize in fattening hogs. Isolation of the nursery pens from the farrowing and fattening units may be good business practice.

Feeding is a large part of the work, and most of it involves the fattening units. The feeding barn may be connected to a plant where grain is stored, ground, and mixed. The grain is moved by some kind of device—an auger, flight conveyor, button conveyor, or air pressure—which moves the feed to the troughs or self-feeders. If the feed plant is away from the fattening units, the feed often is transferred in self-unloading trucks or trailers, which may be emptied into self-feeders. The lots or partitions in the feeding shed or barn are divided to keep the hogs separated according to size.

Another system uses a different means of confinement. We may call it the "cage system," although commercial firms selling equipment for the structures have trade names. The sow farrows in a pen and is removed when the pigs are weaned. The pigs are fattened to market weight as a litter in the same pen or in individual cages. An advantage of the system is that it facilitates keeping of records. The inherited performance of litters from boars and sows can be checked easily to aid in better selective breeding. It is said that one man with half-day help can fatten 7 thousand hogs a year with an investment of 112 thousand dollars.

THE BROODING of several hundred chicks under one hover once seemed to be the only practical way to rear chicks, but experimentation showed that with reasonable care 10 thousand chicks or more can be brooded successfully in one large room. That and the development of bulk handling of feed, automatic feeding equipment, and improved heating systems created a new broiler industry that can produce broilers with such low labor requirement and excellent feed conversion as to make uneconomical the old type of production in small flocks.

Opinions on the proper housing of commercial laying flocks—which went through a similar evolution from the small home flock to large egg industries—vary widely. Climate is one factor; another comes from preferences for systems that actually have the same economy in capital outlay, feed conversion, and labor.

The major difference in housing is between the deep-litter system and the caged-layer system.

Generally poultrymen in the warm regions where rainfall is low have preferred the individual caged-layer system, in which the birds are housed in lightly constructed sheds which may or may not have sidewalls, depending on the climate.

Farmers in Northeastern States prefer multistory buildings, which house chickens on deep litter. In States where the climate is milder but the rainfall is higher, single-story, light-weight structures are employed for housing on deep litter.

A floor area of about 3 square feet for each hen was recommended until experiments demonstrated greater economy of production with housing as close as 1 square foot per bird. Buildup of moisture in the densely populated houses is compensated for by removal of water-laden manure, insulation of the house, forced ventilation, and the use of supplemental heat sources, such as solar heat gain. The changing factors of management systems thus require revision in the design of poultry houses.

A recent development is the temporary shelter for both production of broilers and eggs. The cost of these houses is quite low, but their structural design was not acceptable in engineering codes existing in 1959.

Ventilation of poultry houses has long been a problem. Some farmers have installed heating systems in houses for laying flocks to eliminate the problem of moisture in winter. These systems, properly handled, do the job well, but analyses of the economy of adding supplemental heat to laying houses has neither proved nor disproved the merits of this method. The same applies to the use of air conditioning in poultry production in warm climates. The problem is complicated by the dust that must be filtered out.

STRUCTURES for storing and drying grain function under new conditions, since combines and picker-shellers furnish a supply of wet grain that cannot be stored safely in the presence of air without removal of part of the water present at harvesttime.

Driers for removal of water from hay, cereals, and peanuts consist of machines to deliver either heated or unheated air through the crop being dried. Two general systems have developed—drying in storage and drying in batch bins from which the crop is moved later to storage.

Corncribs for storing ear corn will disappear entirely as the more efficient technique of picking and shelling and drying becomes better established.

Cereal grains usually are stored in circular steel bins or large warehouse-type structures built especially strong to resist the lateral loads imposed by the weight of grain on the building walls. The drying structures often are built of prefabricated steel. Drying bins erected on the farm usually are simple, rectangular bins formed with an airtight chamber beneath a perforated floor, on which the grain rests. Air distribution to the chambers beneath the bins is accomplished through a manifold delivery equipped with valves to control air movement through desired bins.

Better methods are needed of coordinating the handling of grains through driers into storage, from storage into grinding and mixing plants, and from the grinding and mixing plants to distribution systems in the feeding lots or barns.

A new plan of keeping feed grain in a moist condition in airtight storage

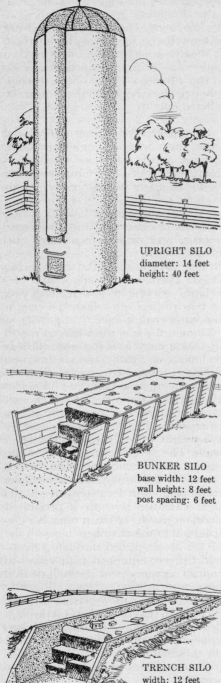

UPRIGHT SILO
diameter: 14 feet
height: 40 feet

BUNKER SILO
base width: 12 feet
wall height: 8 feet
post spacing: 6 feet

TRENCH SILO
width: 12 feet
length: 60 feet
wall: 8 feet

bins may be a valuable development for feeders of livestock. Preliminary trials in several States indicate that the method may be practical, but more research is needed as to the prevention of spoilage and the development of troublefree grain-handling equipment.

Ways of storing forage also have changed. The first silos in the United States were built in Maryland and Michigan in about 1875. Because silage of forage crops gave good results in the feeding of cattle, the use of the silo dominated the dairy industry a long time.

Types of silos changed. Tower silos were most popular in 1900–1920. Trench silos were used in the 1920's and 1930's and were supplemented with bunker silos in the 1940's. Glass-lined, upright silos came in the 1940's.

Field baling of hay changed the type of structures for storing hay. Less space for hay and the greater weight of baled hay led to a gradual move away from big, overhead haymows to smaller sheds, where the heavy weight could be supported on the ground.

Changes in buildings to adapt them to changes in machines require a flexibility in building and pose a problem. A relatively short-lived field machine dictates the nature of a long-lived structure. When we add factors of economy and changes in livestock management and mechanization within the building, the problem of keeping production buildings adequate to the immediate needs of the farm production becomes even more complex. The process of rebuilding is continual.

Liberty Hyde Bailey said in his *Cyclopaedia of American Agriculture* in 1907:

"The old buildings express a former order; however well adapted they may have been to that order, for the most part they are hopelessly inefficient for the new order, and therefore also hopelessly unaesthetic. Nothing is more needed on American farms than new kinds of buildings constructed on correct fundamental ideals."

Our present situation can be expressed no better; rebuilding to fit technologic development has to go on.

# Environment of Animals

T. E. Bond and C. F. Kelly

MORE THAN a hundred years ago A. J. Downing of Newburgh, N.Y., wrote a book, *The Architecture of Country Houses*, in which he pointed out the connection between animal environment and animal production.

He wrote: "As it is well known now that the extra supply of heat needful in the animal economy in cold weather, if not supplied by warm housing, must be supplied by an extra consumption of food, with no increase of flesh or strength, but a great loss of comfort to the exposed animal, this extra consumption of food, in a few months, even where food is cheap, will more than balance all that can be saved by withholding a few feet of boards, and a few hours' labour."

But environment of animals was an old problem even then.

In the first century before Christ, Marcus Vitruvius Pollio, a celebrated Roman architect and engineer, wrote: "The great hall is to be placed in the warmest part of the court; united to this are the ox stalls, with cribs towards the fire and the east for oxen with their faces to the light and the fire do not become rough coated."

Man has striven to improve his environment since the beginning of time. Engineers, physiologists, and doctors have studied man's physiological and psychological reactions to various thermal environments. They have selected optimum conditions and discomfort indexes that now are used by engineers to design heating and cooling equipment so that it is possible to mass-produce "comfort" within the reach of many people.

While man, furless and at the mercy of the elements in all except the mildest climates, was improving his comfort in places to which he chose to migrate, the wild animals and birds relied on instincts and physiological features. Birds migrated to comfortable environments. The bear grew fat during the comfortable summers and bypassed the uncomfortable winters by hibernating. Cattle stayed in the lee side of cliffs and in the forests when winds were cold, and sought shade when the sun was hot.

When man began to domesticate wild animals, he restricted their movement and so kept them from selecting their environment.

An example is a catastrophe in 1955 in southern California. There, in a highly mechanized and modern poultry-producing area, about 1 million laying hens died from heat prostration during a hot spell in August.

One grower lost 31 thousand of his 50 thousand birds. The chickens, most of them confined in cages, could not escape and help themselves when an "unusual" hot spell came. The cages that provided a comfortable environment when the local microclimate was moderate were a death trap during the heat wave. Ranchers who had installed foggers or had enough water and help available to wet the birds by hand, had little or no loss. It was estimated that the deaths and the drop in production of the surviving birds represented a loss of several million dollars.

We all have seen or heard of other examples—confinement of cows waiting for long periods to be milked in an unshaded holding corral in summer or without wind shelter in winter; pigs kept in a concrete-floored pen with no access to a wallow; beef cattle and sheep on pasture without shade in summer or shelter from wind, rain, or snow.

We recall the deaths of beef cattle in blizzards in the 1880's over the Great Plains from Texas to Canada; the spectacular hay drops of 1955 in Nevada;

the unexpected cold-weather losses of livestock in Colorado. Lack of feed was a factor, but low temperatures were the main reason for the high death rate.

Some breeds of cattle, sheep, swine, and poultry selected for survival and production in Europe were low producers in some climates of the United States. Advances in biological and engineering sciences now make it possible to alter environment to match the animal's requirements for maximum production. Today's farmers can fit the environment to the most productive livestock and poultry breeds and fit breeds to the environment.

An animal's environment is the total of all external conditions that affect its development, response, and growth. Literally, it could include, for example, the disposition of the sow or the type or slope of the floor as factors of the piglet's environment—and they may be important factors. But we are concerned primarily with the external factors that affect the regulation and balance of animal heat—the climatic factors which include air temperature, moisture, radiation and light (quantity, quality, and periodicity), and air velocity. Future research may show atmospheric pressure (altitude) and composition of the air to be equally important.

These climatic factors are so closely connected with production and growth of farm animals because all of them are homeothermic—that is, they attempt to maintain a constant body temperature or a balanced exchange of heat. Like human beings, they can exist only within a limited range of body temperatures. To stay within this range, an animal must maintain a rather delicate balance between the heat produced within its body and the heat it loses to its environment or gains from it.

The climate surrounding an animal at any particular instant influences the amount of heat exchanged between it and the environment. Consequently it influences the physiological adjustments the animal must make to maintain a body heat balance. That, in turn, is reflected in its growth, production, and health.

The heat or fuel required to "operate" an animal comes from the food it consumes. In the body processes—metabolism—the chemical energy of the food is transformed into heat energy.

The term "total digestible nutrients," or TDN, refers to the available food energy. Some of it is lost in the urine and in gases. Part of the remaining food energy—metabolizable energy—is available to carry out the body processes. The rest appears in the process of feeding and is referred to as heat increment of feeding. The metabolizable energy, except for the energy equivalent of the gain in weight, appears as excess heat and must be dissipated from the body in order to maintain a balanced state of heat exchange.

This excess heat can be lost from the animal by radiation to cooler walls, floor, ceiling, or other objects whose surfaces are cooler than the animal's; by convection to cool air passing over the body and through the lungs; by conduction, or body contact, with a cool floor, feed, or water; and by evaporation of moisture from the animal's outer surface and respiratory tract.

If the temperature of the air or of objects surrounding an animal is higher than that of the animal's surfaces, net heat transfers by these methods may result in a gain of heat to the animal body. Any improvement of the environment for livestock will necessarily involve a change in one or more of these climatic factors to change the amount of animal heat exchanged by these four methods of heat transfer.

Air temperature has a greater effect than any other climatic element on body temperature response. It is the only climatic factor that affects directly all four modes of heat transfer.

The temperature of the air influences the temperature of walls and other objects around an animal and thereby influences the amount of heat it loses or gains by radiation and conduction.

The amount of heat exchanged by convection is directly proportional to the air temperature. Because air temperature influences both the amount of moisture in the air and on an animal's surface, the heat exchanged by evaporation is affected by air temperature.

When the air temperature is above that of an animal's surface (summer conditions), an excess of heat is transferred to the animal, which the animal generally counteracts by reducing its food (heat) consumption. The reverse may be true in winter, and excessive amounts of feed may be wasted in trying to balance the increased rate of heat loss.

Moisture in the air directly affects only the exchange of heat by evaporation. Low-humidity air is advantageous during hot weather because it readily absorbs moisture from the surface of an animal, removing heat by evaporation. It may be harmful during cold weather for the same reason. An excess of surface moisture increases the rate of evaporation heat loss. That is beneficial in summer but not in winter.

Radiated energy, including light, directly affects only the heat exchanged by radiation between an animal and its surroundings, which include the sun, sky, shade, buildings—any objects or surfaces that may exchange heat with an animal.

Lowering the temperature of the surroundings will reduce the radiation heat load on an animal or increase its radiation loss. We strive to do this during hot weather by shading an animal or by keeping it as far away as we can from buildings and objects that will radiate heat to it. During cold weather we intentionally expose animals to warmer buildings in an effort to increase the amount of radiation the animals receive.

What we have referred to so far is the quantity, or amount, of radiant energy. We may also speak of the quality of radiation, which refers to its wavelengths. We recognize the fact that shortwave solar energy may cause sunburn, whereas the longwave energy we receive while standing in the shade causes no such effect.

The amount of heat an animal exchanges with its surroundings by radiation is determined by quantity of energy, not quality, except that differing qualities or wavelengths will be reflected in different amounts by the animal and also by the surroundings. Light, the visible wavelength, may be an important climatic factor, but this has not been investigated extensively.

Besides quantity and quality of light, there is periodicity, or the period of time an animal is exposed to light. Periodicity has been shown to affect reproduction, growth, and other responses of some farm animals. The natural change in light periodicity due to seasonal changes may affect some animal processes.

Air velocity over the surface of an animal affects only the convection and evaporation forms of heat transfer. If the velocity increases, the evaporation loss will increase (if the air is unsaturated). The rate of convection transfer of heat also will change; whether it is a loss or gain to the animal depends on the relative levels of air and animal surface temperatures—a gain from higher air temperatures and a loss due to lower temperatures. High air velocity during hot weather should generally benefit most farm animals. It may or may not be beneficial during cold weather, depending on the relationship between air temperature and the surface temperature of the animal.

INDICATIONS of thermal stress in the animal alerts the farmer to an unhealthy situation. It is important that he recognize when animals are stressed by either "too cold" or "too hot" environments. Several types of indicators show where an animal stands in relation to the "comfort" range of the average individual of its species. Typical indicators are body and surface temperatures, respiration and pulse rates, rate of production, rates of feed and water intake, and movements and habits.

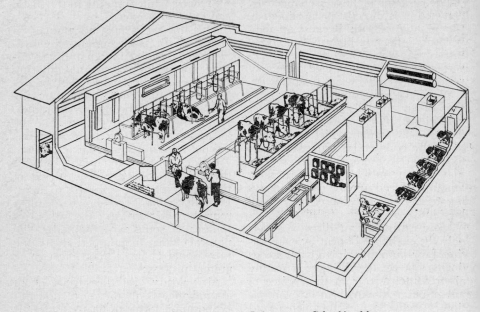

*Interior view of Psychroenergetic Laboratory at Columbia, Mo.*

A person cannot judge "comforts" of livestock by his own reactions in a given environment. He reacts for the most part in an entirely different way. A change in temperature, air velocity, radiation, or other factors of the microclimate (climate near the animal) will probably affect the cow, pig, or chicken faster and to a greater extent than it will affect a man. That is because man sweats profusely when necessary, while most of his livestock cannot. A person can change his clothing, but his livestock can do so only twice each year. A person can seek a more comfortable environment (by a stove or air conditioner), but his animals must accept what is provided.

Differences in the reactions of men and animals produce different levels in physiological measurements for a given microclimate. Man's average body temperature at his "comfortable" environment is 98.6° F. That of dairy cattle, beef cattle, sheep, and swine is about 102°. The average body temperature of laying hens is about 106°. Man can adjust, with little change in body temperature, to temperatures that vary widely on either side of his comfort zone. Animals and birds are not so fortunate.

Tests of research workers of the University of Missouri and the Department of Agriculture indicate that body temperatures in Holstein, Jersey, and Brown Swiss dairy cows remain normal down to air temperatures as low as 0°, but increase rapidly above 80° air temperature, sometimes reaching 108° at an air temperature of only 105°.

Body temperatures of swine also tend to follow environmental temperature closer than do those of man.

In studies by Hubert Heitman and E. H. Hughes at the University of California, the body temperatures of fully grown swine ranged from 101.9° at 40° to 105.5° at 105° air temperature. At higher air temperatures, death usually occurred at a body temperature of 108°.

A pig's reaction to temperatures below and above its comfort zone is exactly the opposite of man's. As air temperature increases, the pulse rate rapidly drops and the respiration rate increases rapidly. The pig, usually considered a nonsweating animal, finds little relief by sending internal body heat to its surface since there is little moisture there to establish an evaporation heat loss (unless it is provided by a spray or wallow). The pulse rate therefore slows down, and the blood flows to the lungs, where there is moisture for evaporation. The respiration rate increases to provide the additional air for this increased evaporation.

Drs. Heitman and Hughes found that the pulse rate of pigs weighing 70 to 144 pounds went down from about 140 per minute at an air temperature of 40° to about 90 per minute at 110°. Over the same temperature range, the respiration rate increased, from 25 to about 150 per minute. In general, cattle and poultry follow the same general trend in their physiological reactions to heat loss.

But when the farmer wants to know if his animals are being stressed by environment, he is not going to obtain rectal temperatures or measure pulse rates with a stethoscope and stopwatch. And he cannot wait to measure production rates or weight gains. If these go down in weather that is "too hot" or "too cold," it will be too late for a remedy by the time the cause is determined.

Probably the best single indicator of the environment is air temperature. All livestock producers should be aware of the temperature in their animal shelters and should analyze mentally the qualifying effects of solar and ground radiation, wind, rain, and snow on the air temperature and the resultant comfort of their animals and birds.

Several "symptoms" warn the farmer to give attention to his animals' comfort—their discomfort may be costing him money. Poultry fluff out their feathers and huddle on their feet when they are cold. When they are too hot, they stand up straight, with outstretched wings and necks, and pant, with open beaks. Cold chicks will "cheep" and

possibly shiver. Pigs, if too hot, seek the shade and eat very little. They will roll in their feces and urine if water is not available for wetting their skins. They also pant and are restless. When too cold, they huddle and try to climb into a deeper pile. Cattle, when they are too hot, seek shade, eat only a little, and may pant and drool. They may shiver and hunch up their backs when they are too cold.

ZONES OF comfort are different for men and for animals. How are these zones defined?

Extensive studies to establish the limits of the comfort zone of people were first with healthy young college men and later with women. The subjects were exposed to different air temperatures, relative humidities, air velocities, and radiant temperatures and were asked at what level of each of these factors or combinations of factors they were most comfortable.

It was realized later that the amount of activity of the subject influenced his comfort zone limits, and the studies were extended to include various stages of activity, such as sleeping, resting, and light and heavy work.

The effect of age was considered next. Only recently has serious thought been given to the increase in work output that might be expected from people in buildings that are air conditioned winter and summer and to whether air conditioning pays.

Studies with livestock and poultry are conducted in the laboratory and in the field. However, it is the laboratory studies that provide the knowledge we need to establish animal "comfort zones." Only under laboratory conditions can we really control enough environmental factors to show the true effects. Field tests are necessary for studying the application or practical usefulness of the laboratory results.

The Psychroenergetic Laboratory at the University of Missouri is such a laboratory for studying the effects of environmental factors on cattle.

It consists of two insulated chambers,

26 by 18 by 9 feet. Each houses six animals. The chambers are equipped with individual air temperature and humidity controls so that animals can be housed in different controlled environments. Dairy cattle, for example, have been subjected to air temperatures ranging from 0° to 110°. The animals are milked, fed, and managed the same within the laboratory as they would be on a farm. This provides an effective means of determining the effect environment may have on various animal responses.

The poultry calorimeter of the Department of Agriculture at Beltsville is used in the study of poultry. The California Psychrometric Chamber at Davis is in use for research on swine. Nineteen colleges and the Department of Agriculture have laboratory facilities for environmental research with poultry, cattle, swine, and sheep.

There has never been much doubt as to how the comfort of farm livestock should be evaluated. Aside from humanitarian considerations in extreme cases of thermal stress, the research agricultural engineer, animal production scientist, and farmer agree that the "comfort" of the animal must be measured by production, feed conversion, reproduction ability, and life or death—things that actually affect the net return from the animals. In other words, if an animal is gaining weight, laying eggs, or producing milk at its highest rate, comfort is assumed. If it dies or fails to reproduce or its feed conversion rate falls, discomfort is assumed. Because the extra milk, eggs, or meat must pay for both summer and winter air conditioning, perhaps livestock may have a more valid reason for air conditioning than do human beings.

Progress has been excellent in the years since the war because of the concerted efforts of many researchers to determine the temperature zones in which animals will produce most efficiently. Swine appear to make most rapid gains between 70° and 80° at live weights of 100 to 150 pounds and between 60° to 70° for larger hogs.

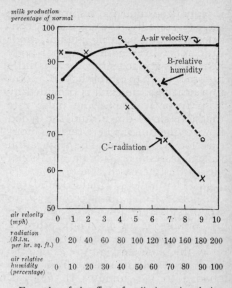

*Examples of the effect of radiation, air velocity, and relative humidity on milk production of Holstein cows. Air temperature for curves A and C was 80° F.; for curve B, 85°.*

The production response of dairy cows to environment varies somewhat with breed. The consensus of several investigators is that milk production of most breeds will be maximum at barn temperatures of 50° to 65°. Lowering the air temperatures slowly lowers production.

At the Psychroenergetic Laboratory at the University of Missouri, Holstein cows withstood air temperatures as low as 10° without a decline in production. Jersey production started to drop at 30°. Partly offsetting this lowering of milk production, however, was an increase in butterfat content—a drop from 61° to 27° was accompanied by an increase in butterfat from 5.4 to 6 percent.

Production dropped rapidly at temperatures above the optimum zone. At 95° the production of Jersey cows was 64 percent of normal and of Holsteins only 51 percent of normal. Several investigators state also that the solids-not-fat content of milk is lower during the summer, presumably because of higher temperatures.

It may be that the effect of environment on the feed conversion rate—the amount of gain or production per pound of feed—is an even more important consideration than actual rate of gain (pounds per animal per day). The studies with swine at Davis, by Drs. Heitman and Hughes, indicate a direct relation. At the most comfortable temperatures for animals weighing 70 to 144 pounds, the pigs gained slightly more than 2 pounds a day and consumed only 300 pounds of feed for 100 pounds of gain. This was at a temperature range between 70° and 80°. When the temperature was increased to 90°, the rate of gain dropped to 1.3 pounds a day, and feed consumption increased to 500 pounds. Lowering the temperature to 50° reduced gains to 1.5 pounds a day and increased feed consumption to 400 pounds for 100 pounds of gain.

H. J. Thompson, D. M. Worstell, and Samuel Brody, at the University of Missouri, obtained somewhat similar results with dairy cattle. A drop in environmental temperatures from 40° to 8° was associated with higher feed consumption, indicating a lower efficiency of milk production. Increasing temperatures above the "comfort" zone apparently affected the relation between feed consumption and milk production even more directly.

H. H. Kibler, at the Missouri Agricultural Experiment Station, found feed conversion in beef cattle considerably reduced by high environmental temperatures. Shorthorns required 4.88 pounds of total digestible nutrients (TDN) per pound of gain at 50° and 5.37 pounds at 80°.

The relation between the quality of ration and an animal's thermal stress is important. Our evidence indicates that it is economically advantageous to feed as little fiber as possible in the summer to dairy cattle. If two animals are receiving 20 pounds of feed a day and one animal gets one-third of this as grain and the other only hay, the one receiving hay and grain would have about 20 percent less energy to

dissipate as heat and 20 percent more energy to use for productive purposes than the animal on the hay diet.

This was reflected in differences in summer gains of beef cattle in our tests in the Imperial Valley. Animals that got a ration with one-third grain gained 1.58 pounds a day, compared to 0.97 pounds a day among animals on a ration of hay only.

Hajime Ota and H. L. Garver studied the effect of temperature on weight gains and feed consumption of Rhode Island Red fryers in the Department of Agriculture poultry calorimeter. One group of 35 birds was kept in a box at 67° through 9 weeks of age. A similar group was kept at 86°. The "cold box" birds used 2.9 pounds of feed per pound of gain; the "hot box" group used 2.7 pounds. There was some evidence that the more comfortable temperature was the higher one during the first 5 weeks and the 67° temperature at 9 weeks.

W. O. Wilson, at the University of California, found that White Leghorn pullets reduced feed intake drastically at high temperatures. Tests of the effects of temperature on laying hens in the poultry calorimeter at Beltsville have shown a wide range of results.

Dr. Ota stated that hens usually lay the most eggs with the least feed at 45° to 70°. Young hens have laid well with good feed conversion ratios at both higher and lower temperatures.

Dr. Wilson reported that both egg weight and shell thickness are lowered almost immediately by high environmental temperatures; 2 to 3 weeks are required for a return to normal.

We have summarized only a few of the points of temperature effects on farm animal production. There is a similar wealth of data relating other climatic factors—moisture, air velocity, and light—to animal production and physiological responses. We hope we have presented enough to indicate to the reader the significance of the problem and the importance of the results.

There are other environmental factors that we know little about. The environment we have been discussing has had to do mostly with factors that affect heat transfer between the animal and its surroundings. Other environmental factors may affect the animal in other ways.

Atmospheric pressure, or altitude, is one. Its effect on livestock comfort could be important.

As people take over low-level agricultural land for houses, factories, and roads, livestock raising will be intensified in the foothills and later in the mountains. A director of an agricultural experiment station in a mountain State once said that our environmental studies at Davis, where the elevation is only 56 feet above sea level, should be supplemented by studies in a low-pressure chamber, so that the results would be applicable where most of the livestock enterprises are in his State, at several thousand feet above sea level. Such studies may also show associated effects.

A. H. Smith, of the University of California, found in preliminary experiments that chickens adapted to oxygen deficiency at the University's White Mountain High-Altitude Research Station, which is 12,500 feet above sea level, when returned to the 56-foot level at Davis, were more heat tolerant than similar birds not so acclimated.

Light is another factor that only recently has been considered for its possible importance to animals. We mentioned some phases of light effects. As with air pressure, there may be effects still unknown that may be even more important. The duration of periods of light and darkness may control the breeding of sheep and the start of laying in turkeys and chickens. Several turkey raisers now produce fresh oven turkeys the year around. The poults are hatched from eggs laid by hens in light-proofed houses; they receive a measured amount of light at carefully spaced intervals so as to bring on the laying season as selected.

Studies are underway to change the

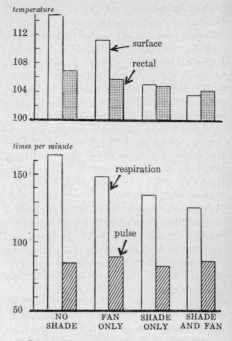

*Effect of shade and wind on several physiological reactions of beef cattle in tests in the Imperial Valley (of California) during a period when the air temperature was 107° F.*

breeding season of sheep through light control, so that lambs will be dropped during good weather rather than in snow and rain, as happens in some of our sheep raising areas.

Studies of light as an environmental factor can offer a great challenge.

Smog is a new environmental factor, born of man's mechanization. Its dangers were first recognized by eye irritation and damage to clothing and, more recently, a possible relation to cancer.

Millions are being spent in research to develop ways to prevent formation of smog at its source and to avoid damage. Its damaging effects to crops, recognized in some areas, have been studied by botanists, engineers, and agronomists. To our knowledge, no one has investigated the effect of smog on farm livestock.

Ions are the electrical charges carried on small particles and molecules of dust, moisture, and gases. They have been under suspicion for their possible influence on various nasal troubles, allergies, and other human disorders. Ions can be large or small and positive or negative. Several scientists have stated that as far as human reactions are concerned, negative ions are good ions and positive ions bad ones.

WHAT EFFECT will ionization of the particles in the air have on livestock? With F. C. Jacob and Hubert Heitman, of the University of California, and LeRoy Hahn, of the Department of Agriculture, we have begun a project to measure their effect on swine. We hope other researchers will become interested in this problem.

No doubt radiation fallout will influence the design of livestock shelters and ventilation systems. Recent studies indicate the amount of strontium-90 (from fallout) in milk may be approaching a dangerous level. The farmer, in the future, may be called upon to protect both animals and feed from such contamination.

Space—the area allotted to one animal and number of animals in a pen—should be given greater study in the United States. European engineers and livestock producers are more aware of this environmental factor than we are. With greater mechanization and a trend toward confining animals to facilitate environmental control, the minimum areas necessary for efficient growth and production must be known.

Even increased weight, as animals are bred, housed, and fed to reach finish at an earlier age, is being studied as an environmental factor. Long-term centrifugation provides a method of determining the effect of weight on the present bone system of chickens. This may provide leads to diseases associated with weight, or even point the way, for the geneticist, toward the development of a better framework for the chicken of tomorrow.

We are confident there will be new developments and new surprises in the matter of animal environment.

APPLICATION of results is the objective of most research. It is interesting to note some of the changes in livestock structures that have resulted from basic and applied research.

In work in a field station and laboratory with the late N. R. Ittner at the Imperial Valley Field Station, we have measured the benefits of increased airflow over beef cattle, cooled drinking water, shade design, wire and cable corrals, and so on during hot weather.

These findings were put to immediate use by several operators of feedlots— sometimes before we were completely certain of the results ourselves. Practically all new construction in California's hot valleys now makes provision for keeping the temperature of drinking water as close as possible to that of the cool well water and uses cable and wire for pens instead of wooden planks, so that cooling breezes can flow across the animals. Shades are placed well off the ground to allow exposure to the cool sky. Sometimes fans are installed.

We can give other examples of improvements from research.

The earliest shelter for the dairy cow was a roof of branches thatched with leaves or straw to protect her from the rain or sun. This structure was not the outgrowth of basic research, but it had the advantage of supplying plenty of fresh air.

The next step was the log barn, in which chinked joints gave weathertight construction. It retained all foul air and moisture, and little sunlight entered.

F. H. King in 1908 pointed out the advantages of fresh air, and a study of ventilation led to fairly well ventilated barns. S. S. Buckley at the University of Maryland in 1913 and J. R. Dice at the North Dakota State College in 1934 tested the idea of milking cows in a barn (to protect man) and allowing them freedom the rest of the time in loose housing or lounging barns.

An agricultural engineer, S. A. Witzell, of the University of Wisconsin, in 1944 proved to the satisfaction of the Midwest dairyman that the cow would produce as much milk or more under the loose housing system, that the building would cost less, and that labor would be less in caring for and feeding the animals. Loose housing is used today on many American dairy farms.

A research team of Samuel Brody, A. C. Ragsdale, H. H. Kibler, physiologists, and H. J. Thompson, R. E. Stewart, Robert G. Yeck, and M. D. Shanklin, agricultural engineers, at the University of Missouri, developed much basic data relating dairy production to environmental temperature, humidity, and airflow.

Producers and engineers the world over have put to use their results in calculating the costs of insulation, air conditioning, and structures. The data have been applied in various profitable ways.

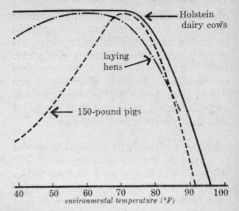

*Influence of environmental temperature on animal production trends.*

THE ECONOMIC implications of improving livestock environment are many. It has become possible to raise livestock and poultry in sections that are climatically marginal for animal production. Examples are the hot, dry Imperial and Palo Verde Valleys of California. Feeding beef cattle there can be profitable on a year-round basis even though the mean temperature during the four summer months may be 90° or above. As the population increases, the use of such areas will become more important.

Improved environment invariably means more efficient utilization of feed by animals. That also is important in land economy and will become more so in the future.

Changes in animal production and management methods have resulted from our increased knowledge of the relation of environment to animals. More animals—particularly swine and poultry—are raised indoors in birth-to-market confinement under crowded conditions. Greater numbers of animals are raised in less land space, and the concentration of animals increases the opportunity for mechanizing the production process.

Environmental control also has helped to smooth out the fluctuating seasonal supply of meat and animal products. Year-round, or multiple, farrowing of pigs is an example. This also utilizes buildings and manpower more efficiently. Animals will reach market weight sooner, and will not tie up buildings, equipment, and labor so long. An increase in average daily gain of only one-tenth pound means that pigs will reach market weight about 10 days sooner. The breeding season of sheep and turkeys can be changed by the light they receive. Egg production and egg quality have been improved by light control.

Improved environment for animals also means an improved environment for the men who manage them.

Not all of the results from research can be applied economically under present conditions, but they can be held for the future, when our human-animal balance will increase the premium on environmental control. It is doubtful that air-conditioned buildings for livestock were profitable in 1960.

Robert G. Yeck, in a report of work at the University of Missouri, stated that air conditioning of dairy stables might be profitable if each cow gives at least 40 pounds of milk a day, the price is at least 6 dollars a hundredweight, the outside air temperature stays above

80°, and the relative humidity is above 65 percent for 60 or more days each year.

Many of the principles developed through research cost little to apply and add nothing to the production costs. For improving the summer environment, a hay-covered shade costs no more than a galvanized steel shade. Wire fences may be less costly than wood for enclosing corrals and pens. It costs little more to add height to shades.

Other improvements that add little or nothing to production costs are corrals and pens located away from hot buildings and with maximum exposure to wind; white-painted animal shelters, rather than "hot" colors; and keeping water cool in lines insulated or buried for short distances.

Researchers at the University of Arizona found that beef cattle with their shade 10 feet from the feed bunk gained about one-third of a pound each day more during summer than a group with their shade 54 feet from the bunk. This was done with 170 pounds less feed per 100 pounds of gain and an increase in net return of 8.68 dollars per head. It costs no more to consider the relative position of shade and feed bunk.

Tests have shown that pigs that can wet themselves in wallows or sprays gain up to one-third pound more a day and have a better feed conversion ratio. Tests at the Oklahoma State University showed that gilts and sows sprinkled with water during pregnancy farrowed 2.35 more live pigs per litter.

Animal shades may be relatively expensive, but generally they can be justified. Some western cattle feeders object to shades of any kind because of dampness under them. Shades oriented toward the east and west are cooler, but dampness will be less if they are kept narrow, 16 to 20 feet, and oriented north to south. In tests in California, shaded Hereford steers gained 191 pounds each during an 84-day summer feeding period in the Imperial Valley. Unshaded steers gained 137 pounds each. The respective feed conversion

rates were 788 and 928 pounds of feed per 100 pounds of gain. With feed at 50 dollars and beef at 28 cents, the shade could be credited with an increased return of 9.26 dollars per animal.

Low temperatures in buildings generally do not cause the severe reduction in animal production and efficiency that high temperatures do. Low temperatures, however, usually are accompanied by drafts, poor ventilation, and dampness that have bad effects, particularly in poultry and hog houses.

Changes that add little to production costs often will improve winter environment in livestock buildings. Good drainage within a building, for example, costs little more than poorly planned drainage. Each pound of water evaporated within a building will waste about 1,060 B.t.u. (British thermal units) of heat. Properly designed and oriented buildings will capture solar heat and reduce wind effects and draftiness. Such considerations may add nothing to building costs.

Tests have shown that hens protected by windbreaks in winter produced more eggs. Poultry buildings can be located and oriented to reduce the effect of winds.

Building insulation, controlled ventilation, and heating for animal production in cold weather add considerably to production cost, but can often be justified by greater animal production and better feed conversion. Longer building life and greater comfort for those who must tend the animals are other benefits.

The latest recommendations for controlling or improving the environment for farm livestock and poultry in a locality can be obtained from the agricultural engineers at State land-grant institutions and extension offices.

IN SUMMARY, we list some general recommendations based on experimental findings.

*For cold weather:*
Insulate buildings to conserve animal heat.

Ventilate animal buildings to remove excess animal moisture.

Control ventilation to reduce humidity and maintain temperature.

Provide constant building temperatures (or reduce fluctuating temperatures) with controlled ventilation and supplemental heating.

Provide good drainage in buildings so that urine and other free water can leave the building as liquid rather than as a vapor in the ventilating air at the expense of animal heat.

Use insulating glass to utilize solar heat.

Provide a "second," or higher temperature, environment for the very young animals—brooders, heat lamps, heated floors, and such.

Design and orient buildings to make use of solar heat.

Provide protection from wind, snow, and rain for animals raised out-of-doors.

Locate outside pens on the south side of buildings, trees, or windbreaks, for protection from cold wind and for exposure to solar radiation.

*For hot weather:*

Shades should be high or louvered to utilize cool sky and should be long and narrow—oriented east and west for maximum coolness or north and south for dryness.

Use shade materials with radiation characteristics of white paint on top and black paint underneath. Use hay where suitable.

Slope slanted shades with the high side north.

Use wire fence or wire cable pens— if board, use wide spacing.

Keep animal pens and corrals away from buildings and other warm or sun-heated objects.

Lower temperature of surroundings with trees and additional shades, but do not block the flow of air.

Keep the area surrounding pens and corrals in alfalfa or some grass.

Locate animals in unobstructed wind path or on a hill.

Paint buildings white.

Keep animal drinking water cool— small shade over shallow trough.

Feed near or under shade.

The foregoing recommendations apply generally to all classes of livestock and poultry.

For beef cattle, provide showers that wet the animal surfaces adequately. Use fans where air movement is low.

For swine on a concrete floor or slab, use a combination of air movement with wallows or sprays.

For poultry, use fine mist sprays.

# Machines to Help With Chores

H. B. Puckett

CHORES still take much of the stockraiser's time. Various types of improved machines and devices perform some specific task and lessen drudgery, but not so much as in field crops. The whole system of using labor for chores will have to be changed drastically if there is to be any big change in labor requirements on farms.

Mechanization has cut the labor requirement for producing feed grains to one-fourth or one-fifth of what it was 40 to 50 years ago. In the same years, the production of meat animals increased only 31 percent per man-hour. Machines have raised production per man-hour 107 percent in poultry and 88 percent in milk production.

Feed is the major item in producing animals; any improvement in the pounds of feed per pound of gain would lower production costs. There is less opportunity to achieve that, however, than there is to reduce the cost of the labor. Labor requirements determine the number of animals that one person can handle satisfactorily.

Good management is necessary, especially in chore work. Many tasks have to be done that require a diverse inventory of equipment. The equipment may be expensive—but labor can be more expensive. Extensive mechanization will not lessen the need for good management. Each individual will be controlling more capital and working at a lower net percentage of profit. He can easily become overextended or develop too great an inventory in equipment. He must use equipment efficiently and effectively if it is to produce a profit.

An element of management that comes up at the very beginning of farmstead mechanization is the organization of facilities for efficient utilization of structures and labor.

The incorrect placement of a building or a fixed piece of equipment can mean a continuous waste of manpower or a higher equipment cost. It can also make future expansion costly.

A facility conceived for any particular operation should have an open-end design, which will permit reasonable expansion later. Multipurpose design of long lasting and expensive units is desirable if it does not result in an unusually high cost or too much of a sacrifice in the functional performance of the facility.

Equipment for doing chores should be selected to give maximum assistance and eliminate nonproductive manual labor. A man is an expensive source of power. If a task he performs can be done by a piece of machinery that will run for many hours for many years at a fraction of his cost, production is more efficient. That is not always possible, however. Infrequent tasks and tasks of unusual complexity may be performed more reasonably by men.

For the most efficient use of machinery, simple decision-making processes should be relegated to automatic equipment, which can handle almost any degree of complexity and number of decisions. The number and the complexity determine the cost of the controlling system. Automatic control usually results in more efficient use of properly designed equipment. In terms of electric power, human labor is worth about 1 to 2 cents an hour, but the human brain cannot be duplicated by controls costing millions or billions of dollars.

The milking parlor is an example of a way to organize facilities and equipment. The structure is designed specifically to reduce travel time and lost motion. The equipment is not moved, and the worker moves very little. Animals are brought to the man and equipment. A pipeline milking machine conveys the milk directly to the cooler. High quality is preserved in a properly functioning and carefully supervised system.

Loose housing of dairy cattle and the use of a milking parlor reduce housing cost and labor and may reduce feeding costs through the use of automatic machinery for feeding. The loose housing facility and the milking parlor can be integrated into a unit to expedite the handling of the cows.

Feeding lots for beef cattle must be arranged for easy handling of the animals and the feeding and cleaning equipment. An inconveniently placed gate or post can cause the loss of many hours in a year. With the larger herds, the loss can amount to a sizable percentage of any prospective profits.

All aspects must be considered if planning is to be effective and efficient. Such things as width of gates, location of feed bunks, and distance between posts and buildings affect the use of equipment. Some stalls are so placed that it is easier to use a pitchfork and shovel to clean them than it is to use a tractor with a front-end loader. The cleaning of properly designed stalls can be done with a single pass of a tractor-mounted blade or scraper.

Keeping animals in a small area lowers the cost of equipment for feeding and cleaning. The cost per animal can be accommodated within the normal profits. Mechanization permits a man to handle more animals and make a greater net profit while taking a lower profit per animal.

Concentrated swine production offers many possibilities for substituting machine power for human labor. The rapid turnover in the herd is one reason. The equipment is used a greater percentage of the time and can be justified more easily. Many producers keep the hogs on a hard surface from farrowing time until they are marketed.

Poultry producers, who have had a highly competitive market, have achieved a high degree of mechanization. The number of birds one man can tend has been increased by good organization of buildings and labor-saving equipment for time-consuming and simple, repetitive tasks. The work of preparing and distributing feed especially has been mechanized. The feed can be 60 percent or more of production costs. Anything affecting the cost of feed will affect profit materially. Growers have switched to bulk feeds or to the preparation of their own feeds to reduce the cost.

Bulk handling of grains, other feed materials, and farm produce has done much to reduce chore jobs.

The hopper-bottom steel tank has replaced feed sacks on many livestock farms; its use can reduce feed costs 4 dollars a ton. New systems of feed handling permit a farmer to take feed from storage to the point of consumption without touching it.

A typical mechanical feed-handling system for a hog or poultry farm has self-unloading bulk storage bins for small grain and supplements, an automatic mill to blend and grind the ration, and augers to convey the ration to the self-feeders or feed distributors. Feed that is milled off the farm is stored in a self-unloading bin near the point of use and augered directly to the distributors. Time clocks or pressure switches control the operation of all equipment. The feed is never touched by hand from the time it is placed in bulk storage until it is placed before the animals or poultry.

The use of mechanical equipment may create new problems. Moisture migration, bridging, or stoppage of the flow of feed in bulk storage systems may make it necessary to modify facilities to minimize or eliminate the difficulty. New feeding equipment may have to be designed.

THE ACCEPTABILITY of various systems of management is determined largely by the machines available to perform choring tasks involved in mechanization of a farmstead.

The objective is the lowest unit production cost for the desired quality. Both the demands for equipment and the design of the equipment are changing rapidly.

The wise manager must exercise prudent judgment in the selection of a particular system to achieve the lowest cost of production rather than selecting an individual machine or device on its merit alone. The system as a whole and its ability to function as a unit determine production cost and capacity.

Labor requirements of all phases of agriculture must be reduced to keep the products competitive in the market and still yield a reasonable profit for the producer. This is a continuing process.

The reduction of labor requirements about the farmstead and in livestock production eventually will lower the cost of animal products and still result in more profit for the producer.

Laborsaving equipment for chores began appearing on American farms about the middle of the 19th century. The first suction water pump, made of wood, was first used about 1840. Animal-powered corn shellers and grinders were first used about 1850. The self-regulating windmill came into use about 1850. The water pump, powered by an electric motor, in the early 1900's gave us the automatic pressure water system. The first vacuum-powered milking machine appeared in the late 1870's and the pulsating milker about 1895.

Animals furnished the first rotating power for farm chores with a sweep mechanism. A tumbling rod transmitted the power from the sweep to the sheller, grinder, elevator, or other choring equipment. The internal-combustion engine replaced sweep power first as stationary engines and later was supplemented with the belt and power takeoff shafts of tractors.

High-line electric power came to the farm in the 1920's and is now a principal power source for farm chores.

Tractor power has become indispensable in the production of field crops. To a limited extent, tractor power also does some of the work performed with the scoop shovel, the bushel basket, and the pitchfork.

It has been hard to mechanize livestock production. One reason is the nonstandard character of such production. Two producers seldom operate the same. A standard machine is not necessarily adaptable. The mechanization that has been accomplished has been to do the same job in the same way but to handle the material in bigger batches. One man has a bigger shovel, a larger pitchfork, or bushel basket.

Tractor power and self-unloading wagons can haul and distribute feed before the stock. The self-unloading wagon represents the larger bushel basket. It is an efficient way of moving material and is well suited to decentralized systems of production.

The same concept of moving larger batches of materials and handling with machinery has been applied to trucks for long-distance moving. Equipment for the handling of bulk feeds, fertilizers, and other granular material has eliminated the feed sack and with it the cause for many backaches. Handling feed in bulk has many advantages for the miller as well as the livestock feeder. It is essential to any successful mechanical feed distribution system, whether it be with permanently installed conveyors or with portable equipment, such as the self-unloading wagon.

MATERIALS handling is a necessary evil in the production cycle. The operation is more efficient if less time and energy are spent in moving or transferring material from one location to another.

Self-feeders save time and energy in feeding operations. Large quantities of feed are transferred at infrequent intervals. This works well with a batch system of transferring feed material.

Bulk storage of feed material, if accomplished with reliable machines for handling into and out of storage, can save many hours in livestock feeding. Bulk storage of feed materials at convenient locations near the point of use is necessary for an efficient livestock feeding system.

The poultry farmer who buys his feed from a commercial miller has little reason to store this feed at some central location and then move it to the various points for feeding. He could provide feed storage in bulk bins adjacent to the point of use and transfer the feed from the bulk storage to the poultry with inexpensive conveyors. That would eliminate any transfer by hand.

Bulk storage bins are available in many sizes, one of which will be suitable for almost any operation.

The farmer who grinds and mixes his own feed would vary this plan. He would prevent duplication of equipment unless it is up to capacity at each location.

Some systems can be built with permanently installed conveyors. They move the feed at a low rate over a long period of time, so that there is no need for manual labor and big-capacity secondary storage.

Anyone who must move feed by hand will find this a wise policy: Do not move it unless absolutely necessary; if it must be moved, move the material in large batches.

Automatic equipment available to farmers eliminates much drudgery.

On dairy farms are electric milking machines, pipeline systems to carry the milk from the cow to the bulk storage cooling tank, and automatic equipment to wash the pipeline in place. Cleaning equipment does this task easier and better than it can be done by hand.

The automatic water heater has done much to reduce time and labor associated with milk production. The use of bulk milk tanks has surged ahead in the past few years and in many milksheds is the only acceptable way to store Grade-A milk on the farm.

Whether the poultry farmer produces birds for meat or for eggs, his production efficiency is improved with automatic equipment.

Egg production is boosted by artificially increasing the hours of light for the laying hens. This is done automatically with a 24-hour timeclock and electric lights.

Automatic poultry feeders remove feed from bulk storage and transport it throughout the poultry house on a preset time schedule. Adequate feed is before the chickens at all times.

Automatic conveyors can collect the eggs from rollaway nests and transport them to the grading and cooling room for immediate processing. Quick cooling preserves quality.

All livestock must have plenty of fresh water. The pressurized electric water system has done more to improve farmstead operations than any one piece of equipment. One has only to turn the faucet to fill the watering trough. Automatic watering cups are commonplace. A drinking cup with a small, thermostatically controlled electric heater assures plenty of fresh drinking water all year without attention. A small automatic float valve on stock waterers costs only a few dollars and saves many steps.

Plenty of fresh water under adequate pressure is an essential item on any well-organized farm. It can become a limiting factor and determine whether or not a livestock feeding system is workable on a farm.

The increased number of pigs saved per litter by swine growers is due partly to automatic choring equipment. Good farrowing facilities are essential. Underfloor heat provided either by electric cable or by hot water pipes embedded in the concrete farrowing house floor controls the environment of newborn pigs.

Electric underfloor heat is easy to install and control. If properly installed and regulated, its cost of operation will not be excessive.

Radiant heat lamps are a convenient method of obtaining additional heat when required. One 250-watt infrared heating lamp furnishes adequate heat to warm a litter of pigs in a farrowing house with an air temperature as low as 30° F. A cluster of four to six of these lamps can warm 300 to 500 baby chicks. One of these lamps will operate 24 hours for 10 to 15 cents.

Liquid feeding of livestock has attracted some interest as a means of reducing labor requirements. Available means of transferring and measuring liquids suggest that complete automation of a liquid feeding system would be simple. Other problems, such as fermentation of nutrients in the distribution lines and the cost of feedstuffs suitable for liquid feeds, dictate caution in the development of a liquid feeding system. Many animals will require some dry roughage in their diet. This would require two feeding systems, instead of the one liquid system. Liquid feeding may prove practical in the future, but now dry feeds are more acceptable.

Significant advances have been made in all phases of farmstead mechanization. The extraction of honey is an example. Labor and the supervision of operators required to prepare the honeycomb for honey extraction and the extraction itself have been high. Machines now automatically uncap the combs and place the combs in the extractor. Automatic controls start the equipment, bring it to speed, stop it, reverse the combs in the extracting drum, and repeat the acceleration program required to extract the fluid honey. The machine will then stop for unloading and reloading.

An INTEGRATED-SYSTEM approach can best succeed in farmstead mechanization. The tasks that must be performed are usually varied, occur often, and are sometimes complicated.

Proper organization will lessen some of the difficulties in designing a system. If equipment is designed to work for the maximum number of hours available to accomplish a given task, small automatic equipment, which costs much less and requires less power for operation, will do the job.

An integrated system will provide for mechanical transfer of feed and other materials from storage to the point of use and for the removal of waste material as the need arises.

Substitution of mechanical power for human power will not necessarily result in an efficient materials handling system. An efficient system will evolve if all tasks are considered and arranged so that they can most easily be accomplished with mechanical power. The method of accomplishing a task may differ greatly from that practiced when it was done manually.

A man's dexterity can compensate for many errors in system design. A machine performs a given task in a given manner, and it cannot deviate to compensate for errors. The only way to do that is to place the machine in the direct control of a man. It is still possible that a man working with conventional handtools could accomplish the job in a shorter time.

Components of an efficient system for handling materials should be sized to handle material at equal rates. This assumes that all components operate simultaneously. The hurry-up-and-wait technique does not contribute to efficient use of equipment or men.

Machinery is most efficient when it is working at peak capacity continuously—when all equipment is operating at the same rate, when that rate represents the maximum capacity of the equipment, and when its size is such that maximum available time is used to accomplish the task. There will be deviations from this, because nonstandard equipment would be required to fit machine capacity exactly to the requirements of the system. In that case, one would use equipment of the size nearest to the demand, which would deliver the desired quantity.

A system should be designed for some growth, by adding additional equipment, by increasing operating time, or both.

Work done by a man or by a piece of equipment is not determined solely by the rate at which it is accomplished but by the rate and time it is operating. Lower powered, low-capacity equipment operating for a longer period of time can accomplish the same amount of work as large equipment operating for a proportionately shorter time. It is important to remember that in selecting machinery. Costs of machinery usually are determined by the rate at which they will do work; operating the equipment at less than its capacity does not reduce the cost of owning the equipment.

The speed at which a job should be done depends partly on whether an operator is required. Manpower is usually the most expensive item to be considered in the performance of a given job. The rate at which it must be done is chosen to utilize the manpower efficiently. If an operator is not required, then maximum efficiency of the machine and system can be the guide. Automatic control of machines to do a given task is necessary for the full utilization of a system and the maximum use of the machinery and power available.

Electric power is the most satisfactory means of operating an automatic system. It is nearly mandatory for the controls system. It is ideal for systems that operate on low horsepower over a long period under full automatic control. Automatic control permits the establishment of a programed system for accomplishing a task which will be repeated time after time until the controls are changed. This simple decision-making equipment often can do a better job of regulating the equipment than would be possible with manual control.

AUTOMATIC CONTROLS perform essentially the operations that would be performed by a man if the equipment were under manual control. They usually are repetitious and can be relegated to "yes" or "no" decisions, which can be easily handled by relays of the proper type and simple sensing devices. Full-range, or proportional, controls are more expensive, and, unless the equipment can perform only with such sophisticated controls, it is better to use the simple automatic-control equipment.

Controls for low-powered equipment are less expensive to buy and maintain. The relatively smaller amounts of power handled by the equipment permit the use of inexpensive relays and control devices.

DEVELOPMENTS like the hogomatic show what can be done with automatic equipment for feeding and cleaning operations. The hogomatic, an experimental system of feeding hogs during the finishing phase of their growth, has been used at the University of Illinois. It represents an integration of equipment and controls to perform automatically the routine operations that normally are performed manually. The controls take over the feeding and cleaning operations completely and only require that an operator set them to perform in the manner desired.

Feed is removed from bulk storage, mixed, ground, and conveyed through a system of pipes and automatic valves to a small holding container on a special feeder. The feeder controls are separate from those of the preparation and distribution system. Feed is maintained in the trough for the hogs at a given level; it is delivered to the trough at any time that the feed level in the control opening drops below the specified amount.

A timeclock controls the entire floor-cleaning operation. It turns on a traversing mechanism, which drives the water nozzles back and forth across one side of the pen. It also turns on the high-pressure pump that delivers water to two nozzles, which operate at a pressure of about 90 pounds per square inch and deliver about 12 gallons a minute. The manure and the cleaning water are discharged through a gutter and pipe system to a septic tank, where the manure is collected.

This system has been in satisfactory operation for more than 2 years.

Plans were made to develop a similar integration of equipment and controls for feeding beef and dairy cattle. It could be applied just as easily to other types of feed preparation and distribution operation. The main difference between the beef- and dairy-feeding systems and the hog-feeding system is the handling of roughages.

ROUGHAGES are harder to meter because they are not uniform, whereas ground feeds are relatively easy to mix, convey, and distribute.

Equipment to overcome the difficulties of bridging and other factors causing nonfree flow of roughage is being developed and studied. Equipment now used to meter roughage is a bin with a steel mat covering the entire floor. The mat is advanced slowly and proportions the roughage with concentrated materials such as corn and supplements. The mixed material then is conveyed in an auger for additional mixing and easy distribution in the feed bunk. The high-pressure pneumatic conveyor used in a hog-feeding system is not feasible for handling low-density roughages.

Distribution of feed by systems suitable for automatic electric control has been studied. The performance of high-volume, low-pressure (less than 2 pounds per square inch) pneumatic conveyors has been reported by engineers at the University of Illinois, Michigan State University, Texas Agricultural and Mechanical College, and the National Institute of Agricultural Engineering, Silsoe, England.

Floyd L. Herum, of the University of Illinois, reported on the performance of augers for conveying at low rates and low speed (down to 50 revolutions a minute) for 20 feet or more. Auger lengths of 100 feet or more would be common for this type of conveying.

Augers are less expensive than some systems of conveying. An auger system costs about 3 dollars a foot. As a simple method of moving material from point A to point B, they are satisfactory. Complications arise, however, if a different type of ration must also be moved from point A to point C through point B.

That is especially true if the two materials should not mix. The operator must operate the auger without introducing additional material until it is cleaned out and then close any intermediate dropouts to prevent mixing of the two materials.

This cleanout operation requires several minutes each time a different material is to be conveyed and makes an auger conveyor unsatisfactory for an automatic conveying system that must handle more than one material through a single conveyor at frequent intervals. A 3-inch screw moves material at the rate of approximately 25 feet a minute at 100 revolutions per minute. Cleanout time is the biggest disadvantage of an auger conveyor in an automatic system.

THE HIGH-PRESSURE pneumatic conveying system has shown promise for use in a fully automatic feed preparation and distribution system. With it, all the main operating equipment is at one place, and feed can be routed through small pipes to the feeding locations. Valves to control the feed flow are simple and easy to operate. They are effective, and the small amount of plugging that occurs with any valve in a pneumatic system does not endanger the operation of the system.

This system uses about 20 to 30 cubic feet of air a minute to deliver 1 thousand to 2 thousand pounds of feed an hour. It requires a pressure of 1 to 2 pounds per square inch per 100 feet of length. The conveying pipe can be suspended overhead or buried underground to connect various buildings to the feeding system. The ability of a high-pressure conveying system to purge itself and to break plugs if any should form makes it well suited for a fully automatic feed preparation and distribution system.

Warren Frye, owner and operator of the Frye Turkey Farm in Peoria County, Ill., installed a high-pressure pneumatic conveying system. This system automatically prepares a feed ration consisting of as many as four different ingredients at a rate of 1,200 pounds an hour. It delivers feed to any one of four different locations up to 400 feet from the mill. All an operator does is to change the constituents to make the desired ration.

Mr. Frye's system was installed with the help of engineers of the Department of Agriculture and the University of Illinois. Previously he needed one full-time man to prepare and deliver feed to the 30 thousand capons and 12 thousand turkeys he raises each year.

He estimates that one-half the time of one man is needed now to do the feeding. He believes he could triple the chicken phase of his poultry operation and require only an additional 84 man-hours a year for feeding the chickens. He hand-feeds the small chickens for the first few weeks until they are able to reach the automatic poultry feeder. No additional feed preparation equipment would be required for him to make this expansion. His feed conveying line would be extended another 200 feet and four more feed control valves would be added to the system.

Dependable sources of ingredients are essential to any satisfactory automatic feeding system. An automatic flat-bottomed bin unloader has been developed that assures a supply of small grain or meal for the discharge auger (or conveyor). It also unloads the bin to within a fraction of an inch of the floor.

The proportioning of ingredients continuously before grinding eliminates the need for a batch mixing system and more attention of an operator—a saving in time and investment. It also assures freshly ground feed for the animals. It has not been proved that freshly ground feed has any advantage over feed ground for a week or longer, but many farmers who are using continuous mixing-grinding systems believe that the freshly ground feed is more palatable to the animals; they eat more and put on more weight per pound of feed consumed.

Interlocks between controls are necessary to assure dependable operation of an automatic system. They permit the establishment of any desired control sequence that can be initiated by the closing of a single switch. The switch might be a timeclock or a pressure switch located at some point in the feeding system.

Another form of interlock essential in an automatic system is adequate protective devices to prevent malfunction of the system, which could cause either the delivery of an improper ration to the feeding point or damage to expensive equipment.

These devices can be connected to identify the cause of the stoppage of equipment. They can also be connected in various parts of the system to give the equipment time to recover from some difficulty and then begin operation again. If this cannot be done in a reasonable time, the system can be stopped; a warning circuit tells the operator that the equipment has stopped.

To MECHANIZE the farmstead further, it will be necessary to explore the basic characteristics of materials to be handled and the requirements of equipment to do the job.

The success of mechanization of the farmstead depends on reliable equipment, which must support its cost and yield a profit to the user. Otherwise it would become nothing more than a toy and would complicate the work and return nothing.

# Engineering the Farmstead

J. W. Rockey and S. S. DeForest

FARMSTEAD engineering organizes the buildings, lots, equipment, animals, workers, and other facilities of the farmstead into an efficient, profitable, integrated production unit for the present and the future.

It also lightens the drudgery of the chores and improves the livability and attractiveness of the farm.

Nearly all chores involve handling of materials—feed, water, bedding, manure, milk, eggs. Much chore labor can be saved by organizing the movements of materials, animals, and workers into a complete, efficient system in keeping with desired management practices.

Few will ever have the opportunity to lay out and build a completely new farmstead. Many will face the problems of improving or adding to an existing one. Some who suffer a catastrophe like fire or tornado may rebuild extensively or build anew.

To improve the efficiency of a farmstead and to be ready when the time comes, our advice is to prepare a long-range layout plan or goal now so it can be put into effect as opportunity occurs. In most instances, improvement will come a step at a time, but each step should be a step forward.

Because larger numbers of livestock are being handled on farms by fewer and possibly less experienced men, in less space, and at smaller margins of profit, a point to remember is that the farmstead should be engineered to hold to a minimum the discomfort or stress among the animals from extremes of weather, changes in ration, sorting, slighted sanitation, and such.

THE ARRANGEMENT of the farmstead has an important bearing on its efficiency, appearance, and livability.

For example, conveniently located feed and bedding storages ease the distribution chore. Paved yards and lots keep animals out of the mud, reduce physical stress on them, ease the cleaning chore, and improve general appearance and livability.

An easily accessible farmhouse, with a nice view and parking area, is an attractive, convenient setting for living and entertaining.

Each farmstead presents its own set of conditions that must be taken into account in planning the layout. Some general principles have common application, however.

The site should be chosen carefully. A poor choice could be a longtime handicap.

Look for favorable natural topography—high, well drained, and level enough for convenient placement of the buildings and easy getting around. Allow room for expansion.

Provide easy access to highway and fields. There will be constant travel with many types of vehicles and equipment in all kinds of weather. The driveways, lanes, service courts, and other areas for vehicles and equipment must have adequate clearances and turnaround space for today's and tomorrow's vehicles.

Take your vehicles and wheeled equipment out in the open and measure the space required for parking and maneuvering and be sure to allow adequate safety clearances. Grades and construction must be suitable for heavy loads the year around.

Make lanes and driveways as short, direct, and free of gates as possible. This will hold down costs of construction, maintenance, fencing, and gates.

Avoid a situation in which livestock must be driven across a busy road.

There has to be a good source of water. The automatic water system, high standards of sanitation and safety, and water-using equipment of the modern farmstead require generous quantities of good water. Wells that may be pumped only at low rates can be compensated for somewhat by large storages, and poor quality can be improved by treatment.

Investigate the water situation to your full satisfaction while your project is in the planning stage. Do likewise for the disposal of wastes carried by water.

Orient the buildings and facilities to take advantage of winter sun and the summer breezes, while protecting against summer sun and winter wind. Sun provides more than light. It provides heat to thaw snow and ice, help dry wet spots, and promote general sanitation and well-being of man and animals. Summer sun can be a disadvantage and may need to be shaded.

Take advantage of natural windbreaks, such as hills or clumps of trees. Use buildings as windbreaks to protect open feeding and service areas.

Place open-front buildings with their closed backs or sides to the prevailing winter winds. This would usually put them along the north or west side of the livestock lot. Close the gaps where necessary with fences or windbreaks.

Look for exposure to cooling summer breezes and shade from the hot sun.

Winds carry odors. Good orientation would let prevailing breezes carry them away from the living area.

Fire always is a hazard. Therefore, if possible, place buildings containing such flammable materials as hay or such heating devices as welding apparatus, heated-air grain or hay driers, brooders, and the like at least 1 50 feet

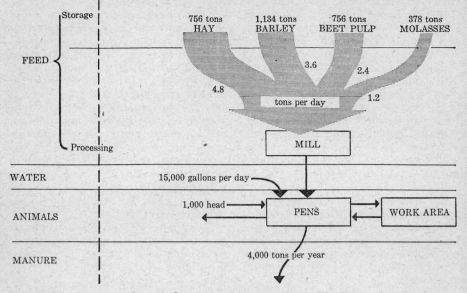

*Example of materials flow diagram for a 1,000-head beef feedlot operation.*

away from other major buildings, particularly the house and barn.

Protect buildings against lightning.

If possible, provide some firefighting facilities, such as fire extinguishers, a 1-inch hose line for the water system, or a farm pond.

Safety should be planned—particularly traffic safety. Avoid blind corners by setting buildings back from driveways and removing plantings that obscure vision. Avoid low overhangs or protruding objects that an unwary person might walk into or stumble over.

Place the farmhouse 100 feet or more from the highway, upwind from the livestock area, and with the kitchen having a view of the entrance drive and service facilities.

Consider an outdoor living area, with shade trees and a fireplace, by the farm pond. Provide adequate parking for visitors near the guest entrance.

PRODUCTION efficiency is a major concern. Locate the buildings, lots, yards, and feeding and other facilities with respect to one another and to the fields and highway so that a minimum of time and travel is required to perform the chore routines.

Allow some flexibility for future changes in scale, nature, management system or equipment of the enterprise. Such changes are inevitable. Do this by making it possible to add to buildings, to convert them from one use to another, to add new buildings or equipment, or to add or rearrange lots or yards at reasonable cost and without reducing efficiency.

Handling large quantities of feed, water, bedding, manure, products, and other materials efficiently—including the animals—requires careful planning. In an operation like a thousand-cow dairy or a layout for feeding thousands of head of beef or hogs, the problems of handling materials can be complex. Just getting the thousand cows back and forth between the milking and resting-feeding areas twice daily is a major traffic problem.

A number of principles applicable to

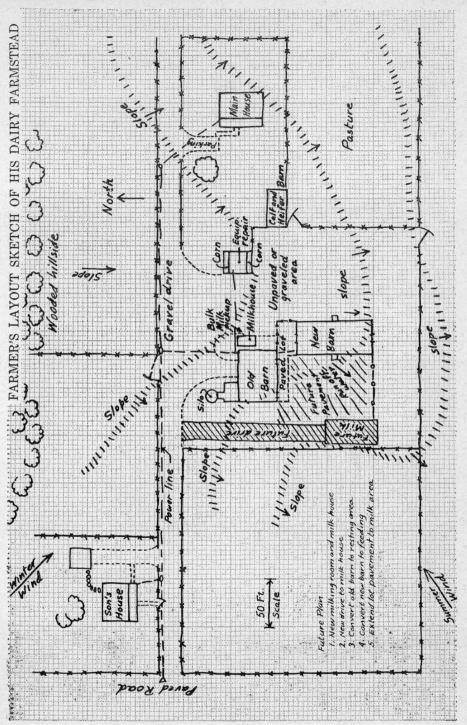

FARMER'S LAYOUT SKETCH OF HIS DAIRY FARMSTEAD

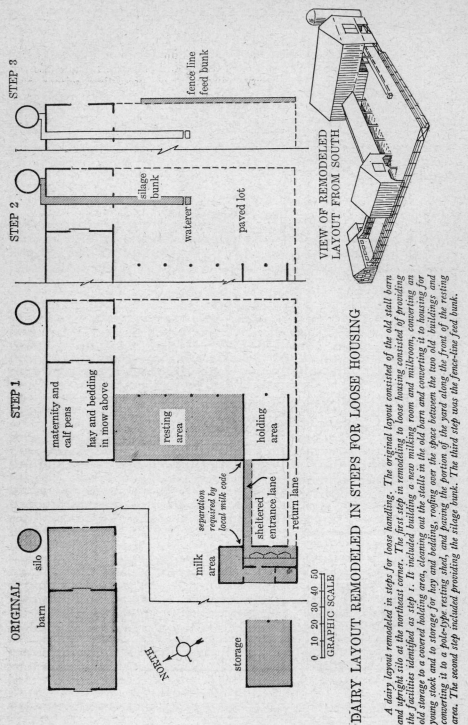

STEP 3

fence line
feed bunk

VIEW OF REMODELED
LAYOUT FROM SOUTH

STEP 2

silage
bunk

waterer

paved lot

STEP 1

maternity and
calf pens

hay and bedding
in mow above

resting
area

holding
area

separation
required by
local milk code

sheltered
entrance lane

return lane

milk
area

ORIGINAL

silo

barn

NORTH

storage

GRAPHIC SCALE
0  10  20  30  40  50

## DAIRY LAYOUT REMODELED IN STEPS FOR LOOSE HOUSING

*A dairy layout remodeled in steps for loose handling. The original layout consisted of the old stall barn and upright silo at the northeast corner. The first step in remodeling to loose housing consisted of providing the facilities identified as step 1. It included building a new milking room and milkroom, converting an old storage to a covered holding area, cleaning out the stalls in the old barn and converting it to housing for young stock and to storage for hay and bedding, roofing over the space between the two old buildings and converting it to a pole-type resting shed, and paving the portion of the yard along the front of the resting area. The second step included providing the silage bunk. The third step was the fence-line feed bunk.*

handling materials on the farmstead have been developed:

Don't move it. Or move it as little as possible. Shorten distances. Let animals self-feed.

Handle larger amounts. Make every trip count. Eliminate small batches.

Make flow continuous. Use machines to move materials automatically.

Condense it. Reduce bulk and weight of materials. Change their shape for easy handling.

Calculate and tabulate the amounts of the various materials to be moved and stored, on a daily, monthly, or annual basis and diagram their flow. The diagram need not be to an accurate scale, but it should resemble the contemplated layout and should be large enough to allow the pertinent information to be shown legibly.

The flow diagram helps you study the location and capacity of mixers, storages, conveyors, chore routes, equipment and the like.

Select equipment to fit in with the management and operational systems to be employed in the enterprise and with the physical arrangement of the farmstead.

Until chores can be turned over to fully automatized systems of equipment and facilities, they will continue to be performed by the combination of men and equipment. So consider the labor on hand, along with the tasks and facilities, in selecting equipment for the layout.

Be wary of overmechanizing to the point where hired help or machines are underutilized.

Consult equipment catalogs and manufacturers' or dealers' representatives for dimensions, power requirements, clearances, capacities, and other engineering information so the layout can be made to accommodate the equipment and so separate items of equipment can be fitted with each other into systems.

PREPARE a layout sketch or map of the entire farmstead and keep it as a permanent record. Show such natural features as hills, streams, and roads and the buildings, lots, lanes, fences, gates, utilities, and other facilities, existing and planned. Include also the direction of prevailing winter and summer winds and the compass orientation.

The layout begins with thinking, discussing, and seeking advice from extension specialists, dealers in buildings, equipment, and materials, power company representatives, and the like.

At this stage ideas can be changed or discarded without even erasing a line on a piece of paper. Then come rough sketches and, finally, a finished layout to scale.

Make every effort to crystallize thinking and ideas during this phase while it is still possible to make changes at little expense. Double check to be sure adequate water, electric power, and means for disposing of wastes are available.

The important thing is to work out an efficient operating system in accordance with desired management practices. Keep in mind that the buildings, facilities, equipment, materials, animals, and workmen are all parts of the system.

Observe particularly the following:

Locate buildings involving appreciable chore travel as close together as is consistent with fire safety and local codes.

Pave livestock yards and lots to the extent possible so as to keep animals, workers, and equipment out of the mud and to make cleaning easier.

Arrange buildings and lots to facilitate movement of trucks, wagons, tractors, manure loaders, spreaders, and the like. Avoid such bottlenecks and obstructions as inadequate headroom under beams or low-hanging overhead wires, closely spaced posts, too-narrow gates, doors, and passageways, and odd-shaped or cut-up lots, which will hamper movement.

Locate feed storage and processing facilities conveniently close to the point of use. Self-feed hay and silage if pos-

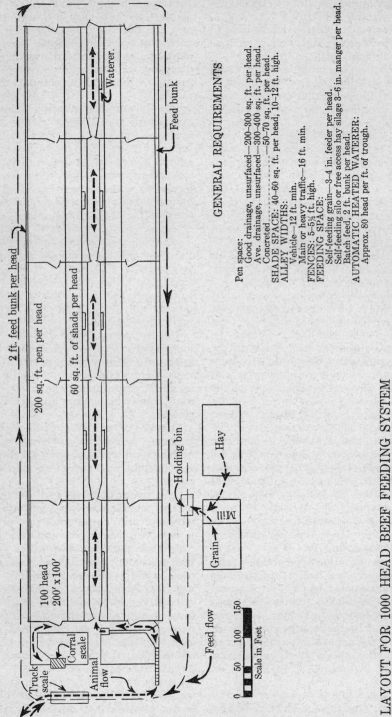

GENERAL REQUIREMENTS

Pen space:
  Good drainage, unsurfaced—200–300 sq. ft. per head.
  Ave. drainage, unsurfaced—300–400 sq. ft. per head.
  Concreted—50–70 sq. ft. per head.
SHADE SPACE: 40–60 sq. ft. per head, 10–12 ft. high.
ALLEY WIDTHS:
  Vehicle—12 ft. min.
  Main or heavy traffic—16 ft. min.
FENCES: 5–5½ ft. high.
FEEDING SPACE:
  Self-feeding grain—3–4 in. feeder per head.
  Self-feeding silo or free access hay silage 3–6 in. manger per head.
  Batch feed, 2 ft. bunk per head.
AUTOMATIC HEATED WATERER:
  Approx. 80 head per ft. of trough.

LAYOUT FOR 1000 HEAD BEEF FEEDING SYSTEM

sible. Arrange feed bunks for filling from a self-unloading truck or tractor-towed wagon, without opening gates. Or use a mechanical conveyor.

It is helpful in making layouts to work on cross-section paper, which you can buy at a stationery store. A common printing is 10 lines to the inch in both directions. Let 1 inch on the drawing equal 20 feet on the ground or each space on the paper equal 2 feet on the ground. That is a good general scale for smaller farmsteads. At that scale, a distance of 300 feet on the ground would be 15 inches on the paper and 10 feet on the ground would be one-half inch on the paper.

For larger, more spreadout farmsteads or entire farms, an overall layout may be made at a smaller scale; 1 inch on the drawing may equal 50 feet on the ground. At that scale, 750 feet on the ground would reduce to 15 inches on the paper. Then details of small or congested areas, such as gate arrangements or building interiors could be shown at an enlarged scale, such as 1 inch to 10 feet or even 1 inch to 5 feet.

Paper ruled with 8 lines to the inch lends itself correspondingly to scales of 1 inch to 16 feet, 40 feet, 8 feet, or 4 feet.

Work lightly in pencil, so that you can make erasures and changes easily. Or use transparent overlays for preliminary trials, which may be discarded in lieu of erasing.

You can try different arrangements easily by using templates, cutouts, or models of the buildings, storages, equipment items, and other facilities made to the scale of the layout. They also help you to visualize the layout and make this phase a family undertaking.

For a remodeling or improvement project, sketch the existing layout on the cross-section paper and use transparent overlays for sketching the improvements. Make and compare several different arrangements. Add them to the original when you have settled them finally.

Analyze the new layout critically.

Question each item to see if it could be eliminated or handled better or more economically by some other means. Consider such things as the amount invested in buildings and equipment, their utilization, probable life and depreciation, maintenance, obsolescence, and flexibility to adjust to future changes. Make any modifications indicated by this evaluation.

THE AMOUNT of investment may dictate a smaller enterprise at the start or a less heavily mechanized operation. If so, you may regard the overall layout as a long-range goal to be achieved in planned steps. This is the practical solution for many livestock producers, but it takes more careful consideration of the steps to achieve a smooth, economical, and nonwasteful transition from one step to the next.

A good example is a 150-acre dairy farm in Maryland that had been producing Grade-A milk for the Washington market with 25 cows in an old stall barn, which could not be adapted for a larger herd without excessive cost. When the son was graduated from college, the father took him into partnership. Together they proceeded to modernize the farmstead.

The first step was to build a loose housing system, which included an elevated-stall milking room, milk pipeline and bulk cooler, and a pole barn, 38 by 76 feet, for 60 cows.

Young stock, hay, and bedding were housed in the old barn. Silage was hauled from the upright silo at the northeast corner of the old barn and fed in movable bunks in the drylot (part of which was paved) southeast of the pole barn. Green chop cut with a field harvester also was fed there.

The second step was to install a mechanical feeder to convey the silage from the upright silo to the feed bunk and to complete the paving of the drylot.

The third step was to construct a fence-line feed bunk for green chop and to bring the herd up to 60 cows. The family did most of the work on

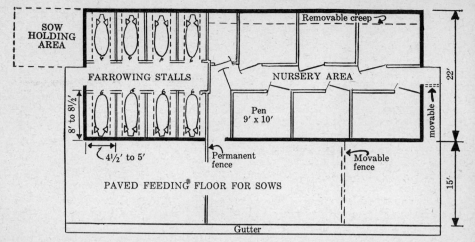

EXAMPLE OF A HOG FARROWING-NURSERY UNIT

the project to hold down cash outlay.

Cash outlay was restricted to the purchase of materials and equipment and occasional hire of part-time help. No record was kept of the amount of family labor, but the cash outlay amounted to 17,100 dollars—or 285 dollars per cow.

The changes reduced the man-hours needed to care for the 60 cows to less than formerly was needed for 25. For example, average man-hours per cow for milking was reduced by one-third and for barn cleaning and silage feeding by about five-sixths each.

The family is going on with additional improvements to reduce labor further and increase the number of cows that can be handled. Several old buildings have been abandoned and will be torn down.

The fourth stage will be to build a new implement storage building with farm shop and a drier for chopped hay. A further increase in the herd, however, will require the purchase of most concentrate feeds.

THE DAIRY farmstead traditionally has been associated with long hours of hard, seven-days-a-week work.

Wider adoption of presently available laborsaving practices and equipment such as milking machines with pipelines and bulk tanks, elevated milking stalls, automatic feeding and watering systems, gutter cleaners, self-feeding, and the like, would do much to reduce the drudgery and improve labor efficiency.

But there is need for still further improvement, which can be provided by engineering research. It has been estimated that the chore labor requirements of good practices can be cut 10 to 20 percent. Far greater savings can be made in enterprises handicapped by poor arrangements and procedures.

In a study of operations on a number of Maryland dairy farms, H. J. Eby, of the Department of Agriculture, found chore labor bottlenecks and handicaps to be widespread. They included such things as awkward locations for milkhouses, silos, and feed storages; dead-end feed alleys that require nonproductive travel; and inadequate doorway size, postspacing, or headroom that prevent use of tractors or other powered equipment in and around buildings for cleaning and other chores. Searching out and cor-

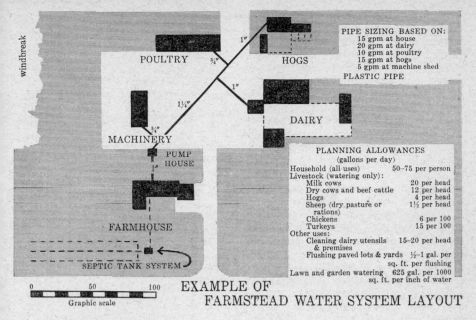

PIPE SIZING BASED ON:
15 gpm at house
20 gpm at dairy
10 gpm at poultry
15 gpm at hogs
5 gpm at machine shed
PLASTIC PIPE

windbreak

POULTRY ¾″

1″

HOGS

1″

1¼″

DAIRY

¾″

MACHINERY

PUMP
HOUSE

1″

FARMHOUSE

SEPTIC TANK SYSTEM

PLANNING ALLOWANCES
(gallons per day)

| Household (all-uses) | 50–75 per person |
|---|---|
| Livestock (watering only): | |
| Milk cows | 20 per head |
| Dry cows and beef cattle | 12 per head |
| Hogs | 4 per head |
| Sheep (dry pasture or rations) | 1½ per head |
| Chickens | 6 per 100 |
| Turkeys | 15 per 100 |
| Other uses: | |
| Cleaning dairy utensils & premises | 15–20 per head |
| Flushing paved lots & yards | ½–1 gal. per sq. ft. per flushing |
| Lawn and garden watering | 625 gal. per 1000 sq. ft. per inch of water |

0        50        100
Graphic scale

EXAMPLE OF
FARMSTEAD WATER SYSTEM LAYOUT

recting such handicaps would help many a dairyman.

Two general systems of handling dairy cattle are employed in the United States—the stall barn and loose housing. Milk of high quality can be produced under either system. The stall barn is traditional, but does not readily lend itself to increasing herd size. The loose housing system has become popular as its advantages in cost, labor, and flexibility for herds of 25 to 30 cows and larger were recognized.

Loose housing is a flexible system of buildings and lots in which the cows are allowed free access to resting and feeding areas until they are brought into the milking room for milking. Resting, feeding, and milking areas usually are grouped around a central paved lot or yard.

In cold climates it is advantageous to locate an open front resting shed along the north side of the paved lot so that it may benefit from the winter sun and break the winter wind for the lot. A covered feeding area works well along the north or west side of the lot for the same reasons, with the open exposure to the south or east. The milking area is normally enclosed and may thus take an exposed location so long as the holding area is sheltered.

The wagon-wheel or pie-shaped layout, as is used in the hot Southwest, uses open corrals and sun shades in the resting areas. It is designed to reduce the cow traffic problem by having one end of each corral at the central hub, near the milking facility. Feeding is along the outer perimeter. At least the holding area and ground near the water and feed should be paved.

The milking rooms used in the loose housing system are usually elevated-stall types, which do away with the tiresome bending and stooping of milking in a floor-level stall arrangement. To the elderly, the arthritic, or otherwise physically handicapped worker this may mean more than a saving in time or money.

Milking rates and movements of operators in these milking rooms vary with the type and arrangement of stalls, the number of stalls and milking machines, skill and energy of the operator, training of the cows, and other factors.

Thayer Cleaver, an agricultural engineer in the Department of Agriculture, found that milking rates ranged from fewer than 10 to more than 40 cows per man-hour and that operator travel ranged from less than 50 to more than 200 feet per cow per milking for conventional side-entering and lane- or chute-type stalls arranged in a single or double row or U-shape. In the herringbone-type milking room, he found rates from less than 30 to more than 60 cows per man-hour and travel from less than 40 to more than 60 feet per cow per milking.

The herringbone milking room is an efficient, compact, elevated-stall, walk-through arrangement with a multiple stall on either side of a central operator area. Each stall has space for several cows, usually four to eight, positioned at an angle of about 30° to the axis of the operator area by the shape of the stall rail and the endgates. There are no separating partitions between the cows. Milk is normally piped to a bulk tank. A milking unit is provided for each pair of cow positions—a layout with space for positioning four cows in each stall (double-4) would thus have four units. Facilities for feeding concentrates during milking are optional.

Among its advantages are: Less distance between udders (36 to 38 inches compared with 8 to 9 feet in conventional milking rooms); less floor space per cow because of the compact arrangement; group handling of cows; and adaptability to different herd sizes and to one or more operators.

Russell E. Larson, an agricultural engineer in the Department, applied an industrial engineering technique and determined that a good size for a one-man operation was the double-4. The operator, working at a normal rate, could break his routine for an occasional fast milker, cope with the usual delays, and still get the machines off 83 percent of the cows as soon as they finished milking. To operate a double-5 successfully and cope with the delays, the operator would have to

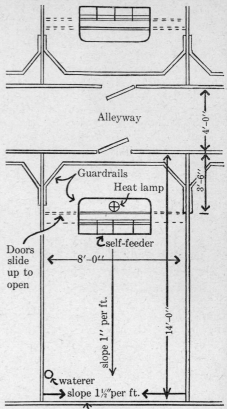

MINIMUM STRESS HOG HOUSE PEN

work at least part of the time at a rate faster than 125 percent of normal.

The double-6 demands a continuously fast pace and high degree of alertness on the part of the operator, well-trained cows, and reliable equipment. It is recommended for one-man operation only when these conditions can be met.

The double-6, double-8, and double-10 are suited to a two-man operation. In new construction, space for five or six stall positions on a side could be provided per operator, but only four positions should be used until the necessary skill and experience are acquired.

FEEDING SYSTEMS for beef cattle are beginning to fit a pattern.

Where 250 to 300 animals are fed at

one time, mechanical bunk feeders are efficient. They are easy to install (especially the auger type) and are adapted easily to existing barns. To combine ration ingredients, silo unloaders feed to a central feed auger; additional small augers introduce grain and supplement. The feed auger mixes the ingredients as the ration is delivered to the stock. Location of silos and feed storage bins is important. Old barns—if they are used—should have widely spaced posts and ample headroom for operation of manure removal equipment.

Mechanical conveyors are impractical for feeding a thousand head or more. The feed processing area then becomes a small feed plant, with provision for measuring accurately all the ingredients of any number of possible rations available to the feeder. Some provision must be made for sorting, handling, holding, and loading cattle. The pens must be arranged so that an unloading wagon can easily maneuver to fill the feed bunks without going through the pens.

In an operation of that size, the accuracy of the feed processing can be lost if the workmen doing the actual feeding are careless.

Hog raising systems are of two basic types.

In the clean-ground system, hogs are dispersed in pastures.

The confinement system was made possible by advances in nutrition developments and disease control. Hogs can be raised where labor requirements are low, utilizing housing to provide an environment most beneficial to small pigs, growing pigs, or finishing pigs. Buildings are kept "working" most of the time by farrowing almost continuously, with intervals to break the disease cycle.

A variety of layout arrangements are suitable for raising hogs in confinement. A practical one is Midwest Plan 72670; its capacity is 80 litters a year from two 20-sow herds, each sow farrowing twice a year.

The insulated farrowing-nursery unit has farrowing stalls, which almost eliminate the crushing of little pigs.

Let us assume that four sows farrow in each 4-day period. Sows about to farrow are washed in the service room. Then they are familiarized with stalls. The first eight go to stalls. As more stalls are needed, sows and litters are moved to the nursery area, two sows and litters to a pen.

During the nursing cycle, the first sows to farrow and their litters are in the pens; the last ones are in stalls. Sows are fed outdoors twice daily and feeders for small pigs are in the creep areas.

The pigs are weaned at 3 to 5 weeks of age. Sows and creep feeders are removed, and the pigs have free access to the feeding floor and the sow feeders.

Pigs are moved to the finishing facilities before reaching 75 pounds.

The farrowing-nursery building is thoroughly cleaned and allowed to stand empty for at least a week for disease control before the second herd of sows starts to farrow.

Finishing layouts are varied, but generally they require a sheltered area for the hogs to sleep, a mechanical means of feeding or filling self-feeders, and a method of removing manure easily and often. Manure gutters should be provided with grating covers to keep the hogs from having access to disease-carrying materials.

Stresses have a strong effect on the ability of livestock to convert feed efficiently. Cold, heat, disease, vaccination, sorting, mixing together, and muddy conditions all create stresses that prevent animals from doing their best.

A house to reduce such stress in hogs was tested by Tillman Bubenzer and Don Fisher at Conner Prairie Farm, Noblesville, Ind. Their system enables pigs to remain in the same pen from farrowing to market weight.

The pigs build up resistance to disease organisms present in the pen when they are born, and they are not

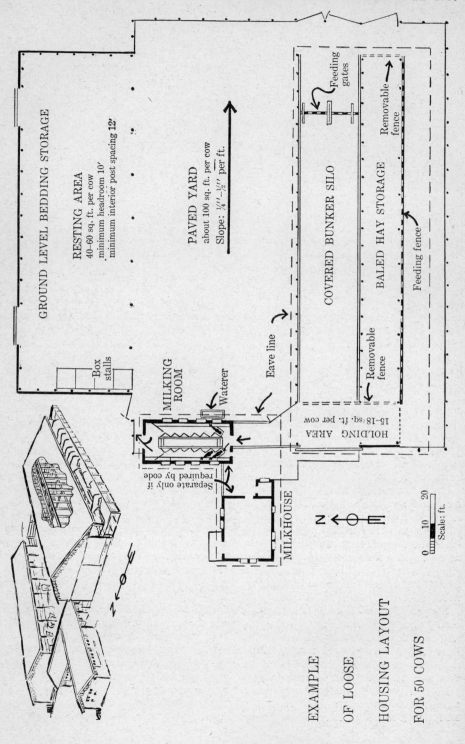

GROUND LEVEL BEDDING STORAGE

RESTING AREA
40-60 sq. ft. per cow
minimum headroom 10'
minimum interior post spacing 12'

Box stalls

PAVED YARD
about 100 sq. ft. per cow
Slope: ¼"–½" per ft.

MILKING ROOM

Waterer

Separate only if required by code

Eave line

Feeding gates

COVERED BUNKER SILO

Removable fence

BALED HAY STORAGE

Feeding fence

Removable fence

HOLDING AREA
15–18 sq. ft. per cow

MILKHOUSE

N   E
Scale: ft.
0   10   20

EXAMPLE

OF LOOSE

HOUSING LAYOUT

FOR 50 COWS

exposed to organisms that may exist in other pens.

The brooder area has an insulated concrete floor and an overhead heat lamp. A curved guardrail causes the sow to lie with her udder toward the brooder. The door arrangement reverses her direction each time she leaves and returns, making for more equal nursing.

A system that may be the next step in raising hogs is a multideck, all-steel, mesh-floor battery of cage-type farrowing stalls that will handle a number of sows and litters on each deck. A special lift cart raises the sow to the proper level. Manure drops to a tray under each stall and is carried away by a mechanical drag. Feed and water are available constantly at each cage. Cooled air is piped to each hog when the weather is hot to reduce stress from heat.

EGG PRODUCING SYSTEMS are of two types: Floor-managed and cage.

In the floor system, the birds are loose and free to scratch, roost, feed, water, or nest.

In the cage system, 1 to 25 birds are confined in a cage. One- or two-bird cages are arranged in rows; water and feed troughs are alongside. Eggs roll to an egg roll-out tray at the front of the cage or the nest for convenient gathering.

Each system has some advantages. According to Hajime Ota, agricultural engineer in the Department of Agriculture, the floor system involves less investment per laying hen and less labor in keeping records and looking after equipment. Cages give lower feed costs, more uniform egg production, and better control of disease.

Thayer Cleaver, also of the Department, and S. A. Hart, W. O. Wilson, and A. E. Woodard, of the California Agricultural Experiment Station, studied floor, cage, and wire-pen housing on 27 poultry farms in California. They reported: Chore time per case of eggs averaged nearly the same for all types of housing, except that it was

approximately half for three community-type cage layouts where egg gathering and cleaning were combined. Chore time and travel varied more widely between poultrymen than between house types. Feeding consumed the least time and most travel; egg cleaning, the reverse. Mechanization of feeding halved the average feeding time. Mechanization of egg cleaning reduced drudgery, but did not save time.

A modern plan for a floor-managed house for 2 thousand layers is Michigan State University Plan 727–C1–87.

This house permits a reduction of the allowance of floor space from the normal 3 to 4 square feet per hen to 2, because of the mechanical ventilation, insulated walls and ceiling, and mechanical removal of droppings. About one-third of the total moisture produced by the flock is removed in the droppings by the mechanical cleaner.

AN ADEQUATE supply of satisfactory water under pressure is essential at the farmhouse, livestock areas, and service areas on the modern farmstead.

Groundwater is the main source of supply for the farmstead. Deep wells usually are more constant in yield and more heavily mineralized than shallow wells, which depend on local rainfall and often go dry during drought. Shallow wells are more subject to contamination. They need a good watertight platform over the top and a tight lining for the upper 10 feet of the walls. Springs also may be found in some areas.

In places where suitable groundwater is unavailable, surface water from ponds or ditches is used. Such water is practically certain to be bacterially unsafe. It should be used only after adequate treatment and approval of the local health officer. The usual recommended treatment is chlorination, preceded by settling and filtering. A bed of activated carbon may remove organic tastes or odors that are present.

Equipment for softening, removing iron, taste, and odor, filtering, or chlo-

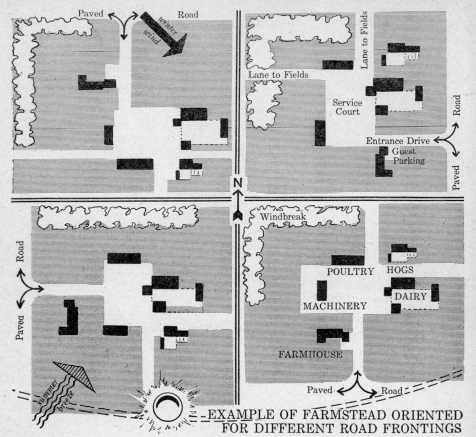

EXAMPLE OF FARMSTEAD ORIENTED
FOR DIFFERENT ROAD FRONTINGS

rinating may be had from dealers in nearly all localities where there is water that can be treated successfully with their equipment.

The water system should have the capacity to meet all the day-to-day demands of the farmstead, including simultaneous use at several outlets.

A rule of thumb for sizing a pump calls for a capacity to pump a day's requirements in 2 hours. Thus, if the estimated daily usage is 1,200 gallons, a 600-gallon-an-hour pump is indicated.

A newer method of sizing calls for furnishing the combined demand of whatever outlets may reasonably be expected to be open simultaneously for more than a few minutes. If 10 gallons a minute are desired for flushing a feedlot at the same time that 5 gallons a

minute are desired for showering and another 5 for watering the lawn or garden, the pump should have a capacity of 20 gallons a minute, or 1,200 an hour—unless available from storage.

When water is used for flushing manure, a booster pump to raise the pressure to 60 to 70 pounds per square inch is desirable.

The service piping should be run as direct as possible. It should be large enough to carry the desired flow without excessive friction losses. Reference charts and tables have been developed for use as guides in sizing piping layouts. Galvanized, copper, and plastic water pipes are being used satisfactorily on the farmstead.

Pipelines, waterers, and other water equipment should be protected against freezing by laying below frost depth, insulating, or applying heat. A simple means of heating is a thermostatically controlled electric heating cable.

Locally available sources of advice on developing farmstead water supplies are the county agricultural agents, health officers, well drillers, pump dealers, and dealers in water-treatment equipment.

FARMSTEAD WASTES, such as manure and sewage, must be handled and disposed of in a sanitary way. These wastes are breeding places of the housefly, stablefly, and other pests that carry diseases and parasites that affect man and animals. The importance of adequate sanitation increases as metropolitan areas reach out into the formerly rural countryside.

The fly lays about 200 eggs at a time. They develop into adult flies in about a week. Cleaning manure on a twice-a-week schedule during the fly-breeding season breaks the breeding cycle and thus helps hold down the number of flies.

Farmers always have spread livestock manure on the fields for its fertilizing and soil conditioning value. The operator with no crop or pasturelands, however, cannot use this method and may be up against a tough problem of disposal. Some operators place manure in trenches and backfill with earth, in a manner similar to the sanitary fills used by some municipalities for disposing of refuse. Some others are lucky enough to be able to sell their manure for use by other farmers or suburbanites.

Mechanical cleaners for barns and poultry buildings are available and save time and labor. The cleaner can empty directly into a spreader as a further laborsaver. Walls and floors can be flushed with a hose.

Paved barnyards, lots, pens, feeding platforms, and other paved areas, indoors or out, may be cleaned by scraping with a blade or flushing with a hose. To facilitate use of power-operated equipment, the pavement should be free of obstacles, either on the ground or overhead. For flushing, the pavement should slope to drain readily, one-fourth inch to one-half inch per foot, and some means of collecting and disposing of the drainage needs to be provided.

Liquid handling of manures has laborsaving advantages. The simplest method is to flush into a 6-inch or 8-inch sewerline leading to a broad, well drained, grassed area for field aeration, but it usually creates a rather unsightly and odorous area at the outlet and is objectionable from this standpoint. Large amounts of water are needed to keep the solids from settling out and clogging.

A variation of this method is to run the sewerline to an open, shallow lagoon or pond, which is cleaned out with a blade, clamshell, or other excavating device when filled. An alternate lagoon may be used while drying and cleaning are in process. Lagoons have been used with more or less success in the Southwest and elsewhere. They are usually not more than 2 to 3 feet deep and have an area of less than one-tenth acre. The frequency of cleaning depends on the amount of solids in the flushings and other factors. Fibrous solids, such as straw, may be screened out by a screening device in the line en route to the lagoon. Lagoons are not entirely free of odor and may be objectionable from this standpoint.

Another method is to run the flushings through a sewer pipe or open gutter to an underground pit and then pump them from the pit either to irrigation piping or to a tank truck or wagon for spreading on a field. This method has the disadvantage that there are times when the material is not wanted on or cannot be applied on a field.

There is little uniformity in the size of pit—it can range from 2,000 gallons upward. Capacity for at least a week's accumulation is desirable. An agitating device may be put in the pit to help prevent settling and keep the

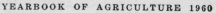

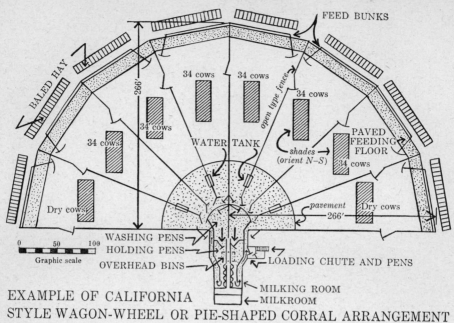

EXAMPLE OF CALIFORNIA
STYLE WAGON-WHEEL OR PIE-SHAPED CORRAL ARRANGEMENT

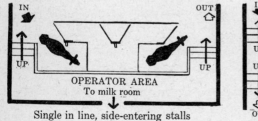

Single in line, side-entering stalls

Tandem, U-shaped, side-entering stalls

Double, walk-through stalls

Herringbone, double

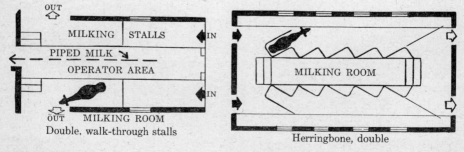

EXAMPLES OF ELEVATED STALL MILKING ROOM ARRANGEMENTS

contents flowable. A nonclogging manure or sewage pump is needed to move the material out of the tank.

The tank wagon is usually made locally by mounting a tank on a chassis and providing a valve to control the flow. An agitator may be placed inside to prevent settling. A baffle or splash device may be used at the outlet.

Soil absorption also is used to some extent for disposal of manure liquids. In this method, the flushings are sewered to a settling tank, the solids are allowed to settle, and the liquid is piped off to a subsoil disposal field. The disadvantages are that the solids do not decompose in the tank and must be removed periodically; an absorbent soil is required, and, even then, the field is apt to clog and become a nuisance in time. A screening device ahead of the tank will keep out some of the fibrous solids and help reduce the load on the tank.

The settling tank is similar to the septic tank commonly used in disposal of domestic sewage.

The disposal field may consist of 4-inch, open-jointed tile, laid at a depth of about 2.5 feet and slope of about 2 to 4 inches per 100 feet, in a trench 2 feet wide, with about a foot of graded gravel under and around the tile.

The length of trench would depend on the amount of liquid and absorptiveness of the soil. It is suggested that the total length be not less than 1 foot for each 5 to 10 gallons of flushings per day. If this gives more than 100 feet of trench, it is suggested that parallel lines be laid, each not more than 100 feet long.

Sewage from the farmhouse and from a toilet room in the milkhouse or elsewhere on the farmstead should be disposed of in accordance with applicable sanitary or health codes that may be in effect in the area. In the absence of applicable codes, a septic tank installation is recommended.

Information on recommended sewage disposal systems is available upon request to most State agricultural extension services and health departments.

# Change on the Range

Robert O. Gilden and F. G. Renner

In the days of the open range, little thought was given to improving the forage resources. Sheep were trailed hundreds of miles to their grazing areas. Cattle were turned out to rustle their own forage, water at dangerous bogholes, and find what little protection they could from pests and storms.

The modern rancher makes every effort to improve his rangelands, provide ample feed and clean water for his livestock, and protect their health and comfort so they will make the gains on which his profits depend.

Fences, which range stockmen once called the curse of the country, first were used to enclose the ranch boundaries to keep the owner's stock where they belonged and to prevent trespass from his neighbors'.

Fences are needed still for that purpose. As more intensive management is practiced, however, the trend is toward cross-fencing. The greater number of smaller-sized pastures or paddocks that results permits separation of a part of the herd for breeding, feeding, and other purposes. The animals can be controlled better. More attention can be given to their individual needs.

Additional fences are used to protect cropland, newly seeded areas, and watering places, and to separate tracts that should be grazed in different seasons or that require other special treatment. A number of fenced grazing units also permit deferred use or other systems of grazing to maintain or improve the condition of the range.

A fence with four or five strands of

## CORRALS FOR BEEF CATTLE

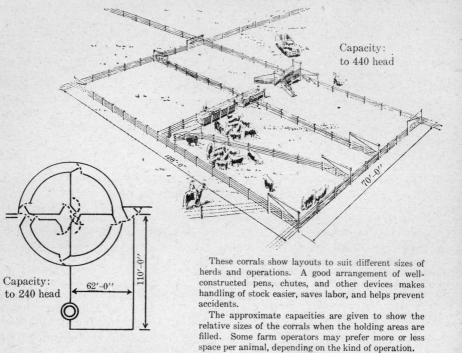

Capacity:
to 440 head

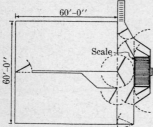

Capacity:
to 240 head

These corrals show layouts to suit different sizes of herds and operations. A good arrangement of well-constructed pens, chutes, and other devices makes handling of stock easier, saves labor, and helps prevent accidents.

The approximate capacities are given to show the relative sizes of the corrals when the holding areas are filled. Some farm operators may prefer more or less space per animal, depending on the kind of operation.

Capacity: to 170 head

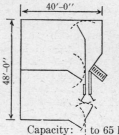

Capacity: to 65 head

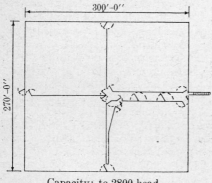

Capacity: to 2800 head

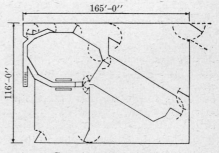

Capacity: to 600 head

barbed wire on posts a rod apart was once standard for cattle over most of the ranching country. Improved breeding has made the animals of today more docile than the wild range cattle of a few years back, and many ranchers have found that such heavy-duty fences are no longer necessary. In many localities now fences have two or three strands of barbed wire and posts at intervals of 2 to 6 rods, with intervening stays. They are effective and less expensive.

WATERING PLACES are being used more and more as a tool in range management—a purpose they serve only if there are enough of them and they are properly located.

Watering places once were considered adequately spaced if they were not more than 4 or 5 miles apart where the topography was flat or rolling and about half that distance in steep, rough, timbered, or brushy country.

Cattle and sheep will travel considerable distances to water, but when they are forced to do so their rate of gain usually is reduced and the range itself may be damaged. It is practically impossible to harvest the forage crop efficiently if watering places are too widely spaced. On one range, for example, 30 percent of the forage was going unused because the watering places were poorly located.

Fewer ranchers are satisfied now with such results. A marked change has been the development of additional watering places for the primary purpose of better range management. The number of watering places probably has quadrupled in recent years in the ranching country.

Farm and ranch ponds, which collect and store surface runoff, comprise most of these new developments. Ponds are easily constructed, require little maintenance, and usually cost less than drilling for underground water. Ponds are sometimes built larger than necessary, but this unnecessary cost can be avoided. A major consideration is the amount of forage in the area the pond is intended to serve. The pond need only be large enough to insure a lasting water supply for the period this area should be grazed.

The ponds have other uses. Many are used for swimming and picnicking and furnish refuge for waterfowl. Some are stocked with fish. They may also provide needed water for fire protection and ice for skating or the house.

Dugouts, a special type of reservoir, collect runoff water for livestock in flat country where other types of pond sites usually are lacking. They are located in natural drainage channels or at low points where water can be collected. They are simply wide, straight-sided trenches scooped out with a bulldozer. One or both ends are sloped to permit access to the water. The sides are fenced to keep livestock away from the steep sides of the excavation. Because of the high evaporation in the regions where dugouts are used, they are made at least 8 feet deep, but otherwise their size can be varied as needed.

Wells may be the only source of enough water to permit the range to be used in places where there are no living streams and the rainfall is scanty or the runoff erratic. Wells are relatively inexpensive if underground water is known to exist at reasonable depths. They have the added advantage of providing good water that can be kept free from contamination.

The operator cannot always be certain of locating underground water, however. Therefore he does not know beforehand how much a well will cost, and he may be unwilling to take the risk of getting a dry hole or an unsatisfactory well. He must also consider the cost of the pumping equipment, storage facilities, and troughs and the continued attention needed to keep them in working order in deciding whether to rely on wells or other kinds of water developments.

CATTLE WALKWAYS are designed to make more efficient use of the millions

## VARIABLE-WIDTH CHUTE FOR CATTLE

The width of this chute may be varied according to cattle size by turning the two pairs of adjusting screws attached to the movable side. A hinged panel permits adjusting the throat width of the crowding chute to reduce bruising.

Length is 28 feet. Construction is of stock sizes of lumber, pressure treated with pentachlorophenol.

Complete working drawings may be obtained through your county agent or from the Extension agricultural engineer at most State agricultural colleges.

of acres of marsh range along the Gulf and Atlantic coasts. Many miles of them have been built. They are low, flat-topped dikes. They extend into the marsh areas and are built with a dragline.

Cattle usually will not graze more than one-fourth mile from firm ground. Walkways constructed every half mile give them access to all parts of the marsh range if the borrow pits are staggered on each side of the walkway.

Walkways also permit more uniform distribution of the grazing animals and consequently more efficient harvesting of the forage crop over the entire range. They provide needed bed-grounds, places where cattle can be fed if necessary or where young calves can rest, refuge from annoying mosquitoes, and protection from unusually

high water that may occasionally cover the marsh.

Walkways make excellent firebreaks. They provide a firm base for fences. They also permit the owner to see all parts of the range and his livestock oftener and greatly reduce the time and work required to move the cattle from one part of the range to another or to round them up for shipment.

WINDBREAKS offer considerable protection to livestock from cold weather. They are being planted increasingly where low temperatures are extreme and other shelter is lacking. They are not needed as a protection for livestock in places where winters are more moderate or where stream bottoms, canyon breaks, or tree thickets offer adequate protection. The heat gener-

## VARIABLE-HEIGHT LOADING CHUTE FOR CATTLE

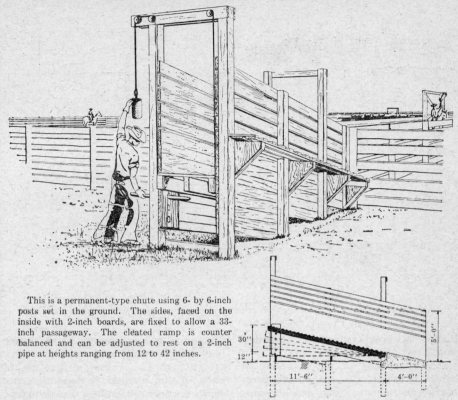

This is a permanent-type chute using 6- by 6-inch posts set in the ground. The sides, faced on the inside with 2-inch boards, are fixed to allow a 33-inch passageway. The cleated ramp is counterbalanced and can be adjusted to rest on a 2-inch pipe at heights ranging from 12 to 42 inches.

ated by digestion and assimilation is more than sufficient to keep the animals warm under most conditions if feed is ample.

Protection from extreme heat, especially when animals are being fed, often is more important than protection from cold. Animals tend to lose their appetite as their body temperatures rise with an increase in the air temperature, and gains are affected.

Research has shown that daily gains of Hereford steers can be increased from 1.63 pounds a day to 2.28 pounds simply by providing shade. Many ranchers therefore are building brush arbors to protect their animals from the direct sun for a part of the day where summer heat is excessive. They usually are 16 to 20 feet wide and 10 to 12 feet high to permit air circulation and long enough to allow 60 square feet for each animal.

LIVESTOCK WORKING structures for the range depend on three factors: Environmental requirements, managerial decisions, and production efficiency.

Since little is known of the limits and effects of environmental conditions on range animals and managerial decisions at best are variable, structures for the range have grown out of production efficiency.

The structures are many and varied. One that satisfies one rancher may not fill the need of another. One rancher for branding may need a complete corral setup that can be operated with little labor. Another rancher may use to advantage a minimum of corral and the maximum of labor because "ro-

## FARM GATES

These gates are suitable for various uses, and can be built of lumber or of metal pipes or channels of equal strength with bolted or welded connections.

Special features shown suggest variations to fit local requirements, materials, or preference. Gate posts should be sturdy. Wood posts should be treated with preservative.

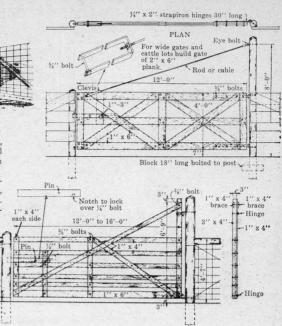

deoing" is a competitive sport and cowboys need a place to practice.

Certain trends in management of range livestock do make structures necessary—for example, trucking instead of trailing; fencing instead of herding; more "horsepower" and fewer horses, and so on. In other words, ranchers are trying to achieve more and more efficiency in production.

The individual features of corrals, such as the working chute, working alley, and holding pen, have shown a great deal of standardization through use.

Users of working chutes formed some principles that underlie the design of chutes: A minimum length of 20 feet; the use of a tapered or adjustable chute, 16 inches wide at the bottom to a maximum of 30 inches at the top so young stock can be worked without turning; a walkway along the chute to facilitate handling of animals and control of grubs; close spacing of sideboards at the bottom so as not to catch legs of animals; taper from working alley into working chute with crowding gate;

placing of the equipment so that animals work uphill and into the sun; prior to squeeze, a small gate to get in back of the animal is desirable; no sharp corners on fencing; no protruding bolts, screws, or nails.

The working corral should be accessible to central operation of cattle at time of use and to a road or transportation if shipments are by rail. Drainage should be good. Corrals in snow areas should be placed so wind will keep them clear of snow for all-weather operations. Water should be nearby. The position of line or drift fences should be kept in mind for they help working cattle into the holding pen.

The working alley is located to facilitate moving cattle from pen to pen and to the working chute. Several points should be kept in mind. The alley should be 12 to 16 feet wide so that horses may be used to move the cattle but narrow enough to span with a gate. A taper or funnel should extend from the working alley into the working chute. It probably will be desirable to locate the loading chute, scales, and

Great changes have been taking place in equipment and structures that are essential in the production of livestock. Now one seldom sees a new barn for work horses or mules, or new bank barns, smokehouses, springhouses, windmills, corncribs. Many new loose-housing systems with pole barns and milking parlors, paved feed yards, bunker silos, crop driers, and feed grinding and mixing plants appear in surprising variety. New types of farmsteads are appearing, such as thousand-cow dairies, pig nurseries, large custom-feed yards for cattle, and multithousand-bird broiler and laying establishments. Materials uncommon 50 years ago, such as concrete blocks, pressure-treated, laminated, and processed wood, lightweight galvanized steel and aluminum sheets, insulation, and plastics provide new opportunities for building design.

The farmstead in the picture above is near Walworth, Wis. The photograph below, taken in 1916, shows part of a large ranch near Bath, S. Dak.

Of all the changes, the improvements in housing and feeding dairy cattle and in milking and handling milk are as kenspeckle as any. Cows may loaf in a 100-foot barn and be milked in a 40-foot parlor nearby (above). A preengineered "package" milking room is used with loose-housing systems.

A pie-shaped corral dairy layout in California has a milking facility at the hub to ease the movement of cows between the corral and the milking room. Feed bunks around the perimeter are filled easily from a self-unloading wagon. Beyond the perimeter is a storage for baled hay. On the Jones farm near Fort Atkinson, Wis. (below), a modern system for feeding silage uses a large-diameter silo with mechanical unloader and a covered bunk feeder with auger distribution. A tractor with a front-end loader is used to clean the paved lot.

On the Jones farm, a man pushes a button on the silo wall (above), and an auger starts the feed on its way to cows.

Chester DeBoer's farm near Hull, Iowa, has no pasture for his 80 head of dairy cattle, which are fed roughage the year around (with some baled hay for young animals) from four structures. The Harvestore and silo at the left store grass, corn silage, soft corn, or grain sorghums. The slatted structures, whose gates can be raised and lowered, are hay driers for self-feeding chopped legume hay.

The cows in the picture below are being sprayed to control insects and diseases.

Sanitation is a constant watchword. Water sprays in the pavement in the picture above wash the udders before the cows enter the milking stalls. For hosing the milking room, water pressure is raised to about 85 pounds per square inch with a booster pump.

Up-to-date methods for removing manure include tractors with scoops or blades. Automatic cleaning, comfortable stalls, exhaust fans, and draft-free ventilating windows (below) mean cleanliness, higher production, and better working conditions.

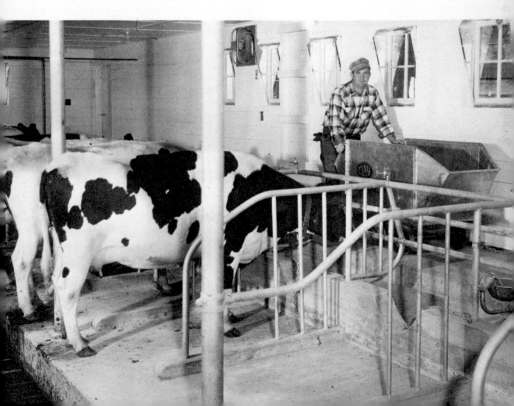

In the herringbone milking parlor, cows stand so close together that each udder is 3 feet from the next and within easy reach of the operator. Time spent in milking is greatly reduced. Feed chutes are above the cows. From the udder, the milk goes directly through a pipeline to a bulk tank.

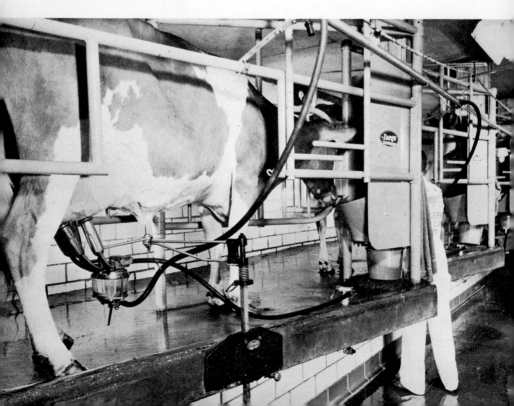

The photograph above, taken on a dairy farm near Anoka, Minn., shows a bulk tank, compressor, milk releaser, milk pipeline, milk pump, and automatic cleaning machine. Below: Milk is bottled in a large plant.

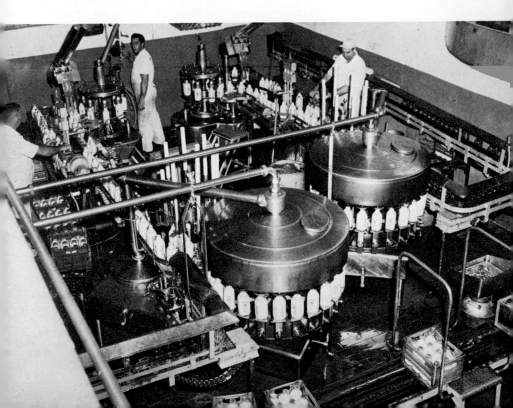

For beef cattle, this modern, mechanized, paved feedlot operation has a capacity of 200 to 300 head. The actual feeding time is 20 to 30 minutes, depending on the amount of grain with the silage. The self-feeder silo in the photograph below eliminates farmstead handling of silage. The animals take their places in a circle without fuss.

This feeding barn for beef cattle is 50 by 180 by 12 feet and has a canopy 10 feet high. It can accommodate 300 head. Wells often are the only source of water in sections where there are no living streams and rainfall is scanty or irregular. The one in the picture below has a 5,000-gallon storage tank and provides water for three pastures.

Hogs are housed in clean, airy, efficient buildings. The picture above shows one of many new types. Raising hogs in confined quarters is a growing practice. The farmer designed this pen arrangement (below) with the plan of finishing 2 thousand hogs a year.

This automatic hog finishing facility—dubbed "hogomatic"—is equipped to feed the pigs and clean the floor under full automatic control. Cleaning is done (below) with two jets of water under 70 pounds of pressure. The revolving boom circles the 21.5-foot exercise area every 2.5 minutes. A 4-inch center drain carries the wastes away.

An automatic hammer mill with a high-pressure pneumatic conveying system prepares and distributes a complete mixed feed in the hogomatic. Pressure switches in the various hog feeders served by this mill will start the mill and route the feed to the feeder through a system of relays and feed line valves. Bulk feed tanks (below), conveniently located, save many steps in handling feed. These three tanks supply the automatic grinding mill.

Ground feed is supplied to the hog feeder through a 1-inch pipe. The feed is deposited in a small hopper and distributed by means of an auger from it to the feeding trough. Another feeding system is illustrated below. In this minimum-stress pen, the shape of the guardrail encourages the sow to lie with the teats toward the pigs. The pigs stay where it's warm—under the heat lamp and behind a guard. The floor is insulated.

The picture above is another view of the minimum-stress hog house. Pigs stay in the same pen from birth until they reach market weight. Feed is distributed by an auger overhead. Below: Hogs in double-deck, all-steel, cage-type farrowing stalls. The pigs are transferred after weaning. Manure is removed by mechanical drags.

This farrowing room, 12 by 64 feet, is in an all-steel, pole-type, prefabricated structure. It has glass-fiber insulation with vapor barrier of vinyl sheets, radiant-type supplemental heat, and power ventilation. Another system is used on a farm near Brook, Ind. Floors of pens slope toward a cleaner outside the pens. The cleaner carries the semiliquid manure to the spreader at the touch of a button.

A well-planned layout of pens, chutes, and loading facilities contributes greatly to the efficiency of the sheep-raising enterprise. The picture below, which was taken in February 1960, shows a sheepherder's camp of the type generally found in the West. It is a reminder that men, horses, and dogs still have a place in a world of pushbuttons.

George B. Sweet, Gaithersburg, Md., put up this prefabricated, 5,000-hen laying house in 1960. The pole-frame, windowless building, 45 by 140 feet, with stressed-skin exterior plywood wall and roof panels, has a fan and pad-type evaporative cooling system for summer, a unique push-pull air recirculation system for ventilation in winter, and separate feed and egg rooms. For warmth in winter and coolness in summer, the 120-foot solar poultry house (below) on a farm near Waterville, Iowa, has south-facing insulated windows and an overhang for shade in summer.

Floyd Smith, Wauseon, Ohio, shows in the photograph above how dry the litter is in his poultry house when temperatures were below zero outside and about 55° inside. The insulated windows make the most of the wintertime sunshine to reduce moisture and keep temperature even. The pole-type, prefabricated-steel laying house pictured below has a slat floor, mechanized feeder, fiberglass insulation, and an interior lining of corrugated galvanized steel sheets sealed with mastic as a vapor barrier. A central ridge ventilator with turnabout fans supply up to 6 c.f.m. per bird. The building, 48 by 64 feet, has an egg and work room 12 by 32 feet.

The structure above was originally a windbreaker, 20 by 50 feet. Additional arches were added later to make it a shed. On a farm near Edgar, Nebr., machines are kept at one end of a frameless steel building. The rest is partitioned to make a storage for corn.

On a farm near Logansport, Ind., a pole-type prefabricated-steel shed, 48 by 64 feet, houses farm machinery and a light plane. The frameless, straight-wall building pictured below is used for storing grain on a farm near Cozad, Nebr. It measures 52 by 100 feet. Its wide doors would permit its use later for storage of machinery.

A self-feeder hay barn is designed to dry the chopped hay in storage, eliminate the need to handle hay at the farmstead, and insure good quality of the forage. A grain bin auger, operated automatically, permits the almost complete unloading of flat-bottomed bins.

A three-man farm crew, with no special equipment, easily puts the roof—of prefabricated, stressed-skin, exterior plywood panels, each 4 by 24 feet—on a poultry laying house. The finished structure was pictured on a previous page. Another type of construction (below) uses laminated glued rafters.

## CATTLE CHUTE AND HEADGATES

TOP VIEW

6'-0''  7'-0''

2-4''

2-ft. gate  4-ft. gate

This chute has a catwalk and a small service gate on one side. Cattle may be let out through the 4-foot gates on either side.

dipping vat (if one is used) from the working alley and keep a taper or funnel approach if possible. It may be well to have an area in the working alley to use as a small holding pen for 10 or 12 animals for spraying purposes. Cutting gates just ahead of the working chute may be useful.

The number and size of holding pens depend on the size of the herd and how it is managed. They should be located and arranged so that the cattle can be driven easily from the range into the large holding pen and from the pen to the working alley. About 15 square feet per head should be allowed in the holding pen if the animals are to be worked through the corral immediately. More space may be needed if they are to be held for a while. Fence boards on the inside of corral should have no sharp corners or protruding hardware. For a single fence that serves more than one pen, boards should be used on each side of a post or the post should be split and one-half used on each side of the boards.

Loading chutes enable cattle to enter or leave trucks by their own effort without injury. As the truck beds are 25 to 50 inches from the ground, the question of the height of the loading chute is often raised. Sometimes the height can be varied, but if a fixed height is used, most plans recommend 40, 42, or 44 inches.

A stairstep type, with a 4-inch rise and a 10- to 12-inch run, has gained favor as a safe loading chute. An earthfill chute also is good. The average width of a chute is 30 inches. Adjustable wing gates at the top, a bumper guard at the end, and walkways on both sides of the chute are desirable.

A more elaborate chute utilizes a movable gangplank to adjust the end of the chute that comes in contact with the truck.

Spraying (with portable sprayers or in the working alley or chute) has been gaining in favor, but many stockmen still used the dipping vat in 1960. One who constructs a dipping vat should keep in mind that animals work easier uphill into sun and on a curve and when they cannot see too far ahead. The chute to the dipping vat should be similar to the working chute with blocking gates and solid sides.

The vat should be about 7 feet deep and 3 feet wide. It may be of the wade-in type, although many ranchers prefer the abrupt drop for complete immersion of the animals. The vat should be 30 to 35 feet long, with the last 10 feet on an incline for the animal to wade out.

Splash boards on top of the vat and two draining pens sloping back to the vat may be used to conserve liquid. While one pen drains, the other pen can be filling up.

Most scales are permanent installations, but portable scales are beginning to be used. A scale should be located so that cattle movement is cut to a minimum. It is not part of the traffic pattern when working cattle. It should be accessible to trucks. Therefore it is next to the corral and connected to it by alleyways, so that the only time cattle cross the scales is when they are to be weighed. The rack for the scale should be mounted on the platform and removable to allow trucks and wagons to use it for weighing hay, grain, and so on.

The squeeze gate and headgate are located at the end of the working chute. Branding, dehorning, and vaccinating are done there. Many types, homemade and commercial, are in use. Most ranchers favor a commercial metal squeeze, but plans for homemade squeeze and headgates are readily available.

Mineral feeders are replacing block salt in exposed locations. The feeders, about 30 inches high at the base and 4 feet high at the top, are roofed to protect the minerals. An effective feeder is a 55-gallon drum, mounted on a swivel composed of a front automobile wheel and axle. The axle is fastened to a base, and a metal vane at the top of the feeder keeps the opening oriented to the leeward.

Backrubbers help control horseflies on range animals. They are made of burlap wrapped around wire or cable and suspended between two posts. The correct oil solution of the proper insecticide is poured on the burlap. The animals rub against it. It is placed where it is easy to service and where cattle gather.

SHEEP WORKING corrals are as many and as varied as those for cattle. Here again, certain fundamentals should be kept in mind. In the holding pens, 10 square feet per ewe should be allowed if they are held overnight. Only 5 square feet is needed if the sheep are being held for sorting.

One who designs a corral system should remember that sheep prefer to be worked uphill and try to get out where they entered. Because shadows make it difficult to work sheep, a north-south cutting chute usually is better. Painting the inside of the chute white will cut down the shadows.

Some sheepmen prefer a grading chute about 66 inches wide, with cross gates every 40 to 50 feet, between the holding pen and the cutting chute. In it the sheep can be graded and marked. They can then be separated by the use of cutting gates as they pass through the cutting chute.

The three-way cutting chute has two gates in the chute and one at one end. By placing these gates at the end of the chute, one man can operate them and cut the sheep four ways. Placing two more gates in the chute makes it possible to cut the sheep three ways—to the left or right of the chute, or straight ahead. The length of the cutting chute depends on how many cuts are made in one operation, but it should be at least 20 feet long.

The cutting chute is made of boards and is 18 inches wide and 40 inches high. Some sheepmen prefer a taper from 11 inches at bottom to 22 inches at top. It should have a crush pen from the grading chute to the cutting chute to help in moving the sheep. A block gate at the beginning of the cutting chute is also desirable.

It is necessary to have a variable-height loading chute in order to load both the top and bottom decks of trucks. The chute should have solid sides, with the last 12 to 14 feet hinged for elevating. The number of animals hauled per load will naturally vary by size of the truck. A rule of thumb for paired sheep (ewe and lamb) and double-deck truck is 3.6 pair per foot of length for the light pairs, 3.5 pair for medium pairs, and 3.4 pair for heavy pairs. In single-deck loading, 50-pound lambs can be loaded at the rate of 4.2 per foot of bed lengths; 75-pound lambs at 3.3; 100-pound lambs at 2.9; 125-pound ewes at 2.6; and 150-pound ewes at 2.2 to 2.3. It is desirable to put fewer sheep on the upper deck when they are shipped any distance.

DUSTING OR DIPPING is done to control ticks. The sheep are driven through the dusters at the end of the chute. Some ranchers use dusting barns in connection with shearing. After shearing, some of the band are driven into the barn, and dust is blown in.

The running chute to the dipping vat should be curved to obstruct the view. The inside should be solidly covered. A small decoy pen just before the dipping vat has been found useful in luring sheep into the vat. Draining pens are needed, as with cattle. The vat should be 2 feet wide and at least 30 feet long.

Not much use is made of lambing sheds in range lambing. Small tents are set up to protect the ewes and the newborn lambs during storms. The high mortality of lambs born on the range has fostered a growing practice of lambing out at lambing camps or at permanent lambing sheds on the range or in the irrigated valleys.

LAMBING camps are a sort of compromise between range lambing and lambing out at permanent lambing sheds. The temporary shelters consist of tents and canvas- or plastic-covered frame buildings.

In the lambing sheds, small pens, or jugs, are used for the ewe and newborn lamb. As the lamb grows older, a number of ewes and lambs are penned together. The jugs are about 4 feet square and 3 feet high, and are movable. One method of making them is to hinge or tie together two panels, each 3 by 4 feet. Two of these connected panels will then make a jug, 5 will make 3 jugs, 6 will make 4 jugs, and so on. The inside panels can be removed to let the ewes and lambs be together.

The minimum area per ewe in the lambing shed is 6 square feet. All gates and doors should be as wide as possible to lessen the chance of crowding and possible injury.

The shearing shed may be next to the working corral and easily accessible to both the range and transportation. Some sheepmen maintain their own shearing equipment. However, there has been a trend to commercial, portable shearing outfits. It is best to have sweat pens where the sheep can be held for sweating and then moved down an alley to small holding pens, about 6 by 6 feet in size.

Back of the holding pens is the shearing floor, which should be elevated 3 to 4 inches above the holding pen and sloping toward it. The floor should be 7 to 8 feet wide, and 4 feet should be allowed for each shearer. The sheep move from the shearing floor through the shed to a holding corral.

The fleece is taken to a tying table, which has a top of spaced rollers of wood or pipe or of meshed wire. The table should be 10 to 12 feet long. A width of 42 inches will allow for two rows of fleece. The fleece can be table-graded and taken to the sacker. The sacking frame, or rack, is about 7 feet high and has a 4-foot base, with steps up one side. It is well to have two or three sackers to receive the graded fleeces.

# Power

# in

# the Market

## The Right Product;
## The Right Place

J. K. Samuels

WHEN a housewife decides to buy a precooked ham, she may not realize— or care—that at least 15 months earlier a farmer in another State decided to produce the meat.

The housewife has some problems in buying the ham, but she knows they are not big ones—a variation of a cent or two a pound between stores or that one ham may be a little leaner than another.

The farmer, on the other hand, must make many important decisions about his pork production and marketing. Should he raise fewer or more pigs this

year? Should he finish them lean or fat? Should he sell at the local auction or directly to the packer-buyer? Or should he consign them to a central market?

How he decides such questions and how he evaluates the market determine largely his profit from his hogs.

He is motivated to produce by the expectation that consumers will buy pork. He raises pigs, however, at his own risk without having advance orders and with comparatively no commitments on anyone's part to buy them at a satisfactory price or to buy them at all.

His problem then is how to gear his production to what he thinks will be the housewife's requirements many months later. The hog producer needs a system of distribution that will guide him in producing the quantity and quality desired by consumers; move his production through marketing channels efficiently; pay him a fair

276

price; and help find and develop new markets.

This problem also concerns the housewife, because she expects the marketing system to provide her a continuous supply of food, processed and packaged to suit her taste and needs and at fair prices.

The meshing of production and consumption of food through the marketing system is far different from what it was in the past.

Our marketing system, both in the central markets and at country points, used to consist generally of many independent firms. Most of them performed a specialized function in distribution. Each operator bought and sold according to the needs of his customers and the supplies available to him.

Production practices on the farm were not so uniform as today. We had a wider range of quality, more varieties, and differences in packaging. Thus we can see the need in earlier days for a large number of specialized handlers who could move these diverse products and qualities through the market to the housewife in a form she would buy.

The marketing of butter is an example. Butter was made and consumed mainly on farms. The surplus was sold directly to local retail dealers and nearby city customers. Some was sold to country buyers for shipment to wholesale butter dealers or renovators.

Later, creameries produced butter and consigned it to receivers or contracted with them for the sale of butter at an agreed wholesale market quotation. Sometimes written contracts were used. Representatives of receivers frequently visited creameries to solicit shipments.

Jobbers bought butter from receivers in carlots or less than carlots and distributed it to stores, hotels, and restaurants. As the market expanded, many larger creameries distributed directly to retailers through branch houses or by contracting with distributing agents in certain territories.

The large meatpackers distributed great amounts of butter through their local branch houses and through a peddler-car system.

Marketing cooperatives often acted as selling agents for local creameries. Butter sales also were conducted in exchanges, such as the New York Mercantile Exchange, and the New York Butter and Egg Exchange, and the Chicago Butter and Egg Board. These sales were in the form of an auction, and each member of the Exchange could put in his offering and bids.

SELLING has always been a risky part of the farmer's business, especially since he moved away from direct contact with consumers. At first there were few itinerant buyers. The farmer made shipments on consignment and then waited for his returns. He had difficulty offering a uniform product. He had little information about the markets.

Under such circumstances, farmers formed marketing cooperatives. Through them, the farmer sought to obtain a better price for his product, secure additional and more dependable outlets, and improve the quality of his products. He expected the cooperatives to collect and disseminate information about markets and advise him on what to grow and how to grow it.

As areas of production spread across the country, the farmer needed reliable information to guide him in producing what the market would want by the time his products were ready for sale.

While the livestock producer could determine how many pigs he would raise, he could only guess how many other farmers would produce and when they would market them.

One of the first activities of the Department of Agriculture was the establishment of a crop and livestock reporting service. It gave farmers and marketing agencies estimates of the national production of farm products.

The Department now reports on the outlook, condition, acreage, production, and intentions to produce for more than 150 commodities.

Market news is another important source of information available to farmers in helping them decide when, where, how, and to whom their products shall be sold. Before the Federal Government began market reporting in 1915, farmers received information on prices and supplies from other producers, buyers, private information services, and trade publications. They still are important supplements to the Government's market news service.

There is now available through the market news service information on prices, shipments, receipts, storage holdings, grades, and other factors gathered from the major producing areas and principal cities.

Better methods of communication have brought about improvements and wider use of production and market reports. The use of radio began in 1921. By 1951 it provided the widest and fastest public distribution of market news. Through 11 thousand miles of leased Teletype circuits, market reporters interchange information, which is quickly available to all agencies in the markets. Many television stations also carry information about food distribution.

Newspapers are an important source of market news for farmers, distributors, and consumers. The Department of Agriculture reports are carried in nearly 1,100 daily papers. The Western Union Telegraph Co., through its Commercial News Dispatch, transmits to subscribers detailed reports of specific commodities from particular markets.

Crop and livestock information and market news are important tools in maintaining efficiency in the flow of supplies from farm to city and in regulating the amounts of food available to consumers.

Hundreds of retailers and many wholesalers and jobbers in a particular market formerly had to gage the needs of their trade and obtain their requirements from closely related suppliers. Today six or eight firms may buy and sell most of the food needed by the people of a city. These organizations, including both corporate and voluntary chains, and the development of the present-day self-service supermarket with its mass distribution of food have facilitated the prompt transmission of consumer demand to the production area.

Hitching together our mass production and mass distribution systems with more direct movement of products has brought about different methods for transferring title and relating production to consumer wants.

Today many large retailers purchase products for their own brands on a straight price specification basis. A retail chain will specify physical standards, volume, and delivery terms. On the basis of these specifications, for example, a canner will make price offers to the chain for his products. Processors and packers, in turn, must procure raw products that will enable them to meet retailers' requirements for uniformity, volume, and continuity of supply.

To meet the requirements of the mass retailer, the farm operation must be geared to deal directly with him or his specialized suppliers. Producers' decisions with respect to management practices and production and harvesting operations must be coordinated increasingly with the requirements of large-scale processors and retailers.

What we are seeing develop is a marketing system that ties together the wants of consumers and farm production through greater coordination among producers, distributors, and retailers.

In the words of George Mehren, of the University of California, "marketing has come to mean a systematic integration of product planning, procurement, manufacturing and merchandising."

MANY DIFFERENT forms of direct and indirect integration and informal coordination have developed among retailers, suppliers, and producers. This is sometimes referred to as vertical integration, which is the linking together of various production and marketing functions.

Vertical integration is as old as the first farmer. In fact, the early farmer who grew his own seed, raised his own horses for power, ground his own flour, and prepared his own meat was completely integrated.

Vertical integration, as we think of it today, has grown out of improvements in the technology of production and marketing and the industrialization that has brought vast markets.

A report on contract farming and vertical integration of the Department of Agriculture in 1958 pointed out that retailers seek a mass market. Increased volume calls for suppliers who can regularly deliver large quantities of uniform products. To maintain volume, continuous supply, standardized quality, and low unit costs, mass retailers integrate more of their activities with processors through contracts or direct ownership. Sometimes they enter into contracts with farmers.

Processors of farm products, in turn, when faced with changes in requirements of retailers and wholesalers, must assure themselves of adequate and timely supplies of raw products with specified quality. By closely tying the farm to his own operations, moreover, the processor can build volume and stable supplies to reduce his costs and increase his returns.

In such a system, producers' decisions and farm production must be fitted directly into the requirements of the trade. This may be done in a number of ways—through informal arrangements between farmer and the buyer, by contract farming, by having processors or other marketing agencies grow their own crops, and through farmer cooperatives.

Processors of vegetables for many years have contracted with producers to grow crops for them. Under such a contract, the processor may furnish the seed and prescribe cultural practices and harvesting methods to be

followed by the farmer. The processor also will provide technical assistance to the farmer to help him grow the best possible crop. The processor thus can assure himself of the volume needed to supply his market. He can get the uniformity and quality of raw product that will enable him to operate efficiently and to produce a uniform pack for large retail buyers.

On the other hand, the farmer's risk is reduced. He knows how much he can sell and what he will get for it. He receives financial assistance either directly or indirectly and also help on production problems. In return, he foregoes at least part of his opportunity to make a profit.

This process has been carried farthest in the integration of the broiler industry. About 90 percent of the broilers in 1960 were produced under contract or some other type of integrated basis, usually between the farmer and a feed dealer, a processing plant, or the farmer's own cooperative. The high degree of integration has improved efficiency and made production of broilers a year-round industry, but problems still exist because of market gluts and periodic unprofitable operations.

An example of integrating production and distribution is the processors who grow part of the crops needed for their operation. Tung oil processors, for example, get a large percentage of their requirements from their own tung orchards. Many of the large concentrators of citrus juice in Florida own groves. Processors also grow certain vegetables and hops. In these instances, the processor has complete control over the product he grows and processes. Usually a company does not produce all the raw product needed for his processing operation.

THE FARMER COOPERATIVE is an important tool in integrating farm production into the marketing system. Through cooperatives, the producer reaches buyers he could not reach by himself.

On the other hand, the cooperative provides service to the mass buyer by pulling together the production of its members for sorting, grading, and processing into the kinds and volumes of products needed by retailers and distributors. Farmers are endeavoring to build cooperatives that will help them regulate their production to the needs of the market.

Through production of high-quality goods and merchandising, many cooperatives have built up consumer demand for their brands and their products. Thus they maintain direct or indirect control over their product as it passes through the marketing system. The cooperative is responsible for determining quality standards and works with farmers in helping them produce the quality and uniformity needed in a branded product.

Merchandising by cooperatives results in gearing production more effectively to demand by endeavoring to give the consumer what she wants, when she wants it, and at a price she is able and willing to pay. Effective merchandising reaches forward to determine, influence, and supply the wants of consumers and backward to make production more nearly meet the requirements of the market.

Cooperatives may process or package products for sale under a buyer's label. Here the buyer determines the specifications as to volume, quality, and regularity of shipment.

Citrus cooperatives have long provided extensive production, harvesting, and marketing services to producers. Some of them have complete control of the members' fruit. Through a contract with growers, the association determines when the grove shall be fertilized, sprayed, pruned, and cultivated. It sets the time of harvest and sends a crew to pick the fruit. It determines—on the basis of quality, variety, and marketing conditions—whether the fruit shall be sold fresh or processed.

This fruit is pooled for payment to producers. All growers in some cooper-

atives receive the same price per box regardless of any variation in the fruit, on the theory that the management decisions of the cooperative have more effect on quality and volume than the land, which is the only factor of production not controlled by the cooperative. True, the cooperative does not control the weather, but it does irrigate groves when necessary.

Under such a system of production, maximum advantage can be gained from technological advance. Production and harvesting can be mechanized to a greater extent than where each producer owns his own equipment. The latest sprays and fertilizer applications can be adopted. Research can be put to immediate use. Production is coordinated directly with the marketing of the crop. Decisions on whether more or less fertilizer should be used, whether to irrigate, and whether to produce for the fresh or the processed market can be made in the light of market conditions and profit potentials.

As processors have turned from the open market to contracts in procuring raw products, farmers have organized bargaining cooperatives to negotiate the price and other terms of the contract. More than 44 bargaining cooperatives have been organized by fruit and vegetable producers—27 of them in 1955–1960. Besides bargaining, many of them provide special services to producers—marketing information, assistance on cultural problems, and short courses. One association has established an experimental center to study ways to combat weed pests and fertilizer problems.

As contracting and other forms of direct dealing between producer and processor, feed dealer, or retailer increase, the significance of open markets declines. Then producers as well as wholesalers and retailers lose an important price reflector of supply and demand.

WE MAY EXPECT further breakthroughs in science and technology, which will alter traditional methods of directing production to the market. The general view is that more, rather than less, farming will be carried on to meet specifications of consumers. Marketing firms will probably become larger and more integrated. We can expect farms to become more specialized.

While closer coordination of agriculture and business is inevitable, even with no further advance in technology, farmers can do several things to strengthen their position.

Through their cooperatives, they can provide alternative integration arrangements and can assemble large volumes of products for sale to mass buyers. Farmers can use bargaining cooperatives to negotiate contracts with processors and marketers.

Farmers may also expand the use of Federal and State marketing agreements and orders. The Department of Agriculture report on contract farming, to which I referred, states:

"Marketing orders are often effective supplements to cooperative bargaining and marketing activities. These devices may need to be refined and given wider application as contract farming expands, particularly if serious pricing problems arise because of a decline in number of buyers or insufficient competition among them, or because of intermittent periods of oversupply."

Markets, too, can be improved to provide for selling according to well-defined grades or specifications. Much can be done through usual marketing channels to improve orderly scheduling of supplies to meet both daily and seasonal requirements of packers and distributors.

Research and education can help farmers maintain freedom of action as further coordination of production and markets develops. Research results available to farmers on new and improved varieties, breeds, rations, and equipment and better marketing methods will help them to maintain their independence and choose how to produce and market their products.

Consumer research can be used more extensively to determine buying habits and buyer preferences and thus assist farmers, processors, distributors, and retailers in supplying this demand. Such research can also serve to guide merchandising and advertising programs so they will effectively motivate consumers to buy a particular commodity or product.

While problems of adjusting production, distribution, and selling methods will remain, we may expect continued benefits to producers and consumers from further technological developments in production and marketing.

# Changes in Marketing Facilities

William C. Crow

MANY TYPES of marketing facilities or structures are required to move products from farms to consumers. In producing areas are livestock auctions, packing sheds, grain elevators, milk plants, and egg assembly plants.

We need processing facilities like creameries, canneries, cotton gins, slaughterhouses, and flour mills; cotton and tobacco warehouses, grain storages, and refrigerated and merchandise warehouses to hold products from one season to another; facilities for wholesalers; and retail food outlets, the facilities closest to the consumer.

All such structures and many others are marketing facilities.

To move the products from one marketing facility to another requires transportation facilities—railroad cars, trucks, boats, and airplanes.

Facilities that are adequate at one time and place may not be at another. Little use is made today of the horse and wagon, the milk depot, the country general store, the cracker barrel, poultry slaughtering equipment in grocery stores, or house-to-house peddlers. Canning plants, poultry processing plants, farmers' markets, wholesale food distribution centers, auction markets, supermarkets, and other useful facilities may be all right in one place but not in another.

I, and every observant reader, can give dozens of examples to show how far-reaching the changes in marketing have been and the effect of the changes on facilities.

Poultry comes first to mind. We remember when poultry reached the retail store in live form and the housewife picked out the chicken in the coop and had it killed and dressed while she waited. Moving poultry through the marketing system in live form was expensive, but that was the way the consumer wanted it, and no other way was known. Now it is assembled, slaughtered, inspected, eviscerated, and packaged in the producing area; moves through the marketing channels dressed; and reaches the consumer ready to cook, at prices lower than they were years ago. Both production and marketing costs have been reduced despite inflation and rising wages of labor. Mechanized poultry processing plants have been developed. Improved packaging, refrigeration, and handling techniques were required. The city live-poultry market is gone, along with the live-poultry car.

Or fruit and vegetables, which now we can get fresh and frozen almost everywhere anytime. To make this possible, it has been necessary to draw on distant producing areas for the fresh and develop a completely new system for freezing and distributing the frozen.

The years have been few but the changes have been many between the time milk was brought to us in a bucket by a farmer and these days of the modern, mechanized dairy farm, tank trucks, and milk plants, which deliver milk bottled or cartoned, pasteurized, standardized, homogenized, vitamin D added, whole, concentrated, or skimmed.

Even the distribution of bread has changed. Years ago farmers took their wheat or corn to the mill and hauled flour or meal home to be made into bread. A generation ago consumers bought flour in 24-pound bags and did their baking. Now large bakers supply many types of bread.

To effect these changes—to meet our growing, changing requirements— more than three-quarters of a billion dollars are expended each year in the United States to build or remodel marketing facilities for farm and food products.

Why?

THE REASONS why facilities must change are many.

In the first place, production areas change.

The cotton-producing areas of the Old South may have had adequate facilities for cotton, but not for grain, livestock, or poultry, the production of which has been increasing. In many southern localities, facilities to store grain are being built. Modern poultry processing plants are turning out ever-increasing quantities of poultry meat at low cost. To provide outlets for the growing livestock production, auction facilities are being established and slaughtering plants built.

Changes in the forms of products also call for changes. Facilities in a producing area may be satisfactory for fresh fruit and vegetables, but the handling of frozen food may require a whole series of changes — freezing plants where the products are grown, mechanical refrigerator cars and trucks, refrigerated warehouses, new equipment for wholesalers, frozen food cabinets for retailers.

And so on.

Changes in transportation called for changes in marketing. When products moved from the farm by horsedrawn vehicles, a large number of cotton gins or milk plants were needed because of the time required to reach them by that slow method of transportation. The coming of motortrucks meant that the small facilities could be consolidated, with "economies of scale"—reduction in cost per unit with increased output.

Many city wholesale food markets, built a century ago on narrow streets, were adequate for horse and wagon, but when the railroad was built it was impossible to place tracks at the buildings. Later, when trucks were developed, the streets were not wide enough for them.

Changes in population made some facilities obsolete: A facility may have been large enough to serve a small town, but not to supply a city.

A highly important cause of obsolescence has been an increase in wages. A facility that was adequate when labor cost 75 cents a day may be almost unusable with wages 2 dollars an hour. Many processing plants, warehouses, wholesale houses, and retail stores in order to survive have had to be rebuilt to accommodate laborsaving equipment and the larger volume necessary to justify the use of such equipment. Sometimes, even, labor cost per unit of output actually has been cut in half by providing facilities of a different design and properly equipping them.

Changes in handling equipment and in the methods of preparing products for the market change space requirements and the layouts of a facility. It may be adequate for two-wheeled handtrucks, but not for unitized handling on pallets—platforms on which many packages are handled at one time—with fork trucks. More space may be needed when a firm must prepackage its products before delivering them.

Other factors that may force changes in marketing facilities include changing habits of consumers and the integration of firms.

The important point is that marketing facilities are in a continual process of change.

When they do not change to meet changing conditions, marketing costs are higher than they ought to be. In a competitive system in which buyers and sellers have choices, high-cost marketing facilities tend to be bypassed. Their operators lose money and eventually fail. Inadequate marketing facilities injure the farmer and the consumer.

Facilities are a pipeline between the grower and the consumer. If the pipeline is too small, runs in out-of-the-way places, has too many bends in it, or any other impediment, it acts as a dam or barrier instead of facilitating the flow of products from the specialized producing areas to consumers.

In some localities that are well suited to production of certain commodities, such production has been delayed for years by an absence of suitable marketing facilities. The failure to improve, rebuild, or relocate marketing facilities adds hundreds of millions of dollars a year to the food bill and causes excessive deterioration and spoilage.

THE CHANGES consumers are most familiar with are the ones at the retail level.

In earlier days, people bought food from peddlers or at farmers' markets. As the population increased, retail stores were built. Some of them handled a fairly complete line of food; others specialized in certain items, such as meat. During the first quarter of the century, many retail stores became "cash-carry" stores, whereas previously they had extended credit and made deliveries.

Chainstores then developed. Soon, in order to compete with the chains, many independent stores became a part of voluntary groups. Since the Second World War, the most rapid expansion has been in the sales of these voluntary groups—stores that work together and with wholesalers without having a common ownership.

Another development of the past two decades has been the rise of the supermarket. So great has been their growth that more than four-fifths of all the food retailing in the country (not counting restaurants) is done by fewer than 90 thousand stores.

The supermarkets handle thousands of items, many of which did not even exist before the war. It costs thousands of dollars to build a supermarket, and many have annual sales in excess of a million dollars. Instead of downtown, they are at places easy to reach, where plenty of parking space is available. In them the consumer can get almost any kind of food she desires in any form. The number of small stores is declining, and those that are left usually perform some special service.

Changes in wholesale food markets in cities have been no less sweeping. When retail food stores began to supply the consumer, the retailers went for supplies to the old market square or market house, the latter having switched from a retail to a wholesale function. Farmers sold bushel baskets or 100-pound bags to the retailers; previously they had sold half a dozen items or a few pounds to the housewife.

Wholesale merchants who handled foods not available from local farmers located in the buildings around the market square—any kind of building that might be available. As the cities grew, space in the old markets became limited, but they continued in these crowded quarters because all wholesale operators had to remain in the area to which the buyers came.

As time passed, the population became too large for the market to handle the food. Tall buildings around the market district blocked any hope of expansion. Products were stacked on the sidewalks and in the streets. Railroad tracks could not be extended to the wholesale stores. Supplies arriving by rail had to be carted to the wholesale house. There was not room in the market for all the trucks, and some were too large to traverse the streets. The results of all this were high rents, big cartage bills, high labor costs, waste of time, confusion, and much deterioration and spoilage.

Efforts to solve the problem brought changes. Railroads built "terminals" (sales buildings) but restricted their use in an effort to compel traffic to

move over their lines. Chainstore organizations, whose retail store operators did not need to visit the wholesale warehouse, built their own warehouses outside the market district. Trucks bypassed the old market to go directly to out-of-town buyers. Split markets resulted in more dissatisfaction.

When men in the central market saw they no longer had a monopoly—that people could get their food somewhere else—they decided to improve its condition.

At first specialized wholesale markets for different food groups, such as fresh fruit and vegetables, were built. Usually they sought less expensive sites at points accessible to both railroads and trucks, where traffic was no problem. These new facilities have rail spurs to the buildings, wide streets, loading and unloading platforms at proper height, front and rear entrances, parking areas, adequate space, refrigeration, handling equipment, and other features needed for the changing times. Wholesale and jobbing functions were combined.

The current trend in these city wholesale markets is toward less specialized, more complete wholesale food districts, sometimes called "food distribution centers." Since retailers are larger and handle more items, they cannot well obtain a few items from each of a large number of wholesalers.

Complete-line wholesalers are developing—larger wholesalers, who need more space and room for equipment for packaging and other processing operations, and who must have one-story buildings to reduce handling costs. If the new market district is properly located, adequate in size, and reasonable in price, such wholesalers usually move into it. When conditions are not suitable for concentrating in one district, these service wholesalers can build their warehouses in another location because they take orders by telephone, mail, or salesmen, and do not depend on buyers' visits to their warehouses. Their close association with their retail outlets makes them more dependent on the retailers they serve but less dependent on the central market.

As the retailers in increasing numbers cease to go to the central market for their supplies, farmers' wholesale markets in cities are dying out. The buyers are not there. Nearby farms, which produced for the farmers' markets, have been taken over for the expanding city. As farm operations become larger, more and more operators do not have time to sell at a farmers' market. Each time these markets have changed, many people have said that city market facilities are no longer needed. Yet wholesale food marketing facilities continue to expand, the volume of food handled in wholesale facilities of all kinds continues to increase, and one set of wholesale facilities becomes outmoded, but the need for proper facilities remains.

Warehousing facilities for farm and food products have likewise undergone change—changes in location, design and methods of operating, and the functions they perform.

The nature of these changes can be illustrated by the refrigerated warehouse for storing perishable food. In the earlier days, products had to be used as they were produced or put into less perishable forms. Then public cold-storage warehouses were built, usually in cities where there were concentrations of various kinds of perishable products.

The earlier warehouses were usually multistory structures with some floors built for cooler storage (above freezing) and a lesser number for freezers. They were designed with little thought for operating economy because labor was cheap and in most cities one firm had a complete monopoly. Since the beginning of the war, nearly all new refrigerated warehouses are one-story structures capable of maintaining any desired temperature in any room.

They usually have railroad tracks beside one platform and truck space at another. All platforms and storage space are on one level for handling by

machines. The houses handle more frozen foods, and find it necessary to perform functions quite different from those performed a few decades ago. With the growth of large marketing agencies and the reluctance of operators of some public cold storages to change their operations, there has been a tremendous increase in the amount of refrigerated storage space built by marketing firms for their private use—meatpackers, frozen food processors and handlers, and food wholesalers.

The past 40 years have been marked by a tremendous increase in the amount of processing done in the marketing channel. At one time most processing was done by the farmer or housewife. Later it was done at the central market. More recently processing has moved closer to producing areas. We see a breakdown of central livestock markets. Poultry processing has moved to the country. Cotton mills have moved to the South.

New kinds of processing have developed. Bread, pies, and cakes are made outside the home. Greens are washed and packaged in consumer packages before they reach the kitchen.

These and many other developments cut the cost of maid service and make life easier, but they raise the cost of marketing and require new marketing facilities or changes in old ones. Each time a processing method is changed, the place of processing is moved, or a new form of processing is developed, changes in marketing facilities follow.

Changes in marketing facilities at some distance from the farm are being paralleled by those taking place right in the producing areas. In many areas the numbers of facilities are being reduced; the volume handled by those remaining is expanding. Common examples are cotton gins, milk plants, and packing sheds. In many other instances, economies could be achieved by such consolidations. Many country-point facilities are being bypassed to go to subterminals, or points of greater concentration, as with some country elevators and livestock shipping pens.

Marketing facilities in producing areas are taking on a number of new operations to cut transportation costs, reduce deterioration and spoilage, and to hold down labor costs. For such purposes, carrots are topped before they are shipped, cauliflower is trimmed, fresh orange shipments give way to orange concentrate, and poultry is processed.

MANY MORE changes are on the horizon. The average size of retail stores will increase further, not because large stores will become larger but because more small stores will close and medium-sized stores will grow.

The number of wholesale establishments will decrease, and the average volume of business increase. Wholesalers will handle more commodities and give more service; thus further changes in their facilities will be necessary.

Greater integration between successive steps in the marketing channel will change practices and facilities.

Greater coordination may be expected among the various forms of transportation. Greater use will be made of transportation equipment that can supply any temperature desired.

A further decline in the relative importance of central livestock markets would not be surprising. Further increases in the amount of processing done in producing areas are in line with the trends.

There may be fewer and larger marketing agencies in producing areas. Producing areas will continue to change the type and variety of products grown. The amount of movement of mixed loads from producing areas directly to retail supermarkets may be expected to rise.

Jobbing and wholesaling operations will continue to merge. Gins may do more cotton compressing. Movement of products directly from the farm to processing plants will grow.

Nearly all food-handling operations will be conducted in one-story buildings. There will be more mechanization at every step in the marketing process to increase labor productivity. More attention will be given to designing facilities and handling equipment to fit each other. More commonly will facilities be located on less expensive land, where highway transportation is good, and on railroads when they are used. There will be more people to feed and a larger volume to handle.

New scientific discoveries and inventions may upset significant parts of the marketing system. For example, radiation may make it possible to stop deterioration and spoilage; refrigeration therefore may not be needed. The use of atomic energy may bring significant changes in transportation. Production of some kinds of food chemically could really shake up the marketing system.

We shall continue to need marketing facilities, but usually not more of the same kind. An official of a large food chain said recently that all his supermarkets would be obsolete within 5 years—a way of describing the dynamic nature of our marketing system.

We should be concerned about marketing facilities for many reasons. When other factors change and marketing facilities do not, problems arise. Products may fail to move. Costs of marketing are made unnecessarily high. Deterioration and spoilage are excessive. Buyers do not get what they want.

These factors give farmers, marketing agencies, and consumers a stake in the continued improvement of marketing facilities.

The development of the right kinds of facilities, in the right places, and with proper methods of operation requires the combined efforts of agricultural groups, marketing firms, and Government agencies.

Research and imagination is needed to find out what to do. When the proper course has been charted, the results need to be applied. The further improvement of marketing facilities will benefit the grower and the consumer, as well as the marketing firms.

# Mechanization
# of Handling

William H. Elliott

HANDLING products into, within, and out of the series of facilities through which they must move, to provide the volumes at the places and times and in the forms required, costs more than any other part of marketing.

The cost would be much higher if we had been content with the methods and equipment of 50 years ago.

Then the marketing system for many staple food items had been fairly well developed. People bought flour, coffee, sugar, canned foods, and such items at retail stores that were supplied by wholesalers. For many perishable food items it was a rather primitive system. It was relatively short, too, because consumers bought produce in season largely from local farmers.

Lack of package and other standardization in those days was no problem: Perishable food was handled only once or twice before it reached the consumer. Labor was plentiful, cheap, willing to work as long as there was a job to be done, and ready to quit when the job was completed. There was no incentive therefore to mechanized handling operations beyond the two-wheeled handtruck or the wheelbarrow. Packages usually were handled one at a time. Unit-load handling was unknown.

Over the years many changes have occurred. The more efficient marketing firms began handling larger and larger amounts of farm and food products as both population and farm output increased. Hourly earnings of labor doubled and trebled. It was not eco-nomical any more to have men do work that machines could do better. The larger firms then could afford to invest in machines if they could use them in the kinds of facilities they occupied. Some left their old buildings because mechanized handling was impractical in them.

Let us consider now the progress made by some types of marketing agencies in mechanizing their operations and some of the possible steps ahead.

COMMERCIAL FRUIT storage and packinghouses of the period around 1910, when some operations began shifting from farm to off-farm points along railroad lines, used about the same methods of handling, sorting, sizing, and packing that were used in farmhouses.

Boxes of field-run fruit were dumped by hand on a workbench, where a worker sorted it into grades, sized it, and packed one box of each grade-size. Fruit was moved to and away from the workbenches either by hand or two-wheeled handtrucks. It took a lot of work and there was very little uniformity among boxes packed out by different workers.

When the Department of Agriculture undertook a research program in 1951 to increase operational efficiency in fruit storage and packinghouses, most houses in the Pacific Northwest were using two-wheeled handtrucks and belt conveyor lines for handling fruit in the mostly multistory facilities. Where possible, the unit-load principle of handling by handtrucks was in use, even though these loads were relatively small.

Besides the manual dumping station and equipment for washing and drying fruit, apple packing lines usually consisted of a belt conveyor or spiral-roll sorting table, two or three sections of weight-type sizing equipment (one section for each grade of fruit), and rotating tubs for accumulating fruit. From these tubs most of the sorted and sized fruit was manually wrapped and place-packed in standard wood boxes.

With 3 different grades and 12 to 16 different sizes of each grade, there were indications that some operations had been overmechanized.

The major emphasis in research and developmental work has been put on the development of improved methods and equipment for handling fruit into, within, and out of storage and packing rooms and for packing fruit.

In the many new, specially designed packinghouses, 48-box pallet loads of unpacked fruit now are picked up by industrial lift trucks from the beds of road trucks or from the apron of the storage house and transported to storage rooms, where they usually are tiered in 3-high (18 boxes) stacks. Fruit is withdrawn from storage and moved to the packing line by the same method. The unit load remains intact until the fruit is dumped.

At the opposite end of the line, packed fruit is graded and sized and put into 40-box pallet loads. It is returned to storage by the lift truck. The unit load remains intact until it is again withdrawn from storage and set in the door of a refrigerator car, or on the tailgate of a motortruck, for shipment.

In these houses, when pallet loads are built in the orchard, one worker and a 1-ton forklift truck can handle as much fruit as five or six workers can handle by two-wheeled handtrucks and belt conveyors.

Many of the older multistory apple houses still in use have adopted 12- and 24-box clamp-type lift trucks for the one-floor jobs of high piling, breaking out high-piled boxes, and transporting to or from the belt conveyor lines.

Another development since 1955 was made possible by the adoption of industrial lift trucks. It is the shift to pallet boxes (variously referred to as bulk boxes, bulk bins, and tote boxes) for handling and storing apples as a replacement for the standard wood box, that also is used as a shipping container. It was estimated that half of the 1959 crop in Michigan, the Pacific Northwest, and the Appalachian sec-

tion was handled and stored in pallet boxes.

The first cost and the maintenance costs of properly designed pallet boxes are less than field crates of standard-box size. Up to 30 percent more fruit can be placed in storage in some plants in properly designed pallet boxes than in standard boxes. Fruit in pallet boxes having 8 to 10 percent open space in their sides and bottom cools faster than in standard boxes; thus 7 to 10 days are added to its storage life. Handling costs in pallet boxes are 10 to 15 percent lower than the costs in standard boxes in 48-box pallet loads. Pallet boxes reduce bruising during initial handling, but after the fruit has been in storage for more than 5 months more bruises may show up than when it is in standard boxes.

Other highlights of the mechanization of apple packing lines are the mechanical box dumper; the float-roll sorting table; an automatic box filler for loose-packing standard boxes; a semiautomatic packer of tray-pack cartons; and a pallet box filler.

Dimension-type sizing equipment, developed primarily for lemons, has been modified greatly. New commercial models have been brought out. Weight-type sizing equipment also has been improved. In both, emphasis has been given to fewer separations by size (usually six to eight) and on group sizing instead of exact sizing. For both types of sizers, rotating tubs are being replaced wholly or partly by improved return-flow belt conveyor tables, on which fruit accumulates and which provide packing stations.

A mechanical box dumper replaces one worker per packing line, and provides a more uniform flow of fruit to other work stations in the line.

On a new float-roll sorting table, developed by men of the Department of Agriculture, fruit rides forward on rotating rolls. The rotating and forward speeds of the rolls can be varied as required for inspection of incoming lots. Lanes also are provided on the surface of the table. One lane is assigned to each worker to eliminate reinspection of the same fruit by several workers. Cull chutes at the side of the table reduce the reach in disposing of this fruit.

The float-roll table increases labor productivity about 17 percent, compared with the reverse roll table, and about 80 percent, compared with the old belt conveyor table. Both improved tables are used widely.

Before improvements were made in equipment for sizing by weight, apple packing lines, which sorted to three grades of fruit and had three double sections of this equipment arranged end to end, stretched out almost 200 feet and required extensive floor space. Fruit of the same grade-size class was accumulated in as many as five different tubs. Shifting packers from tub to tub meant a substantial amount of unproductive time. Moreover, in these lines the sizing operation set the pace for all other line operations, so that there was much idle time. An improved weight-type sizer and a new dimension-type sizer have come into general use, and these problems noted largely have been alleviated.

Improved return-flow conveyor tables have two belts remaining parallel but running in opposite directions. The tables are equipped with movable powered shunts, which transfer fruit from belt to belt, maintain size separations, and circulate the accumulated fruit in front of the packers, who place-pack the fruit in standard boxes. Effort and fatigue are reduced. More important is that heads for bagging, semiautomatic tray packers, automatic standard box fillers, and pallet box fillers can be hooked up with the return-flow belt tables, which automatically feed the other machines. These packing and filling devices could not be hooked up with rotating tubs.

Another is the semiautomatic packer of tray-pack cartons. Although trays for all varieties and sizes of fruit were not yet available in 1960, this packing device has come into widespread use—almost overnight. This device and one worker can pack about five times as

much fruit in tray-pack cartons as she can pack by hand in the same type of container—an increase in labor productivity of 500 percent.

The box filling device for automatically loose packing standard boxes of fruit has come into widespread use in apple and peach packinghouses. It was developed primarily as a means of accumulating in standard boxes some grades and sizes of apples for their return to storage unpacked when no orders for them were on hand. It is used for packing lower grades of apples and all grades of peaches for the market. Boxes of apples packed by this method usually are faced by hand. The only labor required for accumulating loose fruit by this method is that needed to supply empty boxes.

I should point out that few operators of apple packinghouses had adopted all the equipment and devices I have described. In houses that have gone most of the way, reductions of 50 percent in the size of the labor force previously employed are not uncommon. Some operators reported they employed only one-third the labor required by the older and more conventional methods and equipment.

Although I have centered my discussion around apple storage and packinghouses, similar facilities for other fruits and for vegetables also have made rapid strides in mechanizing operations.

Of special interest is the shift to volume-fill shaker-packing devices in California citrus fruit packinghouses and to count-fill shaker-packers in Florida houses. To settle the fruit, both devices vibrate, or shake, the container as it is being filled to either a predetermined weight or number.

The adoption of these automatic packing devices also made central sizing necessary with the abandonment of the single belt-and-roll sizers. On this type of sizer, fruit is moved forward in single file on a narrow belt conveyor line and rides against a parallel, tapered, rotating roll that spins each fruit. At the point where the distances between the belt and the roll approximates the diameter of the fruit, the fruit falls through to a bin. With the count-fill devices, the need for more accurate sizing also is indicated. As the use of these automatic packers is limited to fiberboard containers, houses in Florida are faced with a problem of precooling fruit before it is packed for shipment. They formerly depended on cooling in transit. Relatively heavy expenditures for hydrocoolers or other precooling equipment is a part of the mechanization program.

EARLIER COMMERCIAL EGG grading and packing plants consisted mainly of one or more candling booths plus space for temporarily holding eggs and packing materials. Cases of eggs were brought up to and moved away from candling booths by hand or by two-wheeled handtrucks.

At assembly points, graded eggs usually were repacked in the same cases for shipment to terminal markets. Wholesalers there recandled and cartoned eggs for stores. At both locations, candling booths were the same dark-curtained enclosures having a candling light and workbench. Eggs were lifted, positioned, and held, one at a time, before the candling light for inspection and then packed in cartons or cases.

Candling and cartoning work stations later were connected by powered conveyor lines for moving in ungraded eggs and empty cartons and moving out empty cases and packed cartons. About eight different commercial models of integrated cartoning and candling lines were developed from them. In addition to the cartoning and candling stations, all these lines include a carton makeup machine, carton closing equipment, and a table for packing cartoned eggs in cases. These integrated lines brought greater specialization and productivity of labor.

Still later improvements include the installation of weight-type sizing equipment, tabulating or memory systems for maintaining grade-out records of individual lots, egg transfer devices

and conveyor lines for more efficient presentation of ungraded eggs to the candlers, and chutes for supplying empty cartons. Lights for candling and the arrangement of candling and cartoning workbenches or stations also have been improved to effect economies in motions.

Even with these improvements, however, it became increasingly apparent that grading eggs by inspecting each individual egg before a candling light and cartoning them by hand stood in the way of attaining a high degree of labor efficiency. Some questioned the accuracy of grading all qualities of eggs and the need to grade eggs from controlled-production flocks by full candling.

As a first step in meeting the need for improved methods for grading eggs and for the detection of bloodspots in eggs, scientists and engineers in the Department of Agriculture undertook to develop a spectrophotometric method for detecting blood in eggs. This method involved a comparison of the intensity of light transmitted through an egg at two narrow bands of the spectrum. A commercial model of the electronic bloodspot detector, which had light filters for white-shell eggs only, was ready for testing in 1957.

As the bloodspot detector could not be integrated and tested in a conventional egg grading and packing line, a new, experimental line was designed and constructed in a plant that handled white eggs sized previously on the farm. Geared to the detector's 20 case-per-hour scanning capacity, the experimental line provided for flash candling and cartoning by hand.

Studies of both the experimental and conventional lines in this plant showed that when full candling of high-quality eggs (80 to 100 percent Grade A) was replaced by flash candling and electronic bloodspot detection, a saving of 3 cents a case, on the basis of 1957 wage rates, could be realized. For eggs of lower quality, costs were increased. Breakout tests showed the electronic device to be far more accurate than human candlers in detecting blood-spots.

It became evident that the elimination of the handling that full candling required would not effect a substantial net saving as long as manual cartoning, performed in the same series of motions, was continued. Moreover, it was believed that automatic or semiautomatic cartoning would require less costly and more exact sizing than was done on the farm.

Further work led to modifications of the experimental line so as to incorporate automatic sizing (by weight) and automatic cartoning of eggs. Twenty commercial models of the prototype line were in operation in commercial plants in 1959, and there was a large backlog of orders for the line. It was estimated that the new lines in larger plants could effect an average saving in labor costs of 20 cents a case and increase productivity of labor 100 percent. (Equipment costs were expected to be higher than for conventional lines, and the net savings would be smaller than this figure.)

Even greater mechanization of commercial egg plants will come when we can solve problems of inline cleaning, electronic detection of blood in brown eggs, and automatic removal from the line of eggs having unsound shells.

WHEN POULTRY processing began moving to commercial plants, birds were killed and dressed for individual orders. Coops of live birds were handled by manual methods. Processing equipment consisted of a scalding barrel, a defeathering and eviscerating table, and an offal drum. High inputs of labor and the maintenance of sanitary standards were problems.

Limited mechanization and specialization of labor were introduced in commercial plants when retail food stores began ordering a dozen or more birds from processors, but commercial plants attained their present scale and mechanization of operations only when the industry became aware of the pos-sible economies in processing poultry in the producing sections.

Today's highly mechanized plants, some of which have a capacity of 5 thousand broilers an hour, usually are designed around overhead, monorail conveyor lines, on which birds, as they are killed, are suspended from shackles for scalding, defeathering, and eviscerating. Eviscerating lines move into weight-type sizing mechanisms, from which sized birds fall into chill tanks.

Many of the already highly mechanized processing plants that went under Federal inspection in 1958 soon found that they needed even greater mechanization of some operations. Plants having production capacities of 2 thousand to 5 thousand birds an hour per line needed to install additional eviscerating lines to provide the number of inspection stations needed to maintain production or of modifying existing lines. They also were faced with increased labor costs because of the lack of mechanical methods of transferring birds from the defeathering line onto two or more eviscerating lines. Labor costs for this one operation, on the basis of 1959 wage rates, are about 10 thousand dollars a year in the larger plants.

Engineers of the Department of Agriculture and the Georgia Agricultural Experiment Station initiated research in 1958 on an experimental overhead conveyor line that provides for the automatic transfer of materials from a powered main line onto power-free branch lines. This line offers promise for meeting the need for a mechanized transfer method at a reasonable cost.

Equipment for the inline chilling of poultry, as a replacement for the conventional slush-ice chill tanks, is the next big step in the mechanization of processing plants. Commercial models of inline chilling equipment were installed in a few plants in 1959 and were undergoing the usual period of testing, changing, and improving. The matter of excess water absorption was a problem that remained to be solved.

Greater mechanization of packing

operations is another development. It includes a hydraulic tank tipper, which eliminates the manual transfer of birds from chill tanks to the packing table, and an integrated packing line, which replaces the slatted-top conventional packing table. It was designed to save labor. It has a hopper for receiving birds and a packing apron. It saved more than 5 thousand dollars annually in plants that ice-packed 250 thousand boxes. More than 75 plants had installed the tipper and packing equipment in 1958.

FLUID MILK PLANTS of the early 1900's were no marvels of mechanization as they were in 1960. Back in the days when commercial bottling and distribution plants began supplanting milk depots, mechanical refrigeration, power-driven machines, and mechanically operated bottle filling and capping machines were unknown.

Over the years, dairy plants have had many innovations in mechanization—some new and some borrowed from other industries.

Nearly all types of dairy plants since 1950 have shifted to receiving milk in bulk. Thus cumbersome and costly methods of receiving in cans are ended. Cleaning-in-place methods are improvements on methods in which equipment is torn down, cleaned, and reassembled each day.

Automation has been growing in dairy plants since about 1950. Because of the high degree of mechanization attained in nearly all types of dairy plants in 50 years, it was only natural that the industry's interest would turn toward bringing mechanical operations under automatic control.

Paul H. Tracy, former professor of dairy technology in the University of Illinois, in 1958 studied the impact of automation on dairy plants. He concluded that because of obsolescence many firms would have to scrap their facilities and equipment if they were to make their processing fully automatic. He pointed out that engineers of dairy plants have not kept pace with the needs for electronic controls and other equipment to achieve the desired degree of automation in the fewer and larger plants that will come with full automation.

It may be appropriate to raise here the question as to whether other food handling industries may not also eventually face the same dilemma as a result of advancing technology—or can mechanization in other food industries be aimed more accurately at the ultimate target?

IN LIVESTOCK slaughter plants, the adoption or development of new methods and equipment has not been impressive since about 1910, when overhead, monorail conveyor lines were substituted for tables to provide work stations for skinning or dehairing and related operations and for moving carcasses.

The rearrangement of equipment and work stations in slaughter plants since that time to provide improved layouts, however, has been significant.

To gain greater efficiency through a better flow of product and improved arrangements of work stations, a number of the older multistory plants in national meatpacking centers have been abandoned, usually in favor of smaller, one-story plants at interior points.

In livestock auction markets and terminal stockyards, yarding operations always have involved relatively long drives of each lot of animals to commission firm or sellers' pens and from the pens to buyers' pens following their sale. A lot may consist of one animal or a carload. In terminal stockyards, the pen assigned to a specific lot may be as much as half a mile from the receiving docks. To pen each lot, workers on foot traditionally drive the animals through alleys to the assigned pen, opening both alley and pen gates, to reach it. The workers return on foot, through the same alleys or over catwalks, and repeat the operation.

The mechanization of livestock market operations until 1959 had been limited to the installation of office machines and to hydraulic gates at strategic points in the yards of a few markets. Then the San Antonio Terminal Stockyards began using mechanical cowboys. This device is a modified three-wheeled, battery-powered golf cart, or carrier. One rider uses it for driving cattle in yarding operations. Four of these carts and four drivers can replace six yardworkers who operate on foot—an increase of 50 percent in productivity. An electronic or automatic device for opening and closing pen gates to achieve even greater productivity is needed. It should have wide acceptance with or without the use of the mechanical cowboy.

MANY COTTON warehousemen can remember when they yelled at workers, "lift that bale!" In most cotton warehouses, until labor costs began rising in the 1930's, bales of cotton were stacked and broken out of stacks by hand. Hand hooks were the only concession to mechanization. Bales were transported into, within, and out of warehouses by two-wheeled handtrucks. In a few warehouses, where separated storage compartments increased distances, the cotton was transported on trailers pulled by farm tractors. Open storage yards in the West frequently used road trucks for inplant transportation. In both instances, bales were loaded and unloaded by hand.

The cotton warehouse industry now has almost completely mechanized its handling methods.

The mechanization has centered around the industrial truck. Clamp attachments, instead of forks, are used for transporting and stacking bales. Hook or boom attachments are used for breaking out bales from storage stacks. Electronic scales, mounted on boom attachments, also have come into extensive use in western warehouses.

One worker and a 3-bale lift truck can handle as many bales of cotton as 9 or 10 workers can handle by manual-handtruck methods. But warehousemen, particularly in the West, have

started to shift to 9-, 12-, and 16-bale clamp-type industrial trucks for the inplant transportation of bales. In a warehouse in the Texas Plains, one 9-bale truck does the work of 26 handtruckers or 5 workers and 5 tractor-trailer trains.

In the face of increasing wage rates, the cotton warehouse industry is one of the few marketing agencies that have been in a position to reduce charges. Effective June 1, 1959, warehouses in New Mexico and in the South Bend and Plains areas of Texas reduced storage and insurance tariffs 15 percent. Receiving and shipping tariffs were reduced 45 and 50 percent, respectively.

OPERATORS of grain elevators traditionally have turned grain from one storage bin to another (by conveyors and elevator legs) for the purpose of cooling the grain, equalizing moisture, drawing samples, and fumigating for insects.

Turning thus is the movement of grain through air. As the surface of the grain on a moving conveyor is exposed to the air for only a short time, however, repeated turnings may be necessary to cool warm grain satisfactorily.

Turning grain is a relatively expensive operation, which costs one-fourth to three-fourths of a cent for labor and equipment to turn a bushel once. Grain is turned an average of four times each year in some sections. Furthermore, turning means a loss of storage revenues, because empty storage space must be maintained in which to turn grain. In one small sorghum grain storage in southern Texas, for example, 20 percent of the total space was used to receive turned grain; the loss in storage revenues was more than 4 thousand dollars a year. Turning also causes considerable breakage and shrinkage of grain.

Grain aeration—the movement of air through stored grain—was used first in small bins of the type used on farms, in flat storages, and in ships of the reserve fleets, none of which had equipment for turning grain. Such successful use attracted considerable attention among operators of elevators and other commercial storages.

A number of attempts were made to design efficient and economical systems for upright- and large-flat types of commercial storages. Many were not successful because they ignored sound engineering principles of air movement or were not operated within proper limits.

Engineers in the Department of Agriculture began research in 1954 in cooperation with the engineers of the experiment stations of Georgia, Indiana, Iowa, Michigan, and Texas to develop suitable equipment, methods, and operating procedures for the aeration of grain and dry beans in commercial facilities.

The widespread adoption of their first results prompted the Grain Elevator and Processing Superintendents Association at its 1956 annual meeting to predict that within 5 years 90 percent of the commercial grain storages in the country would be equipped with mechanical aeration systems.

Preliminary data place annual costs of aerating grain at about one-fourth to 1 cent a bushel and annual savings by substituting aeration for turning at one-half cent or more a bushel. If 90 percent of the industry adopted aeration, annual savings should approximate at least 15.7 million dollars.

Increased storage revenues of about 1 million dollars a year also might be realized from existing storages through better utilization of space. Costs of fumigating grain against insect damage also should be less.

PUBLIC REFRIGERATED warehouses, sometimes thought of as part of the intransit bridge between shipping points and terminal points in the food marketing system, receive, store, and ship millions of tons of perishable products each year. Handling of materials may account for 75 percent of the physical operations in the warehouses.

More consideration once was given to the costs of land for warehouse sites

## MECHANICAL AERATION OF GRAIN STORED IN COMMERCIAL STORAGES

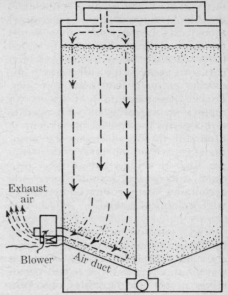

*Aeration is practical in deep tanks as well as in shallow bins for preventing heating, molding, and caking of the stored grain. For less than 1 cent per bushel for power, recommended amounts of air can be moved through grain stored in tanks up to 150 feet high.*

and to refrigerating the structures than to handling costs. All public refrigerated warehouses were multistory buildings, in which elevators generally provided means for handling between floors. Two- and four-wheeled handtrucks and manual stacking methods were in general use.

Designed and financed by the Federal Government as a war measure, the first single-floor public refrigerated warehouse was constructed during the Second World War. In it, industrial forklift trucks and pallets were used for handling products in unit loads. Handling costs averaged about 35 percent less than in multistory warehouses.

Since the construction of the prototype one-story warehouse, few new multistory warehouses have been constructed—nearly all new ones largely have followed the one-floor design.

AT THE TERMINAL end of the marketing system, most wholesalers of some 60 years ago were small, independent dealers. Produce dealers usually operated in established market areas, where the facilities available were designed for other purposes. Wholesalers of dry groceries tended to locate outside the market areas in their own buildings. In both, handling was either purely manual or by handtrucks. Attempts to improve these methods usually were limited to the installation of a few sections of gravity-type conveyors to bridge the differences in heights between railroad car or motortruck floors and warehouse floors. Independent service wholesalers and chainstore warehouses since about 1940 have led the way in the adoption of mechanized handling methods. With the exception of beef carcasses and some other irregular shaped items that do not lend themselves to unit load handling, the use of pallets and skids has come into fairly widespread use. In receiving, unit loads are built as the products are unloaded from railroad cars or motortrucks and moved by skid jacks, pallet transporters, or industrial lift trucks to storage areas. Because of the instability of some types of packages, which limits stacking height of unit loads, pallet racks are coming into general use in wholesalers' warehouses.

With the growth of service wholesaling, methods of assembling products from storage areas and loading delivery trucks also have become more highly mechanized.

In some warehouses, entire unit loads are withdrawn from storage and are brought to the shipping area. In others, orders are totaled to determine the exact amounts of each specific item needed for all orders and only that amount is withdrawn from storage. Portable belt conveyor lines, which extend from the assembly area in the warehouse to the loading face in the truck, can accomplish the last of the shipping operations.

But improved technology in these warehouses has not been limited to greater use of lift trucks and other mechanized handling equipment. Recording and transcribing equipment is employed in at least two ways in addition to usual office methods—for receiving orders from salesmen and to replace checkers who call out items in individual orders as they are loaded.

An obstacle to the more general adoption of mechanized handling by all types of wholesalers is outmoded buildings. Savings in labor of up to 50 percent in facilities of modern design, in which mechanized equipment can be used efficiently, make a convincing argument for abandoning obsolete structures or putting them to other uses.

RETAIL food stores at the turn of the century were purveyors of food that served also as social institutions, extended credit to their customers, and made deliveries. Clerks waited on each customer and bagged and weighed individual orders. Prepackaged items largely were unknown.

When self-service retail food stores eliminated the need for clerks to wait on customers, some experts felt that these stores had no further possibilities to effect savings or to increase labor productivity.

Research in the Department of Agriculture has pointed the way to many additional improvements in operation of retail stores.

Progress in meat departments, for example, began with the shifting of butchers and other workers to a special room designed and equipped for cutting, grinding, and packaging meats and meat products for self-service displays. Except for special cuts of meat, butchers were relieved of responsibilities for direct contacts with customers.

The establishment of meat rooms has permitted the complete mechanization of many operations that formerly required high labor inputs. As an illustration, new equipment now automatically grinds, packages, and prices hamburger as an integrated operation. This equipment plus numerous other mechanical innovations that have come since about 1950 have sharply increased the productivity of workers in meat departments. Beginning with average sales of roughly 25 dollars per man-hour of labor employed about 1950, a number of stores that have moved and mechanized their meat departments reported that 1959 sales per man-hour of labor had increased to 44 dollars. Although increases in meat prices during the 9-year period account for part of the difference, increased labor productivity accounts for the major part.

With the increase in the number of prepackaged items, produce departments in many supermarkets also have been assigned a backroom, where selected products can be trimmed, packaged, and placed on specially designed trays for handling and display.

Thus the shelf life of produce is increased, and waste is minimized. Sales per man-hour of labor also have increased—from about 21 dollars in 1950 by conventional methods to 29 dollars in 1959 by the new methods.

In some stores where improved methods and equipment have made the greatest inroads, sales for the store as a whole have risen from 25,400 dollars annually per worker employed in 1948 to 41,200 dollars in 1958.

ALTHOUGH the effects of the mechanization I have cited have been many and varied, none has had a greater impact than the reductions made possible in the unit costs of handling products as the volumes handled in a single establishment increased.

True, these reductions in unit costs have not been enough to bring about reductions in total costs. But this would be too much to expect when it is recognized that total costs now cover the handling of substantially larger volumes of products and the performance of additional services plus inflation.

Possible economies of scale on the part of marketing firms actually is another way of pointing up possibilities of achieving unit cost savings as volumes handled warrant the adoption of improved technology and of determining, for example, when two industrial lift trucks or another packing line should be installed.

Fixed, or ownership, costs of such equipment should of course be considered in terms of fractional utilization, influenced by seasonal operation and related factors. Possible savings in unit costs, however, usually have been so great, and the expectations of further increases in volumes so well founded, that the degree or extent of utilization of the second or third units of equipment usually has been of relatively minor importance to most of the larger marketing firms.

Just as the mechanization of farms has encouraged a shift to larger units, so has mechanization in the agricultural marketing system encouraged business—and for like reasons.

Despite continued increases in the total annual volume of agricultural products moving through the marketing system and the demand for more and more services, smaller marketing firms have found it increasingly difficult to maintain a share of this business because of the competition provided by larger, more highly mechanized firms.

As a consequence, many of the smaller firms, whose respective volumes of business did not justify heavy capital outlays for equipment, now have sought other enterprises. And with this decline in the number of smaller marketing firms, larger firms usually have taken over both the volumes vacated plus those stemming from increased consumer demand. Moreover, many of the larger firms now are in position to seek out and pay for the consulting and research services needed to increase their competitive advantage among firms of their same relative scale of operations. In this respect, smaller firms also are at a distinct disadvantage.

Farm economists and engineers have pointed out that if the shift on farms from horse-drawn and horse-powered equipment to mechanically powered equipment had not taken place during the first half of the 20th century, our present levels of farm production could not have been attained. But largely because of these multipliers of human effort on the farm, in 1960 only 12 percent of the total population could produce more foods, fibers, and other agricultural products than were in demand by the total population.

The situation has not been so favorable in the agricultural marketing system. The number of workers employed by marketing firms has continued to increase from 2 to 3 percent each year. Thanks to the progress made in increasing worker productivity, this increase is relatively small in proportion to the increased volume of products moving through the marketing system each year and the increase in services rendered in the preparation of oven-ready or table-ready products. If the productivity of marketing labor had not been increased above the levels prevailing around 1910, it is doubtful whether sufficient work stations could be provided in our present facilities for the labor that would be required to move the 1960 volume of products.

But lack of space for workers is not a primary consideration of marketing firms, which have been investing about 850 million dollars each year in new and improved marketing and off-farm storage facilities. Although the replacement of facilities destroyed by fires, hurricanes, and other disasters accounts for part of this amount, a substantial part of this investment stems from the impact of mechanization. Multistory facilities in congested downtown areas, which were designed for a bygone age, are giving way to new structures specifically designed for the operations to be performed and the methods to be employed. Transportation facilities also have been similarly affected by improved methods and equipment and, in some instances, have pointed up the need for greater mechanization. Notable among these shifts are the use of tank trucks for hauling milk, which have replaced expensive labor and equipment in the plant for receiving and handling milk in cans.

Greater mechanization of handling operations also has been directly responsible for reducing the spoilage and waste of perishable items by minimizing the number of times products are handled during the course of their journey from farms to consumers and by providing gentler handling.

In fact, the stimulus for many improved methods now in use has been quality maintenance rather than savings in labor and other costs.

In conclusion, I should point out that the benefits from the mechanization on farms would have been largely dissipated in the marketing of farm and food products if corresponding improvements had not been made in the marketing system.

# Railroads, Trucks, and Ships

John C. Winter

MAY 10 of 1869 was a big day in Promontory, Utah. Amid speechmaking and jollification, a golden spike was driven to mark the coming together of two lines of railroad track, one from the East and one from the West. The Pacific Railroad had been completed. A route was open between the Atlantic and the Pacific.

The oxcart, the mule team, the sailboat, the canaler, and the steamboat had all held worthy places in the Nation's early development. But the development and expansion of the railroads, in which the ceremony at Promontory was an incident, were primarily responsible for the settlement and cultivation of the millions of acres in the West, the Southwest, and the South and provided means for the pioneers to market the fruits of their labor and to obtain other necessities of life and production.

The origins of railroading lie in the industrial revolution in England. Dependence on coal, mined mostly at some distance from canals and rivers, was responsible for early efforts to find a way to move it overland to waterside and industrial localities quickly and cheaply.

The first successful use of a steam engine operating on rails—wooden— was on a short stretch of track in Wales. Shortly thereafter, in 1814, a man named George Stephenson followed with a steam locomotive, named "Blucher," and the introduction of regular steam transportation on the Stockton and Darlington Railroad.

Some experimentation with steam locomotion was done in this country between 1820 and 1830. The famous "Tom Thumb" of the Baltimore and Ohio came in 1829, but the first successful use of the locomotive in pulling a train of cars was "The Best Friend of Charleston," on 6 miles of track of the South Carolina Railroad out of Charleston, S.C., in 1830. This road had 137 miles of track under operation by 1833.

Railroad mileage in 1840 had increased to 2,818 miles. More than 9 thousand miles of track had been laid by 1850.

Robert S. Henry, in his book, *This Fascinating Railroad Business*, wrote:

"Thus, when as yet there were but two states on the western bank of the Mississippi . . . there came to America the combination of a new sort of flexible composite vehicle—the train made up of many separate cars pulled by a unit of power—and a new sort of road, the road of rails. Their combination freed the continent from the limitations of terrain and temperature which so severely restrict the usefulness of rivers and canals, for the railroad could go anywhere at any time. It

could pierce mountains and cross waterless plains. It could run every day in the year, through the frozen winter or the long summer droughts, as well as in the more favored seasons of navigation. And upon its surface of rails the power of men and machines to produce transportation was many times multiplied."

The first rails in this country were of various combinations of wood stringers faced with iron straps, although English roads were using cast or wrought iron rails. Iron was scarce in this country and costly.

Robert L. Stevens, son of the president of the Camden and Amboy, using a block of wood and a pocketknife, in 1830 designed an iron T rail with a flat bottom. It was first spiked to wooden plugs drilled in holes in stone blocks. The blocks were expensive. Quarrying and moving them to the site and drilling the holes were difficult and laborious. So much so, indeed, that in laying track for the Camden and Amboy, the tracklaying crew ran out of the stone blocks and no more were to be had for some time.

Expediency, then, was responsible for the trial of the wooden crosstie, into which the rails were spiked directly. To the astonishment of the builders, it worked. It also provided a more flexible bed over which cars rode better and held the rail in gage better than stone. Timber for the ties was cheap and plentiful. No better method having been found, wooden ties are still used by railroads today.

The first steel rails were imported for use on the Pennsylvania Railroad in 1863, 7 years after the development of the Bessemer process of converting iron ore into steel. The first steel rails were rolled in this country in 1865, although replacement of the iron rail was slow.

In the days before the Civil War, most of the railroad mileage was in short, unconnected pieces and often of different gages, which ranged from 4 feet 9 inches to 6 feet. There were some narrow gage lines, too, but they were mostly for such special purposes as hauling ore from mines or timber from a lumbering site, where grades and curves presented difficulties to the movement of the heavy locomotives and cars built for a wide gage track. Narrow gage was used long after the major railroads had adopted a standard gage, 4 feet 8.5 inches. Narrow gage is still in use in a few places.

The Civil War made urgent the through movements of materials, without the delay and work involved in unloading and reloading at junction points where a track of a different gage was encountered. So began the slow effort to standardize the gage. Two "standard" gages—4 feet 8.5 inches in the North and 5 feet in the South—existed in 1880; in 1886, the southern roads narrowed the gage of their tracks to 4 feet 8.5 inches.

STEADILY, the many short, disconnected railroads of the East and South had been consolidated into a number of large systems with thousands of miles of track. During this time pioneering farmers were moving by wagon train into the Central and Western States. The productive virgin lands were waiting.

The early settlers and the things they raised were far from markets. Investors in the East and in Europe saw an opportunity for gain in the extension of these new builders of wealth, the railroads, to carry emigrants and the things they needed to the open lands and their products to the expanding populations of the East and to the ports from which the products could be shipped to markets overseas.

What was more natural, then, than that these lines should be extended across the prairies and through the mountains?

Railroad land companies advertised the attractions of the new lands. They offered low rates on "emigrant movables" to enable settlers and their families and their goods—livestock, seed, machinery, and anything else they required, including the dog and the cat—to reach the homesteads. Even as late as 1900 the Great Northern Railroad maintained such rates from St. Paul to Minot, N. Dak., 500 miles, as low as 35 dollars a car, and to Havre, Mont., 1 thousand miles, 66 dollars. From Chicago to Pierre, S. Dak., 750 miles, the Chicago and Northwestern charged 40 dollars. The Milwaukee Railroad's rate from Chicago to Miles City, Mont., 1,100 miles, was 100 dollars a car.

Texas, Iowa, Wisconsin, and California had been admitted to the Union by 1850, when there were 9 thousand miles of railroad, all east of the Mississippi River. There were more than 30 thousand miles by 1860. Lines were stretching out into Wisconsin and Iowa and had reached the Missouri River. There were 53 thousand miles when Nebraska, Minnesota, Oregon, Kansas, and Nevada had become States. By 1890, other roads had been extended to the Pacific; Colorado, North and South Dakota, and Washington had been admitted; and the railroads had grown to 164 thousand miles.

Railroads were promoting traffic for their lines by hiring specialists in agriculture to help farmers grow new crops for rotation and diversification and to encourage good farming practices.

Wheat, corn, oats, and barley flowed in increasing volume to Chicago, St. Louis, the Twin Cities, Kansas City, Omaha, Sioux City. The trail herds had vanished—cattle, hogs, and sheep now moved by train to those markets and to Denver and Fort Worth. Flour and feed mills flourished.

In the South, the movement of cotton by water to the warehouse on the levee was supplanted by rail transportation, which stimulated production in places in the South and Southwest that could not be reached by navigable rivers.

So the expansion of the railroads was also the expansion of agriculture in the United States.

Railroad mileage continued to increase at a diminishing rate after 1890 until it reached its peak of 254 thousand miles, but thereafter railroad progress was primarily in the refinement and improvement of services, which had far-reaching effects upon agriculture.

The trains that hauled goods to market were there, but many of the farmer's products were perishable and needed special care if they were to get to the market in salable condition. For livestock, there came the stock car; for poultry, the live-poultry car; for dressed poultry, meats, and dairy products, the refrigerator car.

Do YOU know that the people of this country consume the equivalent of more than a million railroad carloads of fresh fruit and vegetables and almost a million carloads of meat each year? That about 400 carload equivalents of fruits and vegetables have to arrive in New York every day? That Chicago requires 200 cars daily?

About half of these are now received by motortruck, but the refrigerator car started it all.

The first known effort to refrigerate perishable food was in 1851, when several tons of butter were shipped from Ogdensburg, N.Y., to New York City in a boxcar loaded with ice. Other early experiments included boxcars with ice placed on shelves at the ends of the car or in boxes in the doorways. The Pennsylvania Railroad in 1857 added inside linings in 30 boxcars and filled them with sawdust for insulation. Various innovations involving insulation and the placement of ice in the cars followed, and meat rails to carry hanging meat were added.

William Davis of Detroit in 1868 patented a car in which metal tanks along the sides could be filled with ice and salt from the roof.

In the meantime, the growing Chicago meatpacking industry had a problem: How could the packers ship their meat to the growing cities of the East without having it spoil in warm weather?

The Davis car provided the answer. It was used for shipments of dressed beef from Chicago to Boston and other eastern cities in 1869. It is given credit for the growth of the dressed-beef industry. It and similar cars were suitable for meats and dairy products, but some of the early experiments with the shipment of fruit and vegetables were disappointing, because the cars could not carry enough ice. When this became understood and greater capacity was provided, results were better.

Oranges and strawberries were shipped from California to New York in 1888. Oranges moved from Florida to New York in 1889. Before that time oranges had moved in insulated cars, but under ventilation. Thereupon the marketing of fruit from these areas of specialized production increased rapidly. Shipments of deciduous fruit from California increased to 6,900 carloads by 1899, and shipments of citrus fruit rose to 15 thousand cars.

Refrigerator cars then were owned by shippers and by private lines, and the railroads paid them up to three-fourths of a cent a mile for their use. One railroad in one year made mileage payments to 65 different owners of refrigerator cars.

The demand for more and more cars to move the increasing production of fruit and vegetables evidently aroused opposition to control of these cars by meatpackers. In 1906, when the Armour interests owned 70 percent of the refrigerator cars in use, the Congress enacted the Hepburn Act, which gave the Interstate Commerce Commission control over the mileage charges. The Pacific Fruit Express Co., jointly owned by the Union Pacific and the Southern Pacific, was organized in 1906 and acquired 6 thousand of the Armour cars.

Eastern and southern lines continued to use the packer cars until a Federal Trade Commission order in 1920 required the separation of the fruit and vegetable car business from Armour control. In March of that year a group of eastern and southern roads acquired the Armour subsidiary, Fruit Growers Express, Inc., with 4,279 refrigerator cars, and changed the name to Fruit Growers Express Co.

The refrigerator cars in use at the time of the First World War were not good cars by present standards. Losses due to spoilage were heavy. Many had less than an inch of insulation. Few had permanent floor racks. The ice they could carry was limited.

The Department of Agriculture, working with the United States Railroad Administration, in 1919 set up what were then regarded as extremely rigid standards—2.5 inches of insulation, ice capacity of 5 tons, and floor racks with a clearance of 3.75 inches for air circulation under the load.

These standards were observed and somewhat improved by the railroads and refrigerator carlines. Department research workers, through studies and tests of protective services, including ventilation and protection against cold, meanwhile learned a great deal about how refrigerator cars might be further improved.

The United Fresh Fruit and Vegetable Association established a committee to work with the Association of American Railroads and the Department to develop higher standards in the construction of refrigerator cars. Their recommendations have been adopted for new and rebuilt old cars.

One recommendation called for 4 to 4.5 inches of insulation, sidewall flues, elevated floor racks, and fans to provide positive circulation of air around and through the load. It was a major step in providing adequate protection of fresh fruit, vegetables, and other perishables en route to market. Most cars now used for fruits and vegetables are equipped with fans. A new development is the thermostatic control of the operation of the fans to maintain stable temperatures. Many of the water-ice refrigerator cars recently built have more insulation than the amount recommended.

Another development is the mechanical refrigerator car, in which the zero temperatures required by frozen food products are maintained.

The Fruit Growers Express Co. in 1949 built the first experimental mechanical cars, which were powered by gasoline engines. Later cars used diesel motors. A few are powered with propane gas.

Mechanical cars are more expensive to build than water-ice cars but less expensive to operate. Industry and the Department of Agriculture have continued experimentation in the endeavor to lower costs of construction and operation yet maintain the efficiency required. The cars are being used increasingly for fruit, vegetables, meat, and other products besides frozen food.

Mechanical cars in 1959 numbered 3,750 of a total refrigerator fleet of 115,750 cars. Indications were that the mechanical car would eventually replace the water-ice car, long the standby of the perishable food industries. No water-ice cars were on order for construction in August 1959, but 1,250 mechanical cars were being built or were on order.

Advances of the railroads to improve the efficiency of their operations since the war include the virtually complete replacement of the steam engine by the diesel locomotive, trailer-on-flatcar service, centralized traffic control for more efficient operation of trains over single track lines, and the installation of modern facilities of communication.

Many millions of dollars have also been spent on the improvement of yard and terminal facilities. The use of electronic devices and television in pushbutton classification yards has enabled many railroads to reduce costs and speed the handling of cars through them. Many roads use electronic data processing and communication equipment to distribute cars more efficiently, give advance consists of trains to receiving yards, and do many accounting services formerly done at greater cost by clerical labor.

As THE railroads in the 19th century provided a foundation for the nationwide development of agriculture, the motortruck has powerfully influenced the marketing and distribution of agricultural products in the 20th century.

There is a record of an "Atlas Road Engine" made in 1879. By 1905 a considerable number of companies built 750 trucks. In 1907 an International Harvester truck was powered by an under-the-seat, two-cylinder engine, which generated 8 horsepower.

Factory sales for some subsequent years tell the growth of the industry: 1910, 6 thousand trucks; 1920, 321,789; 1930, 575,364; 1940, 754,901; 1950, 1,332,285.

Almost all of the trucks sold before the First World War were of the city delivery and service types. Indeed, the roads in those days did not encourage dependence upon motor vehicles for hauls of any great length outside the limits of cities and towns.

The trucks of that day were far different from the powerful ones we see now on our highways. Experience gained in the manufacture of trucks for use in the war, capable of carrying loads through all kinds of roads and terrain, overcame earlier limitations, and trucks began to be used on farms and for intercity hauling after the war.

Still, the condition of the roads held back intercity movements until the "get-out-of-the-mud" campaigns of the 1920's brought about extensive road surfacing. By 1955, 2 of every 3 miles of the more than 3 million miles of public highways in the country were all-weather surfaced.

That gave strong impetus to highway transportation generally and the direct movement of products by truck from farms to city markets. Before motortrucks and dependable highways became available, products had to be hauled from the farm by horse and wagon, usually to the nearest railroad station, for movement to the city market. The farmer therefore was limited in his choice of those to whom he might sell.

Farmers who acquired trucks found that it was not much harder to drive them 50 miles than 15, once they were loaded, and their choice of available buyers widened. It extended much further when hard-surfaced highways made it possible for them to deliver to places 150 miles or more away. Local trucking firms appeared, ready to haul grain, livestock, fruit, or vegetables to distant markets. Sometimes buyers' trucks came and purchased directly from the farm for more than a farmer could get from his regular local dealers.

American inventiveness and ingenuity are well illustrated by the many ways in which the motortruck has been adapted to the needs of marketing. Mechanical refrigeration of trucks for perishable food products predated railroad mechanical refrigerator cars.

Many trucks have ice bunkers and blower fans. Others use dry-ice systems. Delivery vehicles for ice cream and frozen foods are equipped with hold plates, in which the brine is refrozen overnight and the refrigeration is made available during the day.

Mechanically refrigerated truck-trailers for over-the-road movement of perishable fresh and frozen foods have been improved greatly. Research in the Department of Agriculture has aided the truck-trailer industry in establishing standards for refrigerated trucks. A standard method for rating refrigerated trailers, developed in cooperation with the National Bureau of Standards, was adopted by the industry in 1959.

Trucks for hauling grain are emptied by hydraulic or mechanical lifts.

Equipment for hauling livestock includes special triple-deck vans and sprinkling systems for cooling hogs in hot weather. Some have refrigeration units to supplement ventilation for cooling. Self-unloading tanks are used for delivering dry granular material, such as feed, to farms. Boxes that carry grain or potatoes in one direction are mounted atop tanks, which carry oil or molasses on the return haul.

The availability of motortruck transportation has revolutionized the system of marketing of some commodities. Livestock in the Corn Belt is an example.

In the early 1920's, at shipping time, some farmers had enough animals ready for market to make a full carload. Others did not, and enough had to be accumulated to make a carload. That usually was done by a local buyer or shipping association—at additional expense. The farmer also had to haul the hogs to town by horse and wagon. The whole business was a bothersome chore.

Then came the motortruck and the local hauler, who would pick up a truckload or a few head at a farm and deliver them to a market before it opened the next morning. The farmer was not limited to the markets served directly by the railroad nearest to the farm, but had a choice of a number of places at which he might sell, perhaps at a better price.

Most of the hogs or cattle of a farmer in Iowa very likely had been sold in Chicago because of the dominant east-west pattern of the main and secondary railroad lines through Iowa. But the trucker could now deliver the animals north to Mason City or Albert Lea, south to Des Moines or Ottumwa, or west to Fort Dodge, Sioux City, or South Omaha. Radio and the market news may also have had much to do with it. The farmer, judging from the noon market news broadcast that prices at Dubuque would be good the next day, could telephone his trucker and have his animals there for the market opening.

The effects of these and other factors that may also have contributed to the change in the marketing system are shown by a decline in the slaughter of hogs at Chicago (from 6 million head in 1925 to 2.3 million in 1958) and at six major Midwest markets including Chicago (from 17 million head in 1925 to 13 million in 1958). In the same period, slaughter at interior packing plants, mostly in Iowa and Minnesota, increased from 7 million head to 17 million.

The motortruck also contributed to the growth of direct buying of livestock on farms by the packing companies, livestock auctions, and local and concentration markets throughout the country.

Cotton also was affected by motortrucks. When the only way of moving it from the farm to the gin was by horse- or mule-drawn wagon or by ox-cart, the gin had to be reasonably close. There were more than 18 thousand gins in 1920 in the cotton States, many only a few miles apart. With a truck it was no great task to deliver to a gin 10 or 20 miles away.

Also, since 1920, the trend has been toward gins of larger size and greater efficiency. The combination of these factors contributed to a reduction in the number of gins. Fewer than 6 thousand gins operated in 1959.

THE FLEXIBILITY and adaptability of the truck to almost any transportation requirements have made it of major importance in the marketing of agricultural products.

It can go anywhere there are streets and highways. Products can be picked up at the farm, in the field, at any warehouse or plant that has an access road, and can be delivered directly to a receiver at the market. It can serve any community and bring the finest and freshest of food products to remote places. Some 25 thousand communities in the United States relied entirely on truck transportation in 1960.

Nearly half of the 23 million trucks in use throughout the world in 1956 were in the United States, and more than 3 million were on American farms. Tens of thousands more were employed regularly in hauling agricultural commodities for hire.

FOR-HIRE interstate transportation of unmanufactured agricultural commodities is subject only to regulations of the Interstate Commerce Commission that relate to safety and hours of service of driver employees.

There is no requirement that the trucker establish proof of public convenience and necessity, with attendant hearings and legal expense. There is no limitation as to what he may haul, or where, or when, or how much he shall charge the shipper.

Many thousands of these operators (known as exempt agricultural haulers) serve the agricultural industry. They deliver livestock, or grain, cotton, fruit and vegetables, dressed poultry, and many other commodities to markets hundreds of miles away and return with other raw or processed products. Dressed poultry, for instance, is transported from the Southeast to California and the Pacific Northwest and fresh fruit and vegetables are brought back on the eastbound return.

In addition are common and contract carriers, who also haul farm products free of regulation, the same as the exempt carriers. The movement of agricultural commodities, by helping them to balance their tonnage and reduce the number of empty return hauls, contributes to the efficiency of their operations. Often the rates charged for hauling agricultural products by common and contract carriers are lower than the rates of exempt haulers.

With this freedom and flexibility of action, motor transportation has come to dominate the marketing of many of the most important products of the farm.

All farm products that are marketed move at least part of the way by truck at one stage of the distribution channel or another, of course, but market news reports of the Department of Agriculture and special studies indicated in 1957 motortrucks transported to final markets 85 percent of the livestock, 99 percent of the fresh dressed poultry, 85 percent of the frozen poultry, 100 percent of the live poultry, 99 percent of the eggs, 75 percent of the butter, 57 percent of the fresh fruit and vegetables, and 50 percent of the meat.

THE MAIN REASONS why motortrucks have grown to a position of such great importance in moving agricultural products are that the freight rates charged are usually lower and that service is faster and more dependable.

We have found that those two factors account for about 80 percent of the shift from railroad to truck and that they are of about equal importance. Sometimes a shipper does not care how soon his shipment gets to market, if it is not highly perishable; perhaps if the market is weak, he would just as soon it did not get there too quickly.

Usually, however, the shipper (or receiver, if he controls the routing) will base his choice of the carrier on these considerations:

If the commodity is perishable it may deteriorate if it is delayed.

He can better judge tomorrow's market than the one the day after.

His estimate of a market 3 days away will be better than if it takes 6 days.

Once loaded, the truck can be out of town and on its way in minutes, without the delays of switching and waiting for road trains. At the destination, delivery can be made, even in a large city, in a few hours after arrival. The individual shipment has the personal attention and care of the driver.

Shipments can be made in smaller amounts by truck. This is important in serving small or middle-sized markets. A receiver who can handle 10 tons of a particular commodity may not be able to store or merchandise a rail carload shipment of 20 tons or more.

Loss and damage are less by truck.

If his shipment fails to reach the market when it should, the price may go down and he will lose money. (Exceptions are the established and guaranteed rail schedules from California and Florida fruit and vegetable shipping districts to major markets where the railroads reimburse the shipper for the loss if his shipment does not arrive on schedule and the market goes down.)

If the receiver is a merchandiser or processor, speed and regularity of movement for fast turnover of inventory is of prime importance. The assembly lines of many processors now reach back to the points of production of the raw products, and it is essential that they reach the plant regularly in the necessary quantities.

Several years ago a large organization that operates a chain of retail stores had to build a new warehouse or expand its old one in an eastern city to take care of its growing business. The uncertainty of arrival of a number of important items received by rail forced the firm to hold heavy inventories of them to satisfy the requirements of the stores supplied by the warehouse. Buying trucks and operating them on regular schedules, which assured dependable arrivals, enabled the reduction of inventories of these foods by half or more. The old warehouse continued to serve.

How typical this example may be I do not know, but it illustrates the importance of inventory in merchandising today and the contribution the truck has made to marketing efficiency.

BEFORE TRUCK transportation had assumed much significance, the Class I railroads in 1929 originated 140 million tons of products of agriculture. They originated 149 million tons in 1957, an increase of 6 percent over 1929. But the production of agricultural products increased about two-thirds over the same period, a potential of 235 million tons of available traffic.

If the railroads had obtained only one-half of this increase in tonnage, their freight revenues for 1959 would have been increased by more than 333 million dollars.

Such traffic losses caused the managements to stimulate efforts to improve service and to reduce rates to meet truck competition.

For many years railroad fast-freight schedules for perishables from California were 7 days to Chicago and 10 days to New York. In 1959 they were 5 days to Chicago and 7 days to New York. Faster service was started on potatoes from Maine to New England cities and New York. Westbound schedules from the Midwest to the Pacific coast, including livestock, were reduced.

Those improvements were made where there was a concentration of important movements of traffic. They have not been enough. Management and labor together need to take a critical look at the whole of railroad performance. Railroad jobs and dividends and the country's welfare are at stake—for scarcely anybody questions the importance of a healthy railroad system.

LAKES and rivers were the main means of transportation in the interior of the country during the first half of the 19th century.

The completion of the Erie Canal in 1825 breached the barrier of the Alleghenies and opened an all-water route to the western shore of Lake Michigan and by portage at the Sault Ste. Marie to Lake Superior.

Side and stern wheelers and flatboats plied the Ohio, Mississippi, Missouri, and their tributaries, carrying supplies to early settlers and furs, hides, grain, cotton, and other produce to places where they could be sold.

The coming of the railroads brought an end to the packet boat trade, and river traffic went into a decline from which it did not begin to recover until after 1900.

Interest was revived in the inland waterways as part of the program for conservation of natural resources during the administration of Theodore Roosevelt. Stabilization and deepening of channels for the navigation of barges also was stimulated by rising freight rates of the railroads and the resulting demand for cheaper transportation.

Less romantic than the river packet, the barge is more efficient—efficient enough to hold its own and more against competing forms of transportation. River traffic of such products as grain, sugar, molasses, and fertilizers for farm use has continued to expand. It more than doubled in 1949–1957, when the movement was more than 11.5 million tons.

Traffic on the Great Lakes has increased steadily from the start, although the character of the tonnage has changed. In the early 1900's, a substantial amount of flour moved from western milling centers over the lakes to eastern cities, until the efficiency of the bulk lakers made it cheaper to move the grain to Buffalo and mill the flour and feed there.

The lake boats have continued to grow in size. Single cargoes of as much as 750 thousand bushels of grain were carried in 1959.

On June 26, 1959, in Montreal the Great Lakes-St. Lawrence Seaway was formally opened by Queen Elizabeth II and President Dwight D. Eisenhower. The Seaway was a joint project of the United States and Canada. It has seven locks, and connecting channels have been deepened to 27 feet. A dream long fought for, it permits the movement of ocean-going vessels to Toledo, Detroit, Chicago, Milwaukee, Duluth, and other ports.

The formal opening awaited the convenience of the heads of State, but the first lake-bound, ocean-going vessels moved through it on April 25, 1959. To the midwestern farmer, the importance of the Seaway lies mainly in the reduced cost of transporting grain from Chicago and Duluth to many markets of the world. The reductions range up to 10 cents a bushel. From the opening on April 25 to the end of 1959, an estimated 115 million bushels moved out of lake ports for export through the Seaway.

WHAT CHANGES in transportation may we look forward to?

For one thing, we may expect a great deal more coordination of transportation facilities in getting products to market.

For instance, a service has been developed by the Missouri Pacific Railroad in which motortruck trailers loaded at citrus and vegetable packing plants in the Rio Grande Valley are shunted onto special flatcars and moved in perishable-scheduled trains.

They go to Kansas City, St. Louis, and other cities, where the trailers are again hooked to tractors for delivery to wholesale houses and chain warehouses. Switching delays are eliminated, and the produce is delivered in better condition.

Other piggyback service transports meats from midwestern packing plants to eastern cities. This innovation has grown mightily in the transportation of industrial goods. Although special problems of perishability have slowed its adaptation to the movement of agricultural products, we should see a great deal more of it in the future. Large bulk containers that may be shifted among trucks, barges, ships, and rail cars then may well supplant piggyback operations.

Truck transportation will be faster and more economical when the 41 thousand miles of interstate superhighways, under construction in 1960, are completed.

Further improved mechanical refrigerator cars and truck-trailers will assure better arrival of perishable products at the markets in top condition.

Many branch lines of railroads will be abandoned, and grain will be accumulated by truck for shipment from large elevators on the main lines of railroads. Covered self-unloading hopper cars for grain will provide faster turn-around of cars for the railroads and reduce loading and unloading costs of shippers and receivers.

Livestock will be slaughtered near the point of production—the long-haul movements will be of meat and other livestock products by rail or truck or a coordination of those services. There are good reasons why some of the livestock now moves long distances, but eventually those reasons will be overcome by reductions in the costs of transporting meat.

Upstream reservoirs to stabilize the flow of water and the deepening of channels in rivers not navigable in 1960 will extend the water transportation of commodities, such as grain, and reduce the costs of moving bulk farm supplies, among them petroleum and fertilizers.

Air transportation of agricultural commodities has not realized the potential many people looked for at the close of the war, although relatively small quantities sometimes move by air. The high costs of operation of conventional aircraft have been the major drawbacks. It is difficult to conceive any great volume of agricultural traffic moving by air, however, as long as planes require the long landing strips that are needed now, especially in view of the high density of passenger and air express traffic at airports serving the large cities of the country. Space for large new airports anywhere near these cities has become hard to get. The possibility is in the development of a revolutionary type of aircraft that can take off and land (or drop cargo) in small spaces in and around the cities, where they will be convenient to markets and to industry.

The loosening of the strings of economic regulation of carriers should encourage experimentation and change. Limitation of competition has been a part of the basic philosophy underlying our transportation policy for many years, and competition is the great incentive to technological advance.

The tendency has seemed to be toward less regulation, rather than more. The Transportation Act of 1958 was intended to give the regulated carriers greater freedom in rate-making and in relieving themselves of unprofitable services. A further extensive review of transportation policy was begun by the Senate in 1959 to determine what additional modification might be of benefit to the public.

Finally, tremendous changes in the structure of the Nation—an increase in population; shifts in the population; industrial development of the Tennessee Valley and the Carolinas, the Texas gulf coast region, southern California, and the Pacific Northwest; expansion of older and established industrial areas, all of which absorb more and more of the arable land— point to still greater specialization in agricultural production and to the creation of new transportation problems and new challenges.

Transportation will have to play its part in meeting them, as in the past.

# Measuring and Keeping Quality

Harold T. Cook

MORE THAN 50 kinds of fresh fruit and vegetables may be on display in supermarkets at any time of the year. Some, even though they are highly perishable, have been shipped thousands of miles from where they were grown. They come from all corners of the country or world, but they are of uniform grade and quality.

Technical advances in measuring, controlling, and maintaining quality have made this possible.

Quality is many things. In apples it is color of peel and flesh, shape, size, maturity, ripeness, firmness, texture, juiciness, flavor, and freedom from decay and other defects. In meat cuts it is size, shape, color, grain or marbling, texture, tenderness, odor, flavor, and freedom from slime or mold.

Standards of quality, the basis for grades and inspection, are essential in modern marketing, because a buyer may purchase goods he never sees by telephone or telegraph from a seller who may be thousands of miles away.

Official United States grades have been set for many products. They have national uniformity and mean the same thing in New York as in California, Texas, or Florida. Buyers and sellers use them as a basis for judging the quality of a product and agreeing on a sale price.

Existing standards or grades rely primarily on the judgment of experienced inspectors. They depend on the senses of vision, feel, taste, and smell. They are subject to human variation and may differ from one inspector to another and from one day to another. Instruments that measure factors of quality by chemical and physical means eliminate much of this variation. They have been perfected for some measurements, and other instruments are in the process of development. The day will come when much of the grading may be based on physical and chemical tests made by instruments that measure quality factors accurately, quickly, and uniformly.

LET US consider some instruments that are available now and some that are coming.

Tenderness is important in sweet corn, peas, green beans, asparagus, and other vegetables. Tenderness in corn was measured for many years by the thumbnail test: The corn is considered tender if the kernels break with only moderate pressure from the thumbnail. Tenderness in beans and asparagus usually is tested by seeing if the pods or stalks snap when broken. These tests are not precise. They leave too much to personal judgment and experience.

The tenderometer was introduced in 1937 for measuring quality in peas. Its principle is that firmness or hardness of the peas indicates quality. It measures these properties by determining the force required to shear a certain volume of peas through a standard grid.

A fibrometer was introduced in 1948 to measure quality in asparagus by measuring the resistance of asparagus stalks to cutting.

Another instrument, the succulometer, measures maturity in sweet corn; the amount of juice forced out of a sample of corn under 500 pounds of pressure indicates maturity.

Each of these instruments measures the force needed for a particular type of "chewing" action. The tenderometer measures crushing and shearing; the fibrometer, cutting; and the succulometer, squeezing out juice.

The shear process measures all three factors in many kinds of fruit and vegetables. It has a single power unit equipped with different types of test cells for measuring each factor. Gages of different ranges are used for each kind of vegetable or fruit.

An attachment has been developed for the shear press that transforms the mechanical energy of shearing force into electrical energy and graphs the readings on a roll-type recorder.

Pressure with the thumb has long been used as an indication of maturity and ripeness in apples, pears, and peaches. Of the many types of instruments that measure firmness more accurately, the most widely used has been the Magness-Taylor pressure tester, which was introduced in 1925. It is simple and handy. It consists of a cylindrical metal barrel, about 12 inches long and 1 inch in diameter, within which a plunger works against a steel spring. The end of the plunger has interchangeable screw-on tips seven-sixteenths or five-sixteenths inch in diameter. The tip is placed against a pared spot on the fruit, and the barrel is pressed until the tip penetrates the flesh. Firmness is expressed as the number of pounds of pressure required to penetrate the fruit and is read from a scale on the barrel.

Stayman Winesap apples, for instance, have a pressure test reading with the seven-sixteenths-inch tip of 16 to 20 pounds at time of harvest; at 11 to 14 pounds, they are firm ripe; prime for eating at 8 to 12 pounds; and are overripe when less than 8 pounds.

The pressure tester is used to tell when pears are ripe enough to pick. Bartlett pears, for example, are harvested in California when they test about 18 to 21 pounds or less. It is also used as an index of picking maturity for peaches.

A fault of the pressure tester is that it punctures the fruit and ruins it for market. A "mechanical thumb" works on the same principle as the pressure tester but does not puncture and destroy the fruit. It uses a convex tip that is broader than the regular tips and indents the flesh only about one-eighth inch.

This modified pressure tester makes it possible to test the fruit that is actually to be sold without causing serious damage. It is superior to a person's thumb because it measures pressure in actual pounds.

COLOR measured by sight is not a good indicator of maturity because differences in color are hard to describe and measure by eye, and maturity sometimes is indicated as much by internal color as external color.

Color standards in the form of models and charts are used frequently to indicate the color terminology that the trade has developed for specific products. Books of color charts are available. Among them are those of Robert Ridgway, *Color Standards and Color Nomenclature;* Munsell Color Co., Inc., *Munsell Book of Color;* and A. Maerz and M. R. Paul, *A Dictionary of Color.* They illustrate and classify thousands of colors.

The books are rather unwieldy for direct matching of the color patches with horticultural specimens.

The 40-hue Nickerson Color Fan, by Dorothy Nickerson, is a new form of color chart in which each color sample is easily accessible for direct comparison alongside the specimen. Each of the 40 leaves of the fan displays samples of a single hue, ranging from dark at the bottom to light at the top. The Munsell color notation of hue, intensity, and relative lightness of color is printed on each sample. It is inexpensive and easy to use.

Color intensity may be measured also by extracting the pigments in suitable solvents and passing light of definite wavelengths through the solution; the amount of light transmitted is measured. Photoelectric colorimeters and spectrophotometers are used for this purpose. The color as seen by the human eye may not be related closely to the concentration of pigment in the extract, and the internal color of the product may be overemphasized.

Considerable progress has been made in measurement of internal color of whole fruit as an indication of maturity and quality. This is done with a new instrument, the "Hortispect." The whole fruit is placed in the instrument, and different wavelengths of light are passed through it. The wavelength that passes through most easily indicates the internal color. The test is based on the principle that green light goes most easily through green fruit, yellow light through yellow fruit, and red light through red fruit. The instrument is easy to operate. It does not damage the sample.

Color is important in tomatoes for processing, especially in tomatoes for juice. A new instrument quickly measures the hue, intensity, and relative lightness or darkness of the extracted juice and automatically calculates a color index that corresponds closely to the judgment of a panel of experienced inspectors. Earlier instruments measured only two of the three color factors and did not give a reliable reading of color.

Sugar content or sweetness generally is considered an indication of quality. Sugar content may be determined in the laboratory with the Abbe refractometer. A more rapid and practical instrument for field use is the hand refractometer, which is about 8 inches long and 1 inch in diameter. Only a drop of juice is needed. The instrument indicates the percentage of soluble solids, which is closely correlated with the percentage of sugar. It has been useful for testing citrus fruit, grapes, plums, cantaloups, tomatoes, and watermelons.

Sugar in grapes is determined commonly with a Balling or Brix hydrometer. They are glass cylinders that are floated in the liquid. The depth to which they sink indicates the density of the liquid. The measurements agree closely with the ones by the Abbe refractometer.

Sugar content alone is not a good indication of palatability if grapes are too acid. Quality in grapes therefore often is indicated by a sugar-acid ratio, which is calculated by dividing the percentage of sugar by the percentage of acid.

A similar method is used as a palatability index for citrus fruit. The soluble solids-acid ratio and total soluble solids are the bases for the present laws governing shipment of Florida citrus fruit. Minimum juice content per box of fruit and minimum color requirements are also enforced to prevent shipment of immature, unpalatable fruit.

QUALITY of shell eggs has been determined for generations by candling. In candling, an egg is held before a light projected through an opening so that the rays pass through and show the condition of the interior.

Candling gives an indication of the size and location of the air sac and condition of the yolk and white, but accurate determination of blood and meat spots, green rot, and other defects are beyond its limitations.

By using spectrophotometric methods, in which light of specific wavelengths is passed through the eggs, blood and meat spots and green rot can be detected with a high degree of accuracy. They operate on the principle that the affected eggs have light-absorbing properties different from those of sound, wholesome eggs. The instruments employing this method, which were being tested in egg grading and packing lines in 1960, automatically reject the bad eggs. The one that detects green rot operates at a speed of a thousand eggs an hour. It could be modified to handle 500 eggs a minute, which is about the maximum safe speed for handling eggs.

Quality of the white and yolk is determined more accurately by breaking out a few sample eggs than by candling. The height of the thick white or albumen and yolk indicates quality. Eggs that spread out are of low quality.

The "Haugh unit" is a measure of quality based on the height of the albumen. The height of the albumen is measured accurately with a special micrometer. A correction factor for egg weight is applied and the logarithm of the corrected height figure multiplied by 100 to give the "Haugh unit" score. Eggs of high quality score 72 to 100. Eggs of low quality score 0 to 30.

THE FAT ACIDITY test indicates deterioration of grain in storage. It is based on the fact that acidity increases as a result of chemical breakdown of some constituents of the grain during deterioration. The test is simple. Eight samples can be tested in an hour. The sample of 100 grams of dry wheat is ground in benzene in a special grinder-extractor. The fat acidity is expressed as the number of milligrams of potassium hydroxide required to neutralize the fatty acids in the extract.

Several simple and rapid objective methods measure smut contamination of wheat. In one, a suspension of smut spores is prepared by washing a sample of wheat, and the concentration of spores is measured with a colorimeter. Another method is to allow the spores to settle in a graduated centrifuge tube and measure the amount of sediment. A third method is to strain the suspension through a filter paper and measure the amount of light reflected from the smut-coated paper with a photoelectric reflectance meter. Still another method is to determine the amount of catalase enzyme in the wheat sample, which indicates the amount of smut.

A "smut meter" detects internal as well as external spores of smut. It requires no washing and takes only 45 seconds. The wheat sample is poured in a small container with clear plastic sides. Light of the near infrared wavelengths is beamed through it. The light is absorbed in proportion to the amount of smut present. Measurements made with it correspond closely to spore counts made with a microscope.

The protein content of wheat is a useful index of baking quality. The Kjeldahl protein test sometimes is used but it is too complicated for routine use. A sedimentation test is simple and fast and does not need expensive equipment or technical skill. Flour is prepared by running a sample of wheat through corrugated steel rollers and sifting through a 100-mesh sieve. Some is mixed with water, lactic acid, and isopropyl alcohol in a cylinder and allowed to settle. The volume of sediment after settling for 5 minutes indicates the swelling capacity of the gluten and the baking quality of the flour.

PROGRESS has been made in developing instruments for making objective tests on cotton.

The Suter-Webb Duplex Fiber Sorter separates fibers in the cotton sample by means of a bank of combs and arranges them in orderly groups by length for analysis and measurement.

The Fibrograph, a photoelectric device, measures the length and uniformity of length of fibers in a sample of cotton.

The Micronaire measures the average fineness of fiber and its maturity. It measures the resistance to passage of air through a sample of cotton of constant weight compressed to a given volume in a chamber.

The Causticaire test is made by testing a sample of cotton on a Micronaire instrument, equipped with a Causticaire scale, before and after treatment with caustic soda. From these measurements, fineness and maturity can be obtained.

The Pressley Strength Tester is used widely to find the aggregate strength of a mass of cotton fibers that have been combed into a flat ribbon.

Color is measured electronically with a Nickerson-Hunter Colorimeter, which registers reflectance or luster and degree of yellowness.

An electric meter measures the moisture content of cottonseed in less than 4 minutes; 12 to 18 hours were required by the forced-draft oven method. The seed is placed in a heavy cylinder, and the electrode is lowered until the seed is under specified pressure. The reading is made in milliamperes and is converted to percentage of moisture.

MOISTURE METERS have been used for many years in the inspection of raisins, figs, prunes, and other dried fruits. A sample of the fruit is placed in a cell, and the resistance to electrical conductivity is measured. A curve shows the moisture content at different electrical resistances. Since electrical conductivity depends essentially on dissolved ionized substances in the tissue of the fruit, moisture content is related to conductivity.

Similar moisture meters are used for grain. A meter based not on electrical conductivity but on dielectric properties of the commodity has come into use. In this application, the commodity is placed between two plates of different electric potentials or voltages, and the capacity of the commodity to support the voltage difference is measured. Water has a high dielectric constant as compared with other constituents of food.

THESE ARE only a few of the instruments and methods for objective tests of quality that have been developed for agricultural products. Some have proved to be satisfactory enough for routine commercial use, and some have been adopted for official use in grading. Others were in various stages of development and testing in 1960.

As I said, objective tests may be expected eventually to supplement subjective tests for quality. The result will be more uniform grading and inspection.

SOME OF the principles of objective measurement of quality are used to control quality in packing and processing plants.

The brine method for automatically separating tender peas from overmature peas is based on the differences in specific gravity—that is, relative weight for a given size or volume.

The peas are poured into a swiftly moving stream of brine. The mature peas, being of greater specific gravity, sink and are drawn off at the bottom. The tender peas float and are taken off at the top.

Differences in specific gravity have been used also to separate baking potatoes from boiling potatoes. Potatoes with a high specific gravity are high in dry matter and are best for baking. Those with low specific gravity are best for boiling.

A specific gravity separator for grading potatoes automatically according to cooking quality has been used experimentally in Colorado and Maine. We know that housewives would like to have potatoes of known cooking quality.

The electric eye has found many uses in quality control. I mentioned its use for detecting defects in eggs. It also may be used to separate brown-shelled from white-shelled eggs.

Electronic sorting of dry beans before packaging for retail sale has been used for many years. The automatic sorting device has been modified slightly and certain parts have been waterproofed, so that it can be used to sort soaked or partly cooked beans. The machine sorts the beans more quickly and accurately than hand sorters. When a bad lot of beans is being graded, the hand sorters miss many of the defective ones, and the pack is of poor quality. When good beans are being graded, the hand sorters often pick out many good beans. Sometimes as much as 40 percent of the rejects are usable. The machine can be adjusted to any degree of perception desired.

Grading for size or weight usually is done mechanically. Sifting through a series of sieves with progressively larger openings is used commonly for dry seeds, grain, green peas, and other small products. The smaller sizes, broken seeds, and trash fall through the smaller openings. The larger, sound seeds fall through the larger openings. Grids with large holes may be used for the larger fruits and vegetables. Another type of sizer has wooden or metal rollers set parallel to and above the conveyor belt. As individual fruit pass under the roller corresponding to their size, they are guided into the bin. These separators are entirely automatic and eliminate guesswork from sizing.

Adjustable openings through which the fruit fall into bins commonly are used also to size fruit and vegetables.

Another method of sizing is by weight. The fruit moves along in a pocket conveyor. When it reaches a bin of fruit of similar weight, a tripping device drops the pocket, and the fruit rolls into the bin.

THE CONTINUOUS inspection service that is made available by the Department of Agriculture has done much to improve the sanitary condition and quality of food products. It has been available for meat since 1890. It is now available for fresh fruit and vegetable packing plants and canners and freezers. Continuous inspection means that Federal inspectors are on duty at all times when the plant is operating.

The inspectors check the plant and equipment to make sure it meets sanitary requirements. They maintain a constant watch on the quality of the raw product and draw samples of the packed product from each lot for inspection. They use objective tests of quality and condition whenever such tests and practical instruments have been developed.

Objective tests are those that are made with instruments, equipment, or some method of measurement or enumeration. They do not rely on judgment alone.

Processors who use the continuous inspection services are permitted to use the official shield and the statement, "Packed under continuous inspection of the U.S. Department of Agriculture," on their containers.

MAINTENANCE of quality during marketing has been made possible largely by the development of modern handling, storage, and transportation.

Improvements in harvesting machinery reduce mechanical damage to the crops during harvesting and move the crop to shelter quickly.

Potatoes used to be harvested with diggers, which left the potatoes on the ground to be picked up by hand. The diggers often were set so shallow that some potatoes were cut and others were badly damaged by striking on the unpadded digger chain. Further damage caused by rough handling by the pickers and long exposure to sun and wind before potatoes were picked up promoted discoloration and decay during storage and marketing

Mechanical harvesters have done much to reduce the injuries. They can be set deep enough to avoid cutting the potatoes and carry enough dirt on the chain to cushion the potatoes. The rubber covering on the chain gives further protection. The potatoes are loaded directly into trucks and hauled immediately to the storage house or packing shed.

Some harvesters used for radishes, celery, lettuce, and sweet corn are literally packing sheds on wheels. The vegetables are cut, trimmed, and packed (and, in the case of celery, washed) as the harvester is pulled through the field. There is no delay between digging and packing, and the packed vegetables are hauled directly to the hydrocooler, vacuum cooler, or rail siding for quick cooling and loading. Mechanization has reduced exposure to weather and the number of times the crop is handled. Speed in getting the vegetables cooled and on the way to market retards loss of quality and lengthens the market life.

Refrigeration is the most effective way to maintain quality in perishable foods. It slows down the life process of fruits and vegetables and the microorganisms that cause food spoilage. These processes are reduced about half with each reduction of $18°$ F.

Hydrocooling cools fruit and vegetables as much in 10 or 15 minutes as previous methods did in 8 or 10 hours. Early hydrocoolers were merely large vats of ice water, in which the packed fruit or vegetables were soaked until cool. Modern hydrocoolers are tunnels through which the packed fruit or vegetables are moved on conveyors while they are drenched with cold water from overhead. The water is cooled by adding ice or by circulating over refrigerated coils. This method is used in many parts of the country for cooling asparagus, carrots, celery, sweet corn, radishes, and peaches.

VACUUM COOLING, a new method for cooling vegetables, is based on the principle that evaporated water absorbs heat. At normal atmospheric pressure (29.92 inches) water boils at $212°$ F., but in a vacuum, where atmospheric pressure has been lowered to 0.18 inch of mercury, it boils at $32°$. When vegetables are put under such a vacuum, water evaporates rapidly from the tissues and absorbs the field heat from the vegetables.

The first commercial vacuum cooling plant was built at Salinas, Calif., in 1948. Thirty-four carloads of lettuce were cooled that year. Since then, permanent vacuum cooling installations have been erected in the major vegetable production areas. Portable vacuum coolers can be moved from one locality to another. The early vacuum coolers could cool half a carload at a time. New coolers hold a whole loaded rail car or trailer truck.

Now most of the lettuce is vacuum cooled. About 30 minutes is required to cool lettuce from about $80°$ F. to $38°$. The lettuce is cooled to the center of the head even though packed in a closed cardboard carton and the cartons stowed in a car or truck.

Since cooling by vacuum depends on rapid evaporation of water, the method works best with leafy vegetables that have a large surface from which water evaporates easily. That is why it is used mostly for lettuce. It has also been used to some extent for cooling sweet corn, green salad mix, and celery, but cooling is slower and not so complete. It is not satisfactory for such products as apples and tomatoes, which have relatively small surfaces and a waxy covering that retards evaporation.

Except for a small amount of field packing for nearby markets, lettuce was formerly hauled to a packing shed, where it was trimmed and packed for shipment. Crushed ice was placed between layers of heads and on the top layer. After the crates were loaded in the car, snow (finely crushed) ice was blown over the top of the load a foot or more deep. That made a wet mess to unload at the destination. Many of the outer leaves of the heads were crushed and soaked by the package ice. Decay developed.

When vacuum cooling became available, packing moved from the shed to the field. The lettuce is cut, packed immediately in fiberboard cartons, and moved without delay to the vacuum cooler and rail car or truck. Since there is no soaking from package ice or top ice, much of the lettuce now is packed in fiberboard cartons instead of wooden crates. The present packages hold about half as much lettuce as the standard crate. Space is saved because no room is needed for ice.

ENGINEERING PROGRESS in grading and equipment in packinghouses has reduced mechanical damage, which often leads to decay. For instance, 18 to 60 bruises per 100 apples occurred when apple field boxes were loaded and unloaded from trucks by hand, but only 2 apples in 100 were bruised when the boxes were placed on pallets and handled by forklifts.

The use of automatic dumpers, which dump apples on the grading and sorting belts, has reduced bruising similarly. They lift and pour the apples or other fruit gently on the belt; workmen often dump them with a tossing motion, which causes many bruises. Improved engineering design of graders and sorting tables to reduce the distance the fruit drops from one section or unit to another, smoothing sharp edges or obstructions, and padding with sponge rubber has reduced mechanical damage further.

Improved methods and equipment for handling animals before slaughter are more humane and prevent injuries that affect the quality of the meat. Various methods and equipment, such as stunning guns and electric shock, have been used to render the animals unconscious before killing. But even with them it is not always possible to prevent some struggling, which may cause broken bones and bruising.

Carbon dioxide has been used with hogs. They are exposed to the proper concentration of the gas to become unconscious as they walk through a narrow passage. There is no struggling and bruising, and bleeding is more complete.

Immobilization of poultry with carbon dioxide has been tested.

All these improvements in methods and handling equipment that reduce injury to fruit, vegetables, meat, and other products pay dividends in more attractive goods and less spoilage.

STORAGE REQUIREMENTS are not the same for all food.

Temperatures of 0° F. or lower are best for frozen foods.

Fresh meat, lettuce, sweet corn, carrots, grapes, pears, and strawberries should be kept at near 32°. Many varieties of apples should be stored at 32°, but some are injured by such a low temperature and must be stored at about 38°.

Bananas, cucumbers, and sweetpotatoes are injured if stored at temperatures below 55°. Pears ripen best at 65° and usually fail to ripen at temperatures warmer than 75° to 80°.

Most fresh fruit and vegetables require a humidity of 85 to 95 percent in storage to avoid excessive wilting and loss of weight. Cheese, dried fruit, garlic, and onions require a relative humidity of about 70 percent.

Adequate refrigeration capacity, good insulation, and accurate control of temperature are necessary to provide optimum temperatures for the wide variety of agricultural products that are stored.

The arrangement and size of refrigeration coils and air circulation must be designed properly to provide an even temperature and relative humidity. Humidifying equipment may be necessary to provide a high enough relative humidity for some products.

More carbon dioxide and less oxygen in the storage air extends the storage life of some products.

Fresh beef, which keeps about 40 days at near 32°, remains in good condition for 60 to 70 days in an atmosphere containing 10 to 20 percent of carbon dioxide.

Eggs are benefited by about 0.5 percent of carbon dioxide.

Varieties of apples that must be stored at near 38° because they are injured by lower temperatures will keep longer and have better quality if stored in an atmosphere of about 3 to 5 percent of carbon dioxide and 3 to 5 percent of oxygen than in normal air.

The storage life of Bartlett, Anjou, Bosc, and Comice pears is lengthened 1 or 2 months by increasing the carbon dioxide and reducing the oxygen content of the storage atmosphere.

Commercial controlled-atmosphere storages for apples with a capacity of about 2.5 million bushels were in operation in 1960. They are expensive to construct and operate, but apples can be kept in them longer and the quality is better even after long storage than in ordinary storages. Apples from controlled-atmosphere storages command a premium price on the market that more than pays the extra cost.

Success in controlled-atmosphere storage depends on having a specially designed and constructed storage and on proper regulation of the atmosphere. The storage rooms must be gastight. The walls, ceiling, and floors are lined with sheet metal or aluminum foil or coated with gasproof paint. All joints must be perfectly sealed. The doors must fit very tightly. Fans must be provided to circulate the air. A gas sampling tube, through which samples of the atmosphere may be taken for analysis, and an atmospheric washer, for removing carbon dioxide when it becomes too concentrated, are needed.

The atmosphere must be sampled often to guard against having atmospheres with too much carbon dioxide or too little oxygen, either of which would injure the fruit. When there is too much carbon dioxide, the atmosphere is circulated through the washer. When oxygen is too low, fresh air is admitted until the right concentration is reached.

Several simple methods of controlled-atmosphere storage have been developed in the West where gastight storages have not been built.

In the Northwest, pear boxes are lined with film bags of polyethylene plastic, which are sealed after filling with fruit. These liners are just permeable enough to permit carbon dioxide to accumulate slightly and retard the entrance of oxygen.

Another type of improvised modified atmosphere storage has been tested for Yellow Newtown apples in California. Whole bulk bins have been lined with film. Pallets of apples have been completely enclosed in a cover made of a polyethylene plastic film laminated on kraft paper.

Packaging in the film has been useful for storage of strawberry and rose plants. Because it protects the roots from drying, it is not necessary to wrap the plants in wet moss. The cost is less, and the plants keep better and longer. Strawberry plants can be dug in February and March, when they are in best condition, and stored until fall before planting. The fall plantings yield as well or better the following spring than plantings made in the spring, and they need less cultivation.

SOME PRODUCTS require special conditioning. Aging of meat, curing of sweetpotatoes, and ripening of various kinds of fruit and vegetables were done for many years before the basic nature of these processes was understood.

Fresh beef is aged at 32° to 38° for 10 days to 6 weeks to increase tenderness. The tenderness is brought about by changes that occur in the muscle fibers. The changes would occur much faster at higher temperatures, but so would spoilage by micro-organisms.

Sweetpotatoes are cured 6 to 8 days at 85° and high humidity before the storage house temperature is lowered to 55°. Some of the starch is changed to sugar during this period, and the potatoes become more palatable. At the same time, skinned and cut places heal so the sweetpotatoes will not rot. The storage house must be properly designed and operated to develop good quality in the sweetpotatoes. Vents at the top and bottom are needed for ventilation, and they must be adjusted so that the humidity during curing will be high, but not so high that moisture will drip on the sweetpotatoes. The heating system should be easily controlled, so the temperature can be held within a few degrees of 85° during the curing period. Some houses are heated with thermostatically controlled electric heaters.

Pears will not ripen properly if the temperature is 75°–80° or higher. Many consumers do not know this and wonder why the pears remain hard when kept in their overheated apartment. Pears may be ripened in the car on the way to market or in special ripening rooms at the market. If they are to be ripened on the way to market, little or no ice is used in the car, and the temperature is kept about 65°. Heaters may be necessary in cold weather. Temperature of the ripening room at the market is controlled to provide optimum ripening temperatures. Bananas and tomatoes are handled in a similar way.

White potatoes that have been stored at 40°–50° must be reconditioned before they can be used for potato chips. When potatoes are refrigerated, part of the starch turns to sugar, and the slices turn brown when they are cooked in oil. The sugar will turn back to starch if the potatoes are held for several weeks at about 70°; satisfactory chips can be made from them.

BIOLOGICAL research has shown why products lose quality and spoil and which conditions are necessary to maintain quality.

Engineering research has given us the means to protect quality. It has provided better equipment for harvesting, grading, packing, and cooling, and better storages, better transportation equipment, and better instruments for testing.

Progress in both will continue.

# Power

## and

## Efficiency

## Efficiency
## of Labor

Reuben W. Hecht and Eugene G. McKibben

TODAY a farmer with mechanical and electrical power, modern machines, improved seeds, fertilizers, and pesticides, convenient buildings, and improved breeding stock and feed turns out almost four times as much product each hour of work as a farmer did each hour in the years just before the First World War.

Advances in efficiency of farm labor have resulted directly from fewer hours of farmwork and from greater farm production. Many related and interrelated forces, including engineering and biological developments and eco-

nomic and social changes, have been behind these basic causes.

During the half century since 1910, farm output per man-hour has risen at an average rate of almost 3 percent a year. This gain has not come about gradually.

For the first decade after 1910, farm output per man-hour rose less than 1 percent a year. The increase was due to the expansion in farm output as the labor used on farms also rose.

The two decades between the First and Second World Wars were characterized by a start of a persistent downward trend in the number of workers on farms. Lack of an effective demand for farm products and other factors held the annual gain in farm output to a modest 1 percent a year, but the gain had a greater influence on raising farm labor efficiency an average of 1.6 percent a year than the reduction in the amount of labor used on farms had.

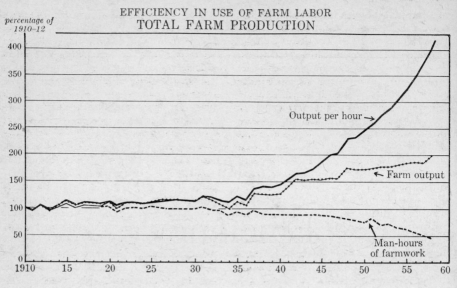

EFFICIENCY IN USE OF FARM LABOR
TOTAL FARM PRODUCTION

*percentage of 1910–12*

The annual increase in farm production and its contribution to the greater labor efficiency that came during the Second World War was without precedent in the history of American agriculture and has not been equaled since. By a fortunate conjuncture of circumstances, farm output rose 3.3 percent annually and was largely responsible for raising production per man-hour to record levels. Efficiency of farm labor rose at the annual rate of 4.8 percent from 1940 to 1945.

The advances in mechanization and the changes that accompanied it have meant an acceleration in the reduction in the man-hours of farmwork since the war. The number of man-hours dropped at an annual rate of 4 percent from 1945 to 1950. Since 1950 the reduction on a percentage basis has been even greater—4.2 percent a year. Expressed in hours of farmwork, the drop in the 5 years following the war amounted to almost 750 million man-hours a year. During the next decade the annual reduction was about 500 million hours a year.

The postwar drop in farm labor input is shown also in the number of workers on farms. There were 10 million on farms at the end of the war. Primarily because of the return of workers from war industries and the Armed Forces, farm employment rose for a couple of years, but after 1947 numbers again turned downward.

In the first 5 years after the war, the reduction was only 15 thousand workers a year, compared with an annual drop of about 200 thousand from 1940 to 1945. Farm employment averaged only about 7.4 million workers in 1959. The annual reduction since 1950 has been almost 20 times as fast as during the first 5 postwar years.

On the other side of the labor efficiency ratio—the production side—additions to farm output after the war continued to contribute significantly to the steep upward climb in labor productivity.

Its effect was less than during the wartime period for two basic reasons, one absolute and the other relative: The annual increase in farm production was less than during the war; the accelerated reduction in labor used on farms lowered the relative effect of additions to farm output.

In line with the great strides made in adding tractors and other forms of mechanical power to farms after the war, work animals disappeared rapidly. From 1945 to 1950, the drop in work animals was responsible for additions to cropland for raising products for human use, amounting to 2.6 million acres a year. The horse-and-mule-release of cropland had equaled 2.2 million acres annually during the war and has averaged 1.5 million acres yearly since 1950.

As only about 3 million head of horses and mules were left on farms and ranches at the beginning of 1960, this source of additional output is about exhausted. However, this aspect of farm mechanization was the prime source of greater farm output for the first half decade after the war. Since 1950, greater crop and livestock production resulting from higher yields has been chiefly responsible for additions to farm production.

While greater farm production helped, the reduction in labor used on farms was the chief cause of the steep upward climb in labor efficiency after the war. It rose at the annual rate of 5.2 percent for the first half decade and 6.5 percent a year since 1950.

MANY adjustments in organization and management of farms and related industries developed concurrently with the advance in farm technology and labor efficiency. Indeed, they were part of it.

We have said that the farm mechanization phase of the technological progress in farming both lowered the amount of labor used on farms and raised the amount of farm products available for human use. That is true, but it is an oversimplification of the complex and interrelated changes that have been part of the technological revolution in agriculture.

An all-inclusive discussion of labor efficiency in farming would include consideration of most of the forces behind growth in the total economy. The more general of these include human desires; stable government and institutions; public and private re-search for new and adaptable products and techniques; education, particularly regarding adoption of the innovations; and a favorable economic climate.

Economic forces express themselves through prices and incomes. Many price relationships and changes in the relationships have profoundly affected advances in technology.

An example is the cost of farm labor and the cost of the items that can be substituted for labor. Much of this kind of substitution has taken place, particularly the replacement of work animals by mechanical power.

To simplify the comparison, we assume that wage rates paid to hired workers reflect the cost of operator's time and that of unpaid labor of his family. (This assumption fails to recognize remuneration for management functions performed by farm operators. On the other hand, they and family workers do many jobs that add little to farm income.)

Farm wage rates were more than 200 percent higher in 1958 than in 1925–1929. During those 30 years, the average prices paid for tractors, trucks, and automobiles rose 190 percent; farm machinery, 130 percent; and fuel, tires, and other motor supplies about 30 percent. A comparison with 1935–1939 would show even greater disparity in the rates of increase.

We could cite other illustrations of the relationship of prices that favor the adoption of technology, such as the prices paid for fertilizer and improved seed, whose cost generally has been considerably less than the value of their additions to production.

THE INCREASE in size and specialization of farms has been one of the most significant changes in farm structure and organization that have come with the adoption of technology.

About a billion acres have consistently constituted the land base in farming, but the number of farms has dropped from about 6.5 million at the time of the First World War to fewer

EFFICIENCY IN USE OF FARM LABOR
CROPS

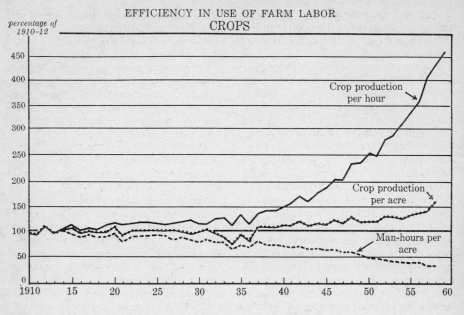

*percentage of 1910–12*

than 4 million in 1960. Each year the fewer remaining farms, on the average, add land to their operations. More than two-fifths of the transfers of farmland are for the purpose of enlarging farms. They were one-fifth of the purchases in 1950.

One might expect that by this time wheat farmers, who were among the first to mechanize, would have pretty well adjusted their operating units to the new machines and methods. A larger proportion of the current transfers of farmland, however, is for farm enlargement in the wheat farming areas than in other parts of the country: Even in the more mechanized areas, innovations are being adopted that save even more labor, and effects of them are being translated into larger farms.

The number of acres is not a reliable measure of size in all farming situations, of course. A poultry farm may have few acres but be a large unit in terms of total investment or in number of birds or eggs produced. Here a major part of the investment is in buildings and equipment that induce large flocks and raise production per hour of labor.

Modern equipment and machines are so expensive in many instances that it is advantageous to the farmer to develop larger farms and enterprises to make full use of the new resources and to hold down unit costs.

Under older systems of farming, a farmer could add acres or animals without increasing proportionally the labor he used. With modern equipment, tools, and methods, the increase in labor needed is even less, relative to the added acres and animals.

The degree of specialization on farms may be indicated by the number of enterprises (such as milk cows or corn) each has. Of 20 major enterprises, the average farm had 5.4 in 1940 and 4.7 in 1954.

Specialization has occurred in both the general and the unusual farm enterprises. The number of farms dropped about 10 percent between 1950 and 1954, but the number of farms with chickens and those having milk cows each fell 19 percent. The number of farmers growing snap beans dropped

35 percent, and the number producing tomatoes, 30 percent. In each instance, the average size of the enterprise was greater in 1954.

Besides raising overall efficiency in farming, specialization has had other effects on farm labor.

One of the disadvantages of specialization is that work may not be provided for all seasons and periods of the year if there are only a few enterprises.

That is particularly significant on farms with a relatively fixed labor force, such as many family farms.

According to the census, workers on farms put in about 5 fewer hours per week in 1959 than they did in 1949. Or on a daily basis—around September 1, 1959—farm operators averaged 9.8 hours of work a day. Hired workers averaged 8.9 hours. Comparable lengths of workdays 10 years earlier were 11.1 and 9.5 hours, respectively.

Specialization, then, has been translated into fewer hours per farmworker as well as into greater production per worker and per hour of work.

We do not mean to stress specialization unduly or to imply the absence of other influences. Many forces have induced changes in input and productivity of labor.

THE INDEX of labor efficiency is the ratio of total agricultural output to the input of labor in farm production. The index thus reflects the net effect of all forces that influence either farm production or farm labor.

Myriad influences underlie changes in the two basic indexes of total agricultural output and labor used in farm production. They are themselves interrelated.

For example: Labor used on farms has trended downward for nearly four decades, and the descent would have been greater were it not for the upward trend in farm production.

In terms of a specific crop, in 1950–1954 it took an average of 69 man-hours to grow and harvest an acre of sugar beets yielding 15.5 tons. The average for the following 4 years was

53 hours per acre, or more than a fifth less, and the drop would have been greater if the yield had not increased. The average yield in 1955–1958 was 17 tons. The combined effect of fewer hours and more tons per acre, including the almost innumerable forces back of these changes, was to raise production of sugar beets per man-hour by more than 40 percent in 5 years.

To understand the meaning of production per hour we have to understand the underlying measures of labor input and production.

The annual series of total man-hours of farmwork are "built up" by individual farm enterprises by applying regional average man-hours per acre of crops and per head or unit of production of livestock to the official estimates of acres and numbers prepared by the Crop Reporting Board of the Agricultural Marketing Service. Time for farm maintenance or general overhead work is estimated separately and added to the direct labor for crops and livestock in arriving at man-hours of all farmwork.

For an individual farm commodity or enterprise, production per man-hour may be expressed in bushels, pounds, tons, or any commonly used measure. Groups of farm commodities or total products, however, because of their diversity, cannot be added directly and must be converted to addable units. Average prices for farm products for a period of years serves this purpose.

Average prices for 1947–1949 are used for the years since 1939.

Total farm output measures the annual volume of farm production available for eventual human use. The output computations are made in such a way that crops fed to livestock, for example, are not double counted, or as part of both crop and livestock production. Eggs used for hatching also illustrate an item that is deducted to avoid double counting. Production of horses and mules and the hay and grain fed to them are likewise excluded from farm output.

## PRODUCTION PER MAN-HOUR

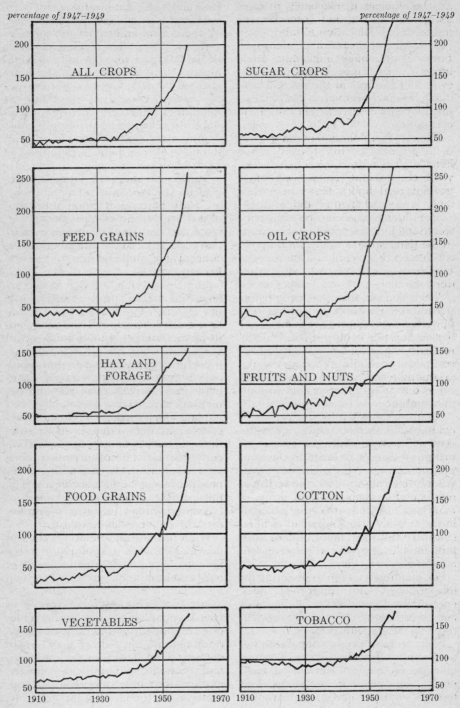

It would not be correct to attribute all the changes in efficiency to farm labor. We should not interpret the indexes as an allocation to labor of all the advances in farming efficiency. Labor is the most important single input in agricultural production, however, and changes in the ratio of production to labor provide a useful measure of changes in efficiency of farm production.

Changes in production per man-hour of labor must be interpreted in the light of changes in mechanization, yields of crops and livestock, and other technological forces that operate on labor input and farm production.

The ideal measure of efficiency would include all production inputs in the denominator of the ratio.

Solomon Fabricant, of New York University, said this regarding productivity ratios:

"As a general rule . . . it is better not to limit productivity indexes that purport to measure change in efficiency to a comparison of output with a single resource. The broader the coverage of resources, generally, the better is the productivity measure. The best measure is one that compares output with the combined use of all resources.

"Information on all resources is not available, however. Until rather recently, economists interested in measuring the rate of increase in national productivity had to make shift with labor input alone—first, in terms of number of workers, then in terms of man-hours. This is still true for most individual industries, narrowly defined even on a historical basis, and for both individual industries and the economy as a whole on a current basis."

His statement about individual industries certainly applies to farm enterprises. It applies at all levels of aggregation or from national data to those for an individual farm.

For a comprehensive measurement of overall efficiency in agriculture, information on the amount of each production resource going to each enterprise would be necessary. Improve-

ment of efficiency in farming results from more efficient production of corn, wheat, beef, or another enterprise. Without total input data for each enterprise, we can learn relatively little of the how and why of total farm efficiency. Capital inputs particularly are difficult to define and to obtain, but we have a wealth of data on the amount of labor used for the individual farm enterprises.

Annual series since 1930 of farm production per man-hour of labor and of production per unit of total input are available for about 17 types of commercial family-operated farms.

Glen T. Barton and Ralph A. Loomis, of the Department of Agriculture, presented an analysis of the trends in these two series in a paper published in the Journal of Farm Economics for December 1957.

They found that the percentage increase in production per man-hour is much larger, but that a close association exists between changes in it and in production per unit of total input. Put another way: A given percentage increase in production per unit of inputs is associated with a much larger percentage increase in production per man-hour.

They stated further: "The high correlation between changes in production per man-hour and in production per unit of input is not surprising when viewed against the background of technological progress in agriculture. The bulk of the innovations adopted in farm production have been of a direct, or indirect, labor-saving nature."

While it has limitations, production per man-hour is reasonably reliable for general purposes as an indicator of total efficiency.

IT IS UNREALISTIC in some respects to view farming as a thing apart. When our Nation was young, that could be done because agriculture was largely self-contained. The draft animals, feed, tools, building materials, implements, manure, the family's food and clothing, material for the farmhouse and furni-

EFFICIENCY IN USE OF FARM LABOR
LIVESTOCK

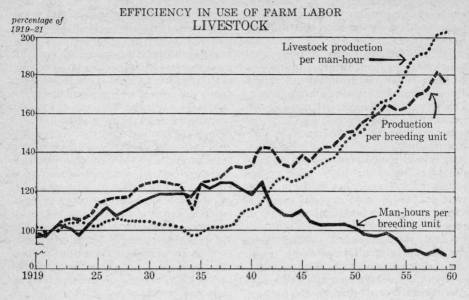

*percentage of 1919-21*

Livestock production per man-hour ➞

Production per breeding unit

Man-hours per breeding unit

ture, and the fuel were all mostly produced on the farm.

Not so today. Now farmers sell most of what they produce and buy what they need on the farm and in the home. There has been a dispersion of jobs or functions from farms to nonfarm business firms.

The modern farmer retains primarily the function of a producer of crops and livestock. This is a different kind of specialization than we discussed previously. The average farmer specializes on fewer enterprises and he also performs fewer functions.

The evolution from self-sufficiency to commercialization of farming may best be portrayed by changes in the distribution of the population and labor force. At the beginning of the 19th century nearly everybody lived in rural areas, and 80 of every 100 persons in the labor force were engaged in farming. Now only 12 percent of the people live on farms, and of each 100 in the total working force, only 9 are farmworkers.

ENTIRELY NEW industries and service institutions have had their beginning and growth in the increasing tendency

of farmers to utilize production supplies originating off the farm.

Complementing this development has been the creation of still another group of business entities with the functions of handling, storing, processing, and distributing food, fiber, and other products from the farm to the consumer. Thus we have three groups of related industries with interrelated functions. Altogether they embrace essentially the functions that the term agriculture denoted 150 years ago.

Their dimensions are large. Consumers in 1954 bought food and fiber worth about 93 billion dollars, or roughly 40 percent of the total consumer expenditures for all products and services.

The total assets of the three segments equaled approximately 220 billion dollars, which was almost three-fifths of the total assets of manufacturing, wholesale, and retail corporations and agriculture.

About 24 million persons, or about two-fifths of the total working force of 64.5 million, engaged in the activities pertaining to agriculture—about 6 million were employed by farm-supplies industries, about 8 million were engaged in farming, and 10 million were in the processing-distribution industries.

The significant point is this: The workers in the farm-supplies industries by taking over functions formerly done by farmworkers have contributed heavily to the advance in farm output per hour of farm labor.

Before going into the extent of this contribution, we should indicate that the processing-distribution workers also do a few functions that were done by farmworkers, but most of their tasks were taken over from housewives.

The processing-distribution workers, that is to say, chiefly perform additional services or processes rather than the functions that farmworkers once did. Processing-distribution workers should be excluded, therefore, in a comparison between farm production or output as it leaves the farmer's gate and the workers who contribute to it.

If we add farm-supplies workers to the farm labor force, however, and compare the sum with farm output, we get a measure of the efficiency of all labor—direct and indirect, farm and nonfarm—that contributes to farm output.

This concept attempts to answer in aggregate a question of which the following illustrates a part of the broader inquiry:

Does using a tractor on a farm still save labor even though we include the miners who dug the iron ore and coal from the earth, the smelter workers who converted these raw materials into steel, the manufacturing workers who fabricated the steel into tractors, and all the other nonfarm workers who assisted in producing and distributing the tractor, the fuel, and the other supplies that it requires?

We cannot give an exact measurement because we lack precise and full data. Some jobs, for example, have been transferred to nonfarm workers and have later been transferred back to farmworkers: Farmworkers once hauled nearly all farm products to a local market. When motortrucks were introduced, many were purchased by commercial truckers, who did a lot of hauling for farmers. When farm trucks became more common, many farmers tended to do their own hauling rather than to hire nonfarm truckers. The exact division of the hauling job between these kinds of workers at a given point in time is unknown.

Estimates by men in the Department of Agriculture indicate that 5 million persons worked in the farm-supplies industries in 1947 and 6 million in 1954. Industrial workers put in about 40 hours a week during this period. Farm-supplies workers therefore spent 10 billion to 11 billion hours in producing goods and services purchased and used by farmers in 1947–1954. At the same time, work on farms took 17 billion to 13 billion hours, or from half to two-thirds of the total.

Similar estimates were made for a few years near the end of the First World War, near the beginning of the Second World War, and for a current period. They help us compare changes in efficiency of farm labor and of total labor for two periods—between the wars, when farmers increased their purchases of supplies from the nonfarm sectors of the economy by about a fourth; and from the beginning of the Second World War to 1958. During the latter period, the quantity of farm supplies, as measured in 1947–1949 average prices, rose from about 7.8 billion dollars to 14.4 billion.

Farm output per hour of farm labor rose by about 40 percent during the interwar period. When the time of the farm-supplies workers is included, the increase is less—about 30 percent. Since the beginning of the Second World War, the gain in farm labor productivity has been a little more than 150 percent. The inclusion of farm-supplies workers reduces it to about 50 percent.

Thus, when farm supplies are converted to labor and added to the farm labor force, the gain in efficiency is not so great as when only farm labor is considered. The increase is still sizable—

more than 80 percent from the end of the First World War to 1958.

The technological revolution has not been limited to agriculture. It has occurred in industrial plants, also; it has meant a gain in productivity of those workers as well as a substantial contribution to the increase in efficiency of workers on farms.

THIS IDEA of laborsaving or gain in efficiency of all labor resulting from the adoption of technology is clearer when it is put in terms of a few important farm machines such as cornpickers, cottonpickers, and milking machines.

First, let us assume that in the late 1950's the average cost of labor going into the production, handling, and delivery of these machines is 2 dollars an hour. Second, let us assume that the total labor represented by one of these machines as received on the job is something less than the delivered cost divided by the average wage. The difference, of course, consists of items— such as natural resources and profit— that do not represent labor.

TWO-ROW mounted cornpickers cost 2,000 to 2,400 dollars delivered to the farm. The farm-supplies labor represented is about 1,100 hours. The use of such a picker may reduce harvest labor requirements by 5 man-hours per acre and can harvest 80 or more acres in a season. This means a total reduction of more than 400 man-hours annually.

Thus, under usual conditions, only a few years would be required for the reduction in farm labor to equal the nonfarm labor required to produce and deliver the machine. A cornpicker, of course, requires a tractor, fuel, and other supplies produced by nonfarm workers. But here, also, a net saving in labor occurs compared with the farm labor required to raise, feed, and work the animals required under older methods of harvesting corn.

One-row, tractor-mounted cotton-pickers cost 4,000 dollars to 8,000 dollars. The off-farm labor used to produce, handle, and deliver such machines may be 2,000 to 4,000 man-hours. Such a picker under normal use will reduce the man-hours needed for cottonpicking from 40 to 50 per acre on 40 to 80 acres. This would be a reduction of farm labor of 1,600 to 4,000 man-hours a year. Again, only a few years would be required to balance reduced man-hours of farm labor against the man-hours of industrial labor required to deliver such a cotton-picker to the user.

A four-unit milking machine costs about 1,000 dollars. The off-farm labor represented must be something less than 500 man-hours. Such a machine will handle 40 or more cows, with an annual reduction of about 30 man-hours per cow compared to hand milking. Thus, the annual reduction of the dairy labor will be 1,200 hours or more. Thus, in many cases, less than a year's use will be sufficient for the reduction in man-hours of dairy labor to balance the man-hours of industrial labor required to make the milking machine available.

These examples constitute further evidence that the increase in time of farm-supplies workers is more than offset by the reduction in time of farmworkers resulting from their use.

EFFICIENCY in farming results from more efficient production of corn, cotton, milk, and other farm products.

How have the different farm enterprises fared in this respect?

How do crops compare with livestock?

If there are differences, what have been the significant causes?

American farmers in 1956–1958 raised more than three times more total crops per hour of labor than they did in 1910–1912. (The 3-year averages are used to add stability.) During the same period, livestock production per hour nearly doubled, and labor efficiency in total farm production rose 2.8 times.

The increase in productivity of the labor spent on crops has been far from uniform among crops and sections and for different parts of the last half century.

There has also been considerable variation during different parts of the period in the relative influence of the two basic factors behind the phenomenal increase in crop production per hour. These causal factors are higher yields per acre, which were largely the result of fertilizer, variety, hybrids, pesticides, weather, and other biological factors, and fewer man-hours per acre, which resulted primarily from mechanization—that is, more effective power sources, machines, and methods.

Man-hours per acre and yield are interrelated. To illustrate: If a greater quantity of fertilizer is applied to a crop and results in a greater yield, additional time is needed to obtain and to apply the fertilizer and to harvest and market the higher yield. The relation between yield and time for harvest depends on the extent of mechanization. Additional yield of a highly mechanized crop adds little to the time for harvesting but for crops that are gathered by hand the increase in harvesttime is almost proportional to the added produce.

For the half century beginning in 1910, wide adoption of mechanized and laborsaving methods of producing, harvesting, and marketing crops resulted in a drop in man-hours per acre of crops at the rate of 2.2 percent per year. Mechanization was the prime cause of greater labor efficiency in producing crops. The increase of 0.8 percent per year in yields also contributed, however, and the combination of the two resulted in the substantial rise—3.1 percent annually—of crop labor productivity. Of the gain in crop efficiency, 72 percent resulted from fewer hours per acre. The remaining 28 percent was associated with higher yields.

Between 1910 and 1920, there was a relatively small but still important increase in the labor efficiency of crop production. Crop production per acre dropped slightly. That had a negative effect on labor efficiency. But changes in equipment and methods, the beginning of the trend toward mechanization, was enough to offset the influence of lower yields and to raise the efficiency of crop labor at the rate of 1 percent annually. There was a trend toward the use of larger teams. Tractors were coming into use, particularly in the western wheat areas. The use of the combine was expanding.

During the depression years of the interwar period, the labor efficiency of crop production continued to improve at the slightly greater rate of about 1.5 percent annually. It was partly the result of moderately higher yields per acre, but a developing mechanization was the dominant factor. It was responsible for about two-thirds of the gain during these two decades. The tractor, particularly the general-purpose tractor with pneumatic tires, was widely accepted in these years. The combine harvester-thresher had almost entirely replaced the binder and threshing machine. Extensive use was made of cornpickers. The adoption of field forage harvesters and field pick-up hay balers was expanding.

During the war years of 1940–1945, the increased demand and prices for crop products resulted in an almost explosive combination of biological and engineering developments, which had been incubating during the depression years. The result was an annual increase of crop production per man-hour of nearly 5 percent. Biological developments in crops, soils, and entomology appear to have made contributions about equal to those of mechanization during this period. The use of hybrid seed corn and heavier applications of fertilizer became almost universal. Laborsaving harvesting machines were generally used, except where wartime limitations on steel for their manufacture prevented.

During the period 1945–1950, labor efficiency continued to increase and at the still higher rate of about 5.3 percent per year. Slight increases in yield per acre occurred during this period,

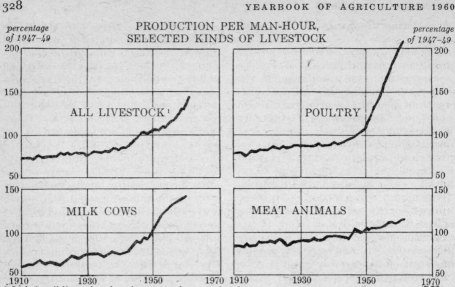

percentage
of 1947–49

PRODUCTION PER MAN-HOUR,
SELECTED KINDS OF LIVESTOCK

percentage
of 1947–49

¹ Includes all livestock and products except horses and mules.

but the major contribution to increased production per man-hour resulted from fewer man-hours per acre, which dropped an average of about 5 percent per year. The Korean situation helped maintain farm prices but did not seriously restrict the production of farm machines. Thus, mechanization developed at the highest rate so far attained and accounted for 97 percent of the gain in productivity of crop labor.

Mechanization, as reflected in man-hours per acre, continued at the slightly lower rate of about 4.6 percent per year from 1950 to 1958 and was the most important factor contributing to rapid increase in labor efficiency.

During this period, though, there was also the highest rate of increase of average yield per acre so far attained— nearly 3 percent annually. An important factor was acreage allotments for wheat, cotton, and a few other crops. With the allotments there was strong incentive to use the best agronomic practices on the best acres.

The combination of this rapidly increasing yield per acre and the reduced labor per acre caused by the continuing rapid development of mechaniza-

tion resulted in a startling 7.4 percent average annual increase in crop production per man-hour. About two-thirds of this phenomenal gain resulted from advances in mechanization and the other third from greater yields.

The biggest gains in labor efficiency have been for the feed and food grains and oil crops, among them corn, wheat, and soybeans, which are among the most completely and effectively mechanized. Farmers in 1956–1958 produced more than six times as much oil crops, six and two-thirds times as much food grains, and almost six times as much feed grains per man-hour as in 1910–1912.

Even greater gains in efficiency were made in the major producing area of each crop.

For sugar crops, mainly sugar beets, the gain in labor productivity for the past 5 decades has been nearly 300 percent, somewhat less than for crop production as a whole. Production of sugar crops per hour from 1950 to 1957, however, rose more rapidly than for any other group of crops except feed grains. Much progress has been made in mechanizing production of sugar beets, which took about 95 hours per acre during the war but only 53 hours in 1955–1958. Also contributing was a significant increase in yield from 12.7 tons to 17 tons an acre.

For cotton, the gain in labor efficiency also has been just under 300 percent. Picking cotton was about one-third mechanized in 1958. Even less progress has been made in mechanizing chopping and hoeing—the most time-consuming preharvest operation.

Production of hay and forage is well mechanized, but the gain in productivity during 1910–1958 was only about three-fifths that of all crop production. That is because baling, one of the modern methods, does not save a great deal of labor as compared with older methods, most notably in the West, where stacking was formerly the prevalent method. Chopping with a field forage harvester, the most laborsaving modern method, has not increased significantly. In fact, the percentage of the hay crop that was chopped has dropped slightly. Advances in the mechanization of tillage and seeding operations have had less effect on the labor for forage production because many acres of forage crops produce for several years with one seedbed preparation and seeding.

The gain in labor efficiency for vegetable production has also been equally low—170 percent—although for certain vegetables as green peas and spinach for canning and freezing production has been completely mechanized.

The mechanization of fruit and nut production has made still less progress. In many fruit and vegetable crops, particularly those produced for the fresh market, the increase in productivity has been low. That is true also of certain special crops.

Tobacco, for example, is an important commercial crop but still requires nearly two-thirds as many man-hours per unit of production as it did in 1910. Because the manual harvesting of this crop has a high labor requirement, the large increase in yield, more than 60 percent, that has

occurred since 1910 has tended to counteract the savings per acre resulting from progress in the mechanization of other operations. In fact, production per man-hour has increased less during this period than the yield per acre, with the result that the man-hours per acre required in 1958 were somewhat higher than in 1910.

WHAT ARE the possibilities to improve farm labor efficiency further for crop production by mechanization?

The complete or partial mechanization of harvesting fruit and vegetables is the most challenging. Another important possibility is the completion of the mechanization of the harvesting and handling of difficult crops, such as for cotton and certain fruit and vegetables, where a good start has already been made. Promising starts have been made on the mechanization of the harvesting of such very difficult crops as tobacco, tomatoes, cucumbers, cherries, and blueberries.

Complete mechanization of weed control in all crops offers a good possibility of further improving the work efficiency of crop production. Peak labor demands for manual weed control and harvesting required almost 1.5 million seasonal workers at the peak in 1958.

We can expect that machines will become reliable—that is, less subject to breakdowns and other interruptions. That could improve greatly the work efficiency of crop production.

More effective machines for planting and applying fertilizers and pesticides might increase work efficiency by reducing the labor cost of replanting and by increasing the yield per acre.

The development of more reliable and effective machines and the more extensive adoption of land forming and stone removal will open the way for the use of wider machines at higher operating speeds. That will tend to contribute proportionately to improved work efficiency.

The possibilities of eliminating operations, such as some of the seedbed and cultivating operations in favor of so-called minimum tillage, or combining operations, such as was done with the combine harvester-thresher, are intriguing but quite unpredictable.

FOR LIVESTOCK production, farm labor efficiency about doubled from 1910–1912 to 1956–1958. It rose at the rate of 1.5 percent a year. That would appear to be good progress when considered by itself, but it is only about one-third of the increase for crop production. It seems to have been the result of more effective application of engineering to crop production, because for the four decades following 1920 the gains from animal science, as reflected in production per breeding unit equaled or surpassed those from plant and soil science.

Production per breeding unit is essentially an average of milk per cow, eggs per hen, and so on. The gain in production per breeding unit was about three-fourths, while the gain in crop production per acre was slightly less than one-half. On the other hand, the reduction in man-hours per breeding unit was less than 10 percent, while the reduction in man-hours per acre of crops was 60 percent.

This gain in production per breeding unit has been continuous throughout the period at a fairly uniform rate. Some acceleration began about 1945, but the gain from 1950 to 1956–1958 was slower. Up to 1937 or so there was little gain in efficiency of labor spent on livestock; the man-hours per breeding unit just about kept pace with the production per breeding unit. The production per man-hour therefore remained virtually unchanged.

Livestock production per man-hour has risen at the rate of 3.7 percent a year since 1950.

The war years were the only period during which the reduction in man-hours per breeding unit was more effective than higher livestock yields in enhancing livestock labor efficiency. Hours per cow, sow, and hen dropped at the rate of 2.4 percent a year and was responsible for more than 90 per-

cent of the gain in labor productivity. There was a great urge to save labor and despite critical shortages of steel and rubber, the number of farms having milking machines more than doubled during 1940–1945. Almost half the farms were receiving central-station electric service in 1945, compared to about a fourth in 1940. Many of the machines and installations that save chore labor depend on electricity.

Declines in man-hours per breeding unit have continued to be a significant factor in greater labor efficiency since the war. They have come through engineering developments, such as more effective buildings and farmstead arrangement; mechanized methods of handling water, feed, bedding and manure; and so on.

Livestock yields also have gone up since the war, however. The average milk cow on farms produced 6,438 pounds of milk in 1959 but only 4,787 pounds in 1945. Rate of lay was in excess of 200 eggs per hen in 1958 and 152 in 1945. Besides, a growing number of the eggs were hatched into broilers; that increases production per hen on farms. These developments were more effective than the reduction in labor in the greater production per man-hour. Since 1950, however, the two basic causes have been about equally responsible for increased livestock labor efficiency.

The dairy and poultry enterprises are the large users of labor in livestock production. The large gains in labor efficiency have been in them.

For meat animals, the gain in labor efficiency was only about a third from 1910 to 1958. This has been a slow but rather constant development throughout the period; it has accelerated somewhat since 1950.

On the other hand, the gain in labor efficiency for dairy production has been over 100 percent. The gain for poultry has been still greater—about 170 percent.

The labor efficiency gains for the egg production phase of poultry is about the same as for dairy, but the production of poultry meat products has been outstanding. Turkeys and broilers have reached commercial status as a farm enterprise since 1940. Turkey production per man-hour has increased nearly 350 percent since 1910, and broiler production per man-hour about 400 percent since 1935.

It is impossible to say exactly what will happen in the way of continued improvement of the labor efficiency of livestock production. It seems certain that for some time the trend will continue to concentrate much of the livestock production in what might be considered livestock factories rather than as secondary or even primary enterprises on general farms. That would mean greater efficiency of the labor spent on livestock.

# Development and Application

R. L. Green and N. L. LeRay

PEOPLE develop and apply technology in agriculture in a way that reminds us of a slow-motion game of leapfrog, in which the time between advancing leaps is months or years or decades.

Geography fixes somewhat the intervals between jumps because of the stages of producing, processing, and marketing crops. In a broader way, the influences of people's moral codes, labor practices, and ways of life limit their initiative in developing and adapting new techniques.

The acceptance of new ideas, a complicated process, involves a series of thoughts and actions that often extend over considerable periods of time. An example: The average timespan between the time an Iowa farmer learns about hybrid seed corn and the time

he accepts it for continued use is 7 years.

George M. Beal and Joe M. Bohlen, of Iowa State University, said the stages in learning about new ideas and adopting them are awareness, interest, evaluation, trial, and adoption.

They classified people on the basis of the sequence in which they adopt or reject new practices as innovators, the first to adopt new ideas; early adopters, those who are among the first to use approved practices in a community, but not the first to try new ideas; the early majority, the ones who must be sure an idea will work before they adopt it; the majority, most of the people in a community who adopt proved methods; and those who do not adopt a new practice even after it has been adopted by most neighbors.

Age, education, social-economic status, and activities in progressive organizations are among the factors that influence the sequence. The more education a farmer has, the greater the likelihood that he will adopt new ideas. Younger farmers are more favorable toward new ideas than older ones. Farmers who belong to farm organizations and cooperatives often are early adopters of new practices.

The differences that make for uneven development and application of technological advances for a commodity include:

Variations in the topography, soils, and climate in areas of production.

Variations in the cultural requirements of crops.

Variations of different production stages in susceptibility to technological advance.

Variations between adapted varieties throughout the area of production.

Variations in the economic feasibility of technological change within the area of production. Feasibility is often determined by ultimate form of a commodity for consumption and the availability and cost of labor.

Variations in the culture of people working with a commodity.

Variations in the prior combinations of these factors, as reflected in present development and adaptation of technological advances. As long as labor is available and cheap, technological change seldom occurs.

Differences exist even in specific operations in the same section, and they in turn affect other enterprises. Some growers of snap beans, for example, have reduced their labor requirements by adopting a mechanical harvester, while others still harvest beans by hand. The reduction in labor required by bean growers in New York by the use of mechanical beanpickers reduced the demand for migrant labor in the community to the point that orchardists found it hard to get workers for harvesting cherries.

The same problem developed in northern Colorado, where increased mechanization cut the need for seasonal workers for sugar beets in spring. The sugar companies recruited fewer workers from southern Texas. Producers of beans, cherries, and other crops in northern Colorado subsequently had labor shortages. They lacked the organization and funds for a recruitment program of their own and could offer workers only short periods of employment.

Cotton is an example of leapfrogging in crop production. Before the invention of the cotton gin, production of cotton was limited by the capacity of hand labor to separate the seed from the fiber. After adoption of the gin, the production was limited by the availability of labor to harvest the crop in a relatively short time to avoid weather damage. Many inventors tried to develop a mechanical harvester, but none was satisfactory until plant breeders developed varieties adapted to mechanical harvesting. Mechanical cotton harvesters since have become quite common. Now considerable time and effort are being expended to develop chemical and mechanical ways to control weeds in cotton fields.

Mechanical harvesters contributed to the shift of cotton production from the Southeast toward the Southwest.

The Southern Piedmont, where cotton was king, is a region of rolling countryside and fields separated by water courses and steep slopes. Fields therefore are small—a point of little consequence when the crop was planted and cultivated with horse- or mule-drawn equipment and harvested by hand, but it is not efficient to grow cotton on small fields with plows and cultivators drawn by tractors. The mechanical cotton harvester contributed to an increase in the size of fields and hastened the discontinuation of the cotton enterprise on small farms.

Much of the rolling Piedmont, which once was covered with small fields of cotton, is now planted to grain, hay, and pasture to support livestock enterprises. In some places broilers have become king.

In the Southwest, on the other hand, sections once too dry for cotton are being irrigated, and the air is filled with sounds of the mechanical cotton harvester. Topography, climate, and availability of labor limited the rate of technological advance. In parts of the Southwest there is insufficient labor to handpick cotton, but the expansion of cotton acreage no longer is prohibited in labor-deficit areas by the cost of importing labor for picking cotton.

The mechanical harvester eliminated availability of labor for picking cotton as the limiting factor. Except for acreage allocations, the limiting production factor now is the labor required to thin the crop and control weeds.

This illustration should establish the fact that technological change usually is the result of a shortage of labor; it does not always displace labor. Another aspect is that industrialization of the Southeast has attracted labor from the farms and so has contributed also to the decline of cotton in the Piedmont.

Corn and small grains respond at all stages of production to the applications of technology and better practices. The labor required per acre of corn grown in the United States dropped from 32 man-hours an acre in 1920–1924 to 25 in 1940–1944 and to 10 in 1955–1958. The average production in those periods was 27, 32, and 46 bushels an acre, respectively. The combination of increased yields and fewer man-hours per acre meant an overall decline from 119 to 23 man-hours per 100 bushels of corn between 1920 and 1958.

The average number of man-hours per milk cow in the United States declined from 142 in 1920–1924 and 1940–1944 to 116 in 1955–1958. Milk production per cow averaged 4,000, 4,653, and 6,071 pounds, respectively, in those periods, and man-hours per hundredweight of milk declined from 3.6 in 1920–1924 to 1.9 in 1955–1958.

THUS we can produce more with less labor.

The decline in labor requirements has permitted farmers to operate larger enterprises. At the same time, investments in land, machinery, and equipment have grown. The average value of assets per farm—land, service buildings, livestock, machinery, equipment, crops held for feed, and demand deposits used for production—increased from 6,094 dollars in 1940 to 33,455 dollars in 1959.

The changes created a need for skilled operators of great managerial ability. A few years ago a sharecropper with little education could earn a subsistence living from a one-horse-crop. Today skill in operating machinery plus ability to manage a business are necessary to pay the higher fixed operating costs and to provide a living wage even for the tenant farmer.

Almost every engineering advance has brought problems that become alternate factors that for a time control production.

The adaptation of the combine for harvesting rice illustrates this shifting of controls. Rice previously was harvested with a binder, shocked, and left in the field until dry enough for storage before it was threshed. In Arkansas it was found that the optimum moisture content of rice for mechanical

harvesting is about 25 percent, but the moisture content must be below 15 percent for storage. The general use of combines was not practical until drying techniques, equipment, and facilities were designed, tested, and made commercially available. The transition from binder-thresher operation to combine harvesting extended over several years.

The gains in labor efficiency because of the adoption of new technology have meant a great gain in the number of people one farmworker can supply with food. Approximately 90 percent of the farm products marketed in 1960 could be produced on about 40 percent of the farms because of the new technology and the use of much seasonal agricultural labor.

TECHNOLOGICAL change and its social and economic effects cannot be disassociated from Government programs. The need for new technology and its adoption often are related closely to agricultural programs. The problems that are met by one change often are intensified by the other. For example, any technology that increases productivity of a surplus commodity will increase oversupplies unless there is a corresponding increase in domestic or foreign consumption or a reduction in acreages or number of units produced.

The benefits of new technology in agriculture have not been distributed evenly among all segments of rural society. The uneven development and adoption of technological advances in agriculture have resulted in many serious social, political, and economic problems.

Some of the effects of the adoption of technological advances can be measured with relative ease.

It is easy to determine the difference in labor requirements in machine-picking and handpicking an acre of green beans and to determine the amount of labor required to plant an acre of corn with one-row, mule-drawn equipment and with four-row tractor equipment.

It is more difficult to determine the amount and effects of the displacement of farmworkers and families.

Most of the labor rendered surplus by technological advances has found employment in industry. Some workers may join the ranks of migratory agricultural laborers during the periods of peak seasonal labor demand. Others may join the ranks of the unemployed and add to existing social and economic problems or create new problems.

Technological advances have intensified the effects of the seasonal nature of some farm enterprises. Many farmers who can meet the labor requirements of land preparation, planting, and fertilizing with family labor and small amounts of hired labor require large numbers of seasonal workers to perform specialized activities that have not become highly mechanized. Large numbers of seasonal workers therefore are needed to perform remaining seasonal tasks, such as harvesting fruit, thinning beets, and chopping cotton.

According to reports of the Bureau of Employment Security for major agricultural areas, about 1,403 thousand seasonal agricultural workers were employed in the peak month of September 1959 and only 321 thousand in February.

Migratory farmworkers are needed because the peak labor requirements for many crops cannot be supplied from local sources. This need is being met by approximately 400 thousand domestic migratory farmworkers, accompanied by about 150 thousand dependents, and by about 450 thousand workers from Mexico, the British West Indies, Canada, and Japan.

The seasonal nature of labor requirements in the San Joaquin Valley further illustrates the effect of uneven technological advances on the need for seasonal workers. In the fertile, irrigated San Joaquin Valley, which includes parts of six counties in south-central California, cotton, grapes, peaches, apricots, potatoes, oranges, figs, and olives are grown.

The number of farmworkers needed there is about 10 thousand in March and more than 100 thousand in October. Grapes in Fresno County usually are harvested between August and the end of October, and in 1958 required about 35 thousand hands at the peak of the harvest season, but almost none from the middle of March to the middle of May. The extra workers came from Mexico, Texas, New Mexico, Arizona, southern California, and other places to harvest the raisin, table, and wine grapes.

The main areas and crops that have high peak seasonal labor requirements are California, for cotton, grapes, tomatoes, potatoes, peaches, pears, apricots, citrus fruit, and miscellaneous crops; the Lower Rio Grande Valley, for citrus fruit, cotton, tomatoes, corn, and miscellaneous vegetables; the cotton areas of Texas, New Mexico, Arizona, and the Mississippi Delta; the Atlantic coast fruit and vegetable areas; the fruit, vegetable, and sugar beet sections of Michigan; and the Northwestern States, for apples, pears, cherries, peaches, sugar beets, and other fruit and vegetables.

The migratory farmworker meets the need of the employer of seasonal farm labor by being available when required for farmwork. He also meets the requirement of the farmer's community by leaving when no work is available. Thus the migratory agricultural worker does not present a major social problem for the farmer or the farmer's community.

The migrants, however, have problems of poor housing, low incomes, and the care and schooling of children.

The rate of turnover among migratory farmworkers is high. Large numbers drop out of the migrant labor force each year and are replaced by new workers. The reasons they give for leaving include steady jobs elsewhere, the low wages, and family and health problems.

Some migrants intermittently enter and leave the migrant streams. Others become established in nonfarm work.

The worker with education and training finds it relatively easy in an expanding economy to leave migratory work and to become established elsewhere. The migrant with little education or nonagricultural skills has little chance but to follow the crops. His lack of training for nonfarm work, lack of resources, and lack of management ability condemn him to his lot. Concerted efforts of public and private agencies and groups are needed to prepare this type of worker for nonfarm work or for employment in mechanized agriculture.

Many operators of small farms have not been able to adjust to the new technology or benefit from Government agricultural programs. As a result, there are areas of low-income farmers and low-income farms in good farming areas. Improved off-farm technology and communications have created a desire for an improvement in level of living, but opportunities for such improvement have not become available.

Other operators of small farms have become part-time farmers who may regard their nonfarm jobs as temporary activities and plan to become full-time farm operators as soon as they can accumulate additional capital. Others consider part-time farming as a transitional step from full-time farm operation to full-time nonfarm work and will leave the farm when they acquire the skills necessary for a well-paying nonfarm job. For others the combination of farm and nonfarm work is a permanent way of life.

A report, "Development of Agricultural Human Resources" issued in 1955 by the Department of Agriculture, summarized the situation of many of approximately 1.5 million low-income farm families: "What they are up against in innumerable cases is lack of enough good land, lack of equipment, lack of credit facilities, and often lack of the management information and skill which might open wider opportunity to them."

Thus the central problem of low-income farm families is lack of resources and lack of opportunity.

The social-economic problems faced by many rural people are not entirely a product of technological advance in agriculture. In the past the surplus farm population was needed by nonfarm sectors of the economy. In many nonfarm sectors of the Nation, however, production has increased at a higher rate than employment because of mechanization. New jobs for unskilled labor were not readily available in 1960 for surplus farm or nonfarm populations as in the past.

UNEVEN DEVELOPMENT and application of technology in agriculture will continue the motions of leapfrog. Production factors peculiar to a crop or geographical area will accelerate development and application of technology segment by segment. Intermittently field production capacity will exceed harvesting capabilities, harvesting capabilities will exceed storage or processing facilities, labor requirements will be unequal to available labor, and market demands will be different from supplies. Development and advancement are regulated by the inevitable laws of supply and demand; improvements in one area tend to create a train of events which will leave behind or overrun segments incapable of an accelerated pace.

Economic checks and balances may be expected to maintain a long-range equality of development and application of technology between various phases of agriculture for maximum benefit to all segments of the American economy.

IN SUMMARY: The social-economic problems that many rural people face are not entirely a product of technologic advances in agriculture. In many nonfarm sectors, production has increased at a higher rate than employment because of mechanization. Methods of solving the future problems of adjustment are available in our national capacity to produce wealth.

# Engineering and Biology

K. H. Norris and W. T. Pentzer

THE EFFECT of controlling the color of the light a plant gets is an example of the place of the biological sciences in modern agriculture and of the need for coordination among the engineers and biologists in their work.

Advances in engineering often create new problems for biologists, and potential engineering advances may not come because the effect on the biological reactions were not foreseen. Only through the combined efforts of the physical and biological scientists are we able to attain the maximum in technologic process.

Plant scientists have known for years that a vital pigment in plants reacts to light to control such functions as growth, flowering, coloration, and germination. Its presence has been demonstrated in seeds, plants, and trees, but only by the physiological response to the light stimulus. Little is known about the pigment, but its importance to agriculture is recognized, and the knowledge we have is used on a practical basis.

We know that the pigment exists in two forms, a red-light-absorbing form and a far-red-light-absorbing form. It can be converted from one form to the other in the plant. By irradiation with red light, the pigment becomes the far-red-absorbing form. By irradiation with far-red light, it becomes the red-light-absorbing form.

In the far-red-light-absorbing form, it acts as an enzyme that promotes germination of seeds, prevents flowering of many plants, prevents stem elongation of seedlings, promotes rooting of plant cuttings, and enhances the red coloring of tomato and apple skins.

In the red-light-absorbing form it causes the opposite reaction. It inhibits germination, rooting, and tissue coloring and promotes flowering and stem elongation. Controlling the color of the light given to a plant makes it possible therefore to control many of the biological responses of the plant.

Florists use the knowledge that plant responses can be controlled with light to provide us with chrysanthemum blooms at any time of the year and the poinsettia at Christmas. These are relatively minor examples of the possibilities that exist for control of plants through the action of this photoreversible pigment, but they illustrate how biological reactions in plants can be modified by physical techniques to produce a desired effect.

Engineering and biological techniques have been combined recently in a study of this pigment, which is so important in controlling plant development. Engineers of the Department of Agriculture have developed extremely sensitive spectrophotometers for study of pigments in biological tissues. The instruments were developed for measuring pigment changes related to maturity and ripeness of fruits and vegetables.

At the same time Department scientists were conducting a long series of experiments to demonstrate that the photoreversible pigment should be concentrated in certain plant tissues and were busily engaged in attempts to detect and isolate the pigment. They were not able to detect the pigment with commercially available spectrophotometers.

Then the two groups combined their efforts with the result that the pigment was detected in a number of plant tissues. With an instrument to detect the pigment, the chemists then proceeded with their isolation procedures, concentrating the pigment into a form suitable for further study. Engineering provided the instrumentation for an important development in biology. Further developments will follow and lead to new applications, which must be engineered.

Animals also respond to light. The egg production of chickens and the fertility of sheep, goats, and turkeys can be altered by controlling the length of day. The mechanism by which this control takes place is not known, but the technique is used to increase egg production during the short days of winter. Further exploitation of this control must wait for understanding of the biological reactions. Any engineering developments are likely to be of minor consequence until more of the biology is known. Once these reactions are known, however, methods will be developed to control the reactions as desired.

THE GREAT STRIDES in the mechanization of crop production have created some serious biological problems. For maximum yields, small grains should be harvested when their moisture content is 20 to 30 percent, but grain of that moisture level soon develops mold when it is stored and is more subject to insect contamination.

Engineers provided a solution to this problem, but in doing so they created new problems in biology. Heated-air driers were developed to dry the wet grain.

If the drying is too rapid, however, the grain cracks, and the yield of final product is less. If the temperature of the grain exceeds a safe limit, the viability is destroyed so that the grain cannot be used for seed. Barley for use in the malting industry is particularly subject to damage from artificial drying. Corn that is dried at a high temperature is much harder to mill. Peanuts develop a bitter flavor under poor drying conditions.

Again, the biological reactions limit the engineering techniques. As a result, close controls are required on the engineering techniques to insure the maintenance of the quality of the product.

Biologists have come to the aid of engineers in the mechanization of grain harvesting. They developed chemicals that cause plant leaves to dry and fall to the ground so that the grain loses moisture faster. They developed grains that are less subject to shattering, so that combine harvesting can be done when the grain has a lower moisture content without excessive losses.

They also have started to develop ways to control the biological reactions in moist grain to permit extended storage of high-moisture grain for specific applications. Wet corn can be stored in gas-tight storage for animal feeding. In such storage not all the biological reactions are stopped—only those that cause mold and decay. The stored corn has a fermented odor, but animals produce as well on it as they do on dry corn. These research developments in biology may provide the answers needed for engineering advancements in grain production.

Harvesting fruit and vegetables requires a high labor cost. The substitution of machines for this human labor has not been practical in many instances because of characteristics of the crop. It may be possible to overcome some of these limitations by engineering techniques, but a better solution is possible if the crop can be modified to facilitate the mechanization.

We can modify characteristics of plants. Radical changes in their shape, size, and other physical aspects are possible by breeding, applying chemicals to regulate growth, and pruning and physically forcing a plant to grow in a specified manner. These modifications are not easy, and they may take years of intensive breeding and plant shaping to obtain the desired change. This should not prevent us from considering at least the possibility of designing the plant to fit a machine operation, rather than always trying to design a machine to fit the plant.

Designing a machine to harvest the crop and modifying the plant to permit the use of the machine demands coordination. Many compromises are required because some problems are solved more readily by changing the machine; others, by changing the plants. The goal is to provide the best product with the lowest cost of production. All decisions must be in line with this goal.

We are not doing all we should be doing to solve cooperatively the problems of mechanical harvesting of fruit and vegetables. Work has started on some crops, but more is needed.

Cooperative work of engineers and plant scientists has brought advances in the automatic harvesting of grapes. Viticulturalists have developed methods of growing grapes on overhead horizontal supports. The clusters of grapes hang below the vines and leaves on long stems. It is relatively easy to design a machine to travel under the vines and harvest the fruit. It will be some time before this development can be used on a large scale, but it should reduce the cost of harvesting grapes.

Cooperative work on the automatic harvesting of tomatoes shows promise of success. Plant breeders are developing tomatoes that mature uniformly to provide an adequate production with a single harvesting. Engineers have been working on equipment to lift the tomato plants and shake the tomatoes into a container.

The equipment will be successful, however, only if a slight force is required to remove the tomatoes from the vine and the tomatoes are firm enough to withstand the treatment given by the machine. The machine must be designed to minimize damage to the tomatoes and to harvest a maximum yield of fruit. All of this plant modification and automatic harvesting must be done without a loss of quality in the final product.

THE STORAGE LIFE of agricultural products can be altered by the storage environment. The maximum storage life of a commodity depends on an exact control of several interacting variables. A fresh fruit or vegetable placed in storage is still a living bio-logical system. It continually undergoes changes. Some of the changes we wish to retard. Others we wish to accelerate, depending on the use of the product.

Efforts to extend the storage life of fruit and vegetables by special treatments and control of environment have not always been successful. For example: Early work with gamma radiation indicated that sprouting of potatoes could be inhibited with a low level of radiation treatment. It appeared that thereby the storage life of potatoes could be extended several months. When an attempt was made to use the radiation treatment to extend the storage life, the potatoes did not sprout but developed rot. The radiation treatment that prevented the sprouting also killed the self-healing properties of the potato skin. Any slight bruise, which would normally heal without trouble, therefore became infected. It may be possible to develop a means of controlling this decay; if not, this promising engineering development cannot be utilized.

Proper control of the atmosphere surrounding a fruit or vegetable can be used to extend the storage life without deleterious effects on the quality of the product. Reducing the oxygen content slows the respiration rate of the plant tissue and reduces the rate of chemical reactions within the product, so that its useful life is extended. The amount of carbon dioxide in the storage atmosphere, however, must also be controlled to prevent deterioration from another source. A careful balance of the oxygen and carbon dioxide level must be maintained. The precise environmental conditions for optimum storage of each product must be determined, and techniques must be developed for creating and maintaining these conditions.

Marketing procedures are increasing the demand for the production of large volume, uniform, high-quality produce at minimum cost. To meet this demand, advancements must be made in the means for measuring and controlling the quality of the product.

Rapid and accurate instruments are required to measure moisture content, color, tenderness, maturity and other important quality factors. Some of them have been developed by cooperative effort of instrument makers and biological scientists. The biological scientists have determined the types of measurements required to express the quality of the product. Specialists in instrumentation have developed methods for making the measurements. So we have automatic machines for sorting lemons, beans, peas, and seeds by color, and for sorting eggs to reject those with defects.

The development of new instruments and procedures will open up larger fields for the application of engineering to biological problems in agriculture.

# Costs of Farm Machinery

James Vermeer and Donald T. Black

THE LARGEST single item of expenditure on many farms in the United States is the cost of owning and operating farm machinery.

Of 30 typical farm situations in the United States, machinery costs in 1958 were more than 40 percent of total operating expenses on three-fifths of the farms. On some farms they made up nearly two-thirds of all operating expenses.

Expenditures for operating and replacing machinery among 30 types of the commercial family-operated farms ranged from about 400 dollars on small tobacco farms in the Coastal Plain of North Carolina to 6,700 dollars per farm on irrigated cotton farms in the High Plains of Texas. The average of the 30 types of farms was about 2,500 dollars.

The value of machinery by type of farm was 1,300 dollars to 18 thousand and averaged 6,600 dollars at the current value. The original purchase price probably was about twice as great. As prices of machines have risen since those investments were made, the cost of replacing 6,600 dollars' worth of equipment at 1960 prices probably would require an investment of 15 thousand to 17 thousand dollars.

Prices farmers paid for motor vehicles and farm machinery were about 2.5 times as high in 1960 as in 1940. For example, prices of 20–29-horsepower wheel tractors rose from 1,020 dollars in 1940 to 2,470 dollars in 1959. The 1940 and 1959 models were not identical, of course; the newer models have extras, such as generators, batteries, self-starters, lights, power takeoffs, power steering, hydraulic controls, and more comfortable seats. Thus the differences in cost of 1940 and 1959 tractors are not due solely to higher prices in 1959.

Many of the improvements in the machines perform more effectively the job for which the machines were designed or reduce the heavy physical labor required of farmworkers. In either case, costs of owning and frequently costs of operating machinery have risen. At the same time, improved machines have contributed to greater output, and machinery costs per unit of product have risen less than the total machinery costs.

THE COSTS of owning machinery often are referred to as fixed costs. All other costs are labeled variable costs.

Some costs are fixed, regardless of amount of use—the interest on investment, taxes, insurance, housing, and usually depreciation. Variable costs include fuel or power costs, repairs, lubrication, and service labor. Some variable costs are proportional to use. Others change with use but are not necessarily proportional to it.

All costs do not fit neatly into these two categories. Depreciation, for example, is classified usually as a fixed cost. As long as the rate of obsolescence exceeds the rate at which the machine wears out, this is a proper classification. If a machine is used so much that it is worn out before it becomes obsolete, however, depreciation becomes a variable cost.

Some ownership costs are applicable to all machines of a given type and size regardless of age or condition. Housing costs are of this kind, because the space required to house a machine of a given size is independent of its age or value. The cost of a license required on trucks, in States where the cost of a license is distinct from personal property tax, likewise is uniform regardless of the age and depreciated value of the truck.

Other ownership costs are related to value and become fixed once the machine is acquired. Taxes and insurance are examples. Usually they are independent of the extent of its use.

Insurance sometimes is considered as a cost only if a machine is insured, but most farmers realize that if they do not insure their machinery against accidental damage or loss through an established insurance company, they in effect carry their own insurance—they must be prepared to suffer some losses, and frequently do.

Another cost related to value is the interest charge on money invested in machinery. This cost often is overlooked, except perhaps for the actual interest paid on money borrowed to buy a machine.

These costs related to value can be kept to a minimum by farmers who can keep older machines in good repair through careful use and regular maintenance. As long as the older machines do not become obsolete—because of the introduction of new machines that will do the job faster or replace more labor—farmers will find it profitable to use older machines with lower charges for taxes, insurance, and interest.

Fixed costs, or costs of ownership, are

ANNUAL DEPRECIATION OF SMALL
TRACTORS WITH DIFFERENT
AMOUNTS OF ANNUAL USE

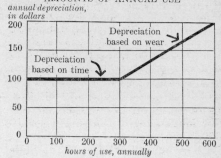

*Charges for depreciation are constant when the rate of obsolescence exceeds wear and tear. They are proportional to use when wear and tear exceeds the rate of obsolescence.*

higher for new equipment. Variable costs, or costs of operation, are higher for old or used equipment.

Fixed costs per hour or per acre of use are higher for equipment that is used only a few days during a year.

DEPRECIATION is one of the major costs of owning machines on most farms.

It is one of the most difficult cost items to estimate. Depreciation occurs for one or both of two reasons.

If a machine is used very little, usually it becomes obsolete before it is worn out. The original cost therefore must be charged off when the machine is replaced.

On the other hand, extensive use will cause the machine to be worn out while it is still the best kind of machine for the job. Again, the original investment in the machine has been used up and must be charged off.

Estimating the expected life of a machine is a highly subjective procedure at best. Records of experience with similar machines are of some help. They indicate the hours or years of use to be expected before the machine is worn out, but they are of little help in forecasting when a particular machine will become obsolete.

Because obsolescence does occur, a

farmer has to make a minimum charge for depreciation even though he uses the machine very little. If the machine is used so much as to shorten its expected life, however, annual depreciation will exceed the minimum charge.

For example: A machine costs 1,500 dollars and its expected life is 15 years, or 4,500 hours, of use, whichever occurs first. Based on the expected life of 15 years, depreciation would be 100 dollars a year. If the annual use exceeds 300 hours (4,500 hours divided by 15), the machine will not last 15 years, and the depreciation charge will exceed 100 dollars. If the machine is used 500 hours a year, its useful life will be reduced to 9 years (4,500 hours divided by 500) and the depreciation charge will be 167 dollars a year (1,500 dollars divided by 9).

A depreciation charge for a machine used very little thus is a fixed cost.

Using a machine enough so that the depreciation from wear is as great as the rate of obsolescence, however, reduces one of the major costs of owning a machine to its practical minimum for each hour of use. Depreciation charges beyond that point are proportional to use—wear.

Some other fixed costs are reduced if a machine is used in excess of the amount necessary to reduce depreciation cost per hour to its practical minimum. Using a machine enough to increase the annual depreciation, and thus reduce the remaining value, more rapidly, reduces charges for interest, taxes, and insurance, which relate to value.

Nearly all new machines are designed to increase the volume of work one man can do. Sometimes they reduce the cost per unit of work performed if a big enough volume of work can be found for them. Associated with the greater capacity of machines has been the demand for more land to increase the size of farms so as to provide more work per machine. Greater demand for land has led to higher prices of land. This is an indirect cost of owning larger machines.

ONE WAY to reduce costs of machinery is to develop cheaper machines that will perform the same volume of work as the machines now in use. Perhaps too little emphasis has been given to this aspect of machine design. In order to reduce fixed costs, or the costs of owning them, the new models would need to be sold for less money than their predecessors.

The design and use of multipurpose machines serve to hold down the fixed costs of machinery per farm. Tillage machines are of this type. They are relatively inexpensive and are commonly used to prepare the seedbed and cultivate all crops on a farm.

Multipurpose harvesting machines have been put on the market. Forage harvesters, with slight adaptations, can be used to harvest green feed from standing grass and legumes, wilted grasses for silage, hay, and row crops, such as corn and sorghum for silage. Combines can be adapted to harvest small grains, soybeans, and corn for grain.

Adapting machines to a number of tasks extends their use and reduces overhead costs per acre or hour of use.

COSTS OF owning and operating machinery usually are not considered independently in deciding which machines or methods to use in performing specified jobs.

Other factors to consider are: What effect the use of a given machine has on other costs, particularly labor; whether the new machine or method will do a better job than the present method does; and whether the capital invested in machinery could be used more advantageously in some other investment or enterprise.

If two types of machines replace equal amounts of labor, the one that replaces hired labor is more likely to be adopted than one that replaces family labor.

Some machines do not necessarily reduce the number of man-hours required; often they make the work easier. If a machine enables a boy or girl in the farm family to replace a hired man, the likelihood is greater that the machine will be adopted.

Other machines can replace hired or family labor. They have an economic advantage on farms operated largely with family labor, however, only if the available labor can be profitably employed in some other way or if the family is willing to use this method to buy leisure.

MACHINERY costs may possibly be reduced by the use of alternative practices or systems for getting a job done. Some machines may be eliminated entirely or may be used for more than one purpose. The combining of operations and machines allows the job to be done faster when timeliness is advantageous and cuts the labor as well. Combinations of operations and reduction in costs go hand in hand. An example is the combined operation of mowing and conditioning of forage for hay. With both the mower and conditioner attached to one tractor, the number of acres handled per hour by one operator and tractor is nearly twice as great as when the operations are performed separately.

Before a new practice is adopted it must satisfy either or both of the following requirements: It must serve to lower costs; the quality of the work the new system does must be as high or higher than that done with the existing practice.

If it meets only one of these—for example, if it reduces costs but also reduces quality—the reduction in costs must be at least as great as the reduction in value of the product.

FORAGE feed crops rank second to corn in value among all farm crops grown in the United States. About 120 million tons of hay and 80 million tons of silage are produced annually.

Methods for harvesting forage have changed rapidly since 1945. The field chopper, forage blower, field baler, hay drier, and a wide variety of other machines have come into general use.

Complete pushbutton feeding equipment is a reality—a great change from the day when haying was done with a mower, dump rake, wagon, and several hand forks. On farms where harvesting forage is a major operation, investments in machinery for this job may be as much as 15 thousand dollars for a single farm.

Because of the importance of forage crops on a large proportion of farms and the opportunities for reducing costs of producing forage by proper combinations of equipment, we pay particular attention here to the harvesting of forage to exemplify ways to reduce costs of harvest.

Among the new methods of harvesting forage are green chopping, by which pasture forage is cut and brought to the animals and fed green; hay drying, either in storage or in a batch system, such as drying on one or more wagons; chopping dry hay in the field and moving it to storage mechanically; and several techniques for preserving the crops as silage.

In determining which of the various systems and necessary equipment are most suitable for his farm, the farmer must consider the two basic items—cost and quality. He should consider also the volumes or amounts of materials to be harvested; amounts of hay, grain, silage, and pasture fed and the number of livestock; the basic layout of the farmstead, hauling distances, and storage and feeding structures; and the additional equipment required for the new practice and its potential use in other new practices.

In harvesting hay, results of research at Iowa State University and elsewhere have shown that the lowest cost method is with the sweep rake, a buck rake, and buck stacker. Where hay must be brought to a central feeding location or sold commercially, this practice obviously must be replaced with some such method as baling to reduce volume and provide easier handling.

If the hay is to be fed on the farm, forage harvesters may be used for harvesting both hay and silage; the same associated equipment such as the mower, rake, and forage blower may be used for handling both types of forage.

As we mentioned before, the tandem operation of mowing and conditioning the hay or (for making silage) both mowing and raking may be performed by one tractor operation.

For farms handling large tonnages of forage, a new self-propelled windrower offers additional savings in cost of equipment and labor. It can mow, condition, and rake a 10- to 14-foot swath in one operation.

Because of the increased interest in the production of better hay through preservation of nutrients during the harvesting and storage phases, artificial drying and practices that speed up natural drying have become common, especially in the East and in sections where weather makes field curing hazardous. Forage begins to deteriorate as soon as it is cut. Deterioration continues rapidly until the crop is completely cured. To reduce the curing time, higher expenditures for equipment have been made for such items as conditioners and drying equipment.

A survey by men at Cornell University revealed that the average cost of drying 1 ton of hay with a heated-air drier was about 6.50 dollars. Fixed costs per ton ranged from 1.15 dollars to 16.06 dollars, while variable costs were 83 cents to 6.20 dollars. Total drying costs for drying in the mow with unheated air, as reported by men at the University of Delaware, were 1.54 dollars to 6.54 dollars a ton.

Variations in cost are due to the type of equipment and the drying system used, the amount of moisture removed, and the number of tons of hay dried. For optimum operating costs in hay drying, the minimum amount of hay appears to be in a range of 75 to 100 tons.

GRASS SILAGE has increased in popularity as a method of harvesting and storing forage crops, primarily because of the recent introduction of direct-cut forage harvesters. The direct-cut system has great appeal to the farmer because it is a once-over operation. This practice, however, results in a high-moisture silage, which means large quantities of water must be hauled for each ton of dry matter stored.

Studies conducted by men of the Department of Agriculture showed that making grass silage by the wilting method requires fewer man-hours per ton of dry matter stored than the direct-cut method. More acres can be cut and stored in an hour, and therefore a large crew is required for a shorter period of time. This method requires equipment for mowing and raking, but such machinery also may be used for haying.

Feeding trials showed that wilted silage was equal to good field-cured hay and superior to weather-damaged hay but had a slightly lower feeding value than barn-dried hay.

GREEN CHOPPING is a way of feeding forage whereby the entire plant growth is cut and fed without drying, curing, or storing. Greater utilization of the forage is possible than with rotation grazing or with continuous grazing, the common method. Losses from selective grazing, trampling, and spoilage from droppings are avoided.

Obviously, however, livestock themselves provide the cheapest method of harvesting, and any degree of mechanization involves additional costs. Green chopping is no exception. A forage harvester and hauling and feeding equipment are necessary. Additional power and labor may be required, and the daily chore of chopping and hauling may interfere with other farm operations.

These additional costs may be offset by increases in income through increase in the size of herd arising from the additional forage available or by reductions in feed costs when more forage can be economically used in the ration. Green chopping may also be used to spread overhead costs to the point at which a forage harvester is economical, whereas it could not be justified solely for use in making silage.

THE MARCH of mechanization requires the use of increasing amounts of capital. Many farmers do not have, cannot borrow, or do not want to risk additional capital for this purpose. Others prefer to use available capital to buy feed, fertilizer, and livestock or for other capital items where the returns per dollar invested may be greater than the return from investment in additional machinery. They are able, however, to take advantage of some of the benefits of mechanization by hiring, renting, borrowing, exchanging, or owning jointly labor-saving machines.

Among the methods used by farmers to reduce their individual investments in machinery, custom work is one of the commonest. About 150 farm operations are performed by custom operators.

Custom work enables a small farmer to obtain the advantages of mechanization without incurring the high overhead costs of owning a specialized machine solely for his own use. These advantages can be obtained in either of two ways. A farmer can hire specified jobs done for him, or he can buy a specialized machine for his own use and spread his ownership costs by doing custom work for neighbors.

If enough custom work is available, the latter method might be preferable. It gives the small farmer an opportunity to sell some of his own labor and the use of his other equipment. By hiring custom work, he would be hiring additional labor and other equipment—for example, a tractor—while his own labor and tractor remained idle.

Rates charged for custom work vary greatly from one part of the country to another. Generally they have been lowest in the North Central States and highest in the Pacific Coast States. In 1957, for example, custom charges for picking corn were about 4.75 dollars an acre in the north-central region, about 6.75 dollars in the Northeast, and 8 dollars in the Pacific Coast States. Costs of operating the machines includ-

ing a charge for labor may have been lower in the Corn Belt than in the Pacific Coast States, but the differences in costs probably were not so great as the differences in custom charges.

The supply of custom operators and their machines and the demand for their services establish the rates. The availability of machines and operators willing to do custom work, on the one hand, and the number of farmers wanting the services of custom operators, on the other, are major considerations.

In the Corn Belt, there were only 72 acres of corn to be picked in 1958 for each machine on farms on January 1, 1958. In the Pacific Coast States, the ratio was 161 acres to one machine. This is one of the factors causing lower custom rates in the Corn Belt than in the Pacific Coast States.

In some areas and among some farmers, custom work is done chiefly as an accommodation for neighbors. Consequently the rates charged are not intended to cover all costs but are only a basis of settlement among neighbors. It may be advantageous there for small operators to hire custom operators to do the jobs that require the use of expensive machines.

The cooperative ownership of machines provides another way of reducing investment per farm and spreading the fixed costs over a larger volume of work.

Because harvesting machines require relatively large investments and are used only a few days a year, they are the ones that are most frequently owned cooperatively. For cooperative ownership to be successful, however, stability of tenure of the operators is highly desirable. The timing of the use of machines on the cooperating farms also requires some planning. For example, two or more farmers could use one combine if they planted some early, midseason, and late maturing varieties of small grains and soybeans. Some jobs, such as filling silos, usually require more help than is available on one farm. The cooperative ownership of silo-filling equipment is a natural arrangement among farmers who exchange work.

LEASING equipment to farmers is a recent addition to the business of some farm machinery dealers. Renting machinery instead of owning it enables farmers to avoid investment in expensive equipment.

Farmers also have the advantage of obtaining the use of only the equipment they need. Renting a specialized machine frequently enables a farmer to make fuller utilization of his own labor and equipment.

If the job can be completed within the time limit of the rental agreement, the farmer has the same control over the time and the way the job will be done as he would have if he owned the equipment. Under unfavorable conditions or adverse weather, however, the lease may expire before the job is done. If the lease cannot be renewed, the loss of a crop or failure to get a job done on time may be greater than all the costs of ownership. Also, because of unfavorable weather, a farmer may have to pay rent on a machine without being able to use it.

The practice of renting machines to farmers also has some advantages for dealers in addition to the income from renting. It gives farmers an opportunity to try machines, and not infrequently they decide to buy.

Rented machines are not always operated properly. Sometimes dealers can improve operating methods by giving farmers instruction in correct operating methods.

The cost of renting machines varies widely from one locality to another. In many communities rental machines are unavailable.

Paul M. Mulliken, of the National Retail Farm Equipment Association, suggested the following rates in an article published in Farm Equipment Retailing, in November 1957:

1 percent of the new delivered retail price of equipment for a 10-hour day.

5 percent of the new delivered retail price for a week.

15 percent on the same basis for a month.

25 percent for a 2-month period.

33.3 percent for 3 months.

The formula applies only to the use of the equipment. Extras, such as an operator, fuel, delivery and pickup service, and supplies, would require added charges. Owners of the machines would be responsible for the usual wear and depreciation, but renters would assume liability for accidents and abuse.

Mr. Mulliken indicated that, to his knowledge, this schedule of rates had not been used by any dealer.

Since then, the published rates of one dealer have come to our attention. In general, rates charged for the use of tractors approximate those suggested here, but rates charged for tractor implements and other equipment were 4 to 6 times as high as those suggested by Mr. Mulliken—an indication that the rates should not be uniform percentages of retail prices. It is likely that costs of sharpening and replacing worn parts on plows, cultivators, mowers, and saws are much higher relative to the retail prices of such equipment than repairs on tractors are relative to their retail prices.

The wide range in rates that are likely to prevail in a new type of service indicates that choice between renting a machine, and owning it, individually or cooperatively, depends largely on local conditions.

Each farmer must estimate what it would cost him to own a machine per unit of the work that he has for it from year to year. If this cost is greater than rental charges in his community, he should consider renting. If costs of owning are less than rental charges, there is little advantage in renting.

TIMELINESS of any operation—harvesting for instance—is an important factor in determining whether to own or lease equipment or rely on custom work.

It may also be important in determining whether to purchase increased-capacity equipment, such as a 10-foot mower rather than the 7-foot model.

Until such time as we can obtain more control over its uncertainty and its effect on crops, weather is a problem that must be contended with. The ownership of any machine or trading for a machine with greater capacity than needed for an average year may be justified on the reasoning that an unfavorable season could mean the difference between a good crop and a poor crop or no crop at all.

A farmer's decision on whether to buy, lease, or hire the job done must be based on the costs involved and his estimate of the risk involved. He may also wish to consider the possibility of alternative practices, such as the making of grass silage when time and weather are not good for curing hay in the field.

Costs of owning machinery can be reduced by the proper selection of the kind and size of machines for the jobs to be done, and by spreading these ownership costs over a sufficient volume of work so that each machine is worn out in normal use before obsolescence becomes significant.

# Management of Machines

Kenneth K. Barnes and Paul E. Strickler

MANAGEMENT of machinery is an important part of farm management. It has become one of the more flexible factors in the control of costs of crop production.

A typical breakdown of the annual costs of producing corn in the Corn Belt would allot 20 dollars an acre to land, 10 dollars an acre to seed and fertilizer, and 20 dollars an acre to costs of labor and machinery. A farmer cannot control the prices of inputs, which are set basically in the marketplace. In selecting and operating machinery, however, he has a wide latitude in the substitution of capital for labor and in the control of per acre costs of machines.

The engineering advances that each year bring improved machines tend to make the machinery-management job more complicated. On what basis should a farmer in the Corn Belt, where four-row planting and cultivating has been standard, decide to buy a 12-row unit? He must select the most profitable size of machine for his operations. The designer of farm machinery must predict the sizes of machines that will be in demand as patterns of agricultural production change.

The decisions cannot be soundly made, and machinery cannot be managed effectively without an understanding of the factors that influence the capacities of machines to accomplish jobs in the field.

THE FIELD capacity of a machine is a function of the forward speed and operating width and of the time losses associated with the operation.

The theoretical field capacity is the rate at which a machine would do a job if there were no interruptions—no clogging, turning, slowing, or filling of hoppers. This capacity is expressed in terms of acres per hour.

The effective field capacity is the average rate at which the operation really moves. If, for example, at the end of 10 hours of picking cotton 8 acres have been picked, the effective field capacity is .8 acre per hour. The effective capacity is less than the theoretical capacity because of the time spent turning at row ends, emptying baskets, and cleaning out the picker.

THEORETICAL field capacity is the forward speed multiplied by the operating width of the machine. The theoretical field capacity (in acres per hour) equals the product of the forward speed in miles per hour and the operating width in feet, divided by 8.25. The factor 8.25 is 43,560, the number of square feet in an acre, divided by 5,280, the number of feet in a mile. It gives a dimensionally consistent equation.

Speed can be estimated conveniently by walking alongside a machine and counting the number of steps taken in 1 minute. Thirty steps a minute is about 1 mile an hour. To determine speed accurately, travel over a measured distance should be timed.

The operating width of a machine may or may not have a relationship to the physical width. The operating width for row-crop equipment is the number of rows times the row spacing.

For such tillage implements as plows, disks, or harrows, the physical width of the soil-engaging parts of the machine is the operating width. For mowers, direct-cut choppers and combines, and similar machines, the physical width of the cutterbar is the operating width. But for balers, pickup choppers, and combines, or other machines that operate on windrowed materials, the center-to-center spacing of windrows becomes the operating width. For such tools as subsoilers or centrifugal seeders, the center-to-center distance between adjacent passes through the field is the operating width.

Time losses are unavoidable, but nonetheless they subtract from the time the machine could be working. Turning at row ends, like all losses of time, varies greatly with the operator's habits and the length of the field. We have found that turning time averages about 30 seconds an acre for four- and six-row planters and cultivators. Although the four-row units make more turns per acre, the six-row units travel farther in each turn.

At 10 seconds per turn, a four-row unit requires 164 seconds per acre for turning with 200-foot rows, 82 with 400-foot rows, 41 with 800-foot rows, 27+ with 1,200-foot rows, and 20+ with 1,600-foot rows.

Turning time can be reduced by operating the long way in rectangular fields, by making fields as long as possible, and by working fields in narrow lands. Gains through reduction of turning time become small as fields increase beyond the rectangular 20 acres a quarter of a mile long.

The time it takes to go from field to field is a sizable loss. Consolidating scattered areas of the same crop into one larger field, when possible, can reduce substantially the time spent in traveling many miles at low tractor speeds.

Field repairs and adjustments to machines are the most insidious sources of time losses in the field. Often they can be avoided.

A field study of a straw baling operation, over three different 2-day periods, gave an example of this type of loss. During the first period, the operator spent 1.2 times as much time on repair and adjustment of the baler as he spent in baling. Much of this repair and adjustment could have been done in slack seasons, or perhaps on rainy days, when labor would not have been at a premium for other activities. After these repairs were completed, only 7 to 10 percent of the actual baling time was needed for field adjustment.

Excessive operating speed also can increase the loss of time spent in making repairs and adjustments. Often the time thus lost more than offsets the gains in theoretical field capacity from the increase in speed.

Handling materials takes much time in many farm operations. In typical planting operations, 85 seconds per acre is required to fill seed and fertilizer hoppers. Changing wagons in cornpicking may take a little less than 1.5 minutes per acre. It used to take about 4 minutes, but the use of the telescoping wagon tongue and quick hitch on corn-harvesting wagons cut wagon-changing time considerably.

In harvesting, changing wagons for balers or choppers, emptying grain hoppers on combines and field shellers, and emptying baskets on cottonpickers are major consumers of time—8 to 12 percent of the field time.

If hauling capacity is not matched to harvesting capacity, however, serious time losses can occur. We have recorded as much as a 30 percent loss of time from waiting for trucks and wagons to haul away harvested materials.

Improved methods of handling materials in the field can reduce greatly the time required.

Filling hoppers with dry and bagged starter fertilizer at the rate of 100 pounds of 5–20–20 per acre required .8 minute per acre. The use of liquid fertilizer and a transfer pump took only .3 minute. With proper equipment, such as portable bins, dry bulk fertilizer can be handled about as readily as liquid.

Insecticide hoppers were filled with dry material in .3 minute per acre. Dry herbicides required a similar amount of time. These figures may seem small, but they may total as much as 1.8 minutes per acre when seed is included, whereas the total field time for a six-row planter may be as low as 8 minutes per acre.

Many miscellaneous time losses depend on individual fields and the operator's habits. Picking up rocks, resting, and visiting with passersby can take much field time.

EFFECTIVE field capacity increases with the width and speed of a machine and drops with time losses. Because many time losses tend to be proportional to area, an increase in width or speed of a machine cannot be expected to result in a proportional increase in effective field capacity.

We have found that increasing the width of a planter 50 percent, from four to six rows, raises effective capacity only 35 percent. A similar increase of 50 percent in width of cultivator gives a 40-percent increase in effective capacity. This failure of a 50-percent increase in width to yield a 50-percent increase in effective capacity arises because time losses tend often to be proportional to area rather than to time.

Time losses incurred in handling materials also tend to be proportional to area because the volume of seed, fertilizer, or harvested crop to be handled per acre is not influenced by the size of the machine in use. Effective capacity can be improved by increasing hopper sizes, however.

WE GET the effective field capacity (in acres per hour) by dividing the product of the speed and width by 8.25 and multiplying that result by the field efficiency expressed as a decimal fraction.

Field efficiency is the effective field capacity divided by the theoretical field capacity and multiplied by 100 to express it as a percentage. Field efficiency is derived by taking the time required per acre at theoretical field capacity and dividing that by the actual time required to cover an acre (including time for turning, stopping, and other activities) and multiplying that result by 100.

Theoretical operating time is 1 divided by the theoretical field capacity. A theoretical field capacity of 2 acres per hour would give a theoretical operating time of 1 divided by 2, or .5 hour per acre. It represents the time required to cover an acre if the machine moved through the field at full width.

As we indicated, the average time required to cover an acre includes various time losses. Some losses, such as those involving materials handling, are proportional to area. These make up the greater portion of losses on most jobs. Losses not proportional to area tend to be proportional to total field time or to theoretical operating time. These include rest stops, lubrication, and miscellaneous items previously mentioned.

With many implements, particularly disks and harrows, it is customary to overlap slightly from one pass through the field to the next to insure complete coverage. This, in effect, reduces the operating width of the machine and increases the time actually spent moving through the field.

For example, a 12-foot disk operated with a 1-foot overlap utilizes eleven-twelfths, or 91.7 percent, of the width. Then the time actually spent in covering an acre would be increased by the difference between the time at theoretical capacity and that time divided by .917. Thus this additional time must be added to the other time losses in determining field efficiency.

As most time losses tend to be proportional to area, the field efficiency decreases as the theoretical capacity increases. This causes some confusion, because many persons think that a larger machine is inherently more efficient. The term "efficiency" is meaningless, however, unless it is defined specifically. A larger machine may reasonably be expected to have a greater effective capacity, but it will have a lower field efficiency than a smaller machine.

Typical field efficiencies for various field operations are: Tillage operations, 75 to 90 percent; drill planting of row crop or grain, 70 to 85 percent; check-row planting, 50 to 65 percent; combining, chopping, and picking, 60 to 75 percent; mowing and raking, 70 to 80 percent; baling, 60 to 75 percent; spraying, 50 to 70 percent.

THE FIELD efficiency of a series of machines working together is determined by multiplying 100 by the product of the field efficiencies of the individual machines involved. The result is then divided by 100 raised to a power equivalent to the number of machines.

An example will clarify this relationship. A field chopper, wagon, and blower have field efficiencies of 85, 95, and 90 percent, respectively. When these are used in series, the field efficiency of the harvesting and placing in storage process is $100 \times 85 \times 95 \times 90/100^3$, or 72.7 percent.

This accounts for the low field efficiencies that frequently are found to exist in complex harvest-transportation-storage systems.

Harvesting activities usually involve a series of machines and operations.

The problem of handling materials boils down to this—the effective capacity of the harvesting machine is limited to the rate at which the product can be hauled away.

IT IS a simple matter to estimate how machines will work together. Suppose a farmer plans to bale hay and store it in his barn. He has a crew of four men: One operates the baler; one loads bales behind the baler; one is at the barn; and one hauls bales to the barn. A bale elevator with a capacity of 15 tons an hour is used at the barn. The farmer has two wagons with a capacity of 2.5 tons each.

The baler is driven at about 3 miles an hour, will take a double windrow, and has a field efficiency of about 75 percent. The estimated yield of the hay is 1 ton an acre. The hayfield is a mile from the barn. The tractor and wagon can be driven at 5 miles an hour over this distance.

The estimates of time losses, in minutes, for hauling the hay are: Changing wagons at the baler, 3; crossing the field to the road, 5; positioning the wagon at elevator and preparing to unload, 5; preparing to return to the field, 1. These total 14 minutes.

Will these machines work together without unnecessary delays? First consider the baler, which has an effective field capacity of 3.8 acres an hour. It thus requires 39 minutes to load one wagon. If the components in the series are balanced, it should take 39 minutes to haul the wagon away, unload it, and return. The time during the unloading cycle in minutes is: Travel in the field, 5; travel on the road, 12; positioning, 5; unloading, 10; rehitching, 1; travel on the road, 12; travel in the field, 5. The total is 50 minutes.

Thus, unloading the wagons takes longer than loading them. In some way the two parts of the harvesting cycle will adjust to each other.

If the baler operator just waits until the empty wagon returns, two men will be idle 11 minutes of every 50. The wagons might be overloaded, but it would take a 40-percent overload and breakdowns could result in serious delays. Another solution would be to drop bales on the ground when a wagon was unavailable. This would keep the baler going, but it would make poor use of the loader's time and more labor would be required later on.

Adding a third wagon would keep the baler going for half a day without delays for wagons and would increase the effective capacity of the baler from the limit of 3 acres an hour imposed by hauling capacity to 3.8 acres an hour, which is the real effective capacity of the baler.

The farm machinery systems should fit together as components of a single production unit. In the complex system of machines on a modern farm, the performance of the best possible machine can be hindered if the system is poor.

The work that field machines do in a year can be considered in terms of the crop acreage that can be handled by a given machine or in terms of the size of machine required for a given crop acreage.

We mentioned the effective capacity of a machine in terms of acres per hour. What does this mean in terms of acres per year?

Two factors, aside from effective capacity of the machine, should be taken into account. One involves the timeliness of the operation to be performed. The other is the hazard of weather to performance of the operation.

Corn generally is planted in May in the Corn Belt. Earlier planting results in poor stands because the soil is cold and germination is poor. Later planting means that the growing season is too short for the crop to develop to full maturity. Corn therefore should be planted sometime in a period of about 30 days. A normal workweek of 6 days reduces that period to 25 days. Bad weather and wet fields may make many of those days unsuitable for planting. A reasonable estimate of the time available for field operations in May is 60 percent. So, in theory at

least, a farmer has 15 days in which he can plant corn. A six-row planter operating with a 12-acre-per-hour theoretical field capacity, 70-percent field efficiency, and an 8-hour day, could plant 1 thousand acres in a season.

The tractor used with the planter, though, may be needed also in preparing the seedbed. If we assume that the seedbed must be disked and harrowed with this tractor, the annual capacity of the planter is further reduced. If 24 minutes are required for disking and harrowing an acre and 7 minutes for planting, the area that the six-row planter can cover in one season is reduced to 232 acres.

Thus in estimating the annual capacity of a machine, one must consider not only its characteristics but the requirements of related activities. Activities that affect the net annual capacity of a machine on one crop may be influenced by tractor and labor requirements on a different crop.

An example is the competition for labor and power between first cultivation of the corn crop and harvest of the first cutting of the hay crop. In judging the annual capacity of a cultivator, one must modify the time available by the timeliness requirements of weed control, the weather hazard in June, and the power and labor requirements for hay harvest.

Thus most farm machines are used only a few days in a year. Tractors, which are used in most field operations, have a great deal more annual use than other machines.

Field machines in the United States have an average annual use of only 50 to 200 acres.

WE CAN estimate inputs of labor and energy in crop production from information on effective field capacities and power requirements of machines and tractor performance data. Power requirements and tractor performances vary with field conditions, as field capacities do. Estimates of power requirements are available for many operations.

Estimates of labor for crop production can come directly from effective field capacities of machines or machine series and the size of crew involved in the operation.

Labor requirements for corn production expressed in minutes per acre, using a 50-belt-horsepower tractor, six-row planter and cultivator, and other machines and implements matched to the tractor's capacity are: Spreading fertilizer, 14; plowing, 38; disking, 17; harrowing, 7; planting, 9; rotary hoeing, 6; first cultivation, 10; second cultivation, 7; and field-shelling with a combine, 30. That makes a total labor input (allowing for harrowing twice) of about 2.5 man-hours per acre.

SIMILAR figures for a 41-belt-horsepower tractor, four-row planter and cultivator, and other equipment matched to the tractor total about 3 man-hours per acre. For a 33-belt-horsepower tractor with two-row equipment, the estimated labor requirement is 4 man-hours per acre. These estimates assume level fields and straight rows. Contour operations on rolling or terraced land are estimated to increase the labor requirements 10 to 12 percent.

Our figures include only time spent in the field. Time for hauling crops and placing them in storage should be added.

Time spent servicing machines in preparation for field operations, buying repair parts, and obtaining seed and fertilizer are all labor items to be charged to crop production. These items are generally estimated as equal to about 20 percent of the actual field time.

Power requirements vary greatly with soil and other operating conditions. Without detailed knowledge of specific conditions, estimates of fuel consumption therefore are somewhat uncertain.

A useful concept in making such estimates is that of "constant energy" per acre for a given job, regardless of the size of machine used.

If we compare a two-bottom and a four-bottom plow operating in the same field at the same depth and speed, for example, the four-bottom plow will require twice the power of the two-bottom plow. Neglecting time losses, the four-bottom plow will cover an acre in half the time required by the two-bottom plow. Thus energy expended, which may be measured in horsepower-hours per acre, will be the same for these plows.

Typical plowing requires about 12 horsepower-hours per acre, disking 5, harrowing 1, rotary hoeing 1, cultivating 2, and cornpicking 6.

These energy levels are the input into the machine. They do not represent the energy output of the tractor engine, which is needed in estimating per acre fuel requirements. Conversion of this energy input into tractor engine output can be accomplished by application of a tractive and transmission efficiency. This efficiency expresses the useful power developed at the drawbar or power takeoff (PTO) shaft of a tractor as a percentage of power developed at the flywheel of the engine.

The tractive and transmission efficiency of a tractor traveling across a field pulling nothing is 0 percent. For light drawbar loads on loose ground, tractive and transmission efficiencies range from 30 to 40 percent. Heavy tillage jobs, such as plowing sod with the tractor operating on firm ground, have 60 percent tractive and transmission efficiencies. Jobs involving PTO-driven machines pulled on firm ground range up to 80 percent tractive and transmission efficiency.

Thus, if the energy input into plowing is 12 horsepower-hours per acre and the tractive and transmission efficiency is 60 percent, the engine energy required for plowing is 20 horsepower-hours per acre. An estimate of the fuel consumption can be made by assuming a fuel use of 10 horsepower-hours per gallon; that is 2 gallons an acre.

Fuel economies of gasoline tractor engines range from 12 horsepower-hours per gallon at maximum load to 0 horsepower-hours per gallon at no load. Fuel economies may be estimated at 10 horsepower-hours per gallon at a three-quarter load, 8 at a half load, and 6 at a one-quarter load. Fuel consumption during time losses usually ranges from .1 to .2 gallon per acre.

Estimates like these yield fuel consumption values for corn production (expressed in gallons per acre) as follows: Spreading fertilizer, .9; plowing, 2; disking, 1.1; harrowing, .3; planting, .6; rotary hoeing, .4; cultivating, .7; and harvesting, 1.

For a system of culture that involves all of these operations and includes harrowing and cultivating two times each, the total fuel consumption is 8 gallons an acre.

This estimate was based on the 50-horsepower tractor and six-row equipment. As wheel slippage, friction, and other energy losses make the constant energy concept not strictly correct, the fuel consumption per acre may be expected to be 8.25 gallons per acre for the four-row machines and 8.75 for the two-row machines. Fuel consumption may be expected to range from 25 percent below to 50 percent above these figures as individual operating conditions vary.

Similar estimates for other crops can be made from available data by comparing the sequence of operations with those used in corn production.

The selection of a machine of a particular size depends partly on the basic capacity and fuel consumption relationships we have discussed. The costs of owning the machine and the returns to be expected also must be considered.

Farmers should select machines that will give the greatest return on their investment compared with other alternatives for use of their capital. This implies knowledge of the return over costs that may be expected from any given size of machine.

FOR ANY CROP, a relationship exists between profit, gross revenue, and cost. This may be expressed as: Profit from the crop is equal to the gross

return minus the production costs. Both the gross return and the production costs depend in part on the size of the machine used on a given acreage of crop.

The dependence of gross return on size of machine results from the timeliness factor present in any field operation. For instance, planting operations have an optimum performance time, as we said. The best time is the time that gives the highest yield. As any practical machine has only a finite width, however, a finite interval of time is required for performance. It is necessary to start ahead of the best time and finish after it, to achieve the highest average yield, and hence the highest total quantity of crop. Furthermore, with a smaller machine, the time between the starting and finishing time is greater so that losses are larger with a small machine.

Production costs depend on machine size through the interplay of fixed and variable costs. A machine too "small" for the area to be used requires a high expenditure for labor. A machine too "large" for the area incurs fixed costs in excess of the value of the labor saved. For a given area there is a machine size which will result in a minimum combination of fixed and variable costs.

This minimum cost size is not necessarily the proper machine to select, however. The farmer wants the machine which will give the greatest return over costs in comparison with alternative investments.

As an example, we may interpret this in relation to planting corn. The return above the cost of planting depends on the total production multiplied by the selling price and the cost of planting. The revenue from corn planted on a given acreage is influenced by the size of the planter used. Suppose a farmer plants 200 acres of corn with a two-row planter. Weather delays and a low planting capacity would, of course, mean that some corn would be planted too early and some too late in relation to the optimum date. The result would be lower yield and lower gross return.

Field tests have shown that the yield of corn may be depressed as much as one-half bushel per acre for each day that planting is delayed beyond the optimum date.

A small planter has low ownership costs and high labor and other operating costs. A large planter gives the reverse situation. For a given acreage and cost structure, there is therefore a minimum-cost size of machine.

But a planter larger than this minimum-cost size will result in increased revenue. The trick is to select a planter that will give the greatest difference between planting costs and revenue. This planter is distinctly larger than the one at minimum cost.

We put together the best information we could find, and formulated some answers.

We found that the planter and cultivator size that will result in the greatest return over machine and labor costs is four-row for 90 acres of corn and six-row for 130 acres of corn.

One more important point is that the return over planting costs drops off much more rapidly for a planter that is too small by two rows than it does for a planter that is too large by two rows. It is better therefore to have machines slightly oversized than slightly undersized. This principle applies also to machines for any operation in which timeliness is a factor.

A machine should get the job done on time in a normal year with a margin to spare for the year in which weather is especially unfavorable. That holds for all field operations.

In practice, of course, row-crop planters cannot be chosen independently of cultivators or harvesting machines. The number of rows for a cultivator must divide into the number of rows on the planter an integral number of times. This is true also for harvesting machines in relation to planters. Analyses indicate that cultivators should be as large as is physically practical for the planter size selected.

Use of this analysis can be hampered severely by lack of the factual knowledge needed to put numbers into the equations. Timeliness functions, for instance, are difficult to come by. Weather, variations in soil conditions and different tillage practices complicate the problem.

CULTURAL practices must be selected with an appreciation of machine capacities and annual use requirements. It makes little sense to select a cultural practice that results in a low labor requirement per acre for crop production if that practice requires an unusually poor distribution of labor. This situation can be illustrated by comparing alternative tillage practices.

Compare the conventional methods of seedbed preparation for corn with a wheel-track planting method. With four-row equipment, the conventional method, including plowing, once-over disking and harrowing, and planting, requires 54 minutes an acre. A wheel-track method that involves only plowing and planting requires 40 minutes an acre.

But wheel-track planting means that plowing must be done only a few days before planting to prevent excessive competition from weeds. Thus the plowing for wheel-track must be done in May. An analysis of May requirements for labor and machines shows that with conventional practice only 24 minutes per acre are needed in May because plowing had been done earlier. With the wheel-track, however, the full 40 minutes per acre is needed in May. A peak requirement of labor and machine time reduces the area that can be handled with a given size of equipment or increases the size of equipment required to handle a given tract of land.

Where 400 acres of corn could be planted with four-row equipment under conventional practice, this size of equipment could handle only 240 acres under the wheel-track planting technique.

To plant the 400 acres with the

wheel-track method would require an
additional 21 drawbar horsepower and
machine capacity to match. Fixed
costs per acre and the labor peak
would be higher for the wheel-track
method. Much of the labor saved by
wheel-track planting is saved at a time
when labor requirements for other activities are not pressing. The economic
saving therefore may be more imagi-
nary than real.

Thus all farm practices should be
selected in reference to the overall farm
enterprise, the distribution of labor,
and the distribution of demands on
machine capacity. Alternative practices cannot be evaluated and selected
intelligently in a framework that takes
into account only a few of the variables.

The operation of a modern farm is as
complex and varied as the operation
of any other type of production enterprise. An opportunity exists to bring
quantitative planning to bear on all
phases of farm management.

SCANT attention has been given to
systematic analysis of farm machinery
management on the basis of the phys-
ical-economic factors involved. We
have tried here to identify some of the
factors and to discuss their implications. Information on the quantitative
values of the factors and their interre-
lationship is meager. Their evaluation
and the development of techniques for
their application to effective management of field operations is a necessity
for the economic institution that agriculture has become.

Further developments in field machines are in the offing. For instance,
in 1959, experiments were conducted
in cultivating row crops with a tractor
which was steered automatically. This
may not only relieve the operator's
tension but enable more precise operation and permit higher speeds. Theoretical field capacities of machines will
be improved as time goes on. Management of machines on the farm will become increasingly important in maintaining a profitable margin between
gross returns and production costs.

# Obsolescence of Buildings

Wallace Ashby and M. M. Lindsey

SOME FARM buildings wear out. Others
lose usefulness because the farmer cannot adapt them to new requirements.
Efficient buildings are long-lived and
easy to keep up to date.

A building is functionally obsolescent
(or perhaps completely obsolete) if it
is not suitable for the service needed
although it is structurally sound.

Once upon a time, when farm practices changed slowly, layouts of farmsteads and buildings were well adjusted
to the farmer's needs.

During the 19th century, for example, the Pennsylvania bank barn,
which had entrances on two levels, ful-
filled well the needs of the time and the
place—the colder hilly regions of the
Northern States.

In the prairie country farther west,
the two-story horse barn and the one-
story general barn, with a haystack in
the center and sheds for livestock on
two or three sides, were in general use
many years.

During such periods of stability in
agriculture, farmers and builders took
pride in barns that would serve the
family for generations.

The great strides in the technology
of agriculture in 1940–1950 taxed
the adequacy of farm service buildings to the limit but did not necessarily
render them obsolete. Since then, however, has come a phenomenal advance
in the livestock enterprise. Many farm
buildings became too small or unsuited
to mechanized operation practically
overnight.

Examples are a cattle barn whose

doors are too small, its posts too close together, or its headroom too low to use a tractor or a truck inside; a dairy barn that cannot meet health requirements; any building where work cannot be done efficiently; and the buildings on a small farm whose fields have been added to another farm.

Obsolescence is more serious with buildings than with tractors or field machinery partly because the building is attached to the land and cannot be traded in on a new model. A building is part of a farmstead and of a system for handling animals, feed, wastes, and products for market. Changes in buildings are harder to plan and carry out than changes in field equipment, and they are put off until the need for improvement becomes urgent.

Obsolescence is a particularly serious handicap for producers of milk and eggs, because they must do much work in the buildings.

OUR INFORMATION on the age and structural condition of farm buildings comes from a few surveys. One was made in 1937—shortly after the depression—by men in the Department of Agriculture, the University of Wisconsin, the University of Georgia, and Kansas State University, and was reported in Miscellaneous Publication 311 of the Department of Agriculture.

It covered 400 farms in typical small sections of Wisconsin, Kansas, and Georgia. The average age of barns was 29 years. A few barns in each State were more than 50 years old. One-third of the barns were in good condition, one-fourth in poor condition, and the remainder in fair condition.

The average age of the other permanent service buildings was 20 to 25 years. Their condition was like that of the barns.

Deane G. Carter reported the results of a survey of farm buildings made in 1944–1945 by the Department of Agricultural Engineering of the University of Illinois. The survey covered 320 farms in 11 counties in Illinois. The average age of the general barns was 40 years; of beef cattle barns, 28 years; and of dairy barns, 35 years.

The engineers who made the survey estimated that the general barns had depreciated 51 percent; the beef cattle barns, 35 percent; and the dairy barns, 39 percent—an average of about 1.25 percent a year. Twenty-seven percent of the general barns, 29 percent of the beef cattle barns, and 28 percent of the dairy barns were considered too poor to be worth renewal.

The average age of other buildings in Illinois was 19 years for silos to 27 years for corncrib and granary combinations. No estimates were made of the functional values of these barns or other buildings.

Bulletin 570 of the University of Illinois Agricultural Experiment Station reported a study of 350 dairy farms made in 1948–1949.

It said: "Most of the buildings on the farms were 40 to 70 years old. They had been built when the farms produced mostly grain and meat animals. With growing populations in the nearby cities of Chicago and St. Louis, changes in food habits, and improved transportation, it was natural that many farmers should add dairying to their enterprises or shift to it exclusively. But few of the buildings were altered to any significant extent. Newer production methods, the introduction of mechanical power, shortage of labor, and its high cost all serve to emphasize the inadequacies of many of these buildings."

Both the functional characteristics and the structural condition of dairy barns and milkhouses were rated, though on different numerical scales.

By rearranging the scales to allow comparison of structural condition and functional usefulness, we find that dairy buildings for the production of Grade A milk were rated 81 out of a possible 100 points on production, health and safety of cows; 71 points on chore labor efficiency and safety of operator; and 74 points on quality of milk. Buildings for production of Grades B and C milk were rated a

little lower in all functional categories.
All buildings were rated "good,"
"fair," or "poor" on structural condition of foundations, floors, walls, and roof. If a value of 2 were assigned to a rating of "good," 1 to "fair," and 0 to "poor," the group rating on structural condition would be 84 out of a possible 100 points.

The study pointed out considerable discrepancies between the structural and functional values of dairy buildings, but a similar study in 1960 would find much greater differences. Loose housing as a complete system was almost unknown in Illinois in 1949. A study of milking operations in 1950–1951 did not find any set of dairy buildings that was considered a satisfactory loose housing system.

Most of the barns used milking machines, but the rate of milking averaged only about 15 cows per man-hour. Few workers exceeded 20 cows per hour. Soon after 1950, the loose housing system, with elevated milking room, came into use in the Midwest.

While the two-stall and three-stall milking rooms first used with small herds gave little increase in the number of cows milked per hour, they reduced the labor of milking and encouraged farmers to increase the size of their herds. With up to four milking machine units handled per man in the newer installations, the average rate of milking increased to 25 or more cows per man-hour.

The herringbone milking parlor—an elevated-floor type in which the cows stand at an angle to the operator's pit with no partitions between them—was introduced in the United States from New Zealand in 1957. It has no special advantage for herds of fewer than 40 cows, but it makes milking of larger herds much faster. Preliminary studies of herringbone milking parlors showed an average rate of milking of 40 to 45 cows per man-hour. Thus the dairy barns that were considered only slightly inefficient in 1949 are much more out of date in 1960.

Probably at least 1,500 new herring-

RATINGS OF DAIRY BUILDINGS ON
350 FARMS IN ILLINOIS, 1948–1949

factors
affecting:

points out of
possible 100

Production, health and safety of cows — 81

Chore labor efficiency and safety of operator — 71

Quality of milk — 74

Structural condition — 84

bone milking parlors were built in 1959, and a much larger number of obsolete buildings went out of use.

Similar advances in design of buildings and equipment for other types of livestock and for crop storage and preparation have been developed or are in progress. They are as much needed as improvements in field equipment and very likely will pay bigger returns.

MANY DIFFERENT situations with respect to building obsolescence are found on farms. We may assume that most of them fall into the somewhat typical classifications we outline here.

*The traditional general farm with little or no hired labor.* Let us assume that this farmer will go along about as usual, making gradual changes to adapt his operations to new market demands but with no change in acreage and no important shift in management. Probably he would gain little from major changes in buildings, but electric lights, running water in the buildings, better location of fences and gates, and paving of lots would considerably lighten his chores. Quantity and quality of production might be improved through the use of insulation, ventilation, refrigeration, or heating, depending on the climate and the job to be done.

*The average-sized family farm that is shifting from general livestock to specialized production but is not increasing in acreage.* Management changes should be considered carefully to make the best use of present buildings, since a building that is an efficient working tool under one type of operation may become obsolete under another.

First consider the various ways of increasing production without major changes in the buildings.

If it is a dairy farm, for example, perhaps space for additional milking cows can be found in the present barn by moving dry cows and young stock to other buildings. Or perhaps returns can be increased by using higher yielding cows and better feed, such as mow-cured hay. If the herd is to be increased to more than about 25 cows, a shift to the loose housing system should be considered.

If the shift is to beef cattle, open-front sheds will furnish cheap additional shelter, and yard space can be made more usable by grading for drainage and by paving. Self-feeding from a bunker silo or some type of automatic feeding for both silage and grain may be considered to save labor.

*The expanding farm, which has been increased in size and production by adding acreage from adjoining farms and also by more intensive farming methods.*

On such a farm, the buildings used before land was added probably are inadequate in size and capacity, and the farmstead may be poorly located and poorly planned as an operating center for the larger unit.

From the long view, it may be desirable to abandon gradually the old farmstead and move to a better location where roads, buildings, and lots can be arranged more efficiently and attractively. This plan, of course, has the disadvantage of splitting operations until the move can be completed. It has the advantage that new structures and the layout of the farmstead as a whole can be designed to meet the requirements of the new farm.

Small buildings can be moved from the old site to the new and located where they will serve the best purpose. Buildings that cannot be moved or used to advantage at the old location can be torn down and the materials used at the new.

Careful consideration should be given to new methods of operation—for example, loose housing of dairy cows and herringbone milking parlors; or multiple farrowing and fattening pigs on concrete; or large slatted- or wire-floor laying houses with mechanical cleaning.

A consulting agricultural engineer or an extension agricultural engineer who specializes in such work could give valuable help in layout of the farmstead, planning the buildings, and selecting equipment.

*The specialized farm that is being forced to change its operations by acreage controls, urban encroachment, or some other cause, or the farm where the buildings have been destroyed by fire or storm.*

Examples are the large farmer in the Mississippi Delta, whose cotton acreage has been cut in half; the dairy farmer near a large city, who has been forced to move to a new location but is selling out at a good price; and the victim of loss covered by insurance.

This owner can plan his farmstead from a fresh start.

*The part-time or shrinking farm.* An increasing number of United States farms produce little for the market and depend largely on off-farm income. Unused buildings may be a burden because of taxes and upkeep.

Several possible uses for such buildings are suggested: Rent as storages or move to new sites; remodel as workshops for home industries; remodel as dwellings for retired persons, urban workers, or summer guests; or wreck and salvage materials for other uses.

AN ENTIRE FARMSTEAD can become obsolete if it is located in the wrong place, or if there is no room for additional buildings or yards.

One safeguard against being caught unawares by farmstead obsolescence is a farmstead map drawn to scale and showing the location of present buildings and lots, the farm drive, lanes leading to fields and pastures, and proposed locations for future buildings, and other improvements.

Before deciding to remodel any building, the farmer should study each important structure of the farmstead to see which one fits best into the new program from the standpoint of location, size, strength, and so on.

IF A BUILDING that can be easily remodeled or enlarged is available in the right place, one should examine the foundation, frame, walls, roof, doors and windows for needed repairs. If the building meets the tests for both suitability and soundness, remodeling is probably worth while, but if it is in bad condition, the cost may be more than for a new building.

Remodeling plans should be worked out carefully on paper before any construction work is started. Ideas can be obtained from plans for new buildings available from a county agent, teacher of vocational agriculture, or building equipment dealer and in bulletins and farm magazines. Plans should be considered for handling the job in an entirely new way, such as loose housing for dairy cattle or raising pigs on concrete.

If the building is a dairy barn or milkhouse to be used for producing Grade A milk, the plans should be approved in writing by the authority having jurisdiction.

Finally, estimates should be compared on the cost of remodeling and the cost of a new building of equal or greater usefulness.

BUILDINGS for the future should be designed with flexibility to meet changing requirements.

Much of the difficulty in mechanizing present buildings is due to lack of space to operate tractors and trucks inside the building or to install conveying equipment.

These faults can be overcome by headrooms of 10 feet or more, wider spacing of supports, or by clear-span construction if the width of the building does not exceed 30 feet or so.

Buildings are remodeled more easily if their weight is carried on columns and the walls are curtain walls that do not carry load. Then walls or doorways and windows can be changed easily. There would be an additional advantage in panel construction for all walls and partitions, so that if changes were to be made, the walls could be unbolted, say, in 4- or 8-foot sections and shifted around to new positions.

The idea of movable walls can be carried further—as is done in some prefabricated buildings, which are bolted together at the site. If the terms of sale specify that the building does not become part of the real estate, it can be taken apart, loaded on a truck, or moved to another farm.

There is an advantage also in strong roof construction, so that if a building were to be used as a cage laying house, for example, the cages could be hung from the roof and the floor kept clear so that cleaning equipment could sweep under the cages without obstruction.

ANOTHER WAY to avoid functional obsolescence is to use short-lived, low-cost buildings for certain purposes, such as for temporary greenhouses. The cost per year of a temporary building while in use may be as much or more than for a longer lived building, and it may give less good service. Its advantage is that when it is no longer needed it can be discarded with little loss.

Examples of plastic-covered buildings include greenhouses, livestock shades, lambing sheds, pig shelters, and poultry houses. In such a building, large sheets of plastic film 4 to 8 mils thick are supported by a light framework. Heavy film may be fastened directly to the frame of the building; if thin material is used, it may be supported on each side by poultry netting to keep it from flapping in the wind. Black or other opaque film lasts longer than most transparent kinds, since sunlight damages them.

The possibility of supporting a plastic envelope over an area by burying the edges of a large plastic sheet in the ground and blowing it up like a balloon has been demonstrated. This sort of tentlike canopy or temporary building requires continual operation of a blower to keep it inflated and a special type of air-lock door to keep the air from escaping too fast. The air pressure need be only a few ounces per square inch.

A number of other comparatively new materials and types of construction give promise of satisfactory use for low-cost, medium-life farm buildings. These should be developed by further research before they are recommended for general use by farmers.

The use of farm-produced materials should not be forgotten. Baled straw and hay make satisfactory winter walls for livestock sheds if animals are kept away from them by fencing. Loose straw or hay, laid over used fencing or brush on a framework of poles, and held in place by chicken wire, makes a good roof for a livestock shade or a temporary winter shelter.

These and similar materials, such as shredded cornstalks, may serve as insulation for temporary use—for example, in false ceilings over farrowing pens, straw lofts of poultry houses, and the like.

SMALL STORAGE structures, such as bulk storage bins of a capacity of 5 to 10 tons, are used on many farms. They can be set outdoors and equipped with conveyors to deliver their contents to a nearby building. Since they can be moved easily from one site to another when empty, they would simplify the problem of changing the farmstead arrangement if changes should be needed later.

The silage stack covered with plastic film is another example of a substitute for a building. If it is built in a well-drained location and the silage is not to be self-fed, a concrete slab is not necessary, and the stack can be built in a new place the next time emergency storage is needed.

MANY FARMERS feel that better banking facilities for building improvements are needed. Some manufacturers of prefabricated buildings have developed time-payment plans for sale of buildings as personal property with no mortgage on the land—so that a fully erected and equipped building may be sold on about the same terms as an automobile.

More rapid depreciation of buildings for income tax purposes on account of obsolescence would help farmers accumulate funds for building replacement.

# Costs of Farm Buildings

Roy N. Van Arsdall and Wallace Ashby

BEFORE he plants a crop, a farmer can test the soil to find out how much fertilizer is needed. He can correct any miscalculation the following year. Guides for the types of service buildings and the amounts to spend for them are not so easy to get, and any miscalculation by the farmer or the previous operator in putting up a building cannot be corrected on an annual basis.

Barns and other service buildings are production tools that can be evaluated on the basis of costs versus benefits.

The costs are the direct expenses of constructing and keeping buildings in use.

The benefits are the effects that buildings have on other costs of production, such as labor and feed consumption, and on the value of products.

Possibilities for gain or loss in efficiency in the production of farm products are much greater in the second category than in the first one.

Investment is one measure of the

360 YEARBOOK OF AGRICULTURE 1960

direct cost of using farm buildings and is a measure of their importance.

The value added to farmland in the United States by buildings totaled 28.6 billion dollars on March 1, 1959, after an almost uninterrupted climb from the depression lows of the early 1930's. This amounted to nearly 25 dollars for each acre of land, or more than 6,700 dollars per farm. Replacement of these buildings would cost more than double their estimated present value, which is an average for buildings in all stages of depreciation—new to nearly useless.

Building values have been increasing, but they have lagged behind land prices. The value of farm buildings in 1959 was 22.9 percent of the total value of farm real estate. This was the second lowest ratio in a downward trend beginning about 1940, when buildings accounted for about 30 percent of the value of farm real estate.

The decline in the value of buildings relative to the value of land is likely to continue as long as the demand for land for farm enlargement continues to be strong.

Farm buildings have limited value to the established farmer in search of additional land with which to enlarge his operation. The farm buildings on land added to existing holdings through purchase or rental often are allowed to go into disrepair or are removed from the property to reduce property taxes and to free the land on which they stand for more productive uses.

Even when a farmer needs additional buildings, he often finds that those existing on a farm that he can acquire are outdated or ill suited to his purposes. Cost of extensive remodeling or removal of the buildings may actually detract from the value of the farm to the extent that the buildings have a negative value.

Building values relative to the total value of farm real estate are greatest in the Northeast, where they commonly account for one-half to two-thirds of the value of real estate. The average building value per farm was just above

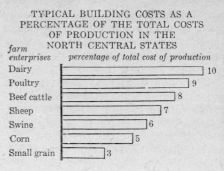

TYPICAL BUILDING COSTS AS A PERCENTAGE OF THE TOTAL COSTS OF PRODUCTION IN THE NORTH CENTRAL STATES

13 thousand dollars in 1959, or 93 dollars an acre.

Building values in the Appalachian and Southeastern States are about one-third of real estate values and generally amount to 3 thousand to 5 thousand dollars per farm and less than 50 dollars an acre. They are about one-fourth of the total elsewhere east of the Plains States. They seldom exceed 15 percent in the western half of the country.

The per acre value of buildings is lowest in the Western States because of large farms and ranches and low building requirements. The value of buildings per farm there ranks higher than in most Southern States—5 thousand to 7 thousand dollars, compared with 3 thousand to 5 thousand dollars—and is nearly equal to building values in the more intensive farming areas of the Midwest. Building values are generally highest where livestock is a major enterprise and where livestock and machinery need shelter.

In the minds of most operators, the farm dwelling is the most important single building on the farm. A dairy barn may add most to direct income, but the dwelling represents the reasons for working, for producing income. A measure of the value of farm dwellings thus indicates both the capital used in agricultural production and the monetary income of farmers.

Dwellings accounted for about half of the value of all buildings on farms in 1959, a slight drop from the 55 percent recorded in 1930. Between 1930 and

1959, however, the average value of farm dwellings tripled, going from 1,126 to 3,400 dollars per farm. Replacement values would be more than twice that amount.

The greater part of the increase came from areas of low dwelling values, thus reflecting a trend toward equalization of living facilities over the country.

The relative importance of the value of dwellings to the value of all buildings varies little among farming regions. The slightly higher ratio in the South reflects a general lack of service buildings. The use of many farm dwellings as residences by nonfarmers keeps the ratio high in some other areas, particularly the Northeast and the Far West.

Building values are higher on commercial farms than is indicated by area averages, which are depressed by subsistence units, part-time operations, and tracts held primarily for residential purposes.

Values of all buildings on commercial family-operated dairy farms in the Northeast and North Central States ranged from 9 thousand to 16 thousand dollars per farm in 1958. Building values on commercial farms in the Corn Belt ranged from 6.5 thousand dollars on hog-beef-cow units to about 15 thousand dollars on farms where hogs and beef are fattened.

Commercial family-operated cotton, peanut, and tobacco farms in the South generally had buildings valued at 5 thousand to 7.5 thousand dollars in 1958. Exceptions included large-scale cotton farms in the Mississippi Delta, whose average building values exceeded 25 thousand dollars and the small-scale cotton farms, whose total building values averaged only about 1.5 thousand dollars per farm.

Building values on most types of commercial farms in the western half of the country averaged 7.5 thousand to 10 thousand dollars in 1958. Building values maintain about the same relationship to land values on commercial family-operated farms as they do on all farms in an area, and range from two-thirds of the total value of the real estate on northeastern dairy farms to about one-tenth of the total on wheat farms in the West.

Dwelling values among the different types of commercial farms are less variable than the values of service buildings. Three-fourths of the major types of farms in the United States had dwellings valued between 4 thousand and 8 thousand dollars. Service buildings covered a range from less than 5 thousand to more than 17 thousand dollars per farm. On these commercial farms, the dwelling usually accounts for a lower proportion of the total value of buildings than on all farms in an area.

THE INITIAL cost of constructing farm buildings depends largely on type of construction, materials, method of erection, structural extras within the building, and labor for construction.

The proportion of cash to the total cost of any building varies from a nominal percentage for simple buildings constructed of lumber from farm-grown timber and erected by unpaid farm labor to the full cost of the building when erected by a contractor.

Cost per square foot or per animal is usually less for large than for small buildings. Costs in the North and Northeast are usually higher than in the West and usually are lower in the South than elsewhere.

Because of these variables, the unit costs mentioned are intended only as guides for making preliminary estimates. Accurate costs should be based on estimates from local builders or suppliers of materials and equipment.

THE USUAL SET of buildings and structural equipment for a commercial family-operated dairy with loose housing facilities cost 250 to 300 dollars per cow in the late 1950's. This included a shelter building, an elevated-stall milking room, paved lots, and feed storage.

The cost of a stanchion barn was usually 400 to 600 dollars per cow.

More elaborate structures sometimes exceeded 1 thousand dollars per cow. Milking machines, milk coolers, and other equipment are added costs.

Facilities to care for beef cattle fattened in drylot in the Midwest cost 50 to 60 dollars per head. Requirements for a herd of beef cows cost about the same to 50 percent higher on a per cow basis if the calves were fattened on the farm. Feedlots for range animals receiving only partial shelter could be built for much less.

Usual pasture systems of hog production required buildings costing about 115 dollars per litter. Confinement systems with central farrowing houses and growing and finishing units pushed new cost of buildings to about 150 dollars per litter. This is on the basis of two litters a year with pasture systems and four litters a year with confinement systems.

Litter houses for laying hens of the type common in the Midwest and Northeast cost 4 to 7 dollars per bird housed, including equipment. Use of mechanical cleaning and ventilating equipment has permitted reduction of floor space and a somewhat lower cost per hen. Prefabricated buildings complete with equipment can be purchased for comparable prices. Costs in the South were about half those in the North. Housing, including equipment, for caged layers cost as much or more than in litter houses if the hens were in single cages one tier high. Use of double cages or two tiers of cages lowered the cost per bird below that in litter houses. Good housing for broilers ranged from about .75 to 1.25 dollars per bird capacity in the South and 1.25 to 2.50 dollars in the North.

Simple shelters without insulation or other structural extras may serve as livestock shelter, hay or straw storage, machinery storage, and many other useful purposes. Such buildings commonly cost about 1.10 dollars per square foot of floor space.

Conventional slatted wood cribs common to Corn Belt farms cost 75 cents to 1 dollar a bushel of storage space for ear corn. Bins for storing shelled corn or small grains cost 30 to 50 cents a bushel of storage space. Concrete bins were the least expensive, particularly for storage of large amounts of grain. Metal bins ranked a close second.

Few two-story barns with lofts for storing hay are built now. Most new structures provide for hay storage at ground level at a cost up to 1.25 dollars per square foot of floor space or as much as 20 dollars for storage space for 1 ton of hay.

Storage space for a ton of silage cost 11 to 15 dollars in ordinary upright silos that hold 150 to 300 tons of silage. The development of silos of larger diameter has reduced construction costs below 10 dollars per ton of storage space. Horizontal silos with paved floors and permanent sidewalls commonly cost 6 to 10 dollars per ton of capacity.

WHEN A BUILDING is erected, a rather large capital investment or commitment is made at one time. Over the years of use, certain expenses must be met periodically to keep the building in use. Certain other anticipated costs must be covered to provide for its eventual replacement.

In the language of the accountant and the income-tax man, these costs include annual charges for depreciation, interest on the investment, maintenance and repairs, taxes, and insurance.

Investment in a building, though made as a lump sum, cannot be charged against production during any one year, but must be prorated over the useful life of the building.

Depreciation is a measure of the decline in value of the building and should be charged against each year's production. The percentage of depreciation per year is based on wear and tear, decay, and obsolescence.

The useful life of a building in the early days was practically synonymous with its wear-out period. Physical depreciation of any building could (and still can) be estimated rather closely; obsolescence mostly was a gradual occurrence that resulted in a small decrease in usefulness each year because of the normal growth of technology associated with the enterprise of which the building was a part. These two kinds of depreciation usually comprised a rather small percentage each year of the original value of a building.

Technological advances have been so rapid, however, that obsolescence often occurs long before the structure is worn out. Thus a farmer may justifiably place a useful life of 15 years or less on a building that he expects to last 30 years. The wear-out period was an acceptable definition of the useful life of a building only when buildings functioned chiefly to exclude the elements and to protect the contents.

Once in a while something occurs to make a building obsolete soon.

That happened to many dairymen who built milkhouses designed for handling milk in 8- or 10-gallon cans and expected the houses to be serviceable for 30 or 40 years. Developments in bulk handling of milk and the usual compulsory shift to bulk-tank storage on farms required extensive remodeling or replacement of many relatively new milkhouses.

Rapid development of laborsaving equipment, which made it possible for a dairyman to handle many more cows, often left supposedly modern dairy barns obsolete because of inadequate size.

Penalties suffered by producers who lacked funds to make changes or whose buildings could not be readily adapted to such advances as automation of materials handling or new knowledge of environmental control for livestock have been severe in terms of labor inefficiencies, hard work, low levels of feed conversion, and so on.

Many of us feel strongly that there is need for a careful appraisal of the rates of depreciation of farm buildings, including a proper allowance for obsolescence caused by our rapidly advancing technology.

THE INTERNAL REVENUE SERVICE has suggested an average life of 50 years for most farm buildings, or an average annual depreciation of 2 percent. Deviations from this rate are acceptable for tax purposes, however. The annual depreciation on a service building is deductible from income as a business expense. Permanent-type buildings are commonly depreciated in 20 to 40 years.

Business accounting procedures provide methods to account for using up the capital invested in the building for tax purposes. Several methods of depreciation can be used for these purposes. The method may result in regular or irregular rates, and the rates may assume any of several patterns.

The accounting technique used for computing annual depreciation may have a significant effect on the farmer's income tax. The total amount of depreciation cannot exceed the cost of a building, but the amount taken each year can be adjusted to fit the financial program of the individual farm business within the limits of acceptable accounting procedures.

The chief methods available for farmers to compute depreciation are the straight-line method, the declining-balance method, and the sum-of-digits method.

The straight-line method is the simplest. The cost of a building, less its estimated salvage value, is divided into equal installments over the life of the building.

For example: A dairyman builds a barn costing 12 thousand dollars. He estimates its useful life at 30 years. He puts the salvage value at zero, as it commonly costs as much to salvage materials from old buildings as they are worth. His annual depreciation allowance for tax purposes is 12 thousand dollars, divided by 30, or 400 dollars.

The declining-balance method allows this dairyman to deduct a higher proportion of the total cost of his barn during the early years of use. Under the 1954 Internal Revenue Code, the rate for the declining-balance method may begin at twice the straight-line rate. The dairyman with the 12 thousand dollar barn would therefore be permitted to take a depreciation allowance of 800 dollars the first year (6.67 percent, instead of 3.33 percent, of the cost), instead of 400 dollars. Each year thereafter he would deduct 6.67 percent of the remaining cost of the barn. Depreciation for the second year would be 6.67 percent of 11,200 dollars or 747 dollars. Depreciation for the third year would be 6.67 percent of 10,453 dollars, or 697 dollars, and so on.

The declining-balance method means that the dairyman recovers about 40 percent of the cost of his barn for tax purposes in the first one-fourth of its estimated life. In the first one-half of its life, he recovers about two-thirds of the cost.

As the depreciation to be charged off is always a percentage of the undepreciated balance, the original cost (less salvage) can never be entirely charged off by this method. The code therefore provides that anyone who uses the declining-balance method may, without obtaining special permission, change over to the straight-line method at any time—so as to be able to charge off any remaining cost during the estimated life of the asset. Any other changes in method of accounting for depreciation require approval of the Internal Revenue Service.

The sum-of-digits method is computed by adding the digits for the number of years of expected life and deducting depreciation inversely in proportion to the position the current year has in the list of years of life.

The dairyman in the example we gave would add the digits 1 through 30 to get a total of 465. He would then divide the cost of the barn by the sum of the digits (12 thousand dollars divided by 465), getting 25.81 dollars as the lowest unit of depreciation that will be taken.

To calculate the depreciation for any year he multiplies the digit for that year by the base rate as follows: First year, 30 × 25.81 dollars = 774.30 dollars (30/465th of 12 thousand dollars); second year, 29 × 25.81 dollars = 748.49 dollars (29/465th of 12 thousand dollars); third year, 28 × 25.81 dollars = 722.68 dollars (28/465th of 12 thousand dollars), and so on to the thirtieth year.

These results of the sum-of-digits method are like those of the declining-balance method in that they account for about 43 percent of the cost of a depreciable asset at one-fourth life and three-fourths of the cost at half life.

The sum-of-digits method differs from the declining-balance method in that it automatically reduces the value of an asset to zero (or to its predetermined salvage value).

The choice of one of these two methods of accounting for depreciation may be particularly valuable to a farmer who prefers an immediate high deduction to the deduction of an equal amount each year.

An expectation of a relatively high income in the immediate future would justify using one of them to minimize taxable income. Uncertainties as to the future status of the farm business often suggest beginning with fast write-off methods of depreciation regardless of income expectations.

If low income is in prospect or if steady disposable income is desired, the straight-line method is more desirable.

Either method of obtaining fast depreciation may also be preferred if a building is expected to outlast the owner. At the death of an owner, his property is revalued at current market prices to obtain a new tax base for the heirs. Since the amount of depreciation deducted has no effect on the new value, the present owner may prefer to take all of the depreciation he can get during his lifetime.

The declining-balance method and the sum-of-digits method usually are more closely related to the market values of business assets than the straight-line method. Secondhand property will seldom bring the price indicated by the straight-line method, especially in the early years of use.

FARM BUILDINGS may present an opportunity for diverting income into capital gains.

A farmowner may use current income to construct barns, sheds, silos, or other buildings useful in his farming operation. He can deduct depreciation on them as an operating expense.

Maintenance and repairs, which are also deductible expenses, can be handled so as to keep the buildings in a high state of repair. This is ordinarily good business management.

If he sells the farm later—at least 6 months after he made the improvements—he can treat any net difference between sale value of the farm and its depreciated cost as a capital gain, which is taxed at only half the rate of ordinary income.

The amount to be treated as capital gains could be quite large, particularly if improvements have been extensive and the owner has used one of the methods of taking fast depreciation during the early years of use.

Farmers who plan carefully, however, limit construction to the type and number of structures that can be used to advantage in the farm business. Investments made without an economically sound basis seldom are recovered at the time of sale.

THE BUYER AND SELLER of farm real estate that includes buildings should examine the terms of the sale contract from the standpoint of their tax management.

If the farm is being bought on an installment basis, it is ordinarily advantageous for the buyer to seek a high-interest, low-cost price contract rather than the reverse.

Interest is a fully deductible expense each year, but payments on principal are not deductible. Outlays for depreciable property may of course be recovered through depreciation deductions. If the seller is financing the purchase of the farm, his interests will be in conflict with those of the buyer on this point, because any capital gains on the higher sale price will be taxed at only half the rate that will be applied to the income from interest.

The buyer should make certain that full purchase price is set on depreciable items, as opposed to land, which is not depreciable. Buildings, particularly structural equipment, fall into this category. The interests of the buyer and seller are alike on this feature on the sale contract.

LEASING, rather than selling, a farm on which there are service buildings and structural equipment of a depreciable nature may be advantageous to a farmowner if the sale would result in a considerable taxable gain.

If a farmowner leases rather than sells a farm he retains the right to claim depreciation allowances. During the early years of use, he can maximize depreciation by using the declining-balance or sum-of-digits method. These depreciation allowances may be especially high if many of the assets are short-lived or are eligible for the extra initial depreciation. Deductible expenses for the first few years may be as large as the annual rent; thus the income is left tax free. The market value of the farm in the meantime may not have decreased in proportion to the amount of depreciation allowed.

Allowable depreciation for income-tax purposes has been used as an incentive for farmers to construct buildings.

During the early 1950's, the Government price-support program began to result in burdensome surpluses of grain. To relieve the pressure on Government-owned storage facilities, farmers were permitted to write off certain grain-storage facilities constructed from 1953 to 1956 over a 60-month period, instead of using the usual normal-life concept. This provision was especially attractive to farmers who expected high incomes during the subsequent 5 years.

The actual rate of building replacement is variable, although the accounting methods normally calculate regular annual amounts of depreciation.

Buildings are allowed to run down during periods of low farm income, and new construction and major repairs are reduced or postponed until the level of income improves. Building reserves are brought to a high level during prosperous years. No other productive factor in farming can be called the residual claimant—the last factor to which funds are allocated—so truthfully as can buildings.

Depreciation of farm service buildings increased with a growth in the value of the total physical plant from 110 million dollars in 1910 to 523 million dollars in 1958. Interrupting this gradual increase was a leveling of the amount of depreciation in the 1920's and a decrease in the 1930's.

EXPENDITURES for new buildings and improvements exhibit a pattern that contrasts sharply with these gradual shifts in depreciation.

They conform rather closely to levels of farm income. Expenditures for service buildings in 1910 and for the next few years ranged from 120 million dollars to 130 million dollars. The amount tripled shortly after the First World War as a result of favorable farm income and increased availability of building materials.

Expenditures were fairly stable during the 1920's, but during the depression of the 1930's they fell to a low of 13 million dollars, less than 10 percent of the high point after the First World War.

Recovery from this level was gradual. It reached 249 million dollars during the early 1940's. The combination of high farm incomes, a built-up need for buildings, and release of building materials from wartime uses resulted in expenditures of 621 million dollars in 1946.

The annual outlay for service buildings grew to more than a billion dollars in the early 1950's. Then it subsided to about 750 million dollars in 1958. The general price level has been a factor contributing to the rise in expenditures since 1940.

Expenditures for repairs and maintenance follow the same general pattern as major capital outlays, but the year-to-year variations are less pronounced, because many repairs must be made when needed if the building or structure is to be kept in use. Also, repairs tend to increase as new construction declines.

When volume of construction falls off, the average age of buildings on farms increases rapidly. More repairs thus are necessary. Even so, farmers may postpone many items of maintenance and repairs to periods of high farm income and still stay in operation.

INTEREST on the investment in service buildings is a direct cost of owning buildings.

If a building is constructed with borrowed capital, the interest charge requires a cash settlement. Farmers who use their own funds to construct buildings also have an interest cost, as they forego the opportunity of investing their money elsewhere.

The minimum interest charge should equal the going interest rate times the value of the buildings.

Average lifetime value is usually taken as the basis for calculating an annual interest charge for service buildings. Using this criterion and a 5-percent interest rate, one finds that farm service buildings, exclusive of dwellings, cost United States farmers nearly 750 million dollars in 1959, either in cash payments or in income that could have been realized from alternative investments.

TAXES also must be added to the list of costs of owning and operating farm service buildings. Taxes require a cash payment and are relatively stable from year to year.

Taxes levied on farm real estate in the United States averaged about 90 cents per 100 dollars of full value in the 1950's. The highest rates were in the Northeastern States, where State averages often approached 2 dollars per 100 dollars of full value. Southeastern and Southern States had rates of around 50 cents. Local conditions may cause large deviations from average tax rates. An allowance of 1 to 1.5 percent of the full value of a building usually is enough to cover the taxes that will be assessed against it.

Risk of loss is the last of the direct costs.

Damage to farm dwellings and service buildings from fire, wind, hail, and floods amounted to 180 million dollars in 1958. Some farmers purchase formal insurance against such losses and can count the cost of the premiums against the buildings. Others accept part or all of the risk themselves. In either case, there is a cost of risk-bearing, and it must be added to the cost of using farm buildings.

The direct annual cost of using farm service buildings thus contains five categories of costs.

They are depreciation (usually 2 to 5 percent of the initial cost); interest on the investment (the going rate times the average lifetime value of the buildings); maintenance and repairs (1 to 3 percent of first cost); taxes (1 to 1.5 percent of full value); and insurance (about one-half of 1 percent of full value).

Added together, direct annual building costs commonly range from 7 to 12 percent of the initial cost, with 8 to 10 percent the more usual figure.

Farm service buildings are not a very large part of the production costs of any of the major farm enterprises, even though they represent substantial investments.

Even in dairy enterprises, which are one of the more intensive users of service buildings, annual building costs average only about 10 percent of production costs.

Representative proportions for other enterprises are 8 percent for beef cattle,

7 percent for sheep, 6 percent for swine, and 9 percent for poultry.

Buildings account for even less of the production costs of most crops, averaging about 5 percent for corn and only 3 percent for small grains.

The relative importance of building costs to total cost of production is greater in cold, humid regions than in areas with warm, dry climates because the need for buildings is greater.

The proportion may shift as a result of some advance in technology, such as the pelleting of hay, which would reduce substantially the requirement for storage space. Individual preference for materials and style of construction also affects the importance of building costs.

Nevertheless, buildings represent a substantial part of the investment in a farm business—sometimes even more than the value of the land.

The costs associated with them are fixed for a long period of time. These annual building costs represent the building input, and they should be consistent with the contribution the buildings make to the enterprise or farming operation.

The dollar value of the contribution of farm service buildings often is hard to determine. A farmer cannot measure the returns from an investment in buildings to the same extent that he can measure the effects of his feeds and fertilizers.

How, then, is he to know whether a contemplated building investment will be profitable?

As a rough guide for keeping the investment in buildings within bounds, a farmer can assume that he will be on reasonably safe ground if he spends about the same amount for buildings as do other farmers in similar situations.

He may do this either by getting information on the amount invested in buildings or by converting the annual cost of using buildings into an investment figure. A dairyman contemplating facilities for a 30-cow herd, for example, may find from talking with his neighbors and studying reports of research that the average investment in dairy buildings on a first-cost basis is about 500 dollars per cow or about 15 thousand dollars for a herd of 30 cows.

Cost account records show that the services of dairy buildings, as an average of many dairy farms, account for about 10 percent of all costs of dairy production.

If annual production costs are averaging 450 dollars per cow, then 45 dollars would be the representative building charge. The guide to investment is obtained by capitalizing the 45 dollars at a rate that will cover the annual charges of interest, depreciation, maintenance, repairs, taxes, and insurance. These charges total about 9 percent of the initial investment on the average dairy farm. Capitalizing 45 dollars at 9 percent results in an investment of 500 dollars per cow, the same as reported for the average farm.

If the rate for depreciation, interest, or any of the other charges differs greatly from the average, however, the rate of capitalization may be above or below 9 percent, thus changing the investment base, even though the annual costs are the same.

When a farmer applies the average investment or annual cost of other farmers as a guide, he should think ahead 5, 10, or 20 years.

Methods of handling dairy cows are changing rapidly, and if present trends continue toward larger herds on the one hand, and higher farm wages and fewer qualified farmworkers on the other, most farmers will wish to mechanize their buildings more fully. That may require a larger than average investment in buildings and equipment.

Well-planned mechanization can double the number of cows per man that can be handled and greatly reduce labor costs. As labor represents about 20 percent of the cost of producing milk, mechanization to cut labor in half would certainly justify an increase in the amount invested in buildings and building equipment.

The scarcity of good renters, managers, and farmworkers makes it more and more important that buildings provide good working conditions and minimize hard, unpleasant tasks.

The average of the decisions of other farmers provides a useful guard against overinvestment. But it places major emphasis on the maximum amount allowable for buildings and equipment—that is, the break-even point.

Any investment in excess of need is an overinvestment even if it is well below the break-even point. Some farmers place a high value on such intangibles as better appearance, uniform architecture, or just plain bigness, and thus try to justify buildings costing far more than these estimates would allow. This is not wrong, but one must remember to charge the extra investment to personal satisfaction or advertising of the farm and not to the enterprise the buildings serve.

The earning power of service buildings is the real measure of how much should be invested in them.

Housing for farm machinery provides an example of the use of this measure to determine how much should be spent for buildings.

Most farmers would like to have machine storage with enough capacity to house all their machinery. Because such satisfactions come at a price, however, a farmer with limited funds might evaluate his problem of housing machinery according to the direct effect of housing on machinery costs.

The first part of the problem is relatively easy. The chief function of machine sheds is to provide shelter from the weather. There are no important alternatives to the one-story buildings available for machinery storage. Only the question of the net value of shelter for machinery remains.

Generally, housing the more complex, high-cost machines increases the life of the machines and reduces repairs more than enough to pay for the annual cost of housing them. Storing machines of relatively low value, particularly those that are bulky and difficult to fit into storage, is seldom profitable, however.

Studies of machinery housing in the Midwest indicate that shelter tends to increase the life of machines and reduce repair costs. But the reduction in annual depreciation charges and repairs, minus the annual cost of housing, may leave little value for the housing. In one example, housing a tractor that cost 2,500 dollars resulted in a net gain of only 4.25 dollars after housing costs were deducted from the savings in its annual depreciation and repairs. The annual cost of housing a side-delivery rake worth 400 dollars was 16.15 dollars more than the reduction in depreciation and repairs gained by keeping the rake under shelter.

These dollar benefits or losses from housing of machinery must be adjusted to compensate for the convenience of having machinery under shelter and close to the farm shop where repairs can be made during bad weather and perhaps for a neater farmstead. The value put on these intangibles may be high or low, according to the importance the farmer attaches to them.

A farmer with limited capital may logically decide to build shelter only for power machines and harvesting equipment, and let paint, grease, rust inhibitors, and a gravel parking strip take care of the rest of his storage needs.

IN CONCLUSION: The greatest economic gain and personal satisfaction will come from buildings and equipment that are doing necessary jobs in the most economical way.

A better yardstick is needed for measuring the costs of buildings and the benefits they bring in reducing chore labor, improving the preservation and utilization of feed, and so on.

The ratio of benefit to cost and the actual investment are important.

More attention needs to be given to the effects of depreciation rates and financing methods on the costs of owning buildings.

# Power

# and

# Its Effects

## Technology and Capital

Wylie D. Goodsell

GREATER changes have occurred in American agriculture since 1940 than in many decades previously.

The average size of farm in the United States increased 46 percent between 1940 and 1958, compared with 19 percent in 1900–1940.

Total capital (in 1940 dollars) invested per farm increased 61 percent in 1940–1958 and 3 percent in 1930–1940.

Investment in machinery and equipment increased 211 percent in 1940–1958. There was little or no change between 1930 and 1940.

Capital invested per person engaged in farming, valued in 1910–1914 dollars, rose from 2,900 dollars in 1870 to 4,400 dollars in 1920. This is an increase of approximately 10 percent per decade.

The increase was 31 percent between 1940 and 1950. It was nearly 34 percent between 1950 and 1958. The number of persons in agriculture, however, dropped 18 percent in 1940–1950 and 19 percent in 1950–1958.

THE TIME at which farmers began to mechanize differed from area to area and from type of farm to type of farm.

Wheat farmers were among the first to mechanize. Early developments in mechanical equipment were readily adapted to grain farming.

Wheat-fallow farmers in the Big Bend of Oregon and Washington increased the size of their farms by about 15 percent in 1930–1940, while operators of dairy, Corn Belt, cotton, tobacco, and

370

related types of farms showed little increase in size of farm.

Capital assets in land and buildings, measured in 1947–1949 dollars, increased by about 15 percent and in machinery and equipment by about 29 percent on wheat-fallow farms in 1930–1940. They remained relatively unchanged on the other types of farms.

Capital investment stepped up rapidly on all farms after 1940. Total capital assets per farm increased by 16 to 18 percent on Piedmont cotton farms and Corn Belt cash-grain farms and by nearly 40 percent on northeastern dairy and wheat-fallow farms. This increased investment on some farms was mainly in real estate; on others, most of it was in mechanical power and equipment.

Mechanization was well under way by 1940 on wheat-fallow farms, but it was just getting under way on the other farm types. Wheat-fallow farmers consequently tended more to increase their acreage so as to utilize more effectively their mechanical power and equipment.

Piedmont cotton, northeastern dairy, and cash-grain farmers were not yet in this adjustment state and were inclined to direct their outlays for capital assets toward more mechanical power and equipment.

As a result, from 1940 to 1958, operators of wheat-fallow farms increased the acreage in their farms by 35 percent, compared with 12 to 24 percent on the other farm types. During this period, however, operators of wheat-fallow farms increased their capital assets in machinery and equipment by 39 percent, compared with 56 to 158 percent on the other types of farms.

Operators of Piedmont cotton farms increased their mechanical power and equipment by 158 percent in 1940–1958 and reduced their total labor by 30 percent. Northeastern dairy farmers increased their machinery and equipment by 109 percent and reduced their labor by nearly 20 percent. Cash-grain farmers increased their machinery and equipment by 56 percent and reduced their labor by about 26 percent. Wheat-fallow farmers increased their machinery and equipment by 39 percent and made only slight reductions in labor used. Much greater reductions were made in amounts of hired labor.

Competent farm laborers became scarce shortly after 1940, and wage rates increased rapidly. After the war, they continued high relative to cost rates paid by farmers for other inputs. A natural consequence was to reduce the amount of hired labor. Operators of the four types of farms reduced the amount of hired labor by 50 or 60 percent.

The effect of the increased outlays for mechanical equipment was a substantial increase in size of farm and total output and a reduction of labor, particularly hired labor. The physical output per man increased as a result from 37 percent on Piedmont cotton farms to 181 percent on wheat-fallow farms between 1940 and 1958.

If we measure this tremendous increase in production efficiency in terms of output per man-hour, we find it increased by 66 percent on Piedmont cotton farms in 1940–1958, 78 percent on cash-grain farms, 98 percent on northeastern dairy farms, and 130 percent on wheat-fallow farms. The output per man-hour from 1930 to 1940 increased only slightly on northeastern dairy and Piedmont cotton farms, but it was 52 and 105 percent higher on cash-grain and wheat-fallow farms. This again indicates earlier capital increases on the latter two types of farms.

ARE FARMERS more vulnerable now to a price squeeze than they were in the 1920's and 1930's, before the large outlays of capital for machinery and equipment and other nonfarm items?

In the 1920's, when I was a boy on a farm, our major cash outlays were for threshing, taxes, and a few harvest hands. We could postpone most expenditures a year or two if necessary. We had most of our labor, grew all our feed, and bred mares for horse replacements. In this respect, we were not very vulnerable to a price squeeze. But our output and efficiency were low, our cash income was relatively meager, and our opportunities for growth and expansion were limited.

Farmers now buy a greater proportion of their total inputs despite reductions in hired labor, which I include here as a purchased input.

On the four types of farms, the proportion of total farm production inputs that are purchased ranged from 53 to 70 percent in 1958, compared with 46 to 61 percent in 1940 and 42 to 64 in 1930. Because all inputs are valued at 1947–1949 cost rates, the effects of changes in prices have been eliminated.

Some of these purchased inputs, such as feed, seed, and livestock, are farm produced, and their prices vary directly with prices of farm products. Prices paid for nonfarm inputs are less variable. They may remain relatively high for a short period in years when farm incomes decline.

Another way of estimating farmers' vulnerability to a price squeeze in view of increased capital assets in mechanical power and equipment is to consider the proportion of purchased farm production inputs that are from nonfarm sources or nonfarm origin.

Because northeastern dairy farmers buy considerable feed, they showed the smallest proportion of inputs purchased from nonfarm sources. They ran about 35 percent of the total in 1930, 36 percent in 1940, and 46 percent in 1958.

On the higher side are the cash-grain farms, on which inputs from nonfarm sources averaged 56, 62, and 68 percent of the total in 1930, 1940, and 1958, respectively.

Farming long has been considered a business subjected to high fixed costs. High fixed costs may become burdensome during declines in prices of farm products. With considerable variation in production from year to year, as is common on many types of farms, high fixed costs can be cumbersome.

Farmers and businesses in general do not like high fixed costs because they place pressure on the business to get high output to meet the costs and also to reduce unit costs. When prices de-

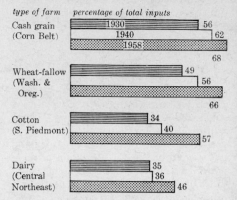

INPUTS FROM NONFARM SOURCES
Selected Commercial Family-Operated Farms

*Farmers are now using more production inputs from nonfarm sources. The prices of these items are less flexible than are prices of farm-produced inputs.*

cline, there is considerable pressure on the farmer to maintain or increase production so as to stabilize his income. A firm with high fixed costs is generally considered one with high leverage. If a high output can be obtained, profits on units in excess of those necessary to meet fixed costs are high.

The question is whether, with the large increase in capital invested in farms, there has been an appreciable increase in variable costs relative to fixed costs.

Variable costs have increased significantly over the years on northeastern dairy farms and Corn Belt farms. On northeastern dairy farms where feed purchases are important, the percentages that variable costs were of total costs, at 1947–1949 prices, averaged 58, 62, and 70 percent, respectively, in 1930, 1940, and 1958. On farms in the Corn Belt, they ran to 34, 40, and 49 percent in these years. Variable costs have averaged 50 to 60 percent of the total costs on wheat-fallow farms, with a slight upward trend in recent years. Variable costs remained around 60 percent of the total on Piedmont cotton farms, with no trend upward or downward in recent years.

One would expect this on Piedmont

cotton farms, as they are not so highly mechanized as the other farms, and reductions in hired and cropper labor have varied greatly from year to year, depending on the size of the cotton crop and on the seasons.

I may point out that farmers now are generally more efficient than they were previously and that in this respect they are in a better position to withstand a price-cost squeeze and to meet certain costs.

A farm operator who faces high fixed costs and is obliged to pay out relatively large amounts for items from nonfarm sources (which tend to have rigid prices) during the production season would naturally feel some insecurity and be impelled to watch his operations carefully so as to meet these obligations. The individual who is considering buying a farm has additional or perhaps even greater problems. His concern is where he can get enough capital and credit to buy a farm and whether his venture will pay.

The total capital assets on a typical cash-grain Corn Belt farm averaged about 111 thousand dollars on January 1, 1959. Those on a typical dairy farm in the Northeast or a Piedmont cotton farm were much less, but those on a wheat-fallow farm averaged much higher.

If any young man were fortunate enough to have 44,400 dollars to use as a downpayment (40 percent) on a typical Corn Belt farm and could amortize the remainder of his payment at 5 percent over 20 years, his annual payment would amount to about 5,340 dollars in principal and interest.

If the operator's income over the next 20 years were to equal that of the last 20 years, he could meet this obligation from farm earnings and he and his family would have an average of 1,720 dollars annually to live on. Similarly, operators of Piedmont cotton farms, northeastern dairy farms, and wheat-fallow farms, respectively, could meet their amortization payments and have approximately 512, 1,441, and 3,189 dollars annually to live on.

The total capital in farm assets has seemed high for several years. They seem formidable to a young man who is contemplating farming. They seem high to the landlord and to the investor. Perhaps they seem high because we know that farm production and prices and consequently farm incomes are subject to considerable variation. But are capital assets in farming too high? Are they high relative to farm incomes?

We do not have data for a long series of years before 1940, as we have for the years since 1940. Also, during the early 1930's, drought and depression occurred. The farm incomes were low therefore relative to values of farm assets. During the late 1930's and early 1940's, however, farm incomes were more favorable.

As a rough comparison, let us assume that a young man bought a typical farm in 1940 and apply the same amortization scheme that we applied in the purchase of the typical farms at 1959 values. Let us assume further that the farmer's annual farm income over the 20-year amortization period averaged the same as the average annual incomes during the 15-year period 1930–1944.

Under this program, operators of cash-grain farms in the Corn Belt could meet their amortization payments from farm income and have approximately 1,023 dollars left. Similarly, operators of Piedmont cotton farms, northeastern dairy farms, and wheat-fallow farms would have about 307, 667, and 869 dollars, respectively, to live on.

According to these estimates, farm assets are not so high relative to farm incomes in recent years as they were in earlier years. Farms purchased now, however, must be paid for to a large extent from future farm earnings. No one can predict the ratio of farm income over the next 20 years to current farm assets.

ANOTHER POINT sometimes overlooked in farm assets and incomes is

## PRODUCTION ASSETS PER WORKER

### SELECTED COMMERCIAL FAMILY-OPERATED FARMS
Value of land, service buildings, livestock, machinery and feed, January 1

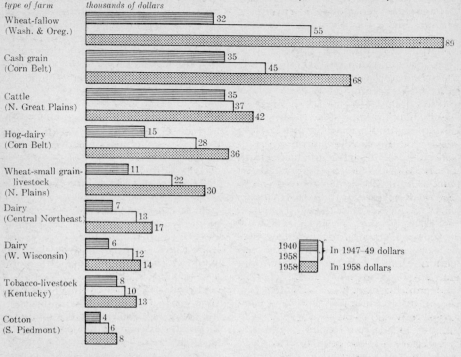

that since 1940 we have had considerable appreciation in farm assets. The total capital assets on the typical cash-grain Corn Belt farm in 1940 averaged about 31,500 dollars. On January 1, 1959, they stood at about 111 thousand dollars.

The typical Corn Belt operator since 1940 has increased the total number of acres operated by about 12 percent.

He has mechanized his operations greatly. He has also adopted a number of technological changes and has made several changes in his operations. If we charge off these purchases at cost at the time they were made, the farm operator has an average annual appreciation in value of capital assets in the amount of 3,575 dollars—about two-thirds of his annual amortization payment. This capital appreciation, together with a net farm income (re-

turn to operator and unpaid family labor for their labor and for assets in the farm) of 7,060 dollars a year, makes a total annual increment of 10,365 dollars. Capital appreciation, therefore, has amounted to a sizable sum.

Capital invested and returns to operators have varied considerably from farm type to farm type. Operators of some types of farms have faced severe competition in recent years. Their incomes have been relatively low and the risk greater than many individuals have wanted to accept.

That is particularly true for poultry producers, especially broiler operators. As a result, the broiler industry has become integrated.

Delaware is one of the leaders in producing broilers. All but a few of the broiler growers in Delaware are producing under contract.

Of the independent growers, a typical one produces about four batches of 10 thousand birds a year. His capital assets are about as follows: Land, buildings, and equipment, 30 thousand dollars; feed, 4,500 dollars; chicks, 1,100 dollars; and fuel, medicine, vaccination, and litter, 650 dollars.

A typical producer who operates under contract has a total investment of about 25 thousand dollars, or about 11,500 dollars less than the typical independent operator. The operator who is under contract in an integrated business produces fewer birds and has no capital in birds, feed, and the related items. As prices paid for feed and prices received for birds vary greatly, the grower who operates under contract has far less risk than the independent operator.

Integrated farming is not new, but it is becoming more widespread and more complex. In it, the farm operator plays a less dominant role. He is less independent, but his risk is less, and he needs less capital.

# Financing Capital Requirements

Fred L. Garlock

MOST OF THE capital invested in agriculture has been provided by the operators and other owners of farms from the cash incomes they received from farming.

The proportion of the capital investment that was financed externally has varied sharply from time to time. In recent years, as in some earlier periods, the rapidly growing need of farmers for capital has forced them to borrow an increasing part of the money.

Moreover, advancing technology in agriculture has complicated the work of financial institutions in financing farmers and led to significant changes in their practices.

A detailed historical study of capital investment in agriculture, and the way in which it was financed, was made by Dr. Alvin S. Tostlebe and reported in Capital in Agriculture, Its Formation and Financing Since 1870, which Princeton University Press published in 1957.

As Dr. Tostlebe was concerned mainly with the buildup of the capital used in agriculture and the investment necessary to accomplish it, he developed measures of the gross investment in farm machinery, farm structures, and improvements and additions to the land in farms.

These investments, added to the increase (or decrease) in crop and livestock inventories and in the cash working balances of farmers, made up the total investment in agriculture for which he accounted.

He did not include in this investment the outlays that farmers and others made to transfer ownership of farms and other farm capital within the industry.

The total investment made to accomplish the buildup of farm capital that occurred in the first half of this century was placed at 79 billion dollars. Dr. Tostlebe credited financial institutions and other lenders with advancing about 17 billion dollars, or 22 percent of this capital. The remaining amount he attributed to direct investment of cash income that farmers and other farmowners received from farming.

Less than half of the amount invested in agriculture during that period was used to increase agricultural capital. The larger part was needed to offset depreciation of machinery and buildings.

Many farmers do not recognize depreciation as a cost except for income tax purposes, but a large part of the investment in agriculture each year is required to replace the capital lost through wear, aging, and other causes. These losses have averaged nearly 4 billion dollars a year since 1955.

Because data were lacking on the volume of credit extended by several important types of lenders, Dr. Tostlebe used net increases in farm debt during 5-year periods as a measure of the contributions of lenders to capital formation in agriculture.

This procedure gives an accurate measure of the net contributions of lenders during 5-year periods, but it does not show the total extent to which lenders financed capital expansion in agriculture within those periods. Large amounts of credit are used and repaid within periods of 5 years and still larger amounts in longer periods.

This point may be illustrated with some estimates that were made by men in the Department of Agriculture.

Farm purchases of all kinds during 1946–1955 were estimated to be about 363 billion dollars. The purchases included the usual production and capital goods and also farm real estate and goods and services for household and living purposes. From estimates of credit extensions, it appeared that credits amounting to 125 billion to 130 billion dollars—about one-third of the cost of the goods and services bought—had been used in making the purchases. Yet farm debt increased only 9 billion dollars because all except a small part of the credit used was repaid within the 10-year period.

No similar estimates of credit extensions have been made for earlier periods, but it is certain that the total amount of credit used in building up the capital assets of agriculture during the first half of this century was considerably greater than is indicated by Dr. Tostlebe's data—probably two to three times greater. Even so, it would still be true that in most years the greater part of the capital invested in agriculture came directly from cash farm receipts.

Lenders financed an exceptionally large part of the investment in agriculture during the first two decades of this century. Rising prices and rapid farm development favored the use of credit during that period, and farm debts were driven up sharply by the speculation in farmland that followed the First World War.

The amount of credit used in financing capital expansion in agriculture dropped sharply in the next two decades. Although the capital investment in agriculture continued to increase, that period included the severe recessions of the early 1920's and early 1930's, which seriously impaired the credit standing of farmers and the lending power of financial institutions.

Lenders continued to occupy a minor role as a source of capital for agriculture during the Second World War. Sharply increased farm receipts allowed the operators and other owners of farms to make most of their investments in farm improvements and machinery directly and enabled them also to build up their financial reserves to record heights.

During the 5 years following the war, increasing use was made of credit as a means of financing capital investment in agriculture. In that period also, however, credit was still of minor importance, compared with cash farm receipts.

Two studies of the financing of farm equipment also throw light on the way in which investment in agriculture was financed in the late 1930's and the 1940's.

Dr. Howard G. Diesslin, in "Agricultural Equipment Financing," Occasional Paper 50 of the National Bureau of Economic Research, estimated that the credit used in purchasing new farm equipment dropped from nearly 30 percent of the cost of the equipment in the late 1930's to about 20 percent in 1941.

In "Financing Farm Machinery and Equipment Purchases, 1947," a Department of Agriculture report, Richard G. Schmitt, Jr., placed credit-financed purchases at only 26 percent of all purchases of new machines and equipment by farmers in 1947.

No later data of national scope are available on credit-financed purchases of farm machinery. A clue to the development that probably occurred is afforded by data on sales of new automobiles collected by the Board of Governors of the Federal Reserve System.

The Board's data indicated that credit-financed sales, which were about 45 percent of all sales of new passenger cars in the late 1940's, had risen to about 65 percent of all sales by 1956–1958. As I note later, there are additional indications that the credit-financed part of the investment in agriculture has risen sharply in recent years.

The buildup of the capital used in agriculture occurred gradually over a long period, and it involved considerably less actual investment than the present value of agricultural assets might suggest—at various times, the physical assets of agriculture have increased greatly in price, particularly since 1940.

In addition to the capital investments covered by Dr. Tostlebe's study, large investments have been required to transfer farms and the other farm capital goods from generation to generation and among individuals within generations.

The entry of a young man into farming may add nothing to the capital used in agriculture, but it often involves a large investment of owned or borrowed capital by the young man or his family.

Capital-transfer problems of large dimensions similarly arise in connection with other transfers of farms, including those for farm enlargement, and in such other areas as transfers of feeder cattle from the range to feedlots.

Some types of capital transfers have been studied quite thoroughly, but only bits of information are available on other types. No measures are available of the amount of credit used in transferring feeder cattle from the range to feedlots, for example, but it is known that cattle feeders usually can borrow the entire purchase price of the feeders. Many follow this practice. There is no measure, except an estimate for 1954, of the value of farms that change ownership each year, but it is known that only about one-twelfth of the farms transferred during recent years were transferred by gift or inheritance and that most transfers involved purchase and sale.

In their studies of the farm real estate market, William H. Scofield and Paul L. Holm, of the Department of Agriculture, have collected data on the capital-transfer problems that arise from sales of farm real estate.

They found that sales of farm real estate, like sales of new passenger cars, are increasingly financed through the use of credit. Approximately two-thirds of all sales in 1958–1959 involved use of credit, compared with a little more than 40 percent in the early 1940's. Of the credit-financed land transfers, more than 40 percent in 1958–1959, compared with about 33 percent in 1955, were financed by the sellers of the land. In the sales financed by sellers, land contracts often are used, and the credit extended usually represents a larger part of the sale price than in sales financed with loans from financial institutions.

An increasing proportion of the farm-land bought is used to enlarge existing farms (42 percent in 1958–1959, compared with 26 percent in 1950–1954). Farms can be enlarged also by renting additional land, a method that has been used extensively.

Renting has some advantages over ownership if the renter is secure in his tenure. It involves a smaller financial commitment. Often the landowner shares risks of the operation by paying a share of the expenses and accepting a share of the crop as rental. With the reduction in number and the increase in size of farms, however, it is becoming harder to lease the additional land needed to create efficient operating units. This element often throws the balance in favor of buying, even though a large debt must be incurred to make the purchase.

The increasing use of credit to finance capital formation in agriculture, purchases of farm real estate, and other transfers of farm capital, raised the farm debt from less than 8 billion dollars at the end of the Second World War to nearly 21 billion dollars at the beginning of 1959. (These figures do not include price-support loans of the Commodity Credit Corporation.)

Moreover, all types of lenders report that the average size of their loans to farm borrowers has been increasing rapidly. As a percentage of the value of farm assets, farm debts rose from less than 8 percent at the end of the war to 10 percent at the beginning of 1959. They probably will continue upward. All indications point to the conclusion that more and more credit is being used to create each additional dollar's worth of capital in agriculture and to effect the necessary transfers of capital within the industry.

The main financial institutions from which farmers borrow and the amounts of farm loans (in millions of dollars) held by each in mid-1959, were: Commercial banks, 6,423; life insurance companies, 2,741; Federal land banks, 2,238; production credit associations, 1,500; and Farmers Home Administration, 890. The total was 13,792 million dollars.

About three-fifths of all farm debts are owed to these institutions, although farmers obtain credit from a variety of other sources—sales finance companies, merchants and dealers, small loan companies, credit unions, relatives, and other individuals.

The demands on the institutions that finance farmers are being increased by the growing complexity of the industry and the uptrend in farmers' needs for credit.

Application of the new technologies, shifts in types of enterprise, and farm enlargements are making good management more essential to success in farming and complicating the task of financial institutions in evaluating applications for loans. These changes have made it necessary for financial institutions to get better qualified personnel and to improve their methods in financing farmers.

Spurred by the recession of the early 1930's and the wave of mortgage foreclosures that followed, the Farm Credit Administration and life insurance companies moved rapidly to improve the caliber of their appraisal staffs and the methods they used.

THE PRODUCTION credit associations and the Farmers Home Administration (including its predecessor agencies) have tried ever since they were first organized in the mid-1930's to get persons familiar with and experienced in farming to handle their loans to farmers. Many commercial banks have appointed men with agricultural backgrounds and educations to handle their agricultural loan business. About 1,200 commercial banks had such officers in 1959.

Usually in cooperation with the State agricultural colleges, lenders also have arranged for periodic farm credit conferences to improve their understanding of changes in farming and the farm credit problems. The conferences often provide opportunities for demonstration and discussion of innovations in agriculture. One such conference group—the National Agricultural Credit Committee—comprises chiefly farm-mortgage lenders. It meets every 4 months to review recent experience with agricultural loans and to assess the current situation and outlook in agriculture.

The Farm Credit Act of 1959 (Public Law 86–168) repealed the limit of 200 thousand dollars on Federal land bank loans to one borrower and authorized the Federal land banks to make unamortized or partially amortized loans under regulations issued by the Farm Credit Administration.

These changes reflect the increase in the capital required for efficient farming and in farmers' needs for credit. The removal of the maximum loan limit will enable the Federal land banks to serve borrowers whose needs for credit have outgrown the previous limit on loans by land banks. The provision for unamortized or only partly amortized loans recognizes that some borrowers can better use their incomes to maintain or increase their capital assets than to reduce their debts.

In the field of production credit, the growing size and costliness of the machines and equipment used in agriculture are bringing some change in the terms of loans made by financial institutions to farmers. Sales contracts that spread payments over several years have long been used by manufacturers and dealers in selling heavy machinery, automobiles, and trucks to farmers, and banks have discounted or bought substantial amounts of these contracts.

Some of the direct loans of both banks and production credit associations to farmers have contained similar provisions. Chiefly, however, the direct loans of these institutions to farmers even for costly equipment have had maturities of a year or less.

This does not mean that farmers have been required to repay their loans as rapidly as this if they needed more time. Usually lenders have renewed the loans or extended the payment dates, as needed by farmers. Lenders, however, have retained the option to collect when these short-term loans were due, even though they often have not exercised it.

The production credit associations have been making more loans with the longer maturities. Some range up to 5 years. These intermediate-term loans give borrowers more protection against untimely demands for payments than do the shorter term loans. They are especially well adapted to the financing of such costly items as bulk milk-handling equipment and heavy machinery.

Whether the lead taken by production credit associations will be followed by banks is not yet clear, but in nonfarm industries, intermediate-term loans largely replaced short-term loans as a means of financing purchases of heavy equipment as long ago as the 1920's.

The Farmers Home Administration has always used intermediate-term loans to finance the working capital requirements of its borrowers, but it serves only a small segment of the farm population.

RAPID TECHNOLOGIC progress in some farm enterprises has changed greatly the relationships between farmers and their suppliers or processors of their products. They are the enterprises in which contract farming has come into prominence—notably production of broilers, eggs, and hogs and feeding of cattle. A variety of contracts is used in each of these enterprises, but more and more the contracts are getting away from the "debtor-creditor" relationship and making the processor or supplier the sole enterpriser or a joint enterpriser with the farmer.

From a viewpoint of financing, the main feature of these contracts is that usually the grower is not obligated to pay for the production items that the supply company or processor furnishes as its part of the deal. The supplier or processor takes a loss if its share of the product sales proceeds does not cover the cost of the items.

Frank D. Hansing, of the Department of Agriculture, studied the broiler industry in Delaware and found that most of the growers were operating under contracts of this kind.

He asked the growers why they preferred contracts—whether it was because they did not have the resources to produce independently. Most of them replied that they could raise the money to produce independently if they wished, but that they did not want to accept the risks of independent production.

This response reveals a motivation that underlies many changes in the methods of mobilizing capital for farming.

The amounts of capital required for efficient farming are now so large and profit margins in some farm enterprises are so low that farmers seek ways of reducing their risks. Suppliers and processors increasingly find it necessary to share farming risks in order to maintain or increase their business with farmers.

# Agribusiness in the Machine Age

Earl L. Butz

MODERN AGRICULTURE is much broader than the narrow dictionary definition—"the art or science of cultivating the ground." It is the whole business of supplying food and fiber for a growing population at home and abroad.

The art or science of cultivating the ground is but one link in the long chain of feeding and clothing people. The chain begins many jobs before we reach the farm and continues several processes after our newly produced food and fiber leave the farm gate. For this whole complex of agricultural production and distribution functions some persons use the term "agribusiness."

The United States has shifted in the past century from a predominantly agricultural economy to an industrial and commercial economy. The industrial sector is now beginning to give way, at least relatively, to a growing variety of personal services. That is possible primarily because we have been able to specialize in our production and processing of food and fiber by the increased use of science, technology, and mechanization and an increasing output per worker in farming and in agribusiness. We have transferred many farm jobs off the farm, such as the shift of farm power from horses and oats to tractors and gasoline, but we do the entire job with much less manpower than formerly.

AGRICULTURE is now in the middle of its third great revolution. Agricultural engineers have had a big part in all three revolutions.

The first revolution came in the middle of the 19th century, when we began to substitute animal energy for human energy. The invention of the reaper is the best known event associated with it. This and other developments called for considerable retooling in agriculture. They increased output per worker on farms and started us on the path of feeding our growing Nation with a constantly shrinking proportion of our total population in the field. Agriculture began to take on some characteristics of a commercial enterprise, although sometimes the change was almost imperceptible.

The second great revolution began in the 1920's, with the substitution of mechanical energy for animal energy. It likewise increased the commercialization of agriculture, shifted a number of production functions off the farm, increased output per worker substantially, and resulted in a further reduction in the proportion of our total working population on farms.

The third revolution is the undergirding of agricultural production and marketing with vast amounts of science, technology, and business management. This revolution has been in progress for a decade or two, but at an accelerated pace during the past few years. This revolution is transferring still additional production and marketing functions off the farm and continues to underscore the importance of specialization at all levels of the agribusiness complex.

Agricultural historians a generation hence may characterize the decade of the 1950's as the decade of the scientific breakthrough. In this decade we experienced an unprecedented number of discoveries, which have changed agriculture from stem to stern.

The decade of the 1960's opens with the march of agricultural science in full stride. Agriculture is changing from a way of living to a way of making a living. It is changing from a business of arts and crafts to a business undergirded with large amounts of science and technology.

IT IS WRONG to think of agriculture as a declining industry.

American agriculture is an expanding industry in every important respect except one—the number of people required to run our farms. Our agricultural plant each year uses more capital, more science and technology, more managerial capacity, more purchased production inputs, more specialized marketing facilities, and more research than the year before.

We do not think of air transportation as a declining industry just because a pilot in a jet airliner can now take 100 passengers from coast to coast in half a day, compared with 20 passengers in a day and half two decades ago. This, like agriculture, is a strong and growing industry.

Although a smaller share of our total population is engaged directly in farming, the agricultural industry is big, broad, and basic. Of 68 million persons employed in America in 1960, about 26 million worked somewhere in agriculture—8 million worked on farms, 7 million produced goods and services purchased by farmers, and 11 million processed and distributed farm products. Hence, almost two-fifths of all our employed people are engaged in work related to agriculture.

The declining trend in farm population is itself a sign of a strong agriculture. Brainpower has replaced horsepower as the essential ingredient on our farms. The total United States agricultural output increased by two-thirds in the past two decades, while the number of farmworkers declined some 3 million. This means that production per worker on our farms has doubled in the past 20 years. This remarkable increase in production efficiency can be matched by no other major sector of the American economy.

Progress of this kind can be continued only if we have capable and well-informed men on our farms. We will need fewer farmers in the future, but they must be better. They will be operating on a fast track, and the race will go to the swift.

WE MUST broaden our thinking about agriculture to include the businesses that supply our farmers with items used in production, as well as the processing and distributing concerns that handle the food and fiber produced on farms.

When the total agribusiness is taken into consideration, approximately one-third of the workers are on farms and two-thirds are off farms. Approximately two-thirds of the capital is on farms and one-third off. Approximately one-sixth of the value added is on farms and roughly five-sixths off the farm.

The farm plant in America purchases each year approximately 17 billion dollars worth of goods and services used in farm production. To this it adds a value of about 17 billion dollars on farms, which means that the total farm produce leaves the farm gates at about 34 billion dollars. Processing and distribution add another 45 billion dollars to this, which makes a total value of output in agribusiness of approximately 80 billion dollars in 1960.

These figures point out the growing importance of agriculture as a market. Industry depends on agriculture as a customer to a greater extent than most persons realize.

A generation ago, farmers were producing most of their own fuel, power, and fertilizer, but now industry is furnishing farmers each year:

6.5 million tons of finished steel—more than is used for a year's output for passenger cars;

45 million tons of chemical materials—about 5 times the amount they used in 1935;

18 billion gallons of crude petroleum—more than is used by any other industry;

285 million pounds of raw rubber—enough to make tires for 6 million automobiles;

22 billion kilowatt hours of electricity—more than enough to serve the cities of Chicago, Detroit, Baltimore, and Houston for a year.

We could go on citing other evidences of the tremendous importance of agriculture in our national life, but the point has been made. Whatever happens to agriculture has a direct and major impact upon industry. And industry, by the same token, has a very great interest in the welfare of agriculture.

The agricultural world and the industrial world are not two separate communities with merely a buyer-seller relationship. They are so bound together and so interrelated that we must think of them jointly if we are to reach sound conclusions about either one.

THE MODERN commercial farm resembles a manufacturing plant in many respects. The large amount of equipment in use on the farm represents a substitution of capital and machinery for labor.

Many family commercial farms today have total capital investment exceeding 100 thousand dollars. It is not uncommon to have capital investment approaching or exceeding 200 thousand dollars on family commercial farms in the Corn Belt. Many Midwest farms have total capital investment per worker in excess of 50 thousand dollars. This is three times the average investment per worker in American industry.

The modern farm operator is much less self-sufficient than his father was. He buys many goods and services needed in his production that father produced on the farm. In a very real sense, he assembles "packages of technology" that have been put together by others on a custom basis. For example, he buys his tractors and petroleum, whereas his father produced horses and oats. Think for a moment of the technology that goes into the modern feedbag, with its careful blending of proteins, antibiotics, minerals, and hormones, as contrasted with the ear corn and a little tankage put out for the hogs in his grandfather's day.

This development obviously calls for a high level of managerial capacity. It is more difficult to manage the modern commercial farm successfully than it is to manage the family-sized manufacturing concern, grocery store, or foundry shop in the city.

The manager of the modern commercial family farm must make more managerial decisions each week covering a much wider range of subject matter than does his counterpart in the city. He has more capital invested, takes greater risks, faces stiffer competition, and has more opportunity for reward if he does a good job.

This kind of "manufacturing operation" means rather narrow operating margins for farmers. In recent years farmers, as a group, have spent some 65 cents of every dollar they take in for operating expense. That is the average. Specialized commercial farmers spend a higher ratio than that for operating expense. They operate on a much narrower margin than their fathers did, but make greater net incomes because of increased volume. A large share of their operating expenses goes for items that their grandfathers produced on the farm himself, but that modern farmers "hire" someone else to produce for them.

TODAY'S farm production is a synthesis of several scientific disciplines.

The earning capacity of the average farmer used to be limited primarily by his physical strength and the amount of work he could do. He substituted some animal muscle for human muscle, but not a great deal. He substituted very little mechanical energy for muscle power. Agriculture was primarily a means of converting muscle energy into farm produce.

Human energy is much less important in today's farm operation. Energy can be purchased so much more cheaply than it can be provided by man. Today's farm operator is a combination manager-applicator of the life sciences, the physical sciences, and the social sciences. The research undergirding modern agriculture ranges all the way from physics to physiology, from biology to business. It is just as complex and just as far on the periphery of knowledge as is the research done in the laboratories of the nuclear scientist, for example.

The first claim of any society upon its total production resources is to get enough food to keep the population alive and well. This is true in primitive societies, in semi-developed societies, and in highly developed societies. We do this so efficiently in this country that almost nine-tenths of our population is available to produce the wide variety of goods and services that make up the American standard of living.

A tremendous amount of research lies behind the production and distribution of those 17 billion dollars' worth of production items farmers bought in 1960. That research must be carefully integrated into the farm operation itself. Indeed, it must go beyond that, to the processing and distribution of the farm product after it leaves the farmers' gates. Increasingly, this kind of research calls for a research team representing various disciplines, and requires careful coordination through the entire process of production, processing, and distribution.

THE TECHNOLOGICAL revolution in the processing and distribution of food and fiber has been perhaps even more spectacular than the technological revolution on the farm. Countless steps in the processing of food and fiber that once were done on the farm have long since moved to the city.

The textile industry was one of the leaders in this field. In the early 1800's, when the mechanical production of textiles began, weaving in the home first declined and then disappeared. A little later, as the migration of population to industrial centers got under way, it was necessary to move food from the farm to urban areas. Inasmuch as the typical food production cycle is annual, and the human hunger cycle is daily, it became necessary to devise means of preserving and storing an annual food supply to meet daily food needs in locations far removed from areas of production. The result was the development of a commercial food processing and distributing industry which today feeds our vast urban population much better than their farmer ancestors fared. The national diet has improved materially in terms of quality and variety.

The interdependence of the various segments of the agribusiness chain is obvious. When these functions were mostly performed on the farm, there was a high degree of integration among them. The individual farm family saw to this, for failure to do so would mean loss of income and perhaps hunger.

In recent times, especially in some kinds of commodities, there has been a pronounced tendency to integrate the various functions of production and marketing through contractual arrangements of one kind or another. This process has come to be known as vertical integration. Although contractual integration arrangements are controversial and are viewed with suspicion by some people, they are a manifest effort on the part of the industry to seek such economies as can be attained by careful coordination of the entire chain of production, processing, and marketing.

Vertical integration is essentially an attempt to combine the advantages of specialization in modern society with the good features of a system in which all the steps were fully coordinated, as they had to be on grandfather's farm. A certain amount of vertical integration is inevitable—and beneficial—in the kind of agribusiness we have today.

Capital requirements per farm and per worker have increased to the extent that it is becoming increasingly difficult for an individual, during his productive years, to accumulate a sufficient amount to finance an economically sized operating unit. This will be still more true in the decades ahead. Moreover, in view of the inheritance tax structure, it is becoming increasingly difficult for a parent to transfer such a unit to his son without substantial operating or financial disruption. This means, perforce, that an increasing share of total farm capital will be supplied by nonoperators. Part of this will be accomplished through some form of vertical integration.

With such large amounts of capital and technology involved, management has become the key factor in successful farm operation. This is in sharp contrast to a generation or two ago, when the farm unit was much more self-sufficient than now, with much less capital involved, with much less science applied, and with many fewer critical managerial decisions to be made.

The movement of population off the farms will continue. They will not necessarily leave the rural community, particularly if urban employment is available within commuting distance. Many of them will find gainful employment in some phase of agribusiness in the city, and will therefore really remain in agriculture.

The question of whether every farm-reared youngster should remain on the farm is no longer a sociological problem. That the opportunity for gainful employment on the farm is not present for all farm-reared boys is simply an arithmetic fact. Fortunately, agribusiness offers a challenging opportunity.

Surveys have shown that in many typical rural areas in the Corn Belt approximately one farm per township per year will become available for new operators in the next generation. In these same townships, the number of farm youth ready for new employment each year ranges from four to eight. Obviously, if they all try to remain on the farm, operating units will necessarily be so small as seriously to limit income opportunities.

The process of "rurbanization" is altering community life in vast areas of our country. Rural and urban cultures are intermingling in countless communities within commuting distance of industrial centers. City folk are moving to the country, and farm families have one or more members commuting to work in the city.

The city limit sign at the edge of your county seat town does not mean the same thing it did just a generation ago. It is now just a tax boundary. It is no longer a cultural boundary, an educational boundary, a social boundary, a recreational boundary, or an economic boundary. The same kind of people live on both sides of that city limit sign. They have the same communications, the same transportation, the same electricity, the same educational opportunities, the same recreational outlets, the same church facilities, the same modernized kitchens, and the same standards of living.

More than half of our farm families have one or more members of the family doing either part-time or full-time work off the farm. On approximately 1.5 million farm units in the United States in 1958, the farm operator either worked off the farm 100 days or more for wages, or his nonfarm income exceeded his farm income. This is one means whereby operators of less than economic-sized units increase their volume and achieve acceptable incomes. There are relatively few farm families who do not live within commuting distance of a nonfarm job.

When this tendency of farm people to get either part-time or full-time work off the farm is put alongside the tendency of growing numbers of urban people to move to a country home, the pattern of our newly rurbanized communities becomes clear. As the farmer himself becomes a well-capitalized, highly specialized producer, a new community culture will emerge in which the farmer will tend to lose his vocational identity, just as the lawyer, the doctor, or the machinist now loses his in his own community.

The very cornerstone of our high standard of life is our ever-increasing efficiency in the production and marketing of food and fiber, made possible by the specialized functions that characterize agribusiness. Increased efficiency in production and distribution of food and fiber and the subsequent release of manpower for other work are the first prerequisites for an industrialized society. The first claim of any organized society on its total production resources is food. The cry for food has echoed through the ages. Food remains man's first physical need.

# Change and Employment

William H. Metzler

ABOUT 2 million young people arrive at working age each year in the United States. One-third of them become housewives. A small proportion inherit farms, shops, or other employment opportunities. More than half enter the job market—some for lifetime careers, others for day-to-day work.

Most of the employment opportunities that are open to entrants in the labor market today arose from technological developments of recent years.

New machines and products created new types of jobs in factories, offices, and laboratories, but curtailed them in others. The invention of the automobile brought rapid expansion of the gasoline, rubber, steel, copper, and glass industries and provided employment for thousands of people besides those who made the automobiles. It spurred the construction of highways, hotels, motels, and resort areas.

On the other hand, the automobile put hostlers, coachmen, carriagemakers, harnessmakers, and livery-stable workers out of employment. It reduced the need for producers of hay and grain and for workers on railroads and steamboats. Thousands of workers had to shift from declining lines of employment toward those that offered a better future.

A myriad discoveries now are creating and curtailing jobs. Some young people will be guided into the paths of technologic and economic growth. Many others, less well advised as to changing opportunities, will move into outdated paths.

528981°—60——26

Wrong decisions may mean years of occupational maladjustment to the youth. They also tend to reduce the balance and productivity of the economy as a whole. Parents and teachers are challenged to provide youth with training that will equip them to function in the scientific world in which they will live.

The hand of the past maintains a firm grip on the average person's economic circumstances, attitudes, and values. The human lag in shifting to new technology and new methods may be due to lack of knowledge, to being caught in a rut of old ideas and habits, or to a lack of capital or managerial ability to make use of the new methods.

All three are powerful deterrents to a smooth adjustment to realities of technology.

The information as to what technology is doing to the economy and to the employment structure has not been worked out clearly enough to meet the needs of career-minded workers. It is not so hard to assess the decline in need for hayfield workers, hand milkers, and cottonpickers as it is to forecast the employment demands of the new industries that are on the horizon. The growth of the plastics industry and its stimulus to the production of some farm products was foreseen only a few years in advance. Today some economists predict a decline in manpower needs in industry because of automation. Others envisage only selective changes from one industry to another.

Of all the occupational shifts that stem from technologic growth, the most far-reaching and most critical is the shift from agriculture to urban business and industrial pursuits. Agricultural technology developed slowly at first, partly because of the multiplicity of small units that were unable to take advantage of it. In the past several decades, though, changes have come with such a rush that timely economic and human adjustments have become difficult.

The practical goal for farm boys at one time was to learn how to farm from their parents and to achieve farm ownership for themselves. Those who did not inherit a farm could start as a farmhand and rise successively to be a tenant and then an owner. The agricultural knowledge required was not great, and farm tools and land were not expensive. The price of success was diligence and hard work.

The growth of agricultural and industrial technology has shifted the demand for workers, and now the success of the farm boy lies in a different direction. Because new technologies have made the farmworker far more productive, the need for manpower in agriculture has dropped accordingly, and the surplus of workers on farms has been estimated at 3 million to 5 million. Ability to readjust these surplus farm people into the nonfarm economy constitutes a sharp challenge to the individual enterprise system.

Adjustment has been taking place. There has been a continuous transfer of people out of agriculture into industry, business, and the professions.

The rate is increasing and has been especially high during periods of rapid industrial buildup in wartime. Yet the shift to nonfarm occupations has seldom kept pace with the reduction in farm manpower needs. Furthermore, the adjustment process has been completely thwarted during periods of industrial depression, when there has been a reverse flow of workers from industry to agriculture.

A few figures indicate the size of the adjustment that is economically desirable. A recent estimate based on census data indicates that 22,747 farm youths are needed each year to replace retiring farmers on commercial farms with sales of 5 thousand dollars or more. But 220 thousand farm youths now reach the age of 19 each year. Only 1 in 10 farm boys is likely therefore to have an opportunity to operate a farm that will provide an adequate income.

An opportunity in farm wage work may still be available for an additional 5 percent of these young men—but often at wage levels that would be less attractive than in urban employment.

Most of the lag in adjustment is concealed almost completely from the public view. The surplus rural youth pile up on farms and have no spokesmen for their economic interest. They are unemployed or underemployed, and small farm incomes are spread thinner and thinner to take care of them.

An excess of 6 million persons had accumulated on farms between 1930 and 1940. The decline in farm population during the Second World War was much greater than in farm employment. The movement was largely of the underemployed.

THE TREND toward more mechanization and less manpower affects all groups in agriculture, but its greatest impact is on small operators and on hired workers. The farm operator with a small enterprise and a small amount of capital is at a great disadvantage in making use of the newer machines and techniques. Between his present inadequate income base and the vagaries of the job market he has a difficult choice. Age and education strongly affect his ability to make an occupational adjustment.

Mechanization not only reduces the number of hired workers that are needed. It also reduces the regularity of their work. Tractors and combines eliminated the need for winter threshing and feeding and for many year-round hired hands. Only one-sixth of the hired farmworkers in 1958 were employed the year around. Harvesting machines cut the harvest season in half.

Short and irregular periods of work do not square up with the need for food and shelter each day. The hired worker has to move from farm to farm or from one location to another in order to avoid numerous periods of unemployment. This type of employment situation produces ready candidates for more regular jobs in town. How farmers will be able to maintain a force of irregular hired workers has become a matter of concern.

It is the youths, however, who are

most likely to be in a crucial situation. Ordinarily they would like to enter nonfarm employment but do not have the job information nor the financial independence to be able to strike out for themselves. Since many have little idea of present technical and capital requirements for successful farm operation, they may follow in their fathers' footsteps because that appears to be the easiest path.

THE ADVANCE of farm youths to positions in law, education, science, and government has been one of the most wholesome aspects of American economic growth. But the big surge of farm manpower is not in that direction. The onetime farmers who are less well educated tend to concentrate in jobs at the lower end of the economic scale. They do day labor on construction jobs, drive trucks, work in canneries and packing plants, and become grease boys in filling stations. They also set in motion an upward movement of the people already in urban employment, however, and a situation of gradual occupational improvement is brought about.

The low economic position of the ex-farmer, therefore, is only temporary. He moves ahead in the occupational scale as he learns new techniques. His children obtain more education than they could have had in the country, and the family makes a significant economic advance. The successful operation of this upward climb is linked to youth and education. Ex-farmers without these assets move ahead slowly.

TO DWELL too long on the displacement aspect of technologic growth is to develop a one-sided conception of the process that is taking place.

The other side is presented in *Careers Ahead*, published in 1955 by the American Association of Land-Grant Colleges and Universities. According to their records, 15 thousand college graduates are needed each year to meet the needs in agricultural research, education, and technology. The colleges have been able to supply only 8,500 gradu-

ates a year to fill those positions. Only half enough farm boys go to agricultural colleges to meet the demand.

New technologies have created demands for new types of technologists. The most urgent recent need has been for electronic engineers, nuclear physicists, mathematicians, and chemists. It has been growing faster than young people can be trained.

The greatest handicap to rapid growth in foreign countries is the shortage of trained personnel to man the new machines, keep them in repair, and to gain from them their full productive capacity. The same situation is developing in this country unless more people become familiar with the devices that are being developed.

The Federal Government has increased its salary scale in an attempt to meet its needs for scientists and technicians. Among the scientists it needed particularly in 1960 were geologists, physicists, geophysicists, chemists, metallurgists, astronomers, and meteorologists; specialists in aeronautical, electronic, forestry, and soils research; architects, engineers, patent examiners, tabulating equipment operators, medical officers, pharmacologists, veterinarians, actuaries, and mathematicians. All are workers in the forefront of technological advance. Public and private agencies are competing for them.

The demand for added workers extends to another level. Industry has recurring shortages of draftsmen, machinists, mechanics, tool and diemakers, welders, and machine repairmen— skilled craftsmen who construct and operate the new machines. The demand for clerical workers, typists, and stenographers became strong in new offices and laboratories.

A publication of the Department of Labor, "Population Trends—Their Manpower Implications," stated that 10 million more people will be needed in the labor force by 1965. Half of the new jobs will be filled by women, as they are entering the labor force in greater numbers. The field of greatest opportunity will be in professional and technical employment, in which the number of workers will increase by 40 percent. The demand for proprietors, managers, clerical and sales workers, skilled craftsmen, and semiskilled workers will be more than 20 percent. The rate of decline in the demand for farmers and unskilled workers is reported to be small, compared to the pyramiding of the demand for workers in the better paid jobs.

Actually, these estimates seem conservative. The rapid growth of new lines of employment can be gaged from census data. The number of technical engineers increased 90 percent between 1940 and 1950, and the number of auto mechanics and manufacturing foremen increased 75 percent. The number of operatives in manufacturing plants rose 50 percent.

More teachers, doctors, nurses, recreational leaders, welfare workers, writers, musicians, and workers in similar fields also will be needed.

EVERY STAGE in technologic development has meant an increase in specialization. Much of the new equipment is both specialized and expensive. Many of the new techniques call for precise knowledge in a limited field. Along with increased capital outlays and a greater division of labor, specialization has meant a large, integrated production structure in a plant and in an industry. So also on large farms.

The many skills needed in a larger farm business may have to be assigned to different individuals. The staff may include an expert cost accountant to ascertain which operations pay, a repair and maintenance crew for the farm machinery, a salesman who knows the market trends and has connections with dependable firms, a production manager who knows the crops best suited to the land and the methods of obtaining maximum yields from each, and a labor superintendent and foreman to direct the crews of tractor drivers, truckdrivers, and handworkers.

Very large farms are pushing technical specialization even further. They have chemists and plant breeders who formulate and produce the fertilizers, sprays, and genetic strains best adapted to the needs of the enterprise. An engineering staff designs and constructs machinery best suited to the operations. Nutritionists plan the livestock rations.

Many tasks have been moved from the farm to the factory, the shop, or the laboratory. The men who plan and assemble farm machines and those who develop and produce effective sprays and fertilizers are among them. Those who specialize in preserving and packaging farm products perform a function of increasing importance. Likewise the people who specialize in agricultural research, agricultural education, inspection, and grading, and market reporting are important parts of the organization that supplies food.

The growth of specialization also means that many jobs within the industrial and commercial structure can be learned in a relatively short time. Job opportunities therefore should be within the reach of many rural people if they are trained properly. They will need to learn to work carefully, rapidly, and accurately at routine tasks, but they will not have to master the business or production principles of the plant in which they are working. Many routine jobs are being eliminated through automation, so their future is less certain than that of jobs of a more technical nature.

Present trends result in a highly integrated employment structure in which there are fewer entrepreneurs and a greater number of hired workers whose activities must dovetail in order to achieve the highest rate of production. To be able to fit into such a structure is difficult for farm people who have taken pride in making all their own decisions. Yet reorganization of operations and jobs for increased productivity and better living overrides personal preferences.

On the other hand, specialization means that a worker becomes so closely identified with a particular job or operation that eventually he becomes dependent on it. Then, if it closes down, he is ill equipped to do other types of work. The industrial, office, or shop-worker is severely handicapped in meeting changes in employment, unless he has had broad occupational training.

THE FLOW of improvements will necessitate a continuous readjustment of the work force. If it can proceed smoothly, it will mean a shift of workers from positions of lower to those of higher productivity. The result will not be unemployment but a continuous growth in output and standards of living.

The major concern in this process is to keep the adjustment channels as open as possible and to provide assistance when the adjustment process lags. The lag in farm-nonfarm adjustment is not because people are unwilling to shift from agriculture. A high proportion do wish to shift but find several barriers in the way.

The first of these is their own lack of technical background. The proportion of urban jobs open to unskilled workers is small, and farm people have few of the specialized skills that are required.

The second barrier, related to the first, is the lack of established procedures for guiding, counseling, and retraining displaced workers. The displaced farmer then can only start at the bottom, but that is not where the demand for workers exists.

The surplus of manpower at the lower technical levels increases with the spread of mechanization and technology. The shortage of specialized technical workers also increases with the growth of technology. Yet the machinery to move workers from one level to the other is entirely inadequate. The technical requirements for jobs are increasing much more rapidly than the general increase in education and technical skills.

If we applied modern administrative technology to our national employment structure, a system of testing, counseling, and retraining all displaced workers would be a regular part of our employment machinery. To achieve that would be easy.

A real economic adjustment to technologic change might go still further. Training and advancement at the more technical levels could be speeded up so as to make room for new entrants in the less skilled positions. Readjustment pay or loans to displaced workers would still permit them to function as parents, consumers, and citizens. Special loans to bring plants and jobs to areas of labor surplus, or to assist workers to move to areas of labor need would be commonplace if we thought in terms of the social responsibility for technical change.

The really tough problem is to have sufficient employment opportunities available both for retrained workers and for new entrants into the job market. Without this, a retraining program may be futile.

The next step in modern technology might well be to determine how to keep our job structure expanding in step with the growth of population and productivity. This is an uncharted course. Only then will we have a completely equitable distribution of the gains from increased productivity.

# Machines and Farm Organization

Orlin J. Scoville

THINGS like fences and tools often have set the pattern, size, diversity, and form of farming and landholding.

The early patterns of landholding in most countries were evolved for farmers whose only tools were hoes and axes. The size and layout of farms and fields depended partly on tradition and arrangements for defense.

Very early it was seen that farmers were more productive if they were given allotments or made responsible for the care of a piece of ground. Tools influenced the size and shape of the holdings. In parts of England, for example, the original allotments were small, square patches to be tilled with a hoe. They were replaced by "the long acre" and narrow allotment strips on open fields when plows came.

Ideas of justice in land distribution also had a part. John Locke, in his second *Treatise of Civil Government* in 1690 said that ". . . every man should have as much land as he could make use of. . . ." How much a farmer could use depended then, as now, on the kind of power and tools he had.

The thread of this idea that the right to land depends on capacity to use it runs through many public policies of land distribution, notably in the United States.

Thus, according to P. W. Bidwell and J. I. Falconer, in their *History of Agriculture in the Northern United States*, the colonial distribution of land in the town of Guilford, Conn., allowed 5 acres of upland and 6 acres of meadow for each 100 pounds sterling of "estate" (a measure of livestock and working capital) and 3 acres of upland and one-half acre of meadow for each head in the family (a measure of labor force).

Many other forces influenced the original size of farms. Often they got only minor attention. The extent and organization of land resources never have been fitted perfectly to the capacities of labor and equipment. Tools have changed with time, and sizes of farms have tended to become even less well adapted to needs for efficient production. The problem of adjusting size, organization, and layout of farms to changes in mechanization has been continuous.

MACHINERY has determined the land that could be cared for at critical periods by one worker in a season. The crew requirements of machines have influenced the number of workers needed to run a farm. Machines have altered the kinds of labor needed—displacing field hands and increasing the need for mechanics and drivers.

The kind of machinery has affected the shape of fields, the location of the farmstead, and the economy of farming scattered tracts from a central place. The rubber-tired, general-purpose tractor has had a great influence in these respects.

The effect of mechanization on the organization of livestock production has been less pervasive, but there have been outstanding contributions. Thousands of farms would not have become livestock enterprises had they not had the pump, windmill, and motor. Our diversified system of crop and livestock farming owes much to the availability of inexpensive and laborsaving wire fencing to confine stock and make possible the rotation of fields and pastures.

The bearing of mechanization on the organization and size of farms has increased as the proportion of work done by machinery has gone up. The standard of a family farm of adequate size is no longer the acreage that the family can care for in a season but what family labor with one or two tractors can do.

Farm machinery, which is being developed toward goals of one-man operation and efficiency under diverse conditions, has strengthened the family farm. Family farms have contributed at the same time to the evolution of farm machines, many of which were farmer-designed to meet specific needs.

Had our national land policy favored peasant holdings, our farm implements would have been smaller, would have made more use of horsepower and manpower, and would be more expensive per unit of work done.

Had our policy favored latifundia, we would have had larger machines, more of them designed for operation by crews, and probably fewer multipurpose machines.

Had our policy been based on large farms and cheap labor, the progress of mechanization of any kind would have been slower. This was, in fact, the policy in the South before the Civil War, and the effects have carried over to recent times.

These are some of the points of interaction between the development of farm mechanization and the manner and scale of farm organization.

A FARM is organized efficiently when the available land, labor, and capital are combined in the proper proportions to give low-cost production. Machines are among the important production resources to be taken into account in organizing the farm, because they influence production costs and the amount of work that can be done in a season. They are "lumpy" resources. A farmer can use a little more or a little less seed or gasoline, but tractors and combines come in large units.

Equipment is a minor consideration in the organization of ranches, but it is very important for Corn Belt farms, wheat farms, and most types of field-crop farms. Where machinery is important, there is a tendency for family-operated farms to adjust to the size that a family can take care of in rush seasons, with the kinds of equipment available.

The work that has affected size of farm in the East has included plowing, mowing, harvesting, and (where corn and other row crops are important) seeding and cultivation.

In the Cotton Belt, before the day of machine pickers, mechanization had less to do with the size of cotton farms than did a family's capacity to chop and pick—about 10 to 15 acres on the average. An early mechanical limitation to the scale of one-man operation in the Great Plains wheat areas was capacity of the binder. With combines, seedbed preparation and fallowing became the busy seasons of the year. Although the adoption of plowless fallow systems has permitted a larger acreage to be cared for, tillage requirements still set the limits to one-man operation.

The time requirements for doing farmwork vary with the size of implement used. That is governed largely by available power and suitable topography.

The power unit has been outstanding among machines in setting the pattern of farm sizes.

E. A. Starch, in Bulletin 278 of the Montana Agricultural Experiment Station, "Farm Organization as Affected by Mechanization," reported that when half of a wheat farm was fallow, a 4-horse team could care for about 200 acres of land; with a 12-horse team, 640 acres could be handled; with a 16-horse team, 800 or 900. With a 3-plow tractor, one man could handle 800 acres; with a 4-plow tractor, 1,100; and with a 6-plow tractor, 1,800 acres.

A study of corn-livestock farms in Nebraska, reported in Technical Bulletin 1037 of the Department of Agriculture, indicated that with a 2-plow tractor and equipment, the maximum crop acreage that can be taken care of is about 155 acres. Acreage is limited by the time required to cultivate corn and put up the first cutting of hay around the middle of June and by a second busy season in mid-July, which includes the second cutting of hay, the cultivation of corn, and the harvest of small grains. With a 3-plow tractor and larger equipment, maximum crop acreage increases to about 170 acres.

C. P. Butler and H. L. Streetman, in a study of farms in South Carolina, found that the typical one-mule cotton farm had about 15 to 25 acres of cropland. With a tractor and complementary equipment, 150 acres of cropland could be handled with little additional seasonal labor except for cotton chopping and picking.

These examples illustrate the continually changing limits to the scale of family farming as power units and machines are improved.

The size of farm does not respond at once to new inventions, however. Instead, great stresses are set up in the structure of farming. Farmers mechanize; then they find that they have machine capacity to handle more land. The search for additional land may cause them to move, to rent additional land, or to bid up the price of neighboring tracts.

The Department of Agriculture reported that 42 percent of all farmland purchases in 1959 were for farm enlargement. Only 23 percent were for this purpose in 1949. For major farming areas, the proportions of land transfers in 1959 that were made to enlarge farms were: Northeastern Dairy, 22 percent; General Farming, 26; Lake States Dairy, 28; Eastern Cotton, 31; Range Livestock, 48; Corn Belt, 48; Western Cotton, 60; and Wheat, 66.

It is not imperative that farmers adjust to the maximum acreage that can be handled with their equipment. Per acre costs for each machine tend to go down as acreage is increased, but the additional reduction tapers off into insignificance as maximum acreage is approached.

The typical relationship between acreage and unit-cost is a curve that shows a steep decline in costs until utilization reaches about one-fourth to one-half the maximum possible with the machine and a very moderate reduction in costs with greater use.

High costs per acre or per hour with limited use reflect the costs of obsolescence for machines that are not used enough to wear out.

Many of the major innovations that have created the pressures and opportunities for farm enlargement have been in use for years. The general-purpose tractor, with mounted implements, was introduced in 1924, for example. Yet many farmers still have not approached the maximum size of farm that is possible with the equipment available.

FARMERS may take an alternative tack. They may hire expensive machines. That, though, sets up stresses of a different kind, because the farm may no longer provide adequate employment.

How extensively custom work is used as a means of adapting the operation of farms to mechanization is shown by these figures of the millions of acres on which custom work was done in 1955: Baling hay and straw, 36.5; combining, 30.5; machine cornpicking, 8; machine cottonpicking, 1.25; mowing, 3.5; plowing, 4; disking, 3.3; and planting and seeding, 5.

Ten million tons of feed were custom ground and mixed; and 577 million bushels of corn were custom shelled.

Not all custom work is done on small farms. Some of it is hired by larger farmers whose farms are too large for one machine and too small for two. Much custom combining is done on farms of all sizes.

Itinerant operators can do this work at rates that are competitive with costs of ownership by farmers because of the high volume of work done per machine.

Custom combine operators harvest grain from Texas, where they commence work in late May, to Canada, where the season closes in September. The possibilities of custom work modify but do not eliminate the influence of machine capacity on adjustment in the size of farm units.

THE DESIGN of field machinery has changed the layout of farms. Rubber-tired tractors, which can travel on roads, opened the way to farming scattered tracts as a single unit and to making farm units of efficient size, particularly in places where land can be rented. The farming of several tracts under one management is common in the Great Plains; often the different parcels are shifted from one unit to another from year to year.

Changes in labor organization and total labor needs have been substantial but machines have changed only slightly the average total labor force on American farms. The census of 1910 reported an average of 2.1 workers per farm, of which 0.5 was hired. For the census of 1954, the figures were 1.8 and 0.4.

This stability through periods of great change suggests that both economic efficiency and the preferences of American farm operators support the

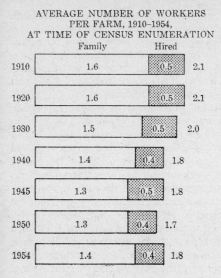

AVERAGE NUMBER OF WORKERS
PER FARM, 1910–1954,
AT TIME OF CENSUS ENUMERATION
Family        Hired

| Year | Family | Hired | Total |
|------|--------|-------|-------|
| 1910 | 1.6 | 0.5 | 2.1 |
| 1920 | 1.6 | 0.5 | 2.1 |
| 1930 | 1.5 | 0.5 | 2.0 |
| 1940 | 1.4 | 0.4 | 1.8 |
| 1945 | 1.3 | 0.5 | 1.8 |
| 1950 | 1.3 | 0.4 | 1.7 |
| 1954 | 1.4 | 0.4 | 1.8 |

organization of production around a family-sized work force. It has been accomplished only because this size of labor force has been taken as a norm in designing the common types of farm equipment.

Mechanization has reduced the number of jobs that require large crews. Grain can be combined, hauled, and stored with a crew of three. A typical crew for binding and shocking in 1900 or so would have included five men, and the threshing crew would have required eight. Hay can be field-baled and stored efficiently with a crew of three, compared with the five or six needed for the old system of stacking or hauling to the mow. American farms well organized around a core of family labor can compete successfully with the "factories in the fields."

Walter Prescott Webb, in his book, *The Great Plains,* listed the Colt revolver, the windmill, and the barbed-wire fence as the strategic inventions in the conquest of the Plains.

Well-drilling machinery and the pump and windmill met the need for an inexpensive source of underground water. This was essential to the settlement of the arid West. The self-regulating windmill was developed in 1854 and the steel windmill tower in 1883.

Windmills made it possible to maintain the pattern of scattered farmsteads in arid regions. They permitted development of diversified livestock farming and of home gardens on dryland farms. Around them were created little oases on the dry prairies.

Engines, electric motors, and turbine pumps further increased the supply of low-cost ground water in arid regions and created new opportunities for irrigated farms. The pump-irrigated units are more diversified, and the family-sized unit has fewer acres than the nearby dryland farms. Pump irrigation helps to stabilize the feed supply in arid regions. It had an important effect on the organization of farms in these areas by reducing the risks of livestock farming.

The buildings, fences, and fixed equipment of the farm influence the choice of enterprises open to a farm manager. The matching of buildings and equipment to the needs of the farm may be difficult on rented farms where tenants make production decisions while landlords furnish the fixed equipment.

Dairy and poultry enterprises can be conducted on a commercial scale only when adequate housing is available. Beef, sheep, and hog production are possible with simple structures.

These differences are reflected in the tenure statistics. Ninety-four percent of commercial poultry farms in 1954 were operated by owners, part-owners, or managers. For dairy farms, the proportion was 86 percent, and for livestock farms other than poultry and dairy, 80 percent. But only 67 percent of cash-grain farms, 57 percent of other field-crop farms, and 41 percent of cotton farms were operated by owners, part-owners, or managers. Buildings are only one of the reasons for these differences, but they are important.

Buildings last a long time, and they reduce the flexibility of management. A farm equipped for dairying will not be shifted to some other enterprise to take advantage of short-run fluctuations in comparative advantage. Existing stanchion barns continue to be used, although other systems of dairying are cheaper to construct and may save labor.

With few exceptions, buildings and fixed equipment are becoming more specialized and thus may further reduce flexibility in management. The stanchion barn can be converted to loose housing or even to poultry housing or to storage, although conversion may be costly. But the walk-through milking parlor has no alternative uses. The modern broiler plant, with its built-in feeders and waterers, also has few alternative uses. Beef and sheep feed yards are becoming increasingly elaborate. On balance, the movement is in the direction of increased specialization. Future obsolescence costs may be high.

Fences are an important item of fixed equipment on many farms. The development of cheap fencing materials has had an important bearing on farm management. On the Plains, neither stone nor wood was available for fences, and hedges would not grow. A settled agriculture would have been impossible without an inexpensive means of enclosure, and the invention of barbed wire in 1884 opened a new era of settlement in the West.

THREE ECONOMIC forces have influenced farm mechanization—the family farm, a high wage level, and cheap land.

Because four-fifths of our farm labor force is family labor, farmers have insisted upon machines that could be run by one man whenever possible. Before self-propelled combines were introduced, many farmers had ingeniously contrived systems of levers, motors, and pushbuttons to control the combine from the tractor seat, or to control the tractor from the combine seat. Farmers were drawing harrows behind plows and drills behind harrows years before the experts had perfected plow-planter units. Among the earliest practical cotton-harvesting machines were the farmer-made sleds that appeared in the Texas Panhandle around 1914.

To a considerable extent, these efforts to save labor were made because hired labor was expensive, but family farmers also sought to avoid the inconvenience and uncertainty of depending on wage hands whenever possible. They did not think of mechanical power in abstract terms but as a means of taking a load off their own backs.

It is the dual role of family farmers as workers and as managers that makes them so effective in promoting farm mechanization. The hired manager can see the need for an improvement and can recommend that it be made, but there his authority ends. The sharecropper can feel the need for laborsaving equipment, but as a rule he can neither finance it nor acquire the additional land to make it worth while to use it.

The third contribution of family farming to mechanization is in our land-tenure arrangements. The American family farm is no hereditary fief. Usually it is partly owned, partly rented. Sometimes it is wholly rented by the operator. Even when it is operator-owned, its boundaries change over the years as land is sold off or bought in, to accommodate changes in the economical size of operating unit. This flexibility of American farm units makes it easier to adapt them to changing mechanization.

The second major economic fact that has influenced mechanization is the rate of wages. Outside of the South, American agriculture has always had to compete with industry for manpower. In recent years this has been so even in the South. Aside from major depressions, wages in industry have been high enough to attract a stream of workers from the farms. In most years since 1916, migration from rural areas has served to reduce the total number of workers in agriculture.

Farm wages have risen as a result of increased productivity and the competition of industrial jobs. Farmers have turned to mechanization as a means of increasing worker productivity so that higher wages can be paid and as a means of getting the work done with a smaller labor force. A part, at least, of the difference between the level of mechanization here and abroad is explained by differences in wage rates. As wages go up, it pays to use more machines and fewer men.

In recent years, for example, it took about 67 gallons of milk to pay for a week's hired labor on a midwestern farm, but only 39 gallons were needed for a week's labor in the eastern counties of England. Two tons of beets or 7.5 hundredweights of grain would pay for a week's labor in the United States, compared with 1 ton and 3.75 hundredweights in England. These differences in the real cost of labor are reflected in differences in mechanization in the two countries.

The third economic factor has been the price of land. Although land values have been rising, land was still cheap enough in 1960 so that it could be left idle if it were not adapted to mechanized farming.

Large acreages of former cropland are now in trees, brush, or weeds. Cropland used for crops in the Northeast has declined from 23 million to 15 million acres, and in the Southern States from 116 million acres to 98 million. These lands are mainly stony, hilly, or not worth draining and poorly adapted to a machine agriculture. Vestiges of arable hill-farming remain, but commercial crop farming is moving rapidly toward the flatlands.

As crop production has moved out of the hills, the organization of hill-farms has been disrupted. Farmsteads have been abandoned and land has been left idle. Improved machinery for grassland renovation and management, together with cheap fencing and live-stock facilities, might make it economical to develop livestock farms in these areas.

WE NEED to have greater flexibility built into our farm structures so that farmers can take advantage of changing economic conditions without incurring heavy obsolescence costs. Perhaps buildings could more often be designed in modular or building-block units, to be taken apart and remodeled as needed.

The peculiar equipment needs of part-time farmers should be taken into account. Their places usually are small; equipment therefore should be adapted to small acreages. But they tend to value their time at off-farm wage rates; equipment capacity therefore should be high. Since the total amount of work done in a year is low, investment in machinery and structures must be kept down. These contradictory needs suggest that special study should be made of kinds of equipment and buildings that would come nearest to meeting requirements of part-time farmers. There are about one half-million part-time farmers, and improvement in their facilities would be worth while.

# Work Simplification

Lowell S. Hardin

WORK SIMPLIFICATION is the systematic development and use of easier, quicker, and more economical ways to do jobs. We study and improve our methods of working to get more and better work done in less time and with less effort.

The approach is simple: We want to eliminate unnecessary work. We simplify the motions of hands and body that are used in doing necessary work. We arrange convenient work areas and locations of materials. We try to use our equipment more fully and improve on its adequacy and suitability. We organize the routine so that machines and men are used effectively.

Work simplification has a place in the operation of a farm, factory, store, office, home—wherever human energy is used.

Efficient production involves two types of decisions.

The first includes the "what-to-do" decisions—what crops, what kinds of livestock, what feed, what fertilizer. The what decisions require understanding of scientific principles of production and business organization.

The second kind we call "how-to-do-it" decisions. They involve practices and operations. Most of us see wasted land, building, or storage space. Are wasted time, energy, and labor just as apparent?

Some persons spend most of their managing time studying what to do. They take the how for granted. Sooner or later, however, we are forced to think of how we do jobs. Work simplification suggests an early, orderly approach to the how decisions.

Robert M. Carter published one of the early and important work simplification studies as Vermont Agricultural Experiment Station Bulletin 503 in 1943. It was made before milking parlors were developed, but it has a lesson for us.

The Vermont farmer in Dr. Carter's study had 22 dairy cows. He was already above average in efficiency. After 4 months of study and a change of chore routines and minor revisions in building and equipment, they showed this progress: The daily chore time had been reduced from 5 hours, 44 minutes to 3 hours, 39 minutes. The saving was 2 hours, 5 minutes a day. The walking was reduced from 3.25 miles to 1.25 miles—a saving of 2 miles a day. The saving of 760 man-hours and 730 miles of walking in a year was made at a cash cost of less than 50 dollars.

Four kinds of changes were made on the farm. The stable was rearranged. Tools and supplies were put in more convenient places. Needed small equipment—shovels, forks, feed carts—was provided. Work routines and methods were improved. Jobs were combined.

A new 4-minute milking routine was established.

The example shows what we can do with thoughtful action without spending much money. Labor and travel might have been further reduced by building a new barn or erecting a new milking parlor. At the time, the dairyman started with a stanchion barn arrangement and continued with a stanchion arrangement. His was not yet the ultimate in efficiency. It was, however, substantially improved, and work simplification had become a part of his thinking.

Savings thus may be made in time and in energy. They may be in quality of work and in total cost. Studies in agriculture show that most jobs can be done easier, faster, and more economically—if we want to give them serious analysis.

SYSTEMATIC APPLICATION of work simplification to industrial jobs has been going on a long time. Many firms have established motion and time departments.

Time study goes back to the work of Frederick W. Taylor, who in 1881 originated it as an aid in improving methods. He used a stopwatch, a keen eye, and his active mind and imagination to make important contributions.

His analysis of shoveling at the Bethlehem Steel Works in 1898 illustrates his use of time studies. Workers used their own shovels to lift 3.5 to 38 pounds per shovel load. Taylor's research showed that 21.5 pounds on a shovel enabled a man to handle a maximum tonnage per day. Shovels were designed of the proper size to accommodate this load. Methods were prescribed. Wage incentive plans were developed. Workers did more, and their earnings rose, but the total cost of handling materials dropped.

Today we probably would move directly to a mechanical solution to such a problem of handling materials. Yet in many businesses we need to examine comparative costs of intermediate solutions that may fall short of complete mechanization.

While Taylor was adding the tool of time study to scientific management, pioneering work in motion study was being done by Frank B. Gilbreth and Lillian M. Gilbreth.

As employees of a building contractor, they discovered that bricklayers used three different sets of motions. One set was used for rapid work, a second for slow work, and a third to instruct someone else how to do the work.

They were challenged to discover whether any one of the three was best. They analyzed them carefully. They replanned the work place and improved the equipment. The number of motions required to lay a brick was reduced from 18 to 5. Again earnings rose as the workers' output increased when they put the new method to work. Construction costs were lower.

Today the work of time-study and motion-study investigators is usually merged into a methods or motion and time study department that analyzes the work and time necessary to do a job.

Chore work with livestock has been especially responsive to their questioning processes. Even the work patterns in using the herringbone milking parlor, pipeline milking machine, and bulk tank on the dairy farm continue to be improved.

THE STARTING POINT in systematic analysis is observation. The necessary facts may be collected in several ways.

We usually break a job down into its parts by preparing a process chart, the key step.

Few of us know exactly how we do a job. It is easier to describe the method someone else uses than to record our own work. Important details escape us even though we do the job hundreds of times. A process chart is a step-by-step outline and description of each detail or operation involved in doing a job. It is helpful on this to record the distances that are traveled, the quantities or kinds of materials that are handled, and the time that is taken. Such a chart

may follow the product or the worker step by step.

FARMERS DO NOT have a methods department on each of their operations. Some farm-supply and marketing firms have research departments, of which methods study is a part.

Alert, progressive farmers naturally believe in work simplification. The farmer's research departments—the Department of Agriculture and the agricultural experiment stations—have spent most of their energies studying what to do, not how to do it. Young farmers have learned how to do jobs mostly from their fathers and from other farmers.

Because he recognized the need for systematic study of ways of doing farm jobs, Dean E. C. Young of Purdue University helped establish a national work simplification project in 1943. It was to deal primarily with agriculture. Agriculturalists in several research institutions learned the techniques of studying motion and time. They modified and adapted them to study and improve ways of doing farm and marketing work. Of a continuing flow of studies and results, some deal with farm production and some with processing and marketing.

You can use any ruled sheet of paper to make a process chart. Distances involved in each operation can be paced or estimated. The time should be checked. You can estimate or check weights of materials handled by sampling. Watch the job all the way through at least once before making the process chart. Then record each operation as it is done.

If you record the time, write down the consecutive time rating each time the worker shifts from one operation to the next. Make your descriptions of the operations brief. After the job is finished, go back and subtract your times to get the elapsed time per operation.

You may find a sketch of the layout of the building and work areas helpful. Once the sketch is made, you may draw in paths of travel. Some place pins in a board on which the layout is drawn. Thread or string is used to join the pins to follow the path of travel.

Several opportunities for improvement become obvious once you understand how a job is actually done. Understanding of principles of effective work, however, prompts the key questions. It often is a good idea to see how others do similar kinds of work.

THE SECOND STEP involves analysis or thinking about the job as a whole now that you have described it. The thinking process, which gives us ideas for improvement, is again rather simple.

All of us do many things from habit. Some of the things that we do are not necessary. We therefore ask first whether we can eliminate or leave out some of the things that we are now doing. Livestock producers have eliminated frequent cleaning of poultry houses as they developed deep litter and roosting racks. Some livestock feeders have eliminated the hand feeding of silage by making trench silos self-feeding affairs. Someone always has to be the first to try doing a job in an easier way to see if it is a good way.

As we puzzle over the way we do the job, we discover that frequently jobs or parts of jobs can be combined. We can do two parts of a job at once. Crop farmers are ingenious in combining tools to make one trip do the work of two. Corn producers are experimenting with devices to plant corn at the same time that the field is plowed. More and more farmers operate two tractors in tandem from one set of controls. The principle here becomes one of doing two or more jobs or operations at once whenever an equally good job can be done.

If elimination or combination is not possible, we examine when the job should be done. That a job or a part of a job has always been done at a certain time of day or at a certain point in the routine does not mean that the time cannot be changed to advantage. The time when the jobs are done often determines the work required and the results accomplished. Cultivation when weeds are at the proper age for destruction may save added cultivations. Timing of spray applications may be the key to successful use of the material. Used oil will drain faster and better when a tractor is hot than when it is cold.

Chores can be organized so that another part of a job is taken up when the first part is completed. Backtracking and empty travel can be eliminated with a little head work. Even the time at which the dairy cow is milked can be adjusted to the family or work schedules.

Locations of feeds and supplies often can be changed to reduce the amount of walking and carrying.

Midwestern farmers have experimented with the grain bank idea. They deposit their grain in the local elevator. On call, the elevator man returns the grain, perhaps in a mixed ration, to the farmer's self-feeder for the livestock. The plan changes storage and feeding practices and makes a new job for the farm-supply business. The grainman takes over certain feeding operations from the livestock farmer. The plan involves a new concept of the whole system of production, building needs, feed handling procedures, and locations of supplies. Much custom grain storage space has been constructed in our feed-producing sections. Should the quantities carried in storage under Government control be reduced, farmers and storage owners may develop further the grain bank system to use excess storage capacity.

Temporary feed storages may save miles of walking and hours of shoveling and hauling. Another way to reduce work is to keep shovels, forks, and other small tools in a definite place near the spot they are used oftenest. People sometimes skimp on small tools. When small items of equipment are used frequently at different places, duplicates should be placed there.

BUILDINGS and work places need to be arranged and located properly.

Almost any layout can be rearranged for greater convenience. New doors, new work centers, and revised storage areas may shorten travel and work routes.

Layout and arrangements of farmsteads are not easily changed. Changes in building interiors usually are less costly and result in more important changes in work methods than shifts in the locations of the structures themselves. One should provide for circular travel whenever possible. Uneven floors, obstructing sills, and other barriers to easy movement should be avoided.

The equipment you use may not be adequate and suitable. Young men sometimes believe all equipment their fathers installed is old fashioned—but they may not be the ones who pay the bills for the new equipment.

Equipment, however, does not need to be expensive to take hard work out of jobs. Water will run, feed will move by gravity, and rolling wheels will carry a load easier than man. Small equipment, such as carts and mechanical water systems and feed storages, often can pay for itself in labor saved.

The importance of substituting mechanical for human power is a continuing force, but that does not mean that we should have too many gadgets. Gadgets frequently prove to be places to spend time and money rather than to save it. Once you adopt key equipment, use it fully. That means keeping it in adjustment. You may need to add companion pieces or change the layout rather than acquire large machinery items themselves.

A hand job, too, can be made less tiring. Handwork has been most economical in harvesting some fruit and vegetables. For such repetitive work, small savings on each performance multiply to significant totals. Arrange hand jobs so both hands can work. Have tools or containers near at hand. Think about your own comfort and the comfort of those who work with you. It is no sin to sit, if almost as much can be accomplished by sitting as by standing.

Adjust work benches to the height of the worker. Small mechanical devices often speed such jobs as milking, hand harvesting, potato cutting, seed treating, egg cleaning, and chicken culling.

The ideas for improvement which result from using the questioning approach should be written down. You have now thought through what you are doing and why you do it that way. Questions have been raised about existing methods and procedures and why you use them.

THE THIRD STEP is deciding. Here we develop new routines and compare them with the present ones. We may copy good ideas, use our own good judgment, bring together ideas seen in many places, or budget a new routine we have created.

We sometimes organize the ideas for a new routine into a revised process chart. Times and distances as well as effects on quality of work can be spelled out on the new process chart alongside the old one. The aim of this step is to work out on paper or in one's mind the best possible improved method before actually trying it.

THE FOURTH STEP involves action. Here we test and use the proved developments. A good idea is of little value until it is placed into use. Put to work the method described in the improved process chart. No method is so good that it cannot be further improved. Too often one change is made without giving thought to further improvement.

This thinking is typified by the farmer who kept his feed in one end of the barn and his livestock in the other end. When asked why he did not store the feed nearer the animals, he replied, "Oh, you should have seen where the feed used to be—over there across the road." He had made one improvement and thought he was finished. The search for a better method is a never-ending process.

These four steps are variations of a scientific method that suggest a way to improve—simplify—work. Principles, however, are involved. Some of them are obvious and need no description. Yet they work for us and are worth our thought.

HERE ARE SUGGESTIONS that research workers have evolved from analyses of work simplification:

Develop a questioning attitude toward precedent as a sole guide to procedures, work methods, and equipment. View your own work as through a stranger's eyes. Imagine that you have taken a moving picture of your work method. By seeing it there and laying it bare, you have defined the problems that give you trouble.

Go visiting. Read. Gather and compare alternatives for cost and for satisfaction. We can easily become so involved in doing our own work that we do not bring to bear on it the ideas and experiences that others would gladly share.

Take time to train yourself and to train others in good methods. Close study is often required before a best method can be recommended. Job training, even with family help, pays big dividends.

Examine carefully the present ratio of wage rates to the cost of equipment. These favor reasonable substitution of capital for labor. They do not preclude improvement of work routines within the framework of existing machinery, buildings, and work places. The key to work simplification is not necessarily the purchase of a pushbutton operation.

Select or develop equipment, forms, and procedures to fit the proper work process. Avoid building a method about a particular gadget, form, or precedent. The work method should be thought out independently of a particular machine, structure, or new piece of equipment. Once you have evolved a method that will be appropriate, efficient, and economical, the equipment and workplace should be modified or acquired to fit this process.

Examine each overall process for possible steps that may be eliminated and combined. Then determine whether

CHART FOR ESTIMATING HOW MUCH IN-VESTMENT WILL BE JUSTIFIED TO SAVE A GIVEN AMOUNT OF LABOR.

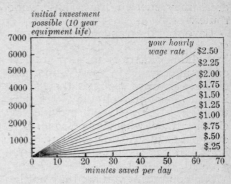

HOW TO USE

Find your time savings on the bottom of the chart, look directly above this to the diagonal line labeled with your hourly wage rate, then by looking directly across to the left of the chart you will find how much you can spend for labor-saving equipment and yet break even

each necessary step is performed where and when it is done most economically. Yes, this is emphasis on the obvious. Examine your own daily routine, however, if you doubt the tendency of people to retain habit-forming patterns beyond their time of usefulness.

Take small savings seriously. They accumulate. Much work is repetitive. Small savings accumulate to major earnings or cost reductions when multiplied by days, weeks, and years.

Make someone definitely responsible. Do not hesitate to delegate or accept delegated responsibility to do jobs and to study jobs. Work will not be simplified and management will not be improved unless someone assumes responsibility.

Insist that the system of payment you use rewards workers for quality and quantity of services rendered. It is not enough for us to get paid for merely being present on the job. Economic progress dictates that earnings be in line with productivity. This built-in incentive system helps each of us to become interested in simplifying our work and adding to the effectiveness of the project.

Remember that the most valuable of

Years ago, when the distance between the farmer and consumer was short, labor was abundant, and volumes were small, products were handled mostly by hand one item at a time. Milk moved from farm to consumer or to a milk depot, where the consumer brought his bucket to have it filled. Fruit, vegetables, poultry, and eggs were sold in like manner. As farms and their output expanded, distant markets were tapped and more handling was required. Wages rose, labor became scarcer, and the incentive for more mechanization was greater. Production tended to move into specialized areas. Farmers now produce for distant, unknown markets, but they must gear production to market requirements. Extensive facilities are needed to assemble, pack, process, store, and distribute the products to consumers. This section illustrates some aspects of modern marketing and research, which have changed greatly since the days when a farmer sold his melons from a 1907 model "High Wheeled Auto Wagon."

More than 50 million pounds of red tart cherries are marketed each year in this way: Pails filled by pickers in the orchards are trucked to a central loading place, where they are poured into tanks containing cold water. The tanks move to a receiving station, where they are transferred to bulk tank trucks, which also contain water.

Time and effort are saved when apples are put into pallet boxes in the orchard and then trucked (as in the photograph above) to the processing plant. A simple dumping arrangement empties the pallet containers at the plant. Other equipment that inverts the containers and returns them to storage also is available.

Peaches in baskets pass through a flood-type hydrocooler. Afterwards, workers select peaches of uniform size and good color and put them in cartons.

Water is removed from citrus juice in a concentrator or evaporator. Then the concentrated juice is blended with fresh juice to restore its proper flavor. It is chilled quickly. Machines like those in the picture below can fill and seal 400 cans of the concentrate a minute. The filled cans move to the freezer, where temperatures are below zero.

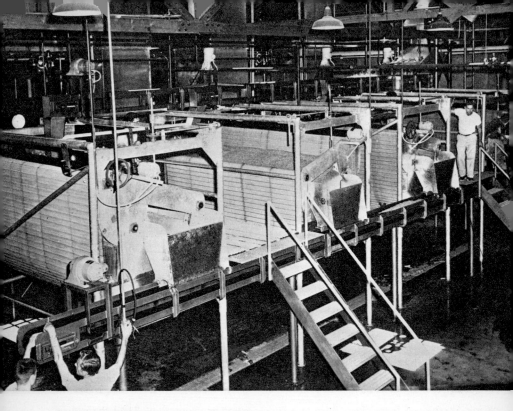

A belt-trough dehydrator, developed by engineers in the Department of Agriculture, reduces the moisture content of pieces of fruit and vegetables. Below, a worker loads trays of cartons of green beans into a plate freezer, in which the beans are quickly frozen.

Of the many operations performed in a sanitary, efficient, modern broiler dressing plant, one is shown in the picture above. As the chickens emerge from a washer, after they have been eviscerated, a worker clips off the neck, which is to be packed with giblets. An automatic machine (below) fills half-gallon cartons with three flavors of ice cream.

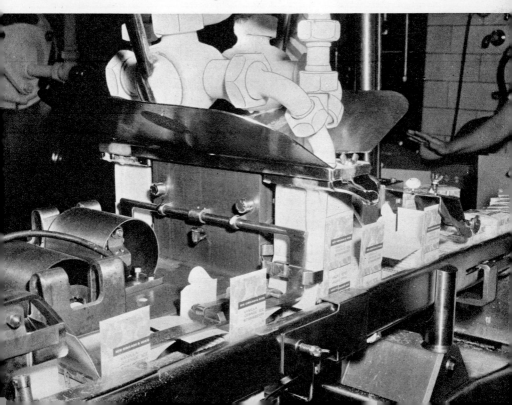

James M. Williams, Jr., an agricultural engineer in the Department of Agriculture, operates a new "flight-bar" cotton gin, which he developed. It separates cottonseed from lint six to eight times faster than conventional roller gins. In a Connecticut curing barn, leaves of tobacco of the cigar-wrapper type are hung on sticks.

Another development is a 1-day haying operation. On a farm in Ohio, hay is cut in the morning, raked in early afternoon, baled, dried in covered wagons overnight, and unloaded into the mow the next morning. Farm products are tested and inspected repeatedly at many stages. An example (below) is the electric moisture meter that determines the percentage of moisture in a rough rice sample.

Most products, as we have seen, do not move directly from the farms or processing plants to consumers. At some point they usually are stored in elevators (above) or warehouses before proceeding to market.

Farm goods are transported to market in several ways. Some go by truck. Pictured above is a refrigerated semitrailer, which hauls perishable products from the Rocky Mountain area to Chicago. Some products go by train. On an average day, 67 freight trains move into and out of Frontier Yard at Buffalo, N.Y.

Some products move by both. Piggyback truck and rail service has grown in recent years. A trailer is loaded at the warehouse and hauled by rail to its destination city, where a tractor pulls it to the door of the market or store. At least one loading and unloading operation is saved thereby. At New Orleans, La., grain is unloaded from rail cars and barges to an elevator and transferred to oceangoing ships.

Above, a city market in 1910. Below, watermelon time at the farmers' market in Cordele, Ga. Growers sell most of their melons to carlot buyers. The melons are loaded into trailer trucks and rail cars for fast shipment to market.

A grocery store in 1910; a supermarket in 1960. And so our story of farm production is almost told: This is the goal of the long chain of endeavor from farmer to consumer. But the farmer's power to produce derives not alone from his muscles, machines, land, structures, skill. At his side always to help him is a phalanx of researchers, engineers, and market specialists, whose work is exemplified in the pictures that follow.

An experimental machine, with an appropriate mechanism to feed eggs into it and remove the eggs after they are sorted, can sort 7,200 eggs an hour. A three-filter photoelectric reflectance measuring instrument (top right) measures the color of raw tomato juice. A recording shear press measures shear characteristics of farm commodities (bottom left). The horticultural spectrophotometer measures the maturity of fruit by transmitting light through the intact fruit to express the flesh color of the sample. Research engineers of the Department of Agriculture helped to develop these useful devices.

At the Agricultural Research Center at Beltsville, Md., a side-delivery rake is used to remove a heavy mulch sprayed with radioactive isotopes. Agricultural engineers and soil scientists designed this and similar tests to find ways of removing radioactive fallout from agricultural lands should the need ever arise. Below: Scientists load belt hoppers and monitor radioactive fertilizer in a fertilizer-placement experiment.

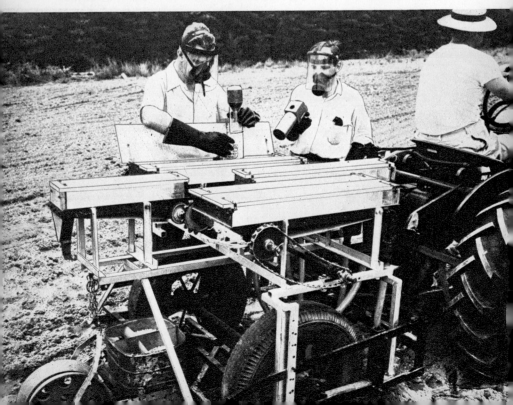

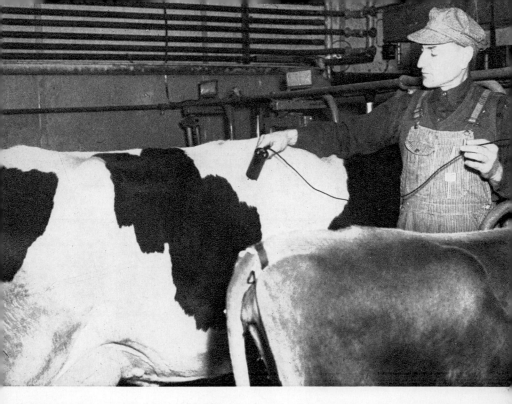

Animal responses, such as surface temperature, can be measured most easily and reliably in a laboratory, where the environment can be controlled. The picture above is of the Psychroenergetic Laboratory at the University of Missouri. The effects of air velocity on the physiological reactions of small animals are studied by means of a wind tunnel.

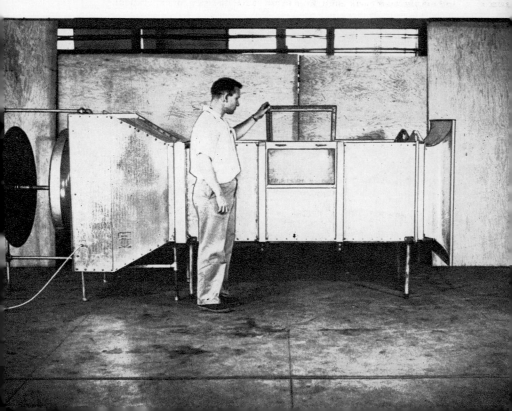

An evaluation of methods of improving an animal's thermal environment must be made on some basis that is independent of the animal in order to reduce the time and effort of the evaluation. Shade materials were compared on a thermal basis to determine their relative effectiveness in reducing the radiation heat loads under them. Below: A portable bulk milk tank under test at Beltsville, Md.

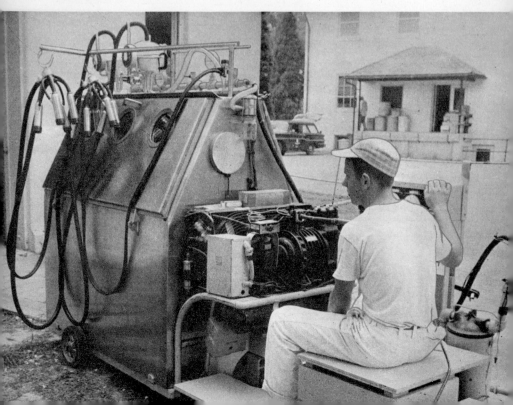

Foundation and fill materials are tested in the Soil Mechanics Testing Laboratory, Albuquerque, N. Mex. Below: This Rainulator (rainfall simulator), developed by men in the Department of Agriculture and Purdue University, enables soil scientists and agricultural engineers to determine the effects of certain farm practices on soil erosion losses in just a few years instead of decades.

Scientists modified a potato planter to study effects of placing fertilizer in two bands 1 inch below potato seed and 7 inches apart. At the National Tillage Machinery Laboratory, Auburn, Ala., Carl Reaves watches what happens when a cultivating tool moves the soil. The tool (a chisel) remains stationary while the field (soil) moves. The white lines (wet facial tissues) show how the soil reacts to the tool.

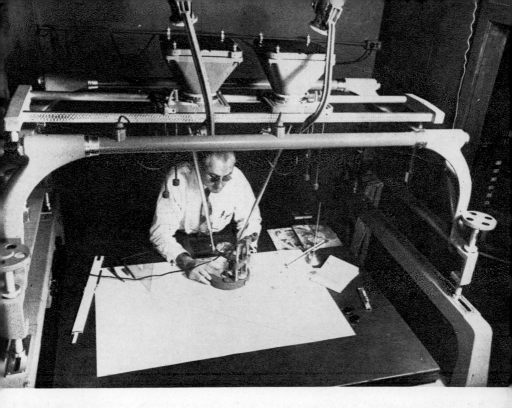

With a Kelsh Plotter, a Soil Conservation Service research worker in Milwaukee, Wis., makes contour maps from air photographs. Below: An engineering drafting room, where farm machines are designed.

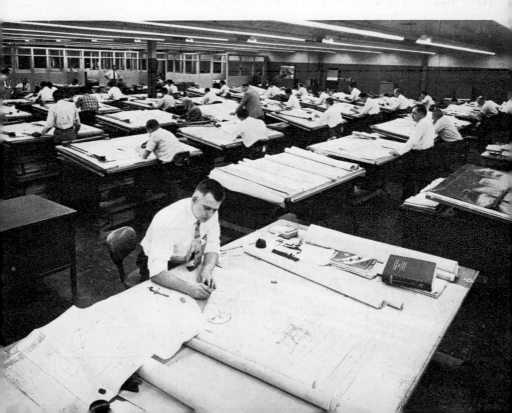

An experimental front-mounted corn planter is being assembled. Below: To learn the strength of the metals they use, engineers put a brittle coating on the front axle of a wagon and study the cracks that indicate stress.

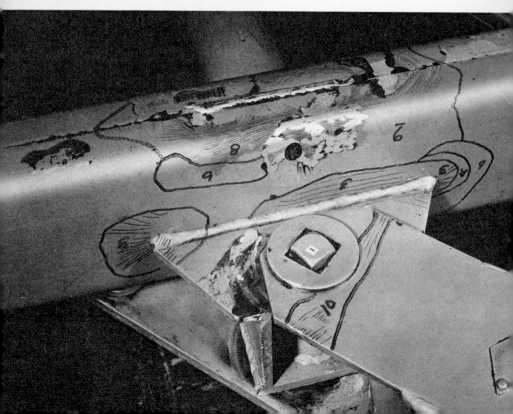

Engineers prepare to drop-test a tractor front end and frame in a laboratory. Below: An experimental cucumber harvester developed at Michigan State University. The vines must be trained to form a row no wider than the pickup unit.

Agricultural engineers at the National Tillage Machinery Laboratory study the relation of soil characteristics to equipment design. A milling company maintains this 1-acre research and demonstration plant near Cayuga, N.Y. It has a unit for boars, a sow colony, farrowing house, nursery, and finishing porch.

all resources is the human resource. Not only is man the indispensable ingredient of farm or nonfarm business. He is the reason that business exists.

Each of us might well build into his approach to work a mental stop-and-go light. Such a mental light flashes red when we do a job in an ineffective, unsystematic, and wasteful fashion. It flashes caution as we think through how the job might be improved. The green light comes on when we have evolved a more effective, economical, and efficient process.

THE AVERAGE AGE of farmworkers is high. The accomplishment of younger workers is greater than that of older persons. Through simplification and mechanization, the less active farmer, however, remains productive.

In a study of 413 farmers in Indiana in 1957, those under 35 years of age had an average work output the equivalent of 32.7 productive work days a month. Those over 65 years of age had an average accomplishment about one-half as great—15.1 productive days a month. Many factors were involved, including health, size of business, and extent of mechanization.

The whole case for work simplification, however, is not in efficiency and reduction of cost. Part of it is in satisfactions—satisfactions to less active (even impaired) workers, who thereby can pursue the career and vocation of their choice.

THE SUBSTITUTION of mechanical power and equipment for human energy continues to move forward more rapidly for crops than for livestock. Part of the explanation rests in the rigidities imposed by existing farm structures. When we make our buildings farm tools to reduce labor and costs, we do several things.

We are practicing closer confinement of livestock. Thus we move toward ever greater control of the environment and of the whole production process.

We are creating shells with flexible interiors and large, clear spans. This

AVERAGE PRODUCTIVE DAYS OF WORK ACCOMPLISHED PER FARMWORKER PER MONTH BY AGE OF OPERATOR, INDIANA STUDY, 1957

| Age of operator | Number of farmers | Average productive days of work output per month |
|---|---|---|
| Under 35 | 31 | 32.7 |
| 35–39 | 40 | 28.2 |
| 40–44 | 47 | 22.7 |
| 45–49 | 70 | 21.0 |
| 50–54 | 41 | 20.5 |
| 55–59 | 74 | 17.8 |
| 60–64 | 84 | 16.4 |
| 65 or older | 26 | 15.1 |
| All ages | 413 | 20.8 |

means that we often store supplies on ground level rather than overhead. We self-feed more. Greater use is made of concrete for feeding and storage areas. Present and future laborsaving equipment are integrated into the structure.

Nevertheless, further mechanization of chore work remains a major challenge. Automation in poultry production may well be a prototype for other classes of livestock. Processes for bulk handling of feed and forages are developing rapidly. Many farmers have eliminated "packaging and unpackaging" of hay (bales) and feed (bags).

Work simplification suggests careful analysis of alternate ways to obtain the use of the new technology. Outright purchase may be more costly than rental, custom, or exchange work.

The principles of work simplification apply also to nonfarm agriculturists— those who work in farm-supply, assembly, processing, and marketing firms. Notable successes have been achieved in simplifying the work of grain elevators, dairy plants, wholesale markets, and retail food stores. Improvements range from new checkout systems to warehouse layout and the design of new markets. Savings in marketing are important to all of us.

Sons of farmers look increasingly to nonfarm businesses for employment. The ability to analyze jobs and improve them stands people in good stead wherever they work.

THE TECHNIQUES of work simplification have been put to another use. Farmers suffering from heart impairments are being helped in their rehabilitation.

Research at Purdue University in energy requirements for work shows the average stress for farmwork to be moderate. Most work may be done with an energy expenditure 3 to 3.5 times the resting rate. Peak stresses, however, may be as high as 8 or 10 times that of resting. The peak stresses are most likely to trouble the cardiac patient. They are associated with such activities as lifting or carrying heavy loads; climbing, running, or chasing livestock; holding animals; and pulling or pushing heavy carts, doors, or machinery in hitching or positioning.

Most of the major physical stresses in farmwork can be reduced. Many can be eliminated.

The pace or rate at which we work is important. Some tasks, like shoveling, have built-in rest periods. We may reduce the pace to our own speed. The same is true of climbing stairs or walking up hills and in loose snow.

Easing or reducing energy requirements—while not increasing costs—is our goal. Store sacked materials on a platform level with the bed of the truck to avoid lifting. Use pressure water systems to avoid carrying. Maybe a mechanical silo unloader and feed bunk are not too costly if a large tonnage of silage is handled.

Stooping to milk cows is virtually eliminated in the two-level parlor. The cow's udder is level with the worker's elbow.

Some activities that use a tractor are relatively high in energy expenditure. Plowing and using a loader mounted on the front of the tractor are examples. Research suggests fitting the tractor with power steering and a comfortable seat. Power steering reduces the peak forces that must be exerted on the steering wheel. Steering shocks are also eliminated. A rough riding seat increases energy expenditure compared to a comfortable one. Modern farming demands long hours on the tractor during rush seasons. Steering and seat conveniences materially reduce driver fatigue.

In such changes as these, we attempt to ease work and increase effectiveness. We may also reduce physical stress by taking frequent short pauses to rest.

When we worked with horses, rest pauses were automatic. Now our mechanical horses need no rest. The worker, however, is not a machine. Several frequent short rest periods reduce stress more than infrequent, longer pauses involving the same total resting time.

The impaired worker, of course, will follow the advice of his physician in his rehabilitation program. The foregoing are only examples of the usefulness of the work simplification idea. Your physician has more specific suggestions. Jobs have been graded and rated according to energy requirements. You may need to avoid some jobs entirely by changing some of your what-to-do decisions. The research assures us, however, that reasonable, productive activity is often good for us.

WE HAVE SEEN here the diverse ways in which the work simplification idea is helpful. Early farm applications were centered about individual cases. Work methods were improved by self-analysis. This approach—observation, analysis, decision, action—is open to all of us, whatever our line of work.

Today we view work simplification in terms of the efficiency with which the labor resource is used. What-to-do as well as how-to-do-it decisions are involved. Capital labor substitution problems are continuously present. So also are the problems of training workers, their selection, and management.

The technique of analyzing and improving each job in its own setting makes a good demonstration and helps individuals to become their own job analysts. This approach, however, does not generally create a new method of doing the job.

For this reason, researchers have set

up semicontrolled situations. Experiments are conducted. Work standards are developed. If presented in detail, labor accomplishment using alternative layouts and methods may be predicted using these standards.

Such standards, however, need constant revision as new technology develops. Further, adjustments for differences among workers and in environment are difficult to make.

As an alternative to development of complete detailed time standards, Wilfred H. M. Morris of Purdue University and others have divided time requirements into fixed and variable components. This provides a tool for studying the effect of size of enterprise on labor requirements. Such data are helpful in farm planning and in budgeting alternative systems of organization and operation.

A word of caution, however: The value of time changes seasonally. An hour saved at the rush season may be worth more than a day saved when work is slack.

# Technology in Homes

Earl C McCracken, Avis M. Woolrich, and Emma G. Holmes

A GENERATION ago many of us thought farm living was substandard living. Farmhouses lacked comforts and conveniences. Farm wives had few labor-saving devices. Farm families usually were isolated.

Today things are different. Most farmers have automobiles, good roads, and communication. Farm homes commonly have the same conveniences as city homes.

We can thank technological advance-ment in farming during the 20th century for much of the improvement in farm living. Better ways of farming increased farm incomes, and farmers had the means to buy improvements for their homes. Mechanized farming lightened farmwork, and farm people got more time for educational pursuits and social contacts. Electricity improved farm operations and also made it possible to install water systems and use household appliances.

The story of the development of equipment for use in farm households is the story of household equipment in general. It would be uneconomical to produce equipment of different design for urban and farm homes, and there is no need to do so. A design with good operating characteristics will perform equally well anywhere. Any difference is in the size of jobs to be done and in the length of time during which the equipment is in use.

Some types of household equipment were adapted from the large-scale equipment developed originally for commercial and institutional use. This byproduct development so often became the "tail that wagged the dog" that development of appliances primarily for household use became an accepted practice.

First came equipment for maintenance of the home and its furnishings—the electrified sewing machine, powered clothes washer, electric hand iron, and vacuum cleaner. Of all other types of household appliances in use today, only the toaster and hotplate had their beginnings in the earliest stage of the development of household equipment.

A full line of electric cooking devices, including the frying pan, and flatirons was exhibited at the World's Columbian Exposition in Chicago in 1893. The heating devices blew up when put into operation, however, and were never sold to the public.

The real advance in appliances for home use had to await the development of the nickel-chromium heat-developing resistance wire and the universal-type small motor. Both came in the first decade of the 20th century, and the technological revolution in household equipment was underway.

WASHING CLOTHES always has been a hard and tedious task. Manufacturers therefore have given much attention to equipment to remove the drudgery from laundering, and homemakers have accepted it eagerly.

The first practical motor-driven washer was introduced in 1908. A motor made for washing machines was put into production in 1913. For many years, however, power for washers on farms was furnished by small gasoline engines, which often were the same ones used for the pump jack when the windmill failed to produce a satisfactory supply of water.

As electric powerlines were extended farther and farther into rural areas, the importance of the gasoline engine as a source of power for laundry equipment diminished. Today the gasoline-powered washer is almost extinct.

The early power washers simply substituted a motor or engine for the hand-crank. Galvanized-iron tubs soon replaced the earlier wooden ones, and the procession of change continued through copper to steel. Now porcelain enamel covers the metal tubs inside and out. Today's colorful laundry equipment is the result of many years of search for a paint that could be sprayed on properly.

The automatic washer, which reduced the homemaker's actual washing labor to a process of inserting soiled clothes and removing them cleaned, came on the market in 1935 after a relatively short period of development. Clothes driers were introduced in 1939. Combination washer-driers appeared in 1953.

One million motor-powered washers had been bought by 1919. More than 1 million have been sold each year since 1934. Of the estimated 50 million-odd wired homes in the United States in 1959, approximately 93 percent had motor-driven washers. Over five times as many automatic and semi-

automatic washers were sold in 1959 as of the conventional types with wringers and spinners. Partly because the water supply on many farms is not always reliable the percentage of rural electric customers who own automatic washers is not so high as urban homes.

Rural homemakers have wide choice in designs of washing equipment. They include washers of the conventional wringer type, semiautomatic and automatic types, and the combination washer-drier. No one type is consistently superior in ability to remove soil. No one type of washing mechanism—agitator, modified agitator, or cylinder—is consistently superior in soil removal.

Purchases of automatic clothes driers rose to 1 million annually in 1951, 12 years after they were introduced. Almost 18 percent of wired homes had driers by the end of 1959.

A report of a study of automatic clothes driers by research workers in the Department of Agriculture said that the most chemical degradation of the fabrics and the most graying and loss of bursting strength occurred in outdoor drying. Tumbler drying caused the greatest shrinkage and visible wear. Gas driers caused the most yellowing. Inside rack and electric cabinet drying usually caused the least change in any property of fabrics.

The report further said that tumbler driers, in comparison with inside rack and cabinet driers, saved about 10 minutes of the operator's time in placing and removing the loads in the tests. In comparison with the outside line, they saved approximately 13 minutes. There is also a saving of elapsed time, which varies according to weather conditions and the work involved in carrying loads to and from the line.

More than a million hand irons have been bought each year since 1915. The steam hand iron appeared on the market in 1926. Models that could be used either dry or with steam followed shortly. More than 6 million electric hand irons were bought in 1959. Ninety percent of the Nation's wired homes have standard electric hand irons. About 55 percent have steam irons of various types.

The electric ironer for home use was introduced early in 1908, but its acceptance has never been so high as that of most of the other major electric appliances. One million ironers had been purchased by 1935. Purchases had dwindled to 40 thousand in 1959 from the peak of 600 thousand in 1948. The steam iron and wash-and-wear fabrics seemingly have made the ironer the victim of technological advance.

A PATENT was taken out in 1859 for a cleaner that had all of the attributes of modern electric vacuum cleaners except the electric motor. Developments came fast after electric power became widely available.

The development of the balanced high-speed motor was a milestone in the attempt to produce a light, high-suction vacuum cleaner. A combination of beating, sweeping, and suction action was introduced. Lighter metals and plastics replaced heavy metals in many parts of the design. Attachments for regular vacuum cleaners and hand cleaners made their appearance.

Tank-type cleaners were followed by those of the canister type.

A report published in the February 1959 issue of the Journal of Home Economics said that for rug cleaning, sweeper cleaners (motor-driven brush or agitator) are superior to canister and tank cleaners and that cleaning efficiency of cleaners is lowered by an accumulation of dirt in the dirt bag— more for some cleaners than for others.

By the end of 1958, 72 percent of the wired homes had motor-driven housecleaning equipment.

THE HOUSEHOLD REFRIGERATOR has done much to raise the standard of living.

It was one of the appliances that first was used commercially. Commercial refrigeration machines were attended by specialized personnel. Home refrigerators, however, had to be operated by nonmechanics. They had to perform automatically the job performed naturally by the melting ice in the iceboxes they replaced and do so without service calls.

Perfection of the household refrigerator involved many hard problems, solutions to which have culminated in the sealed-unit compressor, thermostats and other controls, nontoxic and more efficient refrigerants, lighter and more effective heat-insulating materials, and the elimination of much operation noise. Ninety-eight percent of the wired homes had mechanical refrigerators in 1960.

The establishment of systems for the local distribution of the liquefied-petroleum gases made possible the use of gas refrigerators on farms. With this supply, automatic regulation of temperature was possible to an extent not available with the kerosene-powered refrigerator. The electric refrigerator had such a hold on the rural market, however, that the percentage of farm homes with refrigerators of the gas-absorption type is low. Manufacturers and consumers have shown greater interest in gas refrigerators, however, and it is to be expected that more and more of them will be adopted by farm families.

One million pioneer households had replaced natural refrigeration by mechanical refrigerators by 1928. In 1933, and in each year thereafter, more than 1 million mechanical refrigerators were purchased.

THE HOMEFREEZER, as it exists today, was introduced commercially in 1940. Many of the ideas incorporated in the early models were carryovers from the ice cream cabinet of the local store or soda fountain. One million units had been bought by 1948. About 1 million units have been bought each year since 1953.

The homefreezer market shifted to boxes of a capacity of more than 10 cubic feet in 1950. Fewer than 5 percent of the freezers bought in 1949 were of the upright type. Purchases of upright freezers exceeded those of the chest type in 1959.

The initial cost of an upright freezer is a little higher than that of the chest type of the same storage capacity. Whether one type of freezer is more convenient than another is largely a matter of personal opinion. In a comparison of 11 chest-type freezers of 5.5 to 18 cubic feet and 4 upright-type freezers of 5.5 to 28 cubic feet, little difference was found in the cost of operation between the two types.

A gap in refrigeration facilities on farms was that no commercially built homefreezers were large enough to handle the sides of beef and large amounts of fruit and vegetables that some families wanted to freeze. Commercial locker plants were the answer for some, but many families wanted their own facilities.

Research workers conducted a survey of the existing large, custom-built, two-temperature, walk-in refrigerators on farms to learn the needs of farm people for such facilities and problems involved in their use and upkeep. Thereafter several experimental units were designed and constructed.

From this work came a design for a home-built, two-temperature refrigerator, described in Leaflet No. 320 of the Department of Agriculture. Working drawings (Plan No. 7102) are available from extension agricultural engineers at many of the State agricultural colleges. A farmer, with the help of a refrigerator serviceman, can build the refrigerator at a reasonable cost.

These home-built, on-the-farm installations are particularly valuable on farms far from locker plants. They make it easier to feed the family well. They may help in recruiting seasonal laborers, who are known to choose the farms where they will work on the basis of how good the meals are.

THE MODERN RANGE has thermostats that replace guesswork to determine the temperature of the oven. A regulated heat supply makes unnecessary a knowledge of wind direction in regulating dampers. No need now to stoke the stove. Still, cooking practices have not changed so much as other practices have with the purchase of new types of equipment.

It is a little ironic that the farm wife, with a fine range, has fewer men to cook for than her mother, who was called on at harvesttime to feed a threshing crew but had primitive equipment to do it with: Technology in the kitchen paralleled the development of laborsaving farm equipment, which reduced or eliminated the need for large-quantity cooking.

The development of the nickel-chromium resistance-wire element in the early 1900's made possible practical cooking units. The electric range, which has surface, oven, and broiling facilities in one unit, was introduced commercially in 1909. By 1914, seven companies manufactured them.

In the early days of electric ranges, utility companies feared the effect of an extra electric demand at mealtimes, and insisted that ranges be designed to operate continuously with stored heat. Economically, however, it was found better to take electricity from the line and put it into food in the form of heat as needed. Investigation revealed that the demand of a range did not exceed 700 watts and that many ranges did not impose a load of more than 600 watts each, even at the time of peak demand.

A load-balancing switch and three-wire systems were developed to remove radio interference caused by ranges.

When LP gas began to be delivered in rural places, farm homes could have controlled-temperature ranges that use a fuel other than electricity. Many farmers replaced their wood-coal or kerosene range by the cleaner, faster, and better-regulated gas range.

Thermostats of one kind or another have been used on ranges almost from the beginning. Their development through various types and stages has resulted in the hydrostatic type that is used to control the temperature in ovens and also as the dominant feature in thermostatically controlled surface units.

One million electric ranges had been sold by 1930, and 1947 was the first year in which 1 million were purchased. More than 1.7 million standard gas ranges were purchased in 1959.

The built-in electric or gas oven, paired with one or more sets of separate surface units, is a newer development. It is adaptable to various kitchen layouts. Many women like it. In a few years after they appeared on the market, built-in electric ranges were installed in 4 percent of wired homes. More and more separate gas ovens are bought each year; the total was nearly 360 thousand in 1959.

After the cookstove had evolved into the electric or gas range, more and more of its functions began to be duplicated in specialty items—electric roasters, hotplates, coffeemakers, toasters, and sandwich grills. Rare is the home that does not have at least one of them.

The water heater and sewing machine, the dishwasher, food mixers, ice-cream freezers, and many other items improved household operation and family living on American farms. Scarcely a household activity has not felt the impact of a growing technology in equipment, and scarcely a year goes by but that another hand-operated piece of equipment joins the ranks of the mechanized.

For more details on this and related points, we refer the reader to the October 1952 silver anniversary issue of Electrical Dealer and the golden anniversary issue in July 1957 of Electrical Merchandising, from both of which we have drawn ideas, expressions, and information for this chapter.

CREDIT for the relatively rapid development of household equipment goes to manufacturers who designed new equipment or adapted existing commercial equipment for home use, laboratories that tested and suggested, organizations that participated in standardization activities, the utility companies that supplied the concentrated power to operate the equipment, home management and other extension workers, and the dealers who made the equipment directly available.

Every purchase of household equipment uses money that otherwise would be available for other purposes. The cost of an appliance is always restrictive, regardless of its value. So manufacturers design and redesign to reduce production costs and to suit the equipment better to its task.

Standardization is a benefit we are not always aware of.

There were as many types of plugs in the early years as there were manufacturers. Cycle frequencies varied from 16 to 133; voltage, from 90 to 220. The success of the first attempts to standardize plugs and voltage dispelled manufacturers' initial fears that standardization would curtail their individual freedom of construction and design.

Knowing that sales of their appliances depend on acceptance by consumers, manufacturers of gas and electrical equipment have established departments in which home economists perform various functions. They prepare information on the best ways of using their company's products. They advise the research and engineering departments on features and construction that would improve the appliances.

The utility companies through the years have made engineering improvements to serve consumers better. An example: Electric clocks use only a minute amount of electrical energy, but generating systems were regulated to accurate frequency to assure correct time readings.

A large manufacturer, before adding an electric range to his line, asked several thousand homemakers and scores of dealers what they did not like about present ranges and what they wanted in an ideal range.

Although it was evident that the homemakers usually had had experience with only one range—because the responses were primarily "don't like"—the manufacturer was able to put on the market the first range based, to any extent, on expressed home-makers' needs.

Later, as home economists with special training in the testing of household equipment were hired as home-service employees of the public utilities, as research workers for Government, industry, and college laboratories, and as household management and household equipment specialists in Extension Service, the need for extensive home-maker surveys became unnecessary.

From these home economists came the first indications that specific performance requirements were just as important to users of equipment as features of construction and appearance.

The need for standardization of consumer goods, including household equipment, was early recognized by the American Standards Association, Inc., an association providing means by which organizations and others may cooperate in establishing voluntary American standards in those fields in which engineering methods apply.

Under the jurisdiction of the Consumer Goods Standards Board of the American Standards Association, sectional committees made up of representatives of manufacturers, distributors, consumers, and groups with a general interest in the commodity were charged by the Association with the development of standards for refrigerators, ranges, water heaters, flatirons, hotplates, roasters, toasters, and other equipment.

The initial standards developed by the sectional committees were chiefly standardized test procedures, which are used by manufacturers in developing new designs and by testing laboratories interested in the engineering performance characteristics of different designs of equipment.

Few performance requirements have been developed or even proposed for how well the equipment does the work it is intended to do.

One exception is in the field of household electric range ovens. On the premise that the function of an oven was to bake foods and bake them satisfactorily, a subcommittee of the American Standard Electric Range Committee formulated performance requirements based on standardized tests of the baking ability of an oven. The degree and evenness of browning and the time limits for achieving an acceptable degree of doneness of four baked products—bread, biscuits, and two kinds of cakes—are included in the criteria for evaluating the performance of an oven. Criteria of cake-baking ability also include the factors of evenness of rising and degree of shrinkage of the cake from the pan.

The tests were submitted to a sectional committee of the American Standards Association for approval and inclusion as performance standards in a pamphlet, "American Standard for Household Electric Ranges." If these baking test procedures with oven performance requirements are included in the procedures used by manufacturers in developing electric ranges, they will form a common basis for predicting oven performance of an electric range and can be used as a basis for an informative label stating that the range oven meets the performance requirements of the American Standards Association.

Performance requirements for gas range ovens have been in effect for many years. The American Gas Association in 1925 assumed the responsibility, under the American Standards Association, for developing standards of construction and performance for all gas equipment, including household appliances. By and large, standards for gas household equipment include more performance requirements than do those that have been adopted for electrical appliances. The gap is being narrowed, however, as data are being made available from all groups concerned with and working with electric household equipment. The American Gas Association maintains an extensive testing and accrediting laboratory, which in 1960 had no counterpart in the electrical industry.

Underwriter's Laboratories, Inc., has

done much to take away from the use of household equipment and appliances the fear of personal safety from electrical shock and fire. The UL approval on electrical equipment is proof that they meet the latest standards of safety.

Home economists and engineers in the laboratories of women's magazines, commercial testing and trade associations, and universities have contributed to the betterment of household equipment through their analyses to determine whether a manufacturer's statements of performance were correct and to compare construction and performance with that of competing makes.

Federal and State-supported laboratories have done research on household equipment a long time. One of the earliest studies, done in connection with ice refrigerators—to determine a performance characteristic based on the temperatures required to keep various foods—was carried on in a laboratory of the Department of Agriculture.

Ice then was the only refrigerant generally available to farm families. Their problem of selecting food-cooling equipment was one of choosing between iceboxes of different makes. Both gas (liquefied petroleum usually) and electricity were generally available by the early 1950's for refrigeration and for cooking, and heating of water as well. The problem of choice was between "fuels," rather than among appliances using the same fuel.

Elizabeth Beveridge and Earl C Mc-Cracken of the Department made a comparative study of utilization of energy by electric and liquefied petroleum gas ranges, refrigerators, and water heaters. By applying local rates for each type of fuel to the data on relative efficiency of the appliance in utilizing energy, farm families can compare costs of operating equipment that use different fuels.

Miss Beveridge and Dr. McCracken warned, however, that operating cost is only one of the factors to be considered when selecting the fuel to be used. Also should be considered the installation problems and costs, dependability and convenience of service, the anticipated uses of the fuel, and cost and choice of appliances.

The Government's interest in household equipment has continued through the years and includes participation in the program of standardization as well as research and dissemination of information on the selection, use, and care of all types of household equipment.

Another major contribution of public-supported research laboratories has been possible through close association with engineering and research representatives of industry. Through these contacts, suggestions for improving equipment are relayed more quickly by household equipment specialists to the manufacturers than by the method of waiting for complaints from homemakers.

THE PRESENCE of modern equipment and conveniences in the farmhouse is immediately apparent evidence of the impact of technological progress on the farm homes. Less apparent evidences are the changing patterns of living and housing requirements of farm families.

Because the methods of doing housework are related closely to the equipment and facilities used, an innovation in either usually calls for a change in the work process.

Often the rearrangement—even a relocation—of the activity area is required if full benefit is to be derived from new conveniences. Costs in time and energy of carrying on the activity by the new process or in the new arrangement often differ from those of the old.

Forces operating quite apart from the farmhouse itself also have brought about change in the way farm families live. Specialization in farming and the expansion of the size of farming operations have removed from the farmhouse some of the work formerly done there. Using the farm kitchen for preparing small lots of butter, eggs, and vegetables for local customers, for example, is largely a thing of the past. Utensils connected with milk production are not likely to be cared for in the house, as they formerly were. The greater size and complications of farm business increased the importance of bookkeeping and has intensified the need for a place in the house to keep and work on business records.

Farm family ways with food have changed, too, partly because of changes in farming and partly in keeping with general trends in buying, preparing, and using foods.

Farm families still raise much of their food, but not nearly so much as they used to. They tend to have smaller gardens and grow smaller amounts of vegetables and fruit. They produce more meat for their own use, however. Altogether, the average farm family now gets about 40 percent (by value) of its food from its own farm, as compared with 60 percent in 1941 and 70 percent in 1923.

As farm homemakers used less and less home-produced food, they increased their use of prepared and partly prepared foods. A third or more of the food dollar of the average farm family now goes for prepared and partly prepared foods. This is a substantial increase over the 22 percent spent for such foods in 1941. These foods include items like commercially baked goods, mixes, ready-to-eat cereals, frozen and canned goods, and lunch meats.

Bread baking moved out of the home as incomes increased and access to food stores improved. In 1919, 94 percent of the farm women in 33 Northern and Western States baked their own bread. In 1955, only 22 percent baked any bread or rolls in a week. But though they buy most of their bread and some of their other baked goods, they still do a lot of baking and so need space and equipment for it. In 1955, 93 percent of the farm women made some baked goods during a week.

The introduction of the commercial freezer locker started a revolution in home food preservation, and the home freezer fostered it. Most farm women continue to can foods, but in smaller amounts than before. The average was about 500 pounds of canned food in 1951 but probably no more than 300 pounds now. But they more than made up for the difference by freezing an average of 333 pounds, compared to a negligible amount in 1941. A large proportion of the food frozen by farm families is meat.

All these changes in practices connected with feeding the family have had their effect on the design of farmhouses planned to fit the functions of family living. Changes in other areas of household production and patterns of living have occurred also. The proportion of farm women who do home sewing—three-fourths or more—is large enough to make it important to consider them in planning farmhouses.

Practically all farm homemakers do their own laundry work, or most of it. Because this work is common to most farm homes, we use it as an example of how changes in the processes and supplies involved and the equipment and utilities used affect the space required for a task and the house design.

A homemaker's bulletin on home laundering procedures, published by the Department in 1919, listed 49 pieces of equipment, from clothes boilers to wooden spoons, for doing the laundry. The equipment was to be supplemented by some 20 kinds of supplies, such as soaps, bluing, and stain-removal chemicals. Water usually had to be carried to the house. If there was a water pump, it was usually in the backyard or farther away so it was handy for watering livestock. The welfare of the livestock was of primary consideration, because it was a source of income for the family.

The washing procedure consisted of getting water into the tubs—a hose connected to the yard pump was recommended—then warming it with water heated on the cookstove. Clothes were soaked, scrubbed on the board, and boiled to "sterilize" and remove as much of the remaining soil as possible. Rinsing—more water was carried and heated for it—was next. The final step was to hang the clothes on a line indoors or out for drying.

Small wonder that in many homes laundering was done in the kitchen, where a stove for heating water was nearby and the homemaker could dovetail the tedious, steamy, and smelly job with other household chores that had to be fitted into the day's schedule. Kitchens of the era were large—large enough to dispel the heat and steam arising from the stove and to permit several tasks to be done at one time.

The mechanical washer with wringer attachment made the laundry job easier. The clothes boiler and scrubboard began their journey into oblivion. Laundry supplies were improved. Some houses had piped hot water. But washing with a wringer washer was likely to be a splashy affair, and, regardless of the weather, clothes still had to be hung to dry. So the laundry area was moved out of the kitchen to a less obvious and roomier spot—the basement, porch, or shed. Relieved of this space-consuming job, kitchens were made smaller.

Within the past two decades, further changes in equipment and supplies have revolutionized home laundry methods and brought about further changes in housing requirements for the job. With automatic laundry equipment, no longer is there need for two tubs for rinsing and for baskets and carts to transport clothes from washer to line.

The list of equipment needed for laundering is just about one-third as long as the 1919 list. New finishes for counter tops and floors resist water damage and are easy to keep clean. Multipurpose washing compounds and easy-care fabrics have reduced by one-half the number of supplies needed in 1919 for laundering. The mess is gone, and with it part of the space that was needed to do the job. An area 6 feet by 6 feet, 8 inches, is sufficient for the entire washing and drying process.

Freed of the limitations imposed by the old equipment and old methods, the laundry area has come out of hiding and can be located anywhere. It is not unusual to find it close to the bathroom and bedrooms, which are the main collection points of dirty clothes and household textiles.

Most household activities have undergone changes similar to those that have taken place in the home laundering process. All such changes, taken together, have had influence on requirements for design, arrangement, facilities, and structural materials for the house.

MORE THAN any other consumer goods, houses have a lasting quality.

Created from durable materials, put together with mortar and nails, bolts, and mortised joints, a house is built to stand for 50 years or longer. Once the house is erected, changes in the design or in the spaces that the walls enclose do not come easily. But within the inelastic areas formed by walls are people who carry on a diverse program of household activities, whose tools for carrying on these activities are constantly changing as new equipment, new materials, and new facilities are introduced in their homes and whose needs and preferences for housing are ever changing.

The conflict between the fluid requirements of families for housing and the static quality of their dwellings gives substance to the often-heard criticism that our farmhouses are obsolete—that they simply have not kept pace with present-day needs.

Are we really entering the Space Age with houses more suited to the horse-and-buggy era?

Are we merely refining old ideas and concepts of farmhouses instead of making progress in improving our farm housing?

Answers to these questions must be pieced together from a number of sources.

The 1950 Census of Housing and subsequent special studies describe in part our farmhouses of today. Generally, these houses are in good condition. For the United States as a

*This plan, long the most popular in the Regional Plan Exchange Service, was redesigned to incorporate the changes in housing requirements brought about by new-style household equipment and family living patterns.*

*The Regional Plan Exchange Service is a cooperative operation of the Department of Agriculture and State agricultural colleges. Through it, plans for farmhouses and farm structures that incorporate the latest research findings on functional requirements, construction methods, and materials are made available to the public at nominal cost. The State agricultural extension services distribute the plans, generally through the office of the extension agricultural engineer.*

whole, four out of five farmhouses have none of the faults that would cause them to be classified as "dilapidated." This represents an improvement over 1940—even with a more rigid definition in 1950 of what constitutes poor quality of housing. Nor is overcrowding a widespread problem if we accept the rule of thumb that there should be at least as many rooms in the house as there are persons living there. In no region is the average person-per-room ratio for farm dwellings equal to one. This varies with the size of the house, however; overcrowding in houses of one to four rooms is fairly commonplace.

Electrification has long been of special significance in judging the adequacy of farm housing. Not only does it provide the farm family with the fundamental convenience of lighting. It also makes possible the conveniences of a water system and power for household appliances.

The 28-year span between 1930 and 1958 saw a tremendous growth in the number of electrified farmhouses, from 13 percent to 95 percent of houses of farm operators. Some areas, particularly in the Northeast and West, are completely electrified. Thus one of the most pressing needs of farm housing has been virtually eliminated.

With electricity, installation of a water system becomes a practical possibility. Farm families have taken advantage of it, although not to the extent that one might expect. Possibly the cost of installing a water system accounts for the lag. Almost two of every three farm operator families in this country had running water in their homes in 1956. The proportion varies from one of two in the South to nine of ten in the West. The houses of nonowners fared less well during this decade than did those of owner-operators, and running water in all farm homes is still an achievement for the future.

A substantial number of farmhouses in the United States are large, old houses. More than half of those in the 1950 Housing Inventory were built before 1920. During that period, houses of seven rooms or more were built oftener than any other size. Old houses are not necessarily out-of-date houses, though. They are more likely to be located on high- than on low-production farms. Houses on the better farms exceed the national average in respect to electricity, plumbing, and other modern conveniences.

Newer houses are smaller. More than half of those built during the 1940's had four rooms or fewer. Many were

*Perspective of front elevation, revised design.*

located on low-production farms. In these small houses, whether new or old, the need for improvements in farm housing is most apparent, because the smaller the house, the less likely it is to have electricity, or plumbing, or an adequate number of rooms.

Census data can tell us the number of rooms in a house. But adequacy of space cannot be judged on the number of rooms alone. The size, the arrangement, the uses demanded of each room, and the relationships of rooms to each other are the true keys to judging how successfully a house meets the demands for space and arrangement.

Likewise, a house may be in good condition structurally, be equipped with a bathroom and a mechanical refrigerator, have more rooms than there are members of the household, and show other evidences of modernity, yet it may be obsolete. Mere installation of a modern facility or piece of equipment does not in itself guarantee a house that measures up to the requirements of modern living.

To meet functional requirements for housework, for family group life, and individuals' private life, it is generally agreed that the farmhouse must be so planned and arranged to provide for efficiency in household operation; protection and promotion of health, safety, and comfort of family members; and the development and nurture of the interests and talents of the family.

We do not have accurate statistics on

how well our farmhouses measure up to these livability standards. There are strong indications, however, that the faults are many.

With higher levels of living, more things have to be stored, and houses are straining at the seams to contain the greater number and variety of articles that families find necessary nowadays for their daily living. Data obtained in the 1948–1949 large-scale study of farm family housing needs and preferences showed that at least two-thirds of the houses in two regions had no closets other than clothes closets. Many houses in all regions had fewer clothes closets than bedrooms or no closets at all. Storage facilities in the kitchen were not determined in this survey, but probably they are more adequate than those in any other area of the house because of the educational program of the State extension services on laborsaving kitchens.

The arrangement of rooms and equipment has direct bearing on the time consumed and the human energy expended in carrying on household tasks. The survey, however, showed that rooms in present houses often are not satisfactory from the standpoint of the use that must be made of them. Many families now using the kitchen for washing clothes, cutting meat, ironing, and preserving food want to move those tasks to some other place. Fewer than one-fourth of the western women were content with the location of their

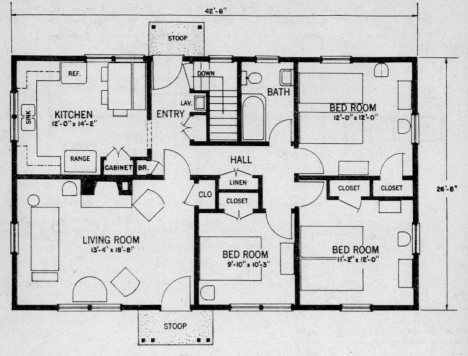

*Floor plan, original design.*

sewing facilities. One-fourth of north-central homemakers reported that they would like to be able to seat more people in the dining room than their present houses permitted.

Housing is an important segment of living costs of families and plays an important role in the satisfactions that the family derives from life.

Housing is of particular importance to farm families because, to a greater extent than in nonfarm occupations, it serves the farm enterprise as well as the business of living. In addition, the farmhouse must serve the family during its entire life cycle; unlike urban families, the farm family cannot shop around for a new house as their living requirements change.

The Congress recognized the part that the farmhouse plays in maintaining a sound and prosperous agriculture and satisfying rural life, when, in the Research and Marketing Act of 1946,

it authorized "research relating to the design, development, and more efficient and satisfactory use of . . . farm homes" and "investigations that have for their purpose the development and improvement of the rural home and family life."

To carry out this directive, coordinated programs of research were conducted cooperatively by the Institute of Home Economics of the Department of Agriculture and the agricultural experiment stations in the four regions.

The persons most concerned with farm housing of good quality—the farm families themselves—were consulted during the first stage of research. This was done by determining the kind and extent of activities carried on in farm homes, preferred locations of activity areas, and kinds and quantities of articles for which storage is needed in the house.

Part of this information went to ar-

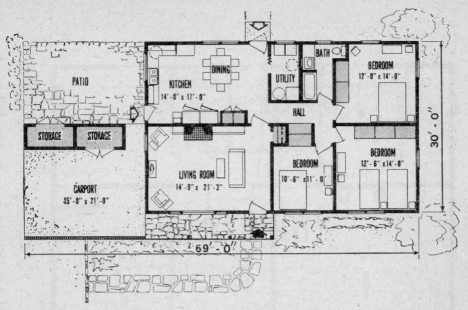

*America on wheels brings the carport to the house in the revised plans. Automatic laundry equipment comes upstairs, and the freezer is established next to the refrigerator. Elimination of one wall increases space for dining in the kitchen. Storage spaces are of a size to accommodate the articles that farm families have to store.*

chitects and others concerned with the design of farmhouses for immediate incorporation into plans for farmhouses.

By far the greatest amount of data became the basis for laboratory studies of space needs and efficient arrangements of space for household activities and storage. The findings of these studies are now being translated into graphic standards for home planners to use in designing new and remodeled farm dwellings.

Paralleling the studies of the need for space have been investigations of expenditures of human energy as related to the use of equipment and facilities of different designs and arrangements. A start has been made on studies of the influence and control of environmental conditions that are related to house design. The characteristics and performance of structural and finishing materials also are receiving attention.

Together, advancing technology and research are providing solutions to some

of the problems that have provoked the criticism that our farmhouses are obsolete. Farm families are spending more than 2 billion dollars a year to modernize farm structures. The farmhouse will claim a large share of this money, for attitudes concerning the value of good housing on the farm have changed as drastically as families' living patterns.

ON THE WANE is the practice of allocating to the farmhouse the income, if any, after needs of farm production have been met. More frequently now the farmhouse is holding its own in competition with farm machinery and farm buildings for a share of the family income.

This is as it should be, for the future ability to maintain competitive and family-type agriculture with trained and highly skilled labor and management is greatly influenced by the attraction of the farmhouse as an efficient and comfortable place to live.

# Power

# in

# the Future

## Mechanization
## and Automation

Carl W. Hall

A TOTAL of about 500 million tons of agricultural products were moved from fields in 1960—6 thousand pounds per person in the United States.

Moving farm crops directly to the consumer can be an efficient process with today's technology and equipment. Marketing the crops as meat, milk, and eggs introduces more steps and more possibilities for reducing labor efficiency. As America has become more prosperous, more crops are being marketed through meat animals.

Increasing efficiency through mechanization of feeding of poultry and livestock and handling and processing meat, milk, and eggs is a great challenge for today's engineering in agriculture.

In the future, automation will be the key which will open the doors to more efficient operations and to greater progress in agriculture. More training will be necessary for the farmer and for those associated with allied fields to take maximum advantage of these new opportunities. Pushbutton farming—automation—is not a dream. It is here.

A gross annual income of 34 billion dollars is received by all farmers for agricultural products, of which 19 billion dollars are for farm foods. The retail cost of the products is 90 billion dollars, of which 48 billion dollars are for farm foods. More engineering effort will be devoted to processing the product on or after it leaves the farm.

The difficulty of mechanizing and automating agricultural processes lies in the fact that many variables must be considered. Considerations of quality

416

and product are more important for agricultural commodities than for the normal industrial products, such as iron and steel. Biological and chemical factors are involved. Furthermore, the handling of animal products is more involved than handling crop products.

Manual handling of materials is the first approach. As soon as it is economical, an animal, a machine, or equipment is used to assist in the movement; or a machine is developed to do the job under the supervision or direction of man; or the machine is directed by timeclocks or control (set by man) to proceed with the operation without direct human control.

This last step is automation. Automation is mechanization with controls.

Feed can be ground manually or by animal power. The animals can be driven or directed by man, or feed can be ground by mechanical means. Corn, wheat, and oats can be moved to the grinder mechanically. A device to assure uniform feeding may be provided. Ground feed can be removed from the grinder mechanically. Automation exists when these units are connected so that instruments and controls relay the function of any one component to the others to assure proper functioning. Automation follows the mechanization of a process, just as mechanization follows manual handling in the evolutionary sense.

Mechanization and automation have been blamed for putting people out of work. Certain individuals are replaced, it is true, but increased productivity per man is one of the great contributions of our society. One element of society cannot lag behind. Agriculture is no exception.

The term "automation" was first used in industry in 1951 and was first used in agricultural publications in 1955. Automation has been applied to handling operations. The development of handling equipment has been pioneered by many of the established manufacturing concerns and by many companies new in the field. A new industry has developed to produce specialized materials-handling equipment and instruments and controls to regulate this equipment.

Reductions in labor costs must occur as more investment is made in equipment. That is true unless the health and safety of operator and animal are given more than the usual direct dollar evaluation. Labor costs can be reduced by less total labor, less expensive labor, more efficient labor (even though it is more costly per hour), or a combination of these. With some operations, like the use of the milking machine, there is an optimum number of units beyond which one man cannot operate properly. These relationships vary with the animal, environment, the operator's skill, and the effect of the operation on the animal.

Labor requirements should not be overlooked when one evaluates an automated system. Supervision and responsibility of operation should be considered; often they were lacking in systems that have failed. Designers are not faultless, but few systems operate perpetually without supervision and maintenance.

The form of a product influences greatly the method of handling and storing it. A crop may be handled in its harvested form—long hay, unchopped straw, stalks of fodder, ears of corn, or kernels (wheat, corn, and oats). Kernels are crop-formed pellets. Long hay, straw, and stalks of fodder are difficult to handle. Cornstalks and straw, which do not lend themselves to mechanical handling, may be assembled in bundles for manual handling.

Additional operations are often carried out on raw materials to facilitate handling. Loose hay as it grows or lies in the field is not easily handled through the operations that follow. Usually we have used the approach of reducing the size of materials to improve handling. Future development will take place in reducing the number of particles to be handled by pressing them together and forming larger, denser particles.

Another way is to cut the size of material by chopping or grinding. Ground forages often are loose and bulky and do not flow freely. To reduce dust and increase flowability, forages and bulky materials can be placed in large packages, like bales. These are heavy to handle. They do not flow easily from one to another piece of mechanical equipment. There is a trend to smaller bales, which can be thrown from the baler to the wagon. These bales flow more readily to the elevator than larger, oblong bales.

Forming forages into smaller packages of various shapes in the fields—biscuits, cakes, wafers, ropes, large pellets—with dimensions of 1 inch to 4 inches is the latest approach. The acceptable size will depend on the requirements and limitations of animals and equipment.

Large stacks of hay or straw can be built in the field on a platform or wagon and moved to the feeding area.

Losses of chopped forage in the field should be kept to a minimum by using a covered or screened enclosed wagon so that chopped material is not lost.

The shape or characteristics of a product can be changed to accommodate mechanization. Through plant breeding, varieties of crops will be selected to facilitate mechanization.

The requirements for mechanization of handling may be different than mechanization of harvest. Eggs in the shells must be handled gently, but removing eggs from shells and packaging them in plastic pockets individually or by the dozen are possible to improve handling. Reduction in the weight of material to be handled is important. With more accurate methods of metering, the amount of filler used in fertilizer will be reduced or eliminated, and a smaller total weight can be applied to get the same nutrients on the field.

Concentrated liquid sprays reduce the amount of water. Further concentration will occur; it and more accurate metering devices make airplane spraying more economical. Pelleting of herbicides will help improve handling.

The maintenance of quality of fresh products is the number one objective during handling and processing. The product does not necessarily dictate how the machine must be built; a machine may be available which with modifications can be utilized; or the machine can be used by changing the product slightly. Both product and machine must be considered.

SPECIALIZATION in the production of agricultural commodities is a trend seemingly great but still in its infancy. Where once a farmer specialized in grain, there will be even more specialization in one grain, such as wheat or corn; specialization in fruit will be specialization in a particular fruit, as apples or cherries.

Specialization and mechanization have developed almost simultaneously. As the farmer becomes a commodity specialist, he will be concerned with more than just production. He will do more preprocessing and storing or processing. He will join with others who produce the same commodity to exchange information; set up grade standards; control processing, distribution, and sales centers; and advertise his product. Because investment in equipment for an automated operation is high, diversification will occur only when the same equipment can be utilized for other products.

Field preparation will require less manpower. Mechanization of these operations has been rapid. Combining two or more operations into one will continue, as, for example, developments in minimum tillage. Automation will develop—tractors, self-propelled units, and implements that operate according to preset directions and adjust themselves for variations in soils and crops. Sensing devices will be developed to determine depth of topsoil, moisture content, soil cover, crop growth, height of crop, and height of heads of crops. Feelers for sensing the location of plants—sugar beets, corn, cotton—will be used for cultivation and harvest.

Moving seed, fertilizer, and chemicals to the field for planting imposes different handling requirements. Bulk handling is taking the place of bag handling of seed and fertilizer. Weaknesses in seed will be detected before planting. Seeds may be placed on soluble plastic tapes with the proper spacing, protected by insecticides and fungicides and laid in a furrow of proper depth for planting. Bulk handling of lime and manure to the field is a normal practice. Dust is reduced, the utilization of nutrients by plants is increased, and uniform distribution is accomplished with granulated fertilizer.

Corn planting could be automated further by replacing the checkwire with a radio beam to place the seeds.

Multiple units and combined operations will develop even more to reduce handling. Planters and seeders will be refilled in a large field while traveling—just as planes can be refueled in flight.

Watering crops in the field and orchard is becoming mechanized and automated. When the soil moisture drops below a certain amount, a plaster of paris block buried in the soil activates a device, calling for water. The irrigation system responds. In the future, if enough rain for the crop is not predicted, the system will respond with water application, thus eliminating the use of water before a heavy rain. Mechanized handling of the irrigation pipe might be accomplished by rolling the large heavy pipe on wheels. Weight is reduced by the use of plastic and aluminum. Further reduction in cost and weight is secured by using a small-diameter pipe. Smaller pipes are made possible by operating one sprinkler head to a lateral at a time. A recent development is valves at the sprinkler head, which open and close in succession along a length of a lateral starting with the main. A pulse of water—set up by momentarily reducing the water supply, which can be automated—actuates the valves.

Irrigation pipe can be rotated around a central pivot, like the spoke of a giant wheel, to cover up to 160 acres. The pipe is supported on pylons, which move on wheels over tall crops on level land. The system can be used to irrigate orchards and trees. The equipment moves over the land, like something dreamed up by Paul Bunyan. To reduce handling of water in pipes over long distances, it will become economical to produce fresh water for coastal areas from the sea.

Reshaping the land for irrigation, drainage, and erosion control will occur as we increase our knowledge of soil, fertilization, and treatment. Consideration will be given to storing water in underground and surface storages during periods of heavy rainfall for use during drought conditions.

PREPARING crops for harvest and new methods of harvesting impose changes in handling considerations.

Many farmers harvest grain early to reduce field and harvest loss and to permit planning of field operations. Crops are mature at a high moisture content—30 percent for corn, 40 percent for wheat—although normally they are stored at a much lower moisture content. Removal of leaves from beans, grains, and cotton for more rapid drying in the field, shelling attachments for field cornpickers, and burning of foliage from such crops as sugarcane are methods of reducing the time that the crops are in the field after maturity. As the field time of a crop is reduced, the possibility of weather damage lessens. New handling equipment and storage units are required and will be developed for high-moisture products.

Preparing forage crops for harvest usually involves harvest earlier than the normal to obtain more nutrients than usual. Yields of forage crops for dry hay drop if the product is left in the field after a certain date. Weather in the humid areas is not conducive to early harvest of field-dried forages. The time that a product, like cut hay, onions, and ear corn, is on the field should be kept to a minimum. Many products can be moved to a drier. Procedures for more rapid drying in the field are being developed. Crushers and crimpers are gaining in prominence—such treatment lowers the drying time by one-half in good drying weather.

A further reduction in drying time can be accomplished by placing the harvested product on a plastic film, which absorbs energy from the sun. The film prevents the moisture in the soil from moving into the hay.

Harvesting and handling the leaves, which contain 70 percent of the nutrients, and the stems, which have a slow drying rate, in separate operations is another approach. Squeezing moisture from high-moisture products at 90 percent down to 70 percent is being developed, and offers promise for removing moisture from some forage crops and from residues of such crops as tomatoes, potatoes, beets, and cane.

Citrus production and harvest will become more mechanized. Lemon trees are now mechanically pruned. Apple, orange, and grapefruit trees will be blocked by heavy-duty cutting bars. Mechanical pickers will remove fruit from the blocked trees. Plant breeders will develop varieties of dwarf types with fruit near the surface area of the trees. All citrus fruit will be handled in bulk. The chemical properties of juices will be automatically determined. Juices will be blended continuously and automatically to provide a beverage of uniform quality throughout the season.

Sugarcane, rice, and cotton can be harvested and handled mechanically. To improve mechanical handling, sugarcane can be chopped in the field with a large heavy-duty harvester similar to a forage harvester. The leaves can be separated or stripped before or during harvest and the low sugar content section at the top of the cane disposed. These residues might be used for silage. Rice can be harvested and handled wet. Combines for threshing of wet grain such as rice, wheat, barley, and oats, will operate on a centrifugal principle, so that the products will not be damaged by a rough, abrasive force. New types of packages, of different sizes, will be forthcoming for cotton.

Faster harvesting and handling after harvest is justified to lower the time that a product is at an undesirable temperature. Direct marketing to the consumer or placing the product in a storage with a desirable environment is done to meet this objective. A desirable environment might consist of proper temperature, availability of oxygen, use of carbon dioxide or other gases for lowering the respiration rate, or the use of other additives to reduce growth of mold, bacteria, and discoloration.

Crop products of maximum quality and quantity should be provided to livestock or for storage in the most economical manner. One procedure is to move livestock to the forage or grain and swine to the corn by pasturing. There are disadvantages to pasturing—loss in quality by harvesting at the improper date; use of energy by the animals for moving, cutting, and chewing the forage; little control of the amount they consume; and direct losses through tramping and weather damage. There is a trend away from moving livestock to the field for harvesting crops to moving all feed to the livestock, usually through a storage.

The storage is required because production is seasonal in most sections and consumption is continuous. The storage acts as a surge tank, balance wheel, or reservoir between periodic production and continuous or nearly continuous consumption. Handling to the storage from the field is done in a short time during 1 or 2 weeks of the season. Handling from the storage for farm consumption is a continuous operation most of the year. Handling from the storage for sale usually must be done quickly. Mechanical equipment for handling must be selected on the basis of harvesting, storing, and unloading (feeding) requirements.

Speed of handling fruit and vegetables is important to preserve quality. Handling picked products in a pail, box, or crate from the field usually is too slow. Unit loads of several pails, boxes, crates, and barrels provide faster and less costly handling. The unit load may be moved by pallet or forklift, on a wagon or, in the future, by helicopter. Quick cooling of fruit and vegetables is obtained by rapid airflow, evaporative cooling of leafy vegetables, or by immersion in cold water. Quality of red tart cherries is maintained and cost of handling is reduced by handling in water from the orchard to the processor. This is a way of applying bulk handling for fruit.

Citrus fruits in Florida and California, which are to be dried, fruits for processing, such as apples, and nuts are handled in bulk wagons or trucks. Sweet corn is handled in bulk into the processing plant. One method is to dump sweet corn on a concrete platform and move the corn to the processing line with a bulldozer with less than the normal damage or loss, at a low cost.

Automation from field to storage is not in the foreseeable future. Mechanical handling from the field to storage will continue to develop. A large belt conveyor could extend from the field to the storage, where the crop can be placed on the belt and conveyed continuously to the storage. During transport, removal of moisture, irradiation for vitamins, addition of minerals, or other treatment could take place. Periodic or continuous sampling of grain and hay on the belt would give needed information as to moisture, color, maturity, and physical properties.

Conveyors, water flumes, or insulated pipes from fields or orchards to processing plants will become practical as producers become product specialists and processing areas come close to the production areas. Complete automation of every phase—handling, quality determination, and processing—can then be a reality. Continuous analysis of chemical content, mold content, color, and hardness will provide for quality control.

On the farmstead, the aim is to place palatable, nutritious feed of the proper quality and quantity before animals at the proper time and at the least expense. Noisy equipment may retard fattening, impair breeding, reduce milk production, or tire the worker so that production is decreased. A low-cost installation therefore may be more expensive because of indirect costs.

Self-feeding from storage is desirable where it is possible. Much self-feeding is done during the step or operation that follows storage. With uncontrolled feeding, however, difficulty of some feeds to flow properly and waste of feeds prevent universal use of self-feeding.

Full self-feeding of silage, although attempted by many, had not become a reality in 1960. Self-feeding hay is being used where storages are properly designed. Some manual work is required to adjust feeders. Silage feeding is mechanized by top or bottom unloading from the vertical silo. Full self-feeding will develop in the future as equipment becomes available to overcome present handicaps of self-feeding.

Handling of feed has become mechanized. Moving feed from bins requires special consideration to prevent lodging or bridging. Proper slope of floor, vibrators, and agitators are involved.

Automation is complete in small feed mills that operate continuously. Each component does its job and operates only if other components are operating properly. Many farm operators, however, purchase a complete feed and handle the feed in bulk. Automation of feeding consists of moving the feed from a bulk storage to the animal. It will be easy to add certain protein, mineral or starch supplements, vitamins, enzymes, hormones, and components yet to be isolated, according to the needs of the animal. The additions could be directed automatically by a punched card or tape.

Automation of the dairy enterprise would refer to completely automatic operation and control of the feeding, milking, handling of cows, and handling of milk. Today's technology consists of automation in some of the components, such as watering, feeding, and handling milk. Watering was the first automatic operation. Feeding of grains has been automated by some.

Automation of milk handling is now a reality. In Switzerland, a dairy farm on a mountainside sends milk by plastic hose to the processing plant in a village some distance away.

An automated dairy farm, according to our definition, would involve interrelated automatic control among the components. If milk is used as a basis for control, the quantity of milk, quantity of fat, solids-not-fat, odor, color, and bacteria content would be used as a basis of control.

Today's fat production for a particular cow would set a memory device so that tomorrow, or perhaps 10 days later, the proper feed mix would be supplied. Or, if milk production of a high-producing cow is limited because sufficient dry matter cannot be fed into the cow because of the excess water in high-moisture silage, she will automatically be given more hay. Likewise, if the temperature of the drinking water goes above 80° F., it will be cooled automatically by a refrigeration unit.

Manure will be continuously or periodically removed. Methods of handling and disposing large quantities of manure will be developed. Decomposition of manure can be carried out to produce gases for fuel and organic matter for soil improvement. Proper ventilation and air conditions would be provided at all times. Cows, milk lines, milker, and other equipment will be cleaned automatically.

How will the milking machines be placed on the cow? An ingenious person can visualize how this operation could take place in a sanitary room. Airplanes can be refueled in the air, submarines can be directed to a particular point, miners can start digging at two opposite sides of a mountain and come together at the center—certainly placing a milking machine on a cow and removing it is not an insurmountable feat.

The butterfat is depressed if only finely ground dry forage is fed to dairy cows. Other effects on cows and other animals might be found. Through feeding trials with animals, tests will be used to determine the form for optimum production of a particular material. Perhaps a compromise will be required—by improving handling we may justify a decrease in feeding efficiency—so that the overall economical returns are greatest.

Sterilization or pasteurization of milk might be done with a small irradiation unit. Imagine the potential of a sterilized milk product with an acceptable flavor, which could be shipped any place in the world without refrigeration.

Automation of cleaning of milking systems is now available. Milk produced under sanitary conditions will be much easier to sterilize than milk now delivered for processing.

All of the dairy operations will not be automated simultaneously. Automation will occur through an evolutionary process as research workers find more information and industry develops components according to economical needs. First each component will be mechanized. Then each component will be automated. Then the whole process will be automated.

FUTURE DEVELOPMENTS are based on the demands and needs of today and tomorrow.

Energy storage will be developed. Storage units will be developed into which can be fed readily available energy—like solar energy during the day, electric energy at night, and energy from surplus products. From these storage units could be removed the appropriate energy desired for the task at hand—heat, electrical, or chemical energy.

A chore tractor will be designed especially for operations around the farmstead. The tractor could operate and be controlled to travel a certain path or track and receive its signals from a tape or a central headquarters manned or preset on a controller by the farmer.

Further developments will be made in pneumatic conveying, vibrating feeders, and meters to determine the milk from each cow. Ground feed may be mixed with water to speed the feeding operation and make handling easier. The health of the animals might be determined at each milking by the body or milk temperature and analysis of excreta or respiration products. Animals with unusual characteristics will be removed for medical treatment if necessary. A small radioactive device in the stomach of the cow will send signals regarding health and digestion.

Seventy-five percent of the silage is made of corn, and 64 percent is stored in tower silos. Mechanization has developed rapidly since 1950. The field forage harvester and chopper and the silo unloader are recent developments. Now nearly 90 percent of the ensilage is made with the field forage harvester and chopper.

More silage will probably be made from crop residues, including potato and tomato vines, sugar beet tops, vines of melons, cucumbers, beans, and peas. The whole tuber or root will be utilized. Vines which are too high in moisture will be dewatered by forcing between mechanical presses or rolls.

An elevator will be used instead of a blower to reduce the power for filling the silo. More uses will be found for the elevator to lower the fixed cost of operation.

To automate silo filling, a better method is needed for moving the chopped forage from the wagon to the silo. As operated now, a person is usually needed to supervise the flow of materials at the silo from the wagon to the blower. Future developments will see the use of a pit or bin into which wagons will be unloaded. An elevator-conveyor will remove material uniformly from the pit. Meanwhile, the operator has returned to the field to get another load of chopped forage. The pit would act as a surge or balance in an automated operation.

Wagons with live bottoms and wagons with hopper construction and bottom unloaders will be used. We will have new methods of handling bales, pellets, or ropes. New methods of storage, in which plastic is used for covering bales or stacks or greater use of acid, alkali, neutral, or liquid-submerged storage will develop. These future developments will be fitted more closely into an efficient feeding operation than has been done previously. Those methods that facilitate feeding will develop most rapidly. Equipment must be provided to fill the silo in a very short time and to remove the ensilage from the silo over a long time.

Commercial production of silage must receive consideration. As specialization in livestock and feeding increases, specialization in silage production can be expected. In California, where considerable specialization exists, 53 percent of the hay was raised as a cash crop in 1959, compared to an average of 10 to 12 percent for the United States.

Possibilities for commercial production and handling of silage include placing silage into smaller packages; special containers for handling silage from conventional silos to avoid damage or spoilage from exposure to air; dehydration of ensilage, followed by reconstitution by adding water to obtain a succulent feed; and use of large, portable silos, like railroad cars or truck trailers.

The feeding and watering of swine were the first areas of automation. Feed preparation and feeding provides a completely automatic operation for some farmers. A small electric motormill, with appropriate metering devices, is used for preparing the feed mixture. High-pressure pneumatic conveying is used to move the material to the swine. An auger feeder may be used to distribute the feed before the animals.

Disease control devices for swine and poultry will be developed for a completely automatic system. Disease control devices may consist of a periodic spray of fumigants, light for killing micro-organisms, and metering of antibiotics into feed or water.

Feeding and watering of poultry are reasonably well mechanized. Egg handling will be greatly improved. Mechanical equipment, much of which is now available, will check the eggs for soundness of shell and yolk, bacteria count, blood spots, and so on. Eggs may be broken from the shell and placed in a plastic shell or package. The selected package will provide proper gas exchange to maintain top quality. Handling and inspecting will be simplified. Perhaps the consumer at the market will purchase a dozen yolks and a half dozen whites, each in its own container. To obtain top quality, separation of the eggs could be provided directly after laying with the yolks and whites going into separate packages. These are handled separately and stored in an environment best suited for each. Rapid handling from the farm to consumer in refrigerated and gas-controlled atmosphere will develop.

Mechanization of handling manure of beef and dairy animals has developed greatly. Mechanization of manure removal for poultry and swine will receive more attention. Litters will be treated to facilitate handling. Mechanical removal of manure from the roosting area works well for poultry. The frequent removal of manure overcomes a major source of moisture, which often causes difficulties with ventilation and condensation. Automatic cleaning of swine houses is being developed: Swine are confined to a concrete platform, and cleaning is accomplished by a stream of water from a rotating boom, which travels over the floor. Water is supplied at about 70 pounds per square inch at 5 gallons a minute per nozzle to dislodge the manure from the floor. This is done 8 to 10 times a day for 3 or 4 minutes each time.

Bacteria that thrive on wastes will be developed. Bacteria have been found that thrive on the gas moving up through the soil from oil deposits. The bacteria aid in prospecting for oil. The action of bacteria of animal wastes might produce animal feed.

Environmental control for animals will become practical and economical: Air-conditioned buildings for productive animals—again the farmer gets the equipment before the housewife!—cooled slabs for swine, and cooled air for poultry. The moisture level would be controlled in a desirable range. Environmental control by zones will provide one zone for production animals, another zone for breeding animals, and another for newborn animals.

PROCESSING and storing activities provide agricultural products for the consumer on a year-round basis, with a minimum of loss, at a low cost. Processing may refer to any activity on the product to improve its marketability. Grinding feed, cleaning grain, drying grain or hay, sorting tomatoes, grading apples, curing meat are all examples of agricultural processing.

Agricultural processing operations for fluid or free-flowing solid products are reasonably well mechanized. Automation of some operations for food processing plants and equipment by cleaning-in-place is developing rapidly. For automation of an entire process, the mechanization of quality evaluation must follow. Possibilities for evaluation are the use of ultrasonic energy transmission, transmission of light, reflection and absorption of energy or light, continuous chemical analysis, spectrophotometric analysis, resilience, and electrical properties.

Some processing operations will be simplified. These will move to the farm and become a part of the production operation. The trend has been in the opposite direction, however, with such operations as milk processing, canning, and freezing, which have moved off the farms. Larger production centers, such as those for poultry and eggs, will do more processing. Large celery and vegetable picking operations will incorporate packing by grades.

Automated grain driers are available. They move grain from a bin to the drier and keep the drier full at all times. The grain is removed according to a preset time or temperature signal. Automatic methods to determine moisture and quality will be developed as a means of controlling the mechanical equipment now available for drying. Designation of quantity of product in hundredweights will replace bushels.

Sorting most fruits and vegetables is largely manual. Sizing most fruit is mechanized with considerable manual supervision. Automation will follow, in which sorting and grading will be done simultaneously and devices will be included for checking various physical, chemical, bacteriological, and biological properties.

Some products, like potatoes, can be separated according to density by placing the potato in liquid. The sorting of lemons and white pea beans according to color is an operation that aids in processing. In color sorting, light is reflected from the surface. The amount of reflected light is a measure of variation in color of a product. Sorting operations for products such as cherries, apples, blueberries, and grapes will be mechanized.

Bacteria counts will be made directly with instruments. Present methods take a lot of time and involve considerable judgment. Chemical, mechanical, or electrical properties might be used to determine the presence and state of growth of bacteria. Live and dead organisms of particular kinds might be determined by fluorescence, change in electrical conductivity, heat production, or light transmission. Devices such as those used for counting blood cells can be developed for counting bacteria—thus completing another link.

DEHYDRATION of products lengthens storage life and reduces losses. The flaking dehydration of potatoes has developed rapidly. Although dehydration of fruit and vegetables has been done for many years, new procedures provide products that are nearly equivalent to the fresh or raw product. Future developments will include powdered fruit juices, powdered whole milk, and tropical fruit.

Automatic operations are necessary to control dehydration. Processors must manufacture a product of uniform quality and taste that can be produced in different sections of the country.

Environmental control during the storage of crops, fruit, vegetables, and packaging materials for them will receive more attention. Ventilation systems will be used for grain to maintain a desirable product, in most cases to cool the product to 30° to 40° in the northern climate, to reduce rate of respiration and damage by insects and mold. Storage for 5 to 10 years of grain will be commonplace and economical. The present annual loss of 5 to 10 percent will be practically eliminated. These aeration systems will be controlled automatically by timeclocks and temperature and humidity controls. A stream of disinfectant fungicide or other chemical will be injected into the airstream if the heat production of the stored grain exceeds the heat carried away by the airstream. Wheat, corn, and rice are now protected to a limited extent with this method.

Controlled atmosphere for storage of fruit will gain. It has been developing rapidly for apple storage. With this procedure apples are held in an atmosphere high in carbon dioxide and low in oxygen. A proper relationship of carbon dioxide to oxygen must be maintained. Too much carbon dioxide will cause scald or damage to the product. Too much oxygen will cause faster deterioration. The storage will have automatic controls to maintain the proper temperature and amounts of gas. Diffusion of oxygen from the outside atmosphere into the storage through doors, cracks, and windows will be automatically compensated for, and the removal of an excess of carbon dioxide will be done automatically.

Handling into storage will receive more attention to reduce cost. Products will be placed in an appropriate form, shape, or container at or directly after harvest. The products can then be easily moved into and out of storage.

Automatic moving of certain varieties to or from a particular bin by chute, flume, or forklift pallets will be commonplace. A forklift truck can be given signals and directions to place and to obtain certain stored products. The fork truck can move without an operator by following a track or wire. Movable storage floors will facilitate handling. Temporary storage on roller conveyors and similar devices will precede a processing operation. Thus it will not be necessary that a processing machine be fed manually for each operation. Instead, cartons or products can be stacked periodically on an incoming conveyor and the machine automatically continue its operation.

Products that require refrigeration will move first through a chiller or hardening room to remove heat and cool the product to the storage temperature. The products will then move to the storage where the temperature is maintained. With this arrangement, the storage may require less expensive refrigeration equipment than if both chilling or hardening are both done with the same equipment.

AUTOMATION does not eliminate the responsibility of supervision and management. As a matter of fact, the responsibility is greater for automated operations.

The dials of meters will be in the control room to give the temperature of product, humidity of storage environment, flow of fluid, oxygen concentration, or speed. Supervision of the operations by observation of many different processes can be viewed from one central control point through television facilities. Television observations can be used to observe operations which are not metered. By tuning in on an appropriate channel, a person can see, by television, the feeding of cans into a filler, the movement of apples into particular bins, and the filling of cartons.

The control center of the farm or enterprise will provide, on request, such information as an accurate and up-to-date inventory of fuel, lubricant, products, repairs and maintenance costs;

hours devoted to each major activity; and the cost per unit of production. Just as a cash register records purchases in a particular column and tells the cashier how much change to give, so the above information will be readily available to the farmer.

Automation is not the answer to all material handling and processing operations. Some operations, in fact, will be more economical with less mechanization or less automation. Each operation must be evaluated separately.

The weather provides one limitation on planning agricultural operations not involved in many industrial operations. Sometime in the future, efforts may succeed in changing the weather, but before then weather forecasting will be improved. Automatically recorded weather data will include radioactivity, evapo-transpiration rate, heat and moisture changes in the atmosphere from pole to pole. Present weather forecasting is based primarily on information obtained near the ground. Future forecasting will involve information from outer space. Satellites will send radio messages to computers on the earth on such information as world sky cover, movement of cloud masses, and formation of storm areas.

Communications in agriculture will be improved to facilitate more rapid and efficient handling. The control center of the automated farm will be equipped with a Teletype that will give market information, weather, prices, and the world situation as it might influence the farmer's decision.

Communications on the farm will be improved. With the operatorless tractor in the field, a panel in the control center will give the information normally on the vehicle dash, such as the temperature, quantity of gasoline, and operation of the electrical system. Such improved communications would help a farmer to operate efficiently on several different areas considerably removed from each other. It would not be necessary then to pay an unusual price for land next to a present operation in order to enlarge a farm.

Computers may use the information supplied by various sources, such as the Teletype, to determine the most economical practice. Memory cells will tell the price of particular products a year ago. Computers will list the various possibilities for decision from which the farmer can select an answer. The computer does not and will not think—the farmer must do that.

WHO WILL PUT these new ideas—supplied by many farmers, engineers, scientists, manufacturers—into practice? Scientists discovered that planting corn kernels with the small end down produces higher yields. Engineers will develop the equipment for seeding to exploit this principle and to make it useful to agriculture. In research, a new kind of engineer—the engineer-scientist—is developing. He will link science and agriculture closer together.

Agricultural engineers will have more concern with the overall farming operations, not just the small components of particular machines, as now generally approached.

Many of the possible developments of the future demand that farm operators have engineering ability. High school training for those going into agriculture must include more of the basic areas for engineering, such as mathematics. These courses will cover those subjects recently covered in more advanced educational studies.

Engineers will help shorten the time between discovery and application of a new principle of finding. America has been made great by the scientific discoveries and the engineering advances of the past century. Underdeveloped areas can make use of this scientific and engineering knowledge and we have a responsibility of helping to disseminate this information to others.

PROGRESS depends on multiplying our efforts in agriculture.

Mainly through mechanization, the efforts of farmers can be multiplied. Automation will follow in many specialized areas. Training in applying engineering to agriculture offers a great hope and challenge. We now have the most efficient agriculture in the world, with the lowest cost of food to the consumer, in terms of hours required to earn food. And the percentage of income devoted to food has decreased in spite of more expensive tastes.

We cannot stop now. We must continue to search, investigate, analyze, and apply our findings for improvement, just as industry keeps looking for fuel and ore deposits and searching for new and more efficient methods of manufacture. We must be ready for these new challenges.

# Systems Engineering in Agriculture

L. L. Sammet

SYSTEMS, defined in terms of "an assemblage or set of correlated members," have been with us for a long time. This quality in a general way describes the universe itself. It characterizes any complex plant or animal organism. More recent than the origin of systems, yet not at all new, is man's recognition and use of the systems concept. This was an important part of early developments in astronomy, physics, and the biological sciences.

Early scientific observers studied natural systems. They focused attention on discovering natural laws as to the behavior of these systems and on explaining the relationships and interaction of many separate parts. This remains the central interest of many scientists, but the growing application of science and technology to man's activities has developed a new interest—that of systems building.

It involves the creation of new assemblages, achievement of improved correlation, and the development of new types of systems members. The procedure, in fact, may extend to the creation of completely new types of processes and products.

Systems characteristics are seen in modern industrial organization as applied, for example, in the manufacture of farm tractors and trucks. We know that this involves design and production scheduling for hundreds of individual parts and that intricate coordination is required to maintain an efficient flow of parts and subassemblies into the fabrication of a final product. This necessary coordination of many separate activities of men and machines creates an assemblage of correlated members, which constitute a system in the sense defined here. Growing attention to the task of coordinating industrial operations has created there a new field of endeavor—systems engineering.

The need for systems engineering in modern industry is easily established with respect to an automated factory or a telephone system. To work at all, such facilities require perfectly integrated performance of many individual parts. Planning and engineering of the system as a whole—as well as attention to individual components and their relation to it—cannot be avoided.

In many industries—and in agriculture—the processes are not rigidly controlled from a single point or otherwise organized as to require an absolutely integrated performance.

Instead, there is some adaptability in the process and component parts. This and time lapse between certain stages—as, for example, between planting and harvesting a crop or between harvesting and processing—lessen the urgency for perfect integration of system components. Greater concentration on individual parts of the system, with reduced interest in the system as a whole, often is evident in such circumstances. But this may bring neglect of important interactions that are present in a comprehensive process.

Neglect of this aspect is not necessarily fatal. Many systems created without comprehensive planning are effective. The case for systems engineering then must be made on the ground that deliberate and comprehensive planning can develop sufficiently improved systems to compensate for the added efforts of systems research and planning.

Wherever applied, systems planning is likely to be difficult. It may require great proficiency in particular fields as well as a broad understanding of major systems objectives. This is especially true in agriculture, where mechanical and electrical processes—those most commonly dealt with in the industrial sphere—are merely important supplements to plant, animal, chemical, bacterial, and many other types of processes involved in agricultural production.

Systems design in this broad framework evidently includes engineering. But the engineer contributes best as one of a team of specialists, each highly skilled in a special field. His concern in agriculture is with materials, machines, labor, and energy and their use to modify natural processes and to control environmental factors in the production of livestock and crops and storage of crops.

THE BOUNDARIES of agricultural systems may be drawn differently by different observers.

If viewed narrowly, many single units of farm equipment may themselves be regarded as "systems." This is true, for example, of a farm tractor, which may be described correctly as a complex, unified system for converting liquid fuels to mechanical power. But this system takes on other dimensions as part of an integrated assembly of tillage and other tools, and it becomes a component of a still larger system when applied in farm operations.

In the production and utilization of forage crops, for example, we have a system composed of major subprocesses or stages, such as soil preparation, planting, harvesting, transporting, storing, handling, and feeding. In these separate stages, the tractor-tool unit serves not as a "system" but as a tool or component. Each production stage includes numerous separate operations and may require the services of many individual components.

Interdependencies among production stages and stage components, a major attribute of systems, are easily recognized in forage production. There are, for example, fixed mechanical interdependencies such as are found in the tractor-tillage unit. There are interdependencies in product form and quality. The harvesting method determines whether materials are produced in loose, chopped, baled, or pelletized form. Selection of harvesting method thus predetermines the opportunities and limitations in subsequent materials handling and storage and may condition usefulness in feeding. The causal relation may, of course, run the other way. Selection of a particular method of handling or storing forage at the farmstead may specify the method of field harvesting.

Other interdependencies in the use of equipment arise when given equipment units—for example, the tractor—are employed in successive stages of the process. This quality is a major consideration in regard to capital investment in machines or structures. Investments in such facilities, made in one time period, are recovered only through their use in several different periods. The possibilities of introducing changes in methods in later periods therefore depend partly on previous technical and investment decisions.

Many other systems of single-crop production could be described, and the concept is easily extended to the production of several different crops on a single farm. Moreover, developments in the procurement of farm supplies and in marketing farm products suggest that some farm systems may extend beyond the farm gate.

A growing number of farm-supply services affect farm operations and equipment. These include bulk feed delivery and custom services for the application of fertilizers and insecticides and for pruning and cultural operations. In the sale and distribution of farm products, similar developments include the use of tank trucks in the farm-to-market transportation of milk and the use of pallet-bins in coordinated grower-processor harvesting of fruit and vegetables, their transportation, and their handling and storage at the processing plant.

Less obvious but important is the growth of contract and specification buying by food processors and distributors whereby type and quality of product as well as on-farm production and cultural practices are specified. The case for extension of system boundaries beyond the farm gate is clearest with respect to integrated production-processing-distribution operations under a single management. Examples of this type of organization are found in some parts of the canning industry and in the production and marketing of poultry.

In agriculture, as in other lines of production, there is evident need to coordinate the many individual operations and stages. When there are numerous alternative techniques for performing particular tasks in the various stages of such systems, it is commonly assumed that the optimum technique should be determined. This implies the selection, from all available methods of performing particular operations, of the particular combination of methods that will most satisfactorily meet predetermined systems goals. Intensive study of individual components and their relation to the system as a whole involves systems analysis.

SYSTEMS ANALYSIS begins with the selection of performance goals and criteria for judging their attainment. These vary with the type of problem under study.

Agricultural systems analysis, for example, might be aimed at minimizing soil loss, maximizing output, minimizing the costs of given outputs or—if directed toward a solution for an individual firm—maximizing profit.

Such goals might be considered singly, or there could be a primary goal modified by subordinate objectives. One could have the single goal of maximum immediate output from given resources, or this goal might be conditioned by certain restraints as to acceptable limits of soil loss.

In any event, the systems visualized, the criteria for judging them, and the optimum solution very likely will be different, depending on the goals sought. Their definition is, therefore, an essential prelude to systems studies.

Systems analysis must also emphasize the fact of numerous production stages with the possibility in each stage of two or more techniques for performing given tasks. This is particularly true in agriculture, where alternative technique must be broadly defined to include different work methods and equipment, different soil and fertilizer treatments, alternative plant and animal strains, and so on.

With the wide range in form of production organization this suggests, some difficulties may be anticipated in finding the optimum solution. With exceedingly simple problems, the alternative forms of process organization could be compared on the basis of controlled experiment. Only a little growth in complexity, however, could make necessary the comparison of many different alternative combinations—usually so great a number as to prohibit comparisons of alternative systems through controlled experiment. For example, a relatively simple five-stage process with two alternative techniques per stage—if all possible combinations of stage techniques are considered—can be arranged in 32 different system organizations. If there were 10 stages and 4 alternatives per stage, the possible number of different combinations would total more than 37 thousand.

When we recognize that the systems of interest generally involve the operating procedures of entire farms and may extend beyond farm limits to include activities in farm-services supply or in processing and marketing, controlled experiment with respect to alternative system organization does not seem a promising means of study.

Synthesis, or model building, offers a useful alternative to experimental comparison of entire systems.

Direct experiment and observation in this procedure is applied at the level of individual operations and stages— that is, to the component parts of the system. Such experiments provide information as to equipment and method of performance; the type, timing, and rate of use of the various inputs; and quantity, type, and quality of output.

From such results, estimates can be made of the type of inputs, their rate of use, and the costs of inputs in a particular operation or stage required to yield a particular *system* output. This kind of determination with respect to each operation and stage and with respect to alternative techniques in each stage provides a set of building blocks, which can be assembled in different combinations, each representing an alternative system organization.

If the basis of system evaluation is cost minimization, comparison of estimated total costs of given outputs from all alternative technical combinations then provides a basis for selecting the optimum system organization. This procedure is not strange to engineers. It has a close parallel in machine or structural design, but with important differences in objectives.

One procedure — synthesis — simulates real systems as a means of evaluating alternative forms of production organization. The other procedure— design—simulates physical equipment and structures as a basis for manufacture and construction.

Interaction and synthesis, the first representing the necessity for systems analysis and the second describing a method of systems evaluation, are illustrated in studies of alternative methods of harvesting and plant-assembly of lima beans and peas for freezing. The studies were reported by the California and Oregon Agricultural Experiment Stations in 1958. The harvesting and assembly activities link together two major phases, farm production and processing, in the production-processing-marketing system for these products.

In the farm production phase, broad categories (or stages) of operation may be recognized, such as soil preparation, planting, cultivation, dusting, irrigating (in some areas), and harvesting. Similarly, within the processing plant, major process stages include receiving the raw product, dumping it into the process flow, cleaning, quality grading, blanching, filling and wrapping containers, preparing for freezing, transporting to freezer, and freezing.

We know that alternative methods are available for performing the various operations in this long sequence. We know also that complexity of analysis grows at an accelerating rate with increase in the number of alternatives considered simultaneously. The problem is simplified, therefore, if the total process can be divided into subprocesses for separate analysis. This can be done if there is no significant interaction between the subprocesses so defined.

This question was considered in comparisons of costs with existing methods of performing the various operations in vining and hauling. Three principal variations in method were observed. All include the same basic operations of cutting, shelling, and transporting. The methods differ with respect to type of equipment, sequence, and location of certain operations.

One method uses mechanical viners fixed in location at a point near the farm producing center. Vines, cut by machine, are draper-loaded into trucks for transportation to the vining center. Here they are unloaded and fed into viner-shellers which remove peas (or beans) from the vines and pods and discharge the vines into a silage pit. Shelled product is delivered to con-

tainers and later loaded for transportation to the processing plant.

In a second method, the operations are essentially the same, except that the viner-sheller equipment is located adjacent to the processing plant rather than in the field. Shelled product is delivered by conveyor or flume directly to the receiving room of the plant for processing.

A third method involves drawing mobile viner-sheller equipment through the field. The vines, previously cut and windrowed, are collected on a drum which feeds them to a conveyor leading to the separator. Shelled beans are collected on a side-delivery conveyor, elevated to a hopper, and periodically dumped into a bulk truck for delivery to the processing plant. The vines are discharged to the ground as the machine moves through the field.

The threshing and separating equipment used with all three methods is essentially the same as to performance characteristics. The principal differences—as indicated in the process chart—are in the handling and hauling operations.

To study the relative costs with the three methods, work measurement procedures as applied in industrial engineering were used to determine output capacities of individual workers on particular jobs and of the various types of equipment.

Standard performance rates per worker and per equipment unit thus determined were the building blocks for synthesis. These were used to estimate the number of workers and quantities of equipment and other services required to produce shelled peas or beans at a given rate per hour. With such estimates of physical requirements, costs were easily computed by the application of appropriate cost rates.

The studies were designed to show the effect on costs of variation in several factors. Length of haul, for example, was considered important in view of differences in density of load in the field-to-plant transportation of field-shelled product, as compared with the

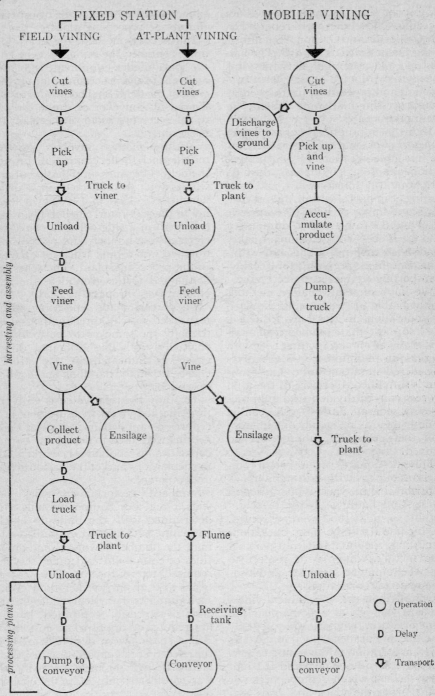

*Process-flow diagram with three methods of harvest and plant-assembly of peas and lima beans for processing.*

hauling of low-density loads of vines to vining equipment stationed at the processing plant.

The possibilities of operating economies with a large-scale installation (where scale was measured in terms of output capacity of shelled product per hour) as compared with small-scale installations were considered.

The substantial differences among methods as to investment requirements for installations of the same scale were also regarded as an important variable.

Still another consideration grows out of the investment problem. Investment costs, which appear in the cost calculations as fixed costs per year, decrease per unit of output as the annual volume produced in an installation increases.

With an installation of given size—and therefore of given investment outlay with respect to each method—annual volume in the fixed harvest season of a given location is varied primarily by variation in hours worked per day. This leads to the problem of optimum adjustment with respect to capacity output rate and hours of daily operation. Since these relationships differ in regard to field and plant operations, solution of this problem requires that vining and processing plant operations be considered jointly. Problems such as the foregoing were considered in these studies.

Comparison of the two methods of field vining showed the mobile viner to be at a slight cost disadvantage when rate of vining is low and hours operated per season small. Mobile vining, where adaptable, offers substantial savings, however, when the size of installation is large and hours operated per season relatively high. As might be expected, at-plant as compared with field vining faces an increasing cost handicap as length of haul with the relatively low-density load of vines increases. Economies gained through direct delivery of shelled product to the plant receiving tanks may be dissipated as size of processing plant grows and its supply area and hauling distance increase.

In the studies, no difference in the methods of farm production before harvest or in plant operation after the receiving stage were attributed to differences in method of vining.

The possibility of subdividing the production-harvesting-processing operations for detailed study then hinge on the extent to which the determination of optimum combination of field and plant capacities and daily operating hours require that these phases be studied jointly. They also hinge on the difference in plant receiving operations with the alternative methods of field harvest.

The first of these problems, while quite important in principle, was found not to be of sufficient practical significance to require simultaneous determination of economical technique in the field and plant operations.

The second consideration may conveniently be handled by defining three major sectors of analysis: Field production; harvesting, hauling, and plant receiving; and plant processing, excluding receiving. In this way, interdependencies in field and plant operations in this example may be adequately treated in the analysis without making the problem unnecessarily complex.

SYSTEMS DEVELOPMENT, involving the creation of new types of equipment, improved farm production methods, and new concepts of process organization, appears to be a logical outgrowth, if not an inseparable companion, of systems analysis.

Ideally, evaluation and comparison in systems analysis would be used to highlight areas within the present systems that offer special promise for more intensive study and development of new technique. In the illustration, for example, measurements of the adverse cost-effect of short-season operation demonstrate potential economies from extending the harvest and plant operating seasons. This suggests plant breeding investigations as a means of developing new varieties for given producing regions that mature at different dates. Or it may be appropriate to consider the production of alternative crops and the construction of processing plants adaptable to several lines of output.

Successful developments of this type would imply important effects on the optimum technical organization of both field and plant organization as well as on costs. They might lead to review and modification of procedures for the coordination of the operations of processors and farmers, and these might call for new forms of contractual relations between growers and processors or even bear significantly on the possibilities and benefits of the integration of growing and processing activities under a single management.

Other illustrations of the possibilities of systems development can easily be visualized. Many of them also would suggest the possibility that systems analysis may stimulate technical developments, which, in turn, create possibilities for new forms of technical organization.

Interaction among the various operating components of agricultural systems evidently has a parallel in the relationship of analysis and development in systems studies.

COMPREHENSIVE SYSTEMS in agricultural production and marketing evidently provide extremely wide possibilities for investigation and analysis and for extending the results of such work into the applied area of systems development.

Such studies embrace the subject matter of many different fields and this suggests the research team as a productive—even necessary—approach. If well organized, such teams would have the capability of deep penetration in special problem areas. They would be equipped for exhaustive search for significant interrelationships among individual system components, but also be prepared to set aside those likely to be of little significance in overall systems operation.

The growing complexity of farm production and marketing operations and the need for improved coordination of existing system organizations and for the development of new process methods and organization may provide a new role—or at least expansion of an old one—for engineering in its service to agriculture.

# Machines for New Crops

Leonard G. Schoenleber

WE CALL castorbeans, kenaf, safflower, sesame, and canaigre new crops because of the new interest farmers and industry have in them.

To produce and sell them and other new crops profitably, new or modified machines usually must be developed to produce, harvest, and process them.

Success in establishing a new crop depends also on efforts of plant scientists, who work to change characteristics of the plants to make them better suited to accommodate limitations of machines and increase efficiency. Developments in machinery likewise take into consideration the characteristics and limitations of the plants.

Such factors as the nature and potential value of the crop, climate and soil conditions, and annual use of the machine dictate which, how, and whether new machines are developed or old ones are adapted. Development of a new machine often requires years of research by agricultural engineers, individual enterprises, and manufacturers.

When the potential acreage or value of a crop does not justify the expense of developing a machine by industry, public institutions may initiate and carry on the development work.

CASTORBEANS contain an oil that is used in the production of more than

200 products. The potential uses of the oil seem unlimited. It is particularly valuable in the manufacture of certain plastics, protective coatings, synthetic lubricants for jet aircraft, all-purpose greases, and hydraulic fluids. It is used in making nylon-type cloth and extruded and molded parts.

The pulp that remains after the oil is extracted is useful as fertilizer. It is known as castor pomace. It contains protein and someday may be used as feed for livestock if a poisonous constituent can be economically neutralized.

Castorbeans were grown commercially, mainly in the Midwest, in the 19th century. Production was hampered by problems in harvesting, handling, and hulling. The large size of the bushy plants, the irregular ripening of the seed, and the susceptibility of ripened seed to shatter made necessary much harvesting by hand as the seed matured. Farmers therefore lost interest in the crop, and production dropped to practically nothing by 1910.

The consumption of oil from castorbeans in the United States has increased steadily since 1900. Most of it was imported. The annual consumption of the oil since 1950 has exceeded 100 million pounds.

The strategic value of castor oil in wartime emphasized the need for a domestic supply. Research was started by employees of the Federal Government to establish production but was discontinued after a while.

World conditions in the 1940's led to the classification of castor oil as a strategic material, and the Government scientists again inaugurated a research program. Intensive studies have been made to develop equipment and better, higher yielding varieties.

One of the first machines was a huller for removing the seed from the pod, or hull. A disk type of huller came into wide use by 1952. The hulling was done by large stationary huller units, usually at a central location, such as a railroad siding, or by small hulling units at the side of the field.

The hullers have a pair of rubber-covered parallel hulling disks. One is stationary and one rotates. They are spaced about three-eighths inch apart. The seeds pass through an opening at the center of the stationary disk. The hulls are removed by the scouring action of the rubber-faced disks as the seed is forced out radially between the disks. A fan separates loose hulls and other foreign material from the seed.

Development of the first experimental harvesting machine started in 1947 in Nebraska. A one-row machine, it used a pair of rotating beaters with canvas flaps for stripping the seeds from standing plants, a cleaner for removing foreign material, and an elevator for depositing the unhulled seeds in a bin mounted on a harvester. Several machines of this kind were built and used.

To encourage the production of castorbeans, the Government began to support prices of the crop in 1949 and contracted with a manufacturer of combines to furnish modified machines that might be used to harvest the castorbeans. The machines had a header attached to a combine to cut the plants near the ground surface. The plants passed through a cylinder and over cleaners that removed the seed capsules, which were deposited in a bin.

A research and development program, started in 1950 by the Federal Government and the Oklahoma Agricultural Experiment Station, led to a machine that used the stripping principles employed on the Nebraska harvester but had modifications to suit the existing varieties.

During the next 2 years, about 200 one-row and two-row tractor-mounted harvesters were built under Government contract to assist in harvesting the greatly expanded castorbean acreage. The machines helped engineers in developing the basic components of effective harvesters, but they only stripped the seed capsules from the plant. Some machines built in 1952 removed foreign material from the unhulled seed, but hauling and handling the bulky unhulled castor material from the harvesters took a lot of time.

At the same time, several companies built a number of one-row harvesters, which stripped the seed capsules from the plant. One company included a huller on one of the harvesters built in 1954. All had many new features.

They made it apparent that a one-man, once-over, two-row machine, which could open a field, strip the seed from the plant, hull and clean the seed, and then place the seed in a bin, would be needed to make mechanical harvesting successful. It became clear also that castorbeans would need to be grown in sections that are relatively dry during harvest. The seed, hulls, and leaves must be dried by frost or defoliation with chemicals to accomplish satisfactory harvesting.

Those principles were taken into account in research by Government workers in 1953 and 1954. They built the first prototype machine in 1955. Machines built since then have included most of the principles they developed.

Higher-yielding varieties, better adapted for mechanical harvesting, have been bred. They are particularly well suited for growing in the Southwest under irrigation. Varieties have been developed also for nonirrigated areas.

Yields of the tall varieties range from a few hundred pounds on unfavorable dryland conditions to yields of 3,500 pounds an acre or more under good management on irrigated areas of California and Arizona.

Dwarf varieties are grown only under irrigation to obtain normal height. In 1960 they were grown in the High Plains of Texas. They normally grow 3.5 to 4 feet tall and are affected little by wind. The crop is much easier to handle than tall varieties, which are 8 to 12 feet tall. Yields of 2,500 pounds an acre of dwarf varieties are common.

Conventional row-crop planters with seed plates adapted for castor seed and regular cultivating equipment are satisfactory. At least 15 to 20 inches of rainfall, well distributed during the growing season, are needed in nonirrigated sections to obtain satisfactory yields.

Castorbeans of varieties now grown commercially need a growing season of at least 180 days for favorable yields.

Four companies were making harvesters in 1960. They were mounted on tractors or were self-propelled and were made in two- and four-row units.

Two companies are providing attachments to mount on self-propelled combines. The changes consist of a header for shaking the seed capsules from the plants with conveyors, a rubber-covered huller with either two rotating drums or one rotating drum and concave, and a bucket or auger elevator for conveying hulled seed.

The two-row machines operate best at 3 miles an hour or less and harvesting at the rate of 2 acres an hour in fields that yield 2,500 pounds an acre. A two-row machine commonly harvests 500 acres of beans a season.

KENAF is a soft-bast, long-fiber plant. In experimental plantings of jute and jutelike substitutes that can be grown in the United States, it was one of the most promising. Such materials are used to make rope, twine, bags, burlap, and similar items. We have depended on imports for them—169 million pounds of raw jute fiber and 753 million pounds of products made from jute were imported in 1956.

Kenaf is less susceptible to diseases and insects and is less exacting in growing requirements than jute. It will grow well in most parts of the South and yields up to 2 thousand pounds of fiber an acre.

It is grown as an annual on land prepared as for other drilled crops. The seed is planted easily with an ordinary grain drill. The rapid growth of the plants chokes out weeds. The stalks are .5 to .75 inch in diameter and are 8 to 12 feet tall at harvest. When seeded at the rate of 25 pounds an acre, the stalks are free of branches except at the top.

Because much hand labor is entailed in cutting, retting, separating, grading, and bundling, agricultural engineers in the Department of Agriculture and the

Florida Agricultural Experiment Station began work to develop machines.

They developed a field harvester-ribboner, which will harvest the stalks and remove the leaves and woody core, with only the bast fibrous ribbons to be taken from the field; a mechanized process of conveying the ribbons through a bacterial retting process; and washing and cleaning machinery for treating the fiber after the ret.

The harvester-ribboner has harvesting, crushing, and ribboning units.

The harvesting unit gathers the stalks from a 32-inch swath, separates those to be cut from those left standing, cuts the swath at the ground, removes 12 to 18 inches of the tops (which contain most of the leaves and practically no fiber), and delivers them to a feed table on the machine.

The crushing unit mashes and breaks the woody core of the stalk at 6-inch intervals. The ribboning drums, 36 inches in diameter with a 20-inch face, have 6 blades with scalping edges. The ribbons from the bast layer surrounding the woody core of the stalks are delivered at the rear of the machine free from leaf material and most of the woody part of the stalk.

Improvements in the machine have reduced field losses, increased the capacity, and reduced the number of men needed to operate it. Three men can harvest about 1 acre an hour. An acre should yield about 3 thousand pounds of dried ribbons, or half that amount of dried fiber after retting.

Ribbons may be treated in several ways. They may be dried and spun into coarse yarns without further processing at harvest. The green ribbons may be mechanically decorticated; the fiber is dried and spun without further treatment. The ribbons also may be chemically or bacterially retted before spinning. Bacterial retting produces a fiber more nearly equal in quality and spinning characteristics to the Indian jute that American manufacturers are accustomed to handling. Most manufacturers demand fiber of the quality produced by water retting.

A number of retting procedures that produce acceptable fiber have been investigated. Methods of securing uniformity and mechanization of the handling processes were being investigated in 1960.

In order to make the production of water-retted fiber feasible in this country, a completely mechanized process of large capacity must be developed. Machinery to do this has been devised and has been undergoing tests and improvements in the fiber laboratory at Belle Glade, Fla.

The process involves a series of squeezing-washing operations to remove slime and loose extraneous material. A scutching operation removes shives, bark, and such from the fiber. Subsequent squeezing removes the last traces of discoloration that may develop from the scutching operation, and the clean fiber is ready for drying and baling. Artificial driers and baling machinery developed for other fibers are suitable for handling kenaf fiber in large-scale operations.

Machinery has been developed for extracting and processing other long fibers—sansevieria for rope and marine cordage, ramie for textiles and industrial products, and lecheguilla for brushes and like products. The machinery for fiber extraction can be used with minor modification on most of the long-fiber plants. Equipment for drying, brushing, and baling can be used for all the fibers with little change.

None of these fibers was grown commercially in the United States in 1960, but the mechanical developments may make it possible to produce enough of them to meet a considerable part of our needs if an emergency occurs.

SAFFLOWER, an oilseed crop grown in India and other parts of the world for centuries, is a new crop for American farmers. Its seed may contain up to 35 percent of oil. Its drying and non-yellowing properties make it useful in paints and varnishes. The processed oil is edible. The seed pulp and hulls that remain after the oil is removed contain about 25 percent of protein, a feed supplement for livestock.

This drought-tolerant plant was introduced in this country on an experimental basis in the 1920's. More than 200 thousand acres of safflower were grown in 1959.

The crop is well adapted to parts of the Western States that have a low relative humidity. Best yields are obtained when the atmosphere is dry and hot during the flowering time and enough subsoil moisture is present throughout the growing season. Irrigation, which is controlled so as not to encourage root rot, a common disease, increases yields when rainfall is deficient.

Safflower, an annual of the thistle family, grows 1 to 5 feet tall. The average yield in California was 1,700 pounds of seed an acre in 1956. Average dryland yields of 700 to 1,200 pounds an acre are common. The seed sells for about twice the price of barley. The oil sells for about the same price as linseed oil or soybean oil.

Safflower can be planted, cultivated, and harvested with the machinery that is used for small grains. Its future as a cash crop in the United States looks bright. Disease-resistant varieties, which produce more seed of a higher oil content, are being developed.

SESAME is one of the oldest oilseed plants known to man. Its seed is used for food and feed. The seeds contain about 50 percent oil and 25 percent protein, which is highly digestible, and are used in baked goods, candies, and other food products. The oil is used in cooking and for making margarine, shortening, paints, soaps, and pharmaceutical products.

This plant, of tropical origin, produces best in places where the temperature remains high during the growing season. This includes the southern half of the United States.

The crop was first grown in this country in the 17th century, but interest in growing it on a commercial scale did not develop until about 1953. The

acreage has increased steadily each year since then. About 15 thousand acres of sesame were grown in 1959.

Yields of more than 2 thousand pounds an acre have been had. Average yields of 600 to 1,500 pounds are commoner.

Sesame, an annual plant, tolerates drought, but responds well to proper irrigation. Plants that stand in water only a few hours are damaged or killed, however.

Sesame can be planted and cultivated with equipment used on other row crops. Seed boxes used for small vegetable seeds can be used satisfactorily for planting the seed of sesame.

Harvesting has been a major problem. The two types of seed—the dehiscent (shattering) and the indehiscent (nonshattering) varieties, both adapted for growing in this country—are difficult to harvest. The dehiscent varieties lose seed readily because the seed pods open during the maturing process and scatter seed. The seed pods of the indehiscent varieties are very tough and hard to open.

Injury to the seed reduces its viability. Seeds even slightly cracked produce objectionable free fatty acids in a short time and become unfit for human food. The dehiscent varieties mostly are grown in the United States.

A common method of harvesting is to cut the crop with grain or row-crop binders and place it in shocks as soon as the plants reach maturity, when most of the leaves drop. The shocks are made compact by tying with twine to prevent loss of seed as the shocks cure. After 10 to 14 days of normal curing weather, the shocks are ready to thresh. Grain combines are used for this purpose.

A platform at the front of the combine helps cut seed losses. The combine is driven to each shock; the whole shock is pushed onto the platform to avoid excessive handling. Bundles are fed from the platform into the machine one at a time. Loose seed that falls on the platform is saved by dumping into the combine. Proper adjustment and speed of the threshing unit is essential; otherwise, seed damage will be excessive.

Research on another type of harvester has been undertaken in California. It picks up windrowed sesame, chops the stalks, knocks out of the pods the seed that has not already shattered, runs the seed over a cleaner, and conveys the seed to a bin on the machine. Four rows of plants are cut with a windrower and placed into an irrigation furrow, which should be wide and shallow. Slicking the furrow with a sled fills the cracks and smooths the surface to provide a suitable area for drying the stalks. Dehisced seed, which falls to the bottom of the furrow, is picked up easily by the gathering arms and air equipment on the harvester.

Sesame can be grown in many sections. Further research is needed to develop higher yielding varieties that are easy to thresh but less subject to shatter than existing varieties, so that direct combining may be done from standing plants. New methods of harvesting may have to be developed also.

CANAIGRE has roots that are rich in tannin, which is important in the manufacture of leather goods and in other uses. Nearly all our tannin has been imported.

This perennial herb, native to the United States, grows from seed, crowns, or root. It tolerates drought and is well adapted to the Southwestern States, but for good yields the crop should be irrigated. Production yields of 15 tons of roots to the acre may be expected under good growing conditions. Yields exceeding 25 tons have been obtained in trials with improved varieties. The freshly harvested mature roots contain about 70 percent of water. The remaining dry matter contains about 35 percent of tannin.

Canaigre roots were used by Indians and early settlers for tanning hides and as a dye and medicine. Now they are used mainly in the manufacture of leather goods. Attempts were made to commercialize canaigre as a source of tannin during the 19th century. The roots were dug by hand from wild stands.

Experimental plantings of canaigre in Arizona have demonstrated that the crop can be handled with ordinary planting and cultivating equipment. The crop is ready for harvest usually by July 1, when the tops die back to the crown.

An experimental digger, built by men in the Department of Agriculture, embodies the main mechanical features of a potato digger but permits deeper penetration of the digger blade to get under the roots. Long shaker chains and a special clod crushing roller aid in the cleaning of the roots. Present commercial potato harvesters with certain modifications should make them adaptable for harvesting canaigre. Bulk methods of handling root crops during harvest and storage can be applied to canaigre.

Roots processed immediately after drying may require further cleaning to remove all remaining soil. Vegetable washers can be used when the agitation of the roots and the rate of cleaning are controlled.

Roots held for later processing require proper storage. The cheapest and best method is to pile the freshly dug, unwashed roots on the ground and cover them with straw to protect them from the hot sun. Undamaged roots stored in this manner should remain in good condition for a year. Good yielding varieties and suitable equipment make possible the production of canaigre on a commercial scale.

THE NEW technology that is accumulating in agriculture and in other industries will have an even greater impact on development of equipment for new crops than experienced in the past. These fascinating new machines and new crops that cast their shadows on the countryside are attracting the attention of farmers and are making possible avenues for new income with efficient farming and better life for the farm families.

# The Dynamics
# of Structures

Mark E. Singley

FARM BUILDINGS are being absorbed into the complete farm design, as were farm tractors after the Second World War. The escape of the tractor from its identity with the horse occurred when its design and use were related to the inherent utility it offered and not to replacement or substitution. Today the tractor performs all sorts of jobs that never could have been identified with the horse.

Buildings are now just emerging from their association with animal housing and feed storage, which are essentially static contributions to farming and do little to make farming easier.

Structures today are evolving as units that contribute to the dynamics of farming. Many will become increasingly difficult to classify uniquely as structures or machines, and their function will range far beyond housing and storage. Machines and buildings have begun to merge to reduce farm labor to a minimum.

Beyond economic progress of our society as a whole lie two reasons of special interest for the changes that are occurring in structures and equipment: Engineering research and industrial development.

Engineering research provides the basis for these changes by improving old methods and creating new ideas.

Industrial development provides the means for making the changes through mass production and distribution of new buildings and equipment.

Research tended in the past to deal separately with the building and the equipment used in it. Today the desire to reduce man's labor has forced a consolidation of research efforts.

Techniques used to create field machines are being applied now to structures. One of them is the combination of several operations in one machine. Today's corn combine picks, husks, and shells corn and by conversion can be used to harvest the small grains. It is truly a remarkable machine. Operations also are consolidated in modern structures where field crops and supplements are received, processed, or processed and converted to new products, usually with the addition of energy.

The integration of operations in one structure is not easily accomplished. One reason is a break with tradition. Another is that a new structure usually is required.

The first and commonest step in change today is the substitution of a machine for a man. Examples are the silo unloader, automatic feed bunk, elevator, conveyor, and automatic poultry feeder. Their common denominator is substitution of a machine for hand feeding. Although substitution is occurring rapidly, much needs to be learned about the machines and the agricultural products they handle.

Man is versatile in his ability to handle feeds with characteristics ranging from the bale form to mixed feeds. Machines generally are not versatile, and the machine is developed to satisfy the characteristics of the material to be handled, or the characteristics of the material are altered to suit the machine design. Therefore the need arises to study machine and characteristics of materials and their relationship to each other.

The need for a machine may be eliminated when the characteristics of the materials are understood. For example, a bin of grain can be emptied completely by machine or by gravity flow and be self-emptying. Research continues to explore both methods.

At the University of Illinois a machine has been developed that consists of a sweep auger that rotates over the floor of a flat-bottomed circular bin and transfers grain or shelled corn to the center of the bin. The material falls onto an auger operating below the floor of the bin and is conveyed to the side, where it empties into a device suitable for the next operation.

This machine is influenced relatively little by the range of characteristics of these materials. Grain or shelled corn that has been tightly packed, or has a moisture content that retards flow, can be removed successfully. This is not true of the conventional self-emptying bin that has a shaped bottom containing a gate to control the flow. Grain that resists flow keeps such a bin from being self-emptying.

For free-flowing materials, a self-emptying bin operates as follows: A vertical core the size of the bottom opening flows out. This opens a channel to the top of the bin. Grain near the channel at the top pours in and falls down through the bottom opening. A funnel is formed that descends as the grain flows. The bin contents literally turn upside down, since the grain at the top empties first.

For funnel flow, the material flows over a constricting surface that exaggerates the resistance to grain flow. A bin discharge device, called the BCR easy-flow bin, enables a large core to flow through a larger bottom opening to which the device is attached. The nature of the core flow is changed. Instead of a funnel, a conical shape is formed. The outside descends first, and the inside is retarded. Flow that occurs over a conical surface to the outside is encouraged.

With a large core removed, the remainder empties by funnel flow. As the diameter of the core opening increases, however, the ability of the grain to flow over a constricting surface is increased. The exact relationship remains unknown. By using the discharge device, which becomes part of the bin, materials with a much wider range of characteristics can be run through a self-emptying bin.

The structure of the machine-emptied bin has no part in the emptying. It is a storage only. In the unloading bins, the structure is not only a storage; it also unloads. This is an old consolidation with new meaning. The self-feeder structure is another example of a building design that eliminates the need for a machine.

Feeds normally are removed from storage to be eaten by livestock. A structure from which feed is consumed by livestock is called a self-feeder. To a vertical silo, in which feed is stored and preserved satisfactorily, another use can be added—feeding.

Such a consolidation eliminates the need to transfer the feed by hand or machine. Before the self-feeder could evolve, some of the characteristics of the materials ensiled in it had to be studied and understood. Silage is essentially a short-cut, fibrous material, which, after packing, exhibits strength when placed in tension, as fibers do when formed into a thread. In compression, however, its strength is low, and the mass can easily be separated and divided. Through research, this weakness was recognized and exploited to create a self-feeder silo. The same material characteristics are important to the researchers who create a machine to handle the material.

It is difficult to determine the relative importance of the self-feeder silo and the machine-unloaded silo. Both contribute to our progress. The self-feeder is probably limited in the physical size that will perform successfully; the machine-unloaded silo is not.

Storage and self-feeding are combined in a hay self-feeder. Research has shown that chopped hay is the best hay form for self-feeding, although hay formed into pellets or wafers may replace it. Chopped hay must be artificially dried in the humid regions of the country to produce consistently a high quality. This is best timed to occur in storage to eliminate the destruction and loss that occurs if chopped hay is handled when dry. This adds another use to the structure and now, like the self-feeder silo, it provides for storage, processing, and feeding. For the combination to be successful, new characteristics that determine the success of drying require study.

The deep-bed drying process of artificially drying agricultural crops, better known as crop drying, uses air as the drying medium. Depths of hay greater than 20 feet and grain and shelled corn greater than 10 feet have been dried successfully, but much remains to be learned about the process.

We still need to determine satisfactory relationships that express the progress of drying through the deep bed based on the original condition of the material and the condition and quantity of the drying air. Minimum quantities of air with specified conditions have been established for drying most crops. The most efficient quantities and conditions have not. When this process is satisfactorily described by mathematical equations, the present method of design by trial and experience will be replaced by the more versatile method of design by calculation. Several groups of researchers have started work to develop these equations.

Engineers also have begun to examine the proper place to dry the crop in the sequence of farm operations. The suitability of drying on the transport vehicle, in a special drying device, or in storage, is questioned for each crop in different farm situations.

The special drying device can be used satisfactorily for crops that flow easily, like shelled corn and grain, because they are not difficult to handle. The time required to transfer the corn and grains in and out of the device is a detraction, however. For materials that resist flow, like the present forms of hay, the transport vehicle or the storage is the place to dry because no handling is added and handling methods have not been as well developed as for materials that flow easily. Like drying in storage, drying in the transport vehicle is a consolidation.

To prevent a crop from becoming too dry when dried in storage, the temperature of the drying air must be limited.

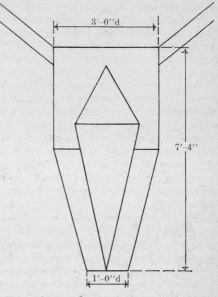

The BCR easy-flow bin is a device that is added to the bottom of a larger bin. A large top opening which encourages flow is reduced to a small bottom opening suitable for delivery to a material handling device. The inverted and upright cone combination in the center causes flow to occur from the outside of the 3'-0" diameter upper opening and this results in expanding flow.

This limits the speed of drying. The amount of water that can be removed with a single drying unit therefore is low. To increase drying speed and capacity, the air is heated and used to dry moderate depths of materials. Four or five layers of baled hay with a depth of about 5 feet are dried on a wagon; the thickness of the wall of grain or shelled corn in a wall-type batch bin drier is about 18 inches. Both are designed to use heated air.

The design of the drying system is of special interest because the drying efficiency can be influenced markedly. Drying does not occur simultaneously in all parts of a deep bed of material. It begins in a relatively narrow zone next to the air supply duct. For drying initiated at the bottom of a mass, when the bottom of the zone is dry, the zone begins to migrate upward through the mass until it emerges from the top.

After emergence, the mass is dry. If the progress of the zone is not uniform, some parts of the mass will be delayed in drying, and the drying time is lengthened. The drying efficiency thus is reduced.

A curved drying zone develops with a nonuniform thickness in a mass of material with a rectangular cross section that is dried by air that enters the material from a duct with a semicircular cross section. The drying zone first emerges directly over the top of the duct. Linear airflow through a uniform cross section is required for uniform drying.

All of the materials I have discussed shrink when they dry. The shrinkage shows itself only as a reduction in depth if they are free flowing and dried in a container. Shrinkage actually occurs in all three dimensions of depth, length, and width, but the length and width are maintained by flowing while drying. A batch of shelled corn 20 inches deep, initially at a moisture content of 25 percent wet basis will be about 17.75 inches deep when dried to a moisture content of 15.5 percent. For material that is not free flowing and has similar shrinkage characteristics, the reduction in depth will not be so great, because the shrinkage in length and width will be expressed and will not contribute to a reduction in depth.

Besides shrinkage, distortion of the material may occur. If pliability increases during drying, distortion will occur when a weight is placed on the material. Bales of hay formed for drying are loose and pliable to allow the air to pass through them. When drying, not only the bale size but the plants comprising the bale shrink.

Bales in the bottom layer sense the weight of the bales above and distort. The distortion counteracts the shrinkage in the length and width of the bales and maintains the original tightness of stacking. Bales in the top layer do not distort, the shrinkage is not counteracted, and they separate as they dry. Bales that are separated dry more slowly than those tightly packed because much of the air will go around rather than through them.

The drying capacity of the air that bypasses the bales is lost when the top layer is dried last by air that enters from the bottom. If the airflow is reversed, the slow-drying top layer begins to dry first, and the air that bypasses it moves through the more tightly packed lower layers. The drying capacity is not lost, and a lower layer begins to dry simultaneously with the top layer. The completion of drying is not delayed while waiting for a slow drying layer to be dried. It occurs simultaneously with the faster drying layers. Total drying time is reduced, and the drying efficiency is improved.

These are some of the contributions to materials handling and processing that have been made by engineering research. They spring from a penetrating study of the characteristics of the materials and processes used. This is the way research works for us.

Energy is used for drying. Unheated-air drying uses the sun's energy after it has warmed the earth's atmosphere. Heated-air drying uses the sun's energy that has been stored in the fossil fuels. Only a fraction of the sun's direct energy is used by mankind today. Methods of increasing its use are being sought.

SOLAR BUILDINGS are an example of a new use to moderate the winter environments for poultry and livestock. For the poultry house environment, winter healthfulness is associated with a moderate relative humidity and temperature.

One of the large contributions of moisture to the atmosphere of the poultry house comes from droppings in the litter. They are not easily dried by air passing over the surface, because the transfer of heat from the air to the litter is slow, and the litter, usually well packed, does not allow air to penetrate. When sunlight falls directly on the litter, only receptivity of the litter determines how much energy it will absorb. As the energy is absorbed, the temperature of the litter rises and the rate of water transfer to the air increases. In addition, warmth of the litter, which acts as a radiator, warms the air and moderates the air temperature of the house.

Ventilation, either natural or mechanical, is used to change the air in the house and remove the moisture. To prevent the house from overheating in summer, the sun's rays must be excluded. An overhang, to provide shade for the transparent face of the building when the sun is high in the summer sky, and the angle of the face combine to exclude most of the rays. The maximum amount of energy passes through when the rays of the sun are perpendicular to the transparent face. When they strike at a sharp angle, most of the energy is reflected and little passes through.

THE COUNTERPART to the use of the sun's rays for heating is the use of a cool area in the sky for radiation cooling.

At the University of California, the sky is being studied to learn how the cool area can be used effectively to cool livestock during the hot months. Although the area moves with the movement of the sun, the north sky at an angle of about 60° above the horizontal is usually the lowest radiating or coolest direction during the hot period of the day. A difference of about 28° F. between air and sky is available as a cooling sink at an air temperature of 100°.

When overhead shade is used to intercept and reflect much of the sun's energy and reduce the radiation from the ground by creating a shadow, the overhead heat load is reduced by as much as 65 percent and the ground heat load by 25 percent.

Combining shade with radiation to the cool area in the sky offers the possibility of improved livestock comfort in summer. This is an example of one of the advantages offered by Nature when it is understood.

Environment contributes much to improving the uniformity of production

of eggs, meat, and milk by reducing stress caused by the extremes of temperature and humidity.

The effect of humidity and temperature on cattle is part of a long-term study at the University of Missouri. When the relative humidity ranges between 55 and 70 percent and the dry bulb temperature between 40° and 75°, milk flow in dairy animals was not affected. Milk flow fell off severely above 75°. The different breeds reacted differently to temperatures below 40°. Holsteins are most tolerant of cold.

Environmental requirements such as these, along with geographic location and animal size in relation to the size of the structure, determine what equipment and structural design must be used to create a suitable environment for each kind of poultry and livestock.

An integrated, efficient farm operation exists when these requirements are satisfied in one or a group of structures that contain systems to supply feed and water, to dispose of wastes, and to remove animal products. Reliable plans can be made for production.

To COMPOSE this kind of farm operation requires that it be studied in its entirety by a group drawn from several research disciplines, with the engineer a prominent member. Research patterns of this kind, although usually incomplete, have been developing. The Agricultural Research and Marketing Act provided funds for basic studies of the effects of housing conditions on the growth, production, and feed consumption of cattle, swine, and poultry. These studies, in which the Department of Agriculture and the Missouri and California Agricultural Experiment Stations cooperate, involve both engineering and animal physiology. Regional projects that combine the research efforts of workers at a group of experiment stations in a geographic region and the Department also have been developed.

SEVERAL manufacturers of farm machinery and buildings recognize the need for this kind of research. They have made grants of money and material to encourage study at widely separated experiment stations. The American Society of Agricultural Engineers is placing more emphasis on the collection and dissemination of information on a common subject or area of study through sponsored meetings and publications.

AN EXAMPLE of group effort is the Fiddlers Creek project. It is a study devoted to the production of beef, in which roughages are the principal feed, and is conducted cooperatively between Paul M. Mazur, owner of Fiddlers Creek Farm, near Titusville, N.J., and the New Jersey Agricultural Experiment Station. The departments of agricultural engineering, animal husbandry, and farm crops are the principal cooperators, but other departments of the station contribute as needed.

From studies begun in 1946, new equipment, buildings, and methods have been developed by avoiding the substitution method. This kind of farming is examined as a whole in order to learn if a new system can be devised. The use of a conservative approach has meant that farm labor has been reduced drastically and the need for much equipment has been eliminated. Beef animals self-feed from the time of purchase to time of sale from vertical self-feeder structures for chopped hay, silage, and ground feeds that are emptied from the bottom. Initially on a high roughage diet of hay and silage, they are finished on the ground feed. Hand feeding is used only during a short adjustment period to transfer the animals from roughage to concentrate feeds.

The single handling of the roughage required when elevated into the self-feeder makes a simple, efficient handling system. While originally explored for winter feeding of preserved feeds, the simplicity of the system suggested year-round use. Year-round use eliminates the need for pastures; their elimi-

nation changes the complexion of the whole farm operation.

High-yielding annual crops, harvested once, can be grown in place of usually lower yielding pasture crops. By proper selection, Mr. Mazur can grow two annual crops each year—one that matures in the spring, a second in the fall. It is called double cropping. Different species of plants can be grown together and selected to complement each other and provide nutritious, balanced feeds. The combinations of soybeans and sorghum, winter wheat and vetch, and spring oats and peas are examples.

Feed mixtures are largely composed in the fields. They are already mixed when they are run through the field machines and self-feeders. Supplements may be added if necessary when the structures are being filled.

THE ELIMINATION of pastures and the use of preserved feeds all year has been named "zero pasture." New cropping patterns, animal responses to combinations of plant species, and the performance of the machinery and structures require concurrent study. They become completely interrelated to form a new farming system. The key piece to this change has been the simplification and efficiency of handling large weights and volumes of crops. Buildings normally used once are now used twice a year and contribute more to the farm operation. This is the first case, to my knowledge, where structures and equipment have been the cause of a change in field practices of this kind.

Thus far I have tried mainly to examine part of the surface of engineering research and now and then dip below the surface for a more penetrating look. Research related to farm structures and the equipment associated with them has begun to expand.

Traditionally, next to land, buildings have been the most permanent part of agriculture and most neglected by research. The new research indicates that they will become less permanent, as

new methods and ideas are developed
and demonstrated. Only then can old
buildings be recognized as obsolete.

It is evident that farm specialization
occurs when crops are suited to structures and structures to animals. The
fitting of structures to animals is occurring at a rapid rate for the production of poultry and eggs and at a
moderate rate for swine. This is specialization that requires new structures
and equipment. On most farms where
these new systems are being put into
use, this is the first time a building
change has been made. There is every
reason to believe that the next change
will occur in a much shorter time.

MANUFACTURERS can begin to supply
buildings in an economy where periodically they become obsolete and are
replaced. Preengineered structures for
mass production are being designed and
marketed nationally today. They range
from components of a system to "turn
key" jobs. Some of them are completely
functional. Others have wide flexibility. Farmers now can order the complete assembly for a few farming needs
from one dealer, but farmers of tomorrow will be able to order complete assemblies for nearly all types of farming.

The stanchion barn of today represents the epitome of acceptance of a
standard design and arrangement that
evolved out of a long past. Designs for
the future are coming fast. No longer
will a long period of time elapse before
a design wins acceptance. This promises
to keep the development of farm structures dynamic.

Instead of the maze of buildings now
assembled on most farms, in the future
we can expect one roof to shelter a complete farmstead. A geodesic dome can
be used to cover large areas while
inflated buildings can enclose smaller
ones. These can be expected to develop
naturally with the creation of new materials and designs.

RESEARCH at the farmstead has
hardly begun. One can only ask—
What kind of future can we expect?

# Marketing
# in the Future

Harry C. Trelogan

KEYDOOZLE was the name given to a
proposed new type of grocery store—
one in which the customer merely
looked at a display of samples and indicated through a key device the products she wanted. When she finished
shopping, she went to the front of the
store to pay. The order was assembled
automatically and mechanically while
she was paying her bill so that it was
ready for her to pick up on her way out
of the door.

The name and the idea originated
with Clarence Saunders, who built and
operated a Keydoozle in Memphis,
Tenn., some years ago.

Twenty years earlier he had originated the self-service grocery store, the
Piggly Wiggly, and made it a fabulous
American success story. He died in
1953. He did not have enough time to
perfect the Keydoozle and the Food-
electric, another of his schemes for reducing costs in grocery stores.

Nor did he have the advantage of
electronic computing machines, transistors, transparent film wrapping materials, prepackaged fresh meats, fruits
and vegetables, and other technological developments that would have
helped to implement his ideas.

All these innovations and more have
come since and await another Clarence
Saunders, whose genius will effectively
bring them together into an arrangement unknown to us today.

Most marketing changes are not spectacular. Many changes are so commonplace the casual observer hardly notices them. Only the cumulative changes

of several years give them their proper proportions. The supermarket did not exist 30 years ago. Now it is displayed around the world as a symbol of American life. One-third of the items on the supermarket shelves have been created within the past decade. Even though those shelves usually carry some 5 thousand different items, only the best of the new products have managed to squeeze onto them.

The panorama of the grocery showcase is evidence that changes have been forthcoming so consistently it would be foolhardy to suggest they would not continue. The accelerated pace at which they have been appearing is likely to persist. More research and more specialized research workers are directing efforts toward finding ways to ease and expand the flow of farm produce into consumption.

Only a fraction of the new forms and packages that are now on the drawing boards for products of agricultural origin will find space on the store shelves of tomorrow. Only a few of the manifold ideas for new ways to perform marketing functions will stand the severe tests of our competitive economy.

Labor is the most expensive resource used in marketing. Innovations therefore are likely to emphasize laborsaving features.

Cost analyses, the antennas of the market researcher, invariably point up the importance of labor expense incurred in moving products through our marketing system.

One reason is that products are handled many times on their way from the farm to the city household. They are picked up and put down as they move into trucks on the farm; as they arrive at assembly points; as they arrive at, move through, and leave processing plants; at terminal markets; and at retail stores in the backroom, on the display shelves, at the checkout counter. A product may be picked up and put down 25 times before the consumer takes it home. Most of the picking up and putting down is done by men.

Machines can do more of the picking up and putting down. Trucks with power lifts, palletized loads, mechanical conveyors, and power equipment for transferring products into, within, and out of warehouses, storages, and processing plants can be extended to many more marketing operations and products if they are made into larger packages and loads.

The number of times products are handled can be reduced by combining successive operations into a more coordinated, compact pattern.

The presorting of apples into different sizes and qualities immediately after harvest and before they are placed in storage is illustrative. The sorted apples are put into large, film-lined boxes so that the apples may be held until the market is ready to take them; then the entire box can be moved directly to the point where they are to be put into packages for consumers. Similarly, the loading of products on trailers, which can be hauled to railheads and transferred in their entirety to rail cars for shipment to team tracks and direct delivery with tractors to warehouses, eliminates handling as products are transferred from one form of transportation to another.

Automation can reduce the need for individually operated controls and close personal supervision. Power trucks move unattended in warehouses as they are directed or driven over established routes with sensitized lines in the floors. Automatic casers, stackers, destackers, in-floor conveyors, automatic traffic regulators, and case-counting devices are used in modern milk plants.

Sequences of activities carried out in this way are like the series of operations that go on in an automatic dishwasher in the kitchen once the sequence is started. Unlike the kitchen dishwasher, in which different treatments are given at one place, automation in a plant frequently carries the products to different places for successive treatments.

These developments represent a logical extension of automation applied to continuous-flow processes that have replaced batch methods for liquid or other free-flowing products. Flow meters, tank weighing scales, electronic memory systems, and mechanically operated valves are items incorporated in the automatic lines leading up to milk bottle fillers. The fillers are also geared into the complete line operations as glass bottles or paper cartons are fed to them. Washers carry the bottles through a sequence of spraying, soaking, brushing, sterilizing, and drying. Carton machines incorporated with the filler form, glue and wax the cartons before filling and close, staple, code, and discharge them as filling is completed. Automatic temperature and speed regulators synchronize the movement of containers with the flow of milk being automatically pumped into the filler. The packaged and cased milk may pass directly to a loading-out area for placement in trucks, which likewise are fitted with mechanized refrigeration and automatic temperature regulators.

GREATER PRODUCTIVITY of labor is the objective of all these types of developments. They will progress as long as the substitution of capital equipment for labor pays off in reduced costs and greater profits.

Farmers expect the laborsaving developments in marketing to progress much further in light of their own experience.

Fewer and fewer farmers are serving more and more people in our economy. During the past decade about 300 thousand farmworkers have been leaving farming each year. That rate cannot continue indefinitely—there would be no farmer left in another 20 years. Besides, the growing population and rising incomes will call for more farm output in the future.

The shift from farming is likely to persist as long as farmers are able to produce more than is required for current needs.

Abundant production can be attributed in large measure to the ability of farmers in the past two decades to achieve gains in labor productivity that have outstripped other sectors of the economy.

Between 1937 and 1948, farm output per unit of labor input increased an average of 3.8 percent annually, compared with 1.9 percent in the nonfarm sectors of the private domestic economy. Increases in the output of farm labor between 1948 and 1957 reached the phenomenal rate of 5.7 percent a year, compared with 2.6 percent for the nonfarm sectors.

Farmers are convinced they are only in the early stages of a technological revolution that will enable them to surpass the records they have already established if markets can absorb the expanded output.

Farmers therefore look at the marketing system that handles their products to see how well it is progressing.

They know that improvements in farm production and marketing often go hand in hand.

One of the developments contributing to marketing efficiency has been the growth of larger, more specialized farms that produce more uniformly good products. Assembly costs are lower as a result; the expense of gathering full truckloads or carlots for efficient delivery to market receiving points is cut, and less sorting is needed to obtain the uniform lots of produce required for a mass distribution system.

Successful mechanization of farming, particularly harvesting, often depends on the ability of market agents to perform new or different services. Mechanical harvesting of potatoes, for example, requires that storage houses be prepared to handle products that are much more vulnerable to physical damage. Since the potatoes are not given time to dry in the fields until the skins harden, receiving plants must be equipped to protect and condition the potatoes for storage and shipment.

INCENTIVES are available within the marketing system itself to assure progression toward better handling methods.

Market agents and even systems of

marketing for agricultural products vie with each other for greater volume. The competition may take any of several forms, such as price competition, striving for lower costs, or for more acceptable products.

Inasmuch as price competition almost invariably encounters prompt retaliation, those who take the initiative in establishing lower prices may not be able to hold or protect price-induced volume gains. This approach, moreover, incurs risk of price cutting, deleterious to profit positions. Innovations leading to less expensive handling methods or superior products are more likely to give lasting competitive advantages.

Competitors therefore strive to find new ways to perform marketing functions that will result in more attractive products at less cost. This type of competition is just as keen as any other type employed to obtain greater share of the market and to improve profit positions.

Competition for economies of scale promises to become even more intense because marketing firms, like farms, are becoming fewer in number and larger in size.

One of its forms is to bring together successive marketing functions under the control of unified management so that they can be better coordinated to maintain higher capacity operations in larger units. Economic integration of this sort has been rapid in agricultural marketing. An example is the broiler chicken industry, in which mixing of feed, hatching of chicks, growing chickens, and operating dressing plants are closely meshed. Through contractual relationships, single firms can dovetail these operations so that they can be planned, financed, and carried out as a unified, efficient, cost-saving operation.

Retailers welcome large-scale producers of uniform products. Supermarket chains that advertise throughout a metropolitan area must have huge quantities of standardized products so that qualities as well as prices are the same in all of their stores. They find integrated firms better able to meet their specifications. The pressure for uniformity incurred by technology in distribution imposes the need for specialization on farms, groups of farms, and production regions.

Organizers of integrated growing and distributing activities are simply adapting to other parts of the market system principles and methods adopted earlier in food retailing.

The first chainstores brought together management of numerous stores into single companies and combined warehousing with retailing. The cost advantages from unified control of wholesaling and retailing forced independent competitors to copy the methods through establishment of service wholesalers and voluntary chains. The changes in organization of market units were accompanied by growth of self-service retail stores and later supermarkets.

As economic integration is extended back toward the farm for more and more products, equally radical alterations in farm production and produce assembly systems may be anticipated.

Harbingers of things to come are cow pools, in which groups of farmowners turn over their cows to pool operators for feeding and milking at central points, and in pig hatcheries and pig put-out systems that are used to assure a steady flow of pigs to market outlets. Beef cattle feeding operations also are conducted on a contract or custom basis for market agents, such as packers or chainstores, who want an assured supply of beef of a particular quality for their customers.

Behind these developments are innovations that facilitate centralized management. Chainstores could not have succeeded in the absence of double-entry accounting systems and cash registers. Neither could they have taken full advantage of warehousing opportunities in the absence of adequate inventory controls. The adaptation of electronic devices to recordkeeping for purchasing, receiving, delivering, ordering, and billing was necessary to enable chains of supermarkets to handle thousands of items in each store in a systematic fashion.

By a comparable way, self-service retailing would have been impossible without packaging of most goods. Packages not only facilitated handling, shelving and display, but also permitted point-of-sale information, promotion, and advertising. The laborsaving features for conserving salesmen were equally important as those for conserving store clerks. Regional or national distribution could not have occurred without the standardized, branded packages that could be brought to the attention of mass audiences through radio and television.

Improvements in communication are being extended within marketing agencies and to the public. Tape recordings are being used to receive, hold, and transmit orders so that they will be available at proper times and places to be handled automatically with less dependence on handwritten records, human memory, and word of mouth. Closed-circuit television, moving pictures, and visual aids are used to train and direct personnel throughout store systems.

THE KEY technological breakthrough leading to improved marketing practices may come from any point in the marketing channels—including the farm. The distribution of broiler chickens as we know it stemmed from disease control and feeding efficiency on farms. Modern frozen foods became possible when new processing methods were found. Sanitary packaging permitted the sale and distribution of process and natural cheeses in convenient shapes and sizes. Home refrigeration improvements opened the way for larger milk containers. Apartment living gave rise to demand for prepared foods in small packages, especially in lighter, disposable containers.

Few changes of consequence can be made, however, without need for adjustments throughout the whole complex of production, distribution, and consumption. In the past, innovations like frozen fruits and vegetables were delayed because advances made in freezing processes could not be utilized until transportation facilities, warehouses, retail stores, and homes were equipped to handle, display, and hold the products at low temperatures.

Tremendous investments of risk capital were required before the obviously superior products could be brought to consumers. Market agents in each of the successive stages of marketing had to be convinced that the new products would sell at a profit before they would make the investments. New firms and systems of distribution in many instances had to be developed to surmount the handicaps encountered when literally hundreds or thousands of independent business judgments were being exercised.

Integration probably creates an environment that permits coordinated planning for comprehensive changes of this sort. Presumably with the finance and business decisions resting in fewer hands, the prospects for introducing new products or methods involving pervasive changes will be more favorable. Mistakes in business judgment are likely to incur larger losses and may deter risk taking with new or different ventures. The prodding influence of effective competition will have to be retained, therefore, if this presumption is to be valid. It is entirely likely that the small independent businessman will continue to have a major part in pioneering new technologies less broad in scope.

Any society that devotes substantial resources to research is bound to experience new concepts ultimately expressed in ways of doing things that break sharply from traditional or conventional methods.

In light of the increased emphasis on research in the United States today, radical changes may be anticipated. It makes little difference whether the research is directed toward civilian or military objectives in the first instances, for discoveries are likely to find applications in different parts of the economy.

Moreover, there is an interaction between advances made on different fronts in the drive toward greater efficiency of use of physical resources.

The proliferation of technological improvements since the industrial revolution is a heritage upon which our society will doubtless build for a long time to come. We have acquired attitudes favorable to acceptance of new methods and expectation of progress. Agriculture has and will continue both to contribute and receive new ideas for accomplishing marketing objectives.

On the horizon one can easily visualize possibilities for such developments as atomic power and radiation, ultrasonics, thermoelectronics, cybernetics, plastic tools, and silicones being brought to bear on problems of agricultural marketing.

Experimentation with radiation already is underway on a broad front. With further technological breakthroughs, radiation may join such recently developed methods as vacuum cooling, hydrocooling, aeration, and fumigation in providing more effective quality maintenance for foods.

Conversely, contributions of agricultural research such as antibiotics, the vitamins, aerosol dispersion, virus chemistry, graphic correlation, and prefabricated housing find wide application transcending agriculture itself. There is every reason to believe that these research sources will be as productive in the future as in the past.

Part of the research will be directed toward improvement of products and methods as we now know them. It will be concerned primarily with cost reductions and greater efficiency in the performance of existing functions. A more significant part will be devoted to the creation of goods and services unimagined at present.

For a substantial share of these to be accepted, it may also be necessary to create the wants for them.

How could the cotton manufacturer know that he wanted to produce wash-and-wear fabrics before competitive synthetic textiles had acquainted consumers with products having similar properties?

How could a housewife know that she would want brown-and-serve rolls or prepared biscuit dough prior to the time she had a low-temperature freezer in the home?

How could she anticipate a want for water piped into her refrigerator before she became familiar with concentrated fruit juices or milk that enabled her to turn a valve to get satisfactory reconstituted products out of special compartments of the refrigerator?

She knows now that she would like better TV dinners, but a decade ago that want did not exist. The preparation of foods frozen on dispensable aluminum platters and wrapped in moisture-proof foil or film had to be perfected and translated into this widely distributed end product. Moreover, development of this convenience food had to coincide with changes in habits of living inconceivable before television made such demands upon the time of her family and herself.

Enterprising marketing firms will be on the alert to supply new wants and for opportunities to instill new wants as technology opens the way for their fulfillment. In fact, they will extend the use of recently introduced psychological techniques to disclose unexpressed individual wants occurring to perceptive minds.

Similar techniques from other social sciences will be used to forecast changes in ways of living and to ascertain factors affecting group acceptance rates for innovations. More tangible technological innovations also suggest indulgence in fantasy as well as prediction as a prerequisite to visualizing the future.

Space travel obviously will need food and clothing with characteristics beyond our present conception. Marketing services to provide them are still further removed from our comprehension.

How could the ship chandler for Columbus in 1492 have dreamed that his counterpart of 1958, supplying sailors of uncharted seas, would have a list of food supplies so different from his own?

How could he have foreseen the vast changes in technology of food preparation to contrast with the open firebox, equipped with a back to screen it from the wind and sand on the floor to hold the wood fire, on the *Niña*, *Pinta*, and *Santa Maria*?

He could not have imagined that food for 100 men in a nuclear-propelled submarine crossing the North Pole would be prepared in a space 10 feet long and 7 feet wide with two electric ranges (including four griddles and two ovens), a deep-fat frier, a 20-quart mixing machine, an ice cream machine, and a coffeemaker.

Come to think of it, the list of foods and the variety of foods served at each meal would have surprised our own grandmothers almost as much as the equipage aboard the U.S.S. *Skate* when it accomplished the feat of staying submerged 31 days and of traveling 2,405 miles, much of the time beneath ice-packs 12 feet thick.

Rapid as advances have been, food technology is confronted with a clear challenge to keep abreast of modern military and civilian requirements.

In general, one may anticipate that agricultural marketing will create and promote developments that will foster the continued movement of specialized activities off farms into the hands of market agents. This will include market agents who sell products (fertilizers, petroleum products, electricity, machinery) and services (feed-mixing, artificial breeding, bulk milk assembly, aerodusting and spraying) to farmers as well as those who buy products from the farm.

Within the marketing system we may look forward to shifts of marketing functions from one place to another. Expansion of consumer packaging of fresh fruits and vegetables will be accompanied by a general transfer of this function away from retail stores toward points where the products are assembled from farms.

Similarly, packaging of products subject to limited processing will shift to the points where the processing is per-formed. Manufacture of products from farm raw materials is likely to be concentrated further in fewer and larger plants.

Research analyses indicate that the ultimate in economies of scale have hardly been approached even in our biggest and most modern plants for dressing chickens, crushing oilseeds, and other processing where new technologies have become available.

This prediction rests on the assumption that transportation services will advance sufficiently to permit the assembly of raw materials and distribution of end products at costs which will not nullify gains from other economies of scale. It further assumes that full realization of the advantages may have to await the need for replacement of smaller plants that will meet the competition until such time as they are worn out or have become obsolete.

The weight of available evidence suggests that we may expect all the marketing and transportation facilities in the country will be rebuilt within relatively few years.

Newer handling facilities will be invented, better ways of retarding deterioration, spoilage and damage will be discovered and a more streamlined flow of products from farm to consumer will evolve.

During the course of these changes, false starts, mistakes, and only partial solutions may be anticipated. The waste of resources occasioned by transitions of such magnitude can be materially reduced with careful planning utilizing fully the most recently proved technologies.

Advantages will accrue to farmers, marketing agencies, and consumers from judicious decisions as the changes proceed.

At the other end of the marketing chain, there is also likely to be a continuing transfer of activities out of the homes into the hands of market agents. Greater varieties of products and associated services are likely to be offered in the stores, vending machines, and restaurants of tomorrow. They will be

## FOOD LISTS FOR PIONEER VOYAGES

|  | *Niña, Pinta, Santa Maria* | U.S.S. *Skate* |
|---|---|---|
| Milk group: | Cheese | Milk (fresh, dried, evaporated)<br>Cheese (canned)<br>Butter<br>Cream (dried, stabilized)<br>Ice cream paste |
| Meat group: | Salt meat (beef and pork)<br>Salt fish (barreled sardines and anchovies)<br>(fishing tackle) | Pork cuts (frozen)<br>Prefried bacon, pullman hams, brown-and-serve sausage (canned)<br>Beef, boneless (fresh, frozen, canned, corned, dehydrated)<br>Veal, boneless (frozen)<br>Liver, prefabricated (frozen)<br>Luncheon meats (fresh, canned)<br>Chile con carne (dehydrated)<br>Poultry (chicken cuts, frozen; turkey logs, canned)<br>Fish (frozen, canned, dehydrated)<br>Eggs (fresh, frozen, dried) |
| Vegetable-fruit group: | Chickpeas<br>Lentils<br>Beans<br>Rice<br>Raisins<br>Almonds<br>Garlic | Potatoes (fresh, canned, dehydrated granules, dehydrated diced)<br>Cabbage, string beans, peppers, onions (dehydrated)<br>Peas (dehydrofrozen)<br>Beans (dried)<br>Other vegetables and fruit (fresh, frozen, canned, dried)<br>Tomato juice, concentrated (canned)<br>Orange, grapefruit juice (dehydrated crystals)<br>Lemon, concentrated (frozen)<br>Apples, pie style (dehydrated)<br>Applesauce (instant)<br>Soups: Potato, onion, vegetable (dehydrated)<br>Soup bases<br>Jellies, jams (canned)<br>Sauces (canned)<br>Peanut butter |
| Bread-cereal-wheat group: | Flour (salted at milling)<br>Biscuit (well seasoned, good, not old) | Flour<br>Flour mixes; bread, rolls, doughnut, cake, pancake<br>Oatmeal<br>Cornmeal<br>Breakfast cereal, assorted<br>Bread (fresh)<br>Brown bread (canned)<br>Cookies<br>Macaroni, spaghetti, noodles<br>Crackers |
| Other foods: | Olive oil<br>Honey<br>Wine<br>Vinegar | Shortening, hydrogenated<br>Salad oil<br>Dessert powders<br>Catsup, chili sauce<br>Pickles, olives<br>Vinegar<br>Sugar, sirups<br>Candies<br>Spices, condiments<br>Coffee (ground, instant)<br>Tea<br>Cocoa |

# TYPICAL MENUS ON PIONEER VOYAGES, 1492 AND 1958

## Niña, Pinta, Santa Maria

### Daily ¹

**Monday:**
Salt fish, 12 ounces
Dried beans, 4.3 ounces
Biscuit, 24 ounces
Vinegar, oil, garlic
Wine, 4 cups

**Tuesday:**
Salt pork, 6 ounces
Cheese, 2 ounces
Biscuit, 24 ounces
Vinegar, oil, garlic
Wine, 4 cups

**Wednesday:**
Salt fish, 12 ounces
Dried peas, 4.3 ounces
Biscuit, 24 ounces
Vinegar, oil, garlic
Wine, 4 cups

## U.S.S. Skate

### Breakfast

**Monday:**
Chilled fruit juice
Chilled fresh fruit
Minced beef on toast
Hash-browned potatoes
Grilled pork sausage
Assorted cereal
Fresh milk
Toast, jam
Coffee

**Tuesday:**
Chilled fresh fruit
Chilled fruit juice
Assorted cereal
Fresh milk
Eggs to order
Crisp bacon slices
Toast, jam
Coffee

**Wednesday:**
Chilled fruit juice
Chilled fresh fruit
Assorted cereal
Fresh milk
Grilled ham slices
Poached eggs on toast
Toast, jam
Coffee

### Dinner

**Monday:**
Barbecued pork loins
Barbecue sauce
Parsley potatoes
Buttered peas
Salad
Chocolate cake
Bread
Coffee, milk

**Tuesday:**
Grilled rib steak
Sauted mushrooms
Julienne potatoes
Buttered golden corn
Salad
Cherry pie, alamode
Bread
Coffee, milk

**Wednesday:**
Southern fried chicken
Giblet gravy
Mashed potatoes
Creamed peas
Salad
Chocolate sundae
Bread
Coffee, milk

### Supper

**Monday:**
Grilled cheeseburgers
Mustard, catsup
Baked potatoes
Green beans with onions
Salad
Butterscotch pudding with cream
Bread
Coffee, milk

**Tuesday:**
Breaded veal cutlets
Tomato gravy
Mashed potatoes
Steamed spinach with eggs
Salad
Fruit jello, cookies
Bread
Coffee, milk

**Wednesday:**
Deviled frankfurters
Mustard, relish
French-fried potatoes
Buttered lima beans
Salad
Coconut cream pudding with cream
Bread
Coffee, milk

¹ Daily ration based on description of the expeditions of Columbus and 16th century voyagers. Only one hot meal was served each day; balance of ration was eaten as desired.

designed to meet the multiplying individual wants and the tastes of willing buyers in a growing urban population.

These changes will be hastened as consumers acquire incomes that enable them to satisfy further their insatiable wants for more choice in the goods and services they buy. Technological advances enable sellers to exercise greater imagination and aggressiveness in creating as well as fulfilling new wants for farm products.

Regardless of the source of the wants, their fulfillment is likely to contribute to more satisfactory living and satisfying life.

# Electric and Telephone Systems

R. W. Lynn and J. E. O'Brien

RURAL ELECTRIC and telephone systems are elements of a vast nationwide complex of power and communications facilities. Since 1882, when the first central electric generating station went into service, the country has been covered with a network of transmission and distribution lines, fed by generating stations and interconnected to provide maximum reliability of service and the most economic use of facilities.

Generating plants are the points at which electric systems begin. They are of three types: Steam, hydraulic (water), and internal combustion (diesel).

Today most new generating capacity is going into steamplants. Advances in technology have brought great improvements in the fuel economy of turbine-driven generators. The amount of coal required to generate 1 kilowatt-hour of electric energy has dropped from about 10 pounds to less than 12 ounces in the largest generators, which may have rated capacity as high as 300 thousand to 500 thousand kilowatts.

The economic benefits of such equipment are available to rural consumers when they are served by systems that have high-performance equipment. When generating equipment is part of a purely rural power system, the unit sizes are smaller and generation costs are higher than those of the larger machines. But because rural generating plants may be located closer to their loads, transmission costs may be reduced and the overall cost of power to the consumer may be competitive with that purchased from the largest suppliers of power.

One further advantage accrues to the users of the small generators: There is a large body of experience with them. They can be used without many of the risks associated with new and untried equipment.

Diesel plants and hydroplants also are used in the rural systems, but in recent years their total capacity has changed little. Most of the total growth in generation has come from the installation of steam capacity.

WHAT OF the future?

Electric loads are increasing, and the utility industry must expand to keep abreast of its responsibility. The Federal Power Commission has forecast that electric utility systems in the United States should be ready for a potential demand of 366 million kilowatts in 1980. That would make necessary an installed generating capacity of 421 million kilowatts. The peak demand was 128 million kilowatts in 1959, with 156 million kilowatts of capacity installed.

Rural loads are keeping pace with the national trend and in some instances are exceeding it. To meet increasing demands for electric power, more generating capacity will be needed. In rural systems financed by the Rural Electrification Administration, this will be made up largely of steam units, with a trend toward larger ratings. The average REA-financed steam unit in operation in 1956 was less than 10 thousand kilowatts. The largest single unit was 30 thousand kilowatts. The average size of 15 steam units installed in 1958 in the rural electrification program was more than 33 thousand kilowatts and included sizes ranging between 12,650 kilowatts and 100 thousand kilowatts.

Serving increasing loads means more than simply enlarging capacity. It means improving reliability and lowering costs. These responsibilities will be met by using larger and more economical generators and a variety of interconnections and system integration arrangements with neighboring power systems. Tying systems together provides flexibility in maintaining reserve capacity and permits postponement of capital investment in certain instances until larger and more economical generating units can be installed.

The possibility of developing new sources of energy to supplement (and perhaps eventually replace) coal and petroleum is being examined continually.

We now foresee the possibility of using nuclear fission as a source of heat to power turbine generators for producing electricity. Tremendous progress has been made since the first controlled nuclear reaction took place in 1942. Much work needs to be done before nuclear power becomes competitive with that generated by conventional means. Our reserves of coal and petroleum, in a broad sense, give us time to devote to the development of more attractive nuclear reactors, so that we need not accept the first promising type that comes along.

Research in nuclear power is being watched carefully by men of the Rural Electrification Administration so that the new source of energy may take its place in the rural electrification picture at the appropriate time.

Of particular interest is a project of the Atomic Energy Commission at Elk River, Minn., a 22-thousand-kilowatt plant on the property of the Rural Cooperative Power Association. Plans were made to put this boiling water reactor into service early in 1961. Its operation as part of a rural power system should give usable information. The association served more than 40 thousand rural consumers in 1960 and operated 64 thousand kilowatts of generating capacity and a transmission network of almost 900 miles. The nuclear reactor was designed to supply steam to an existing turbine generator.

TRANSMISSION of electric energy between generating plants and load distribution centers, or between two or more load distribution centers, is accomplished by high-voltage transmission circuits of appropriate capacity. These may be installed above ground or buried. In rural areas the standard practice is to use overhead transmission lines.

Improvements in the design, construction, and operation of transmission lines are being made continually. They reflect the development of new and better materials and engineering practices. Standard practice employs high-strength conductor made of steel core surrounded by aluminum strands carried on wood poles or steel towers. There is some interest in the use of aluminum for line towers and substation structures, because of its light weight and low maintenance needs.

A long-standing problem is vibration of conductor. Wind causes it, and the result is conductor failure and interruption of service. Dampers consisting of weights clamped to the conductor near its supporting insulators have been used to minimize vibration.

The development by the telephone industry of small, light-weight, plastic sleeve dampers has led to research in the development of a similar device for application to electric powerlines. Such a development has significance to rural power systems because of their large number of miles of exposed overhead lines.

The use of higher transmission voltages as a means of increasing the capacity per circuit to meet heavier powerloads is a historical trend that has economic advantages. Transmission voltages in the range of 200 to 300 kilovolts are common in the larger systems and are being considered for wider use in rural systems.

One of the most exciting fields of research is the use of transmission voltages in the range of 300 to 500 kilovolts. Several lines are operating at 345 kilovolts, and a few experimental lines have been tested up to 500 kilovolts. Behind this research is the need for greater capacity for anticipated future loads and the growing difficulty in obtaining rights-of-way for transmission lines, particularly near cities and other built-up areas.

Furthermore, increases in the size of generating units and in the capacity of powerplants produce results in larger blocks of power, which must be transported to load distribution centers consisting of substations from which distribution lines fan out to serve individual loads.

High load density is characteristic of large urban power systems. Rural power systems are low load density systems because of the dispersion of loads in rural areas. A transmission network serving rural load centers may require 10 to 30 miles of transmission line for each load center. The investment in transmission per dollar of revenue therefore is high.

Just as the trend in rural generation is following the electrical industry trend of increasing generation sizes, but at a lower level of unit sizes, so is the rural transmission trend following the trend of the industry but at a lower level of operating voltage. The basic rural transmission voltage is 69 kilovolts. It is sometimes desirable to superimpose on the basic 69-kilovolt system a higher voltage of 115 kilovolts or above for bulk supply. The higher voltage may be used in the future also for basic transmission in order to serve increased loads.

Wood poles are the economic choice for rural transmission lines and are used for single-pole and H-frame structures. Wood pole structures of standard design, high-strength conductor, which permits the use of long spans, and highly mechanized, mass-production construction techniques are elements that combine to reduce costs and lower the high investment that is characteristic of rural transmission systems.

Distribution lines deliver power to the consumer. The establishment of the Rural Electrification Administration in 1935, with its mission of financing central-station electric service for unserved persons in rural areas, focused attention on electric distribution systems.

Here was a situation in which large investments were to be made for the construction of entirely new distribution systems in thinly populated rural areas where requirements and costs differed radically from industry's experience in cities and suburbs. The question was not one of adding to existing systems but of engineering entirely new systems from the ground up. Costs had to be watched closely to keep rates reasonable and still permit good systems to be built and maintained. Many small savings became substantial when multiplied by the millions of items to which they applied.

Out of this experience came many contributions to the electric distribution industry: High voltage distribution; vertical construction for single-phase circuits; standardized procedures and practices; mass-production construction techniques; as well as standards and specifications for a wide range of materials and equipment used on rural lines.

About 80 percent of the total investment in REA-financed rural electric systems now is in distribution facilities.

Of the total investment of 3,433 million dollars among REA borrowers to 1960, 2,787 million dollars were in distribution facilities, 321 million dollars in transmission facilities, and 325 million dollars were in generation facilities.

Early experience with equipment that performed satisfactorily on urban systems showed the need for lightning arresters, kilowatt-hour meters, and insulators with greater resistance to damage from lightning. Long periods of service interruption occasioned by the blowing of line fuses led to the development of the automatic circuit recloser. The need for rapid communication led to universal use of mobile radio systems linking the system headquarters with the work crews in the field.

The materials and equipment making up transmission and distribution lines are under constant scrutiny in the interest of improvement. Poles and crossarms, which amount to about 27 percent of the cost of the powerline, are receiving increasing attention with regard to their preservation from the effects of decay.

Long-range engineering plans outline the essential elements of a rural system designed to carry four to six times the present load. The plans are reviewed periodically and are modified to reflect changing conditions. Annual work plans fit in with the long-range objectives.

The high-speed digital computer is increasingly important in utility engineering. Some use of it has been made in rural systems for transmission and distribution system design and for system planning. It permits more detailed calculations in system design than is feasible with desk calculators. In system planning, it permits the development of several plans based on different assumptions to provide a range of plans from which the most desirable may be selected.

Increasing attention has been given to the coordination of each distribution transformer to the load it serves. That is particularly important for rural systems, where a transformer usually serves only one consumer. A closer match between the rating of the transformer and the requirements of its connected load will reduce the investment in transformers and lower the operating costs.

Operation and maintenance are particularly vital for rural electric systems. Savings here offset rising costs of material and equipment, over which management has little control. Good operation and maintenance require good management and competent employees. These requirements point up another example of how the factor of size distinguishes the rural system from the larger electric utilities.

The large utility has a sizable engineering staff that includes specialists in many fields of design, construction, and operation. The employees are trained within the company and pass on their accumulated knowledge to new employees. There is within the organization a reservoir of knowledge and experience which can be brought to bear on the day-to-day operation of the system. A rural system that has fewer than 100 employees for all departments and activities usually obtains engineering assistance on specific problems through consultants. Use of consulting service has been effective in engineering and has been used to a limited extent in other specialized fields. But the problem of training system employees in specialized techniques is a challenge for the future.

This problem is met in various ways.

Management institutes, designed by a firm of management consultants, are available to managers and directors of rural electric systems. The Graduate School of the Department of Agriculture offers a correspondence course in bookkeeping for rural electric systems.

Job training and safety programs in most States provide instructors who visit participating systems and instruct line crews in safe work practices. This program is sponsored by the State departments of vocational education, the Office of Education of the Department of Health, Education, and Welfare, and the participating systems. At statewide conferences, line foremen and superintendents study supervisory techniques. At hot-line schools, linemen receive intensive instruction in hot-line construction and maintenance procedures.

Meter schools have been conducted at colleges and universities with the support of all segments of the electric utility industry and the meter manufacturers. They offer instruction in the adjustment, repair, and application of meters.

The University of Wisconsin in 1959 offered an engineering institute on wood utility poles. Other universities planned similar short courses.

THE TYPICAL rural telephone system of just a few years ago was the hand-crank, magneto type. One or more operators at the central office handled all the calls. Often service was available only during the daytime. Sometimes 20 or 30 parties were connected to the same line, and the operator signaled the wanted party with an assortment of long and short rings. Delays in reaching the operator were unavoidable with so many people having access to the same line. Voice transmission frequently was weak and had to compete with line noises. Some systems of this description were still in operation in 1960.

The increasing wage cost in recent years of providing employees in central office switching, together with the demand for modern high-speed automatic service, is making the conversion to dial operation inevitable.

Between 1949, when the Rural Electrification Act was amended to permit telephone loans, and 1960, REA provided 633 million dollars in long-term loans to 686 borrowers for modern dial service to 1,289,000 subscribers in rural areas. Of these companies and cooperatives, 570 had already placed in service 2,259 new dial central offices by January 1, 1960.

The constant search for better methods and materials to improve rural service and reduce costs requires the evaluation of new ideas that are generated within the telephone industry and support and assistance in developing promising ideas.

Telephone equipment manufacturers customarily engineered each separate order for central office switching equipment individually. Rural Electrification Administration developed a standard specification that enables the manufacturers to bid competitively and provide modern central office switching equipment at a lower cost to borrowers.

Multipair distribution wire consists of several pairs of plastic-insulated copper conductors wound around an insulated steel wire used to support the facility and attach it to the telephone poles. When multipair distribution wire was originally developed it was considered an expedient for interim construction. It was designed to reinforce existing facilities temporarily in areas of unexpected growth and to provide temporary service during road widening or major rebuilding work.

The results, however, were so good that the industry was encouraged to improve the physical characteristics to increase its life expectancy. One of the improvements was to fortify the single extrusion of polyethylene-insulated conductors with an outer covering of polyvinyl chloride. The addition of polyvinyl chloride increased the abrasion resistance and offered the possibility of color coding so that each pair could be easily distinguished from all other pairs. The life expectancy has increased from the original of from 2 to 5 years to at least 20 years. Multipair distribution wire is now considered permanent-type plant for rural service to be compared on an annual cost basis with open wire and cable facilities. The physical characteristics of the multipair distribution wire make it easy to install. It can be salvaged and reused.

Polyethylene may be used as an insulation for cable conductors to replace the paper or pulp insulation used in lead-sheathed cables. Because polyethylene in an extruded jacket is quite flexible, has excellent aging characteristics, and offers high resistance to moisture, it is valuable as an outer jacket on communication cables. New cables are available to the telephone industry which have plastic sheaths and paper-insulated conductors, as well as plastic sheaths and plastic-insulated conductors. The plastic-insulated conductors are color coded for ready identification of each pair at every sheath opening.

FOR MANY YEARS telephone men have wanted to bury communication lines in the ground, where they would be relatively free from storm damage. Many important long-distance trunk cables have been placed underground in the Bell Telephone System. The maintenance experience through the years has been very favorable compared with aerial type of construction. The high cost of burying cables and the high cost of the special underground cables have restricted the use of buried plant to these high-grade telephone circuits. Polyethylene insulation, being moisture and corrosion resistant, has made it possible to lower the initial cost of the materials involved in buried plant. Improvements in cable laying techniques have materially decreased the expense of placing cable underground. It is possible now to plow cable and single-pair wire into the ground at a rate of from 4 to 9 miles a day for a single cable plow.

Such accessory materials as terminals and splice enclosures for buried facilities had to be developed to enable telephone companies to take advantage of improvements in the cable and construction techniques. With the cooperation of hardware manufacturers, a complete line of terminal housings, which should have a life expectancy of 20 years or more, was developed.

Today buried plant is considered a standard form of construction in rural areas to be compared with aerial-type plant on an annual cost basis. In 1959, 3,500 miles out of a total of 40 thousand route miles of telephone construction was placed underground. We expect at least 25 percent of the total route miles constructed each year in the telephone program will be buried plant before long.

Transmission on rural lines has been further improved by developments in electronic terminal equipment. They are mainly in devices such as carriers, which provide a number of simultaneous talking and signaling paths over one wire pair, and repeaters, which amplify weak message signals so that they might be better heard. Both effect substantial savings in outside plant conductor materials by superimposing moderate-cost electronic hardware on the circuits.

Costs of voice repeaters were lowered considerably with the development of series-type negative impedance repeaters. Newer types, which added a shunt repeater to the series repeater, take advantage of the plug-in concept, which permits rapid maintenance.

Discovery of the transistor in 1948 and succeeding developments which improved its stability and reliability brought additional improvements. Less than a decade after the first negative impedance repeaters employing vacuum tubes were placed in service, transistorized repeaters came. They embody the interchangeability advantages of later tube types and are smaller and use less power. Replacement of transistors is expected to cost much less than replacement of vacuum tubes.

CARRIER SYSTEMS that provide circuits between central offices are called trunk carriers. Those that provide circuits between a central office and one or more telephone subscribers are subscriber carriers.

Early designs of trunk carriers were complex and expensive. Before 1925 it was not considered economical to superimpose them on wire lines of less than 200 miles. Improved vacuum tubes and electronic techniques have reduced costs of carrier equipment until it is considered economical to use some trunk carriers for distances of less than 20 miles. The first carrier equipment produced specifically for serving rural subscribers became available after the Second World War. This equipment utilized electric distribution lines rather than conventional telephone lines as a transmission medium.

Years ago it was realized that a subscriber carrier system was needed that would provide full selective multifrequency ringing to party-line subscribers and would perform satisfactorily with conventional telephone plant without requiring expensive line treatment apparatus. Such equipment has been developed and approved.

Several subscriber carrier systems having the features desirable for rural service were available by 1955. Their use was encouraged where economies in plant costs could be effected. Since that time, the use of subscriber carrier has reduced the cost of providing circuits; provided an economic means for adding circuits; provided service to individual line and party-line subscribers in areas beyond the economic or transmission limits of conventional wire facilities; and eliminated the need for some small but expensive central offices which would be equipped for only a small number of lines.

Because subscriber carrier equipment costs have been relatively stable while material and labor costs for various types of wire plant have been rising, use of this equipment will probably increase in rural telephone systems as service is extended to new areas or existing facilities are expanded to meet growth requirements.

Statistical data on annual charges are compiled by telephone companies on the operation of trunk and subscriber carrier equipment, as well as on the operation of other items of telephone plant. In carrier equipment the annual costs are principally for vacuum tube replacements, electric power consumption, and the normal expense of keeping the equipment performing satisfactorily.

The Rural Electrification Administration has been conducting field trials of transistorized subscriber carrier equipment since 1957. Annual charges have been closely observed. Trials proved that the annual charges will be substantially lower than those for vacuum-tube types of equipment because of the longer life expectancy and lower power consumption of transistors. The trials also proved that tran-

sistorized equipment has a high degree of reliability.

The first field trial of a fully transistorized trunk carrier system began in 1959. Early reports indicated that the trial will provide a way to lower annual charges for trunk carrier equipment.

In the near future most new installations of trunk and subscriber carrier equipment in rural telephone systems will be transistorized completely.

FOR OPEN WIRE trunk routes, a number of transposition systems have been available for some time, but they have disadvantages for rural systems.

Engineers therefore started development in 1955 of a new transposition system, designed to overcome some of the objections to the transposition systems then available.

Among the objectives were: Maximum average transposition pole spacing greater than 300 feet; a maximum of eight wire pairs; ability to use either point or tandem transposition brackets; negligible absorption peaks (excess loss over and above attenuation due to a sort of resonant coupling to surrounding media) up to 360 kilocycles; good crosstalk characteristics (high crosstalk losses) on approximately half the wire pairs, up to 350 kilocycles, and on the remainder, good characteristics up to 150 kilocycles.

The system was constructed and tested in 1957. The measurements were a gratifying confirmation of the theoretical predictions of the design.

MOBILE RADIOTELEPHONE service has been offered to the public by the telephone industry since 1946. The service was confined generally to urban areas and under the control of a special operator who manually connected the calling party with the called mobile radiotelephone subscriber, and vice versa.

During the early stages of the rural telephone program, it became apparent that mobile radiotelephone would be useful outside cities. A method was needed, however, which would not depend on the services of an operator, because practically all exchanges were unattended dial central offices.

A specification embodying performance requirements consistent with existing dial operation was written by the Rural Electrification Administration and circulated among manufacturers with an invitation to bid on the development of such equipment. Two manufacturers undertook this development work, and pilot systems were installed in Virginia and in Florida in 1957. The systems proved that dial radiotelephone, with some modifications, was practicable and, as a result, other systems ordered equipment to serve rural areas.

This wider use revealed further minor modifications necessary for the equipment to function properly with the various makes and types of central office equipment. During 1959 many telephone borrowers purchased mobile dial radiotelephone equipment.

THE FIRST point-to-point commercial overseas radiotelephone circuit was placed in operation in 1927 between the United States and England. Service between principal cities of the world was established during the next decade. Most of the overseas radiotelephone circuits were in the shortwave range of frequencies between 3 and 30 megacycles.

A system concentrating a large number of circuits on a single radio channel was placed in service in 1947. In a system of this type, the radio channel operates at a frequency of thousands of megacycles, known as microwaves, over line-of-sight paths. Microwave relay systems carrying long-haul, high-density telephone circuits and television channels have been operating in many parts of the world for the past decade.

Telephone borrower systems of the Rural Electrification Administration generally are confined to small areas, and the volume of traffic is relatively low. Microwave, therefore, usually is not feasible except in certain special

instances. It has been used where the terrain is such that land line facilities are too expensive to construct or where the number of circuits is likely to expand beyond the capability of the land line facilities. At the end of 1959 approximately 15 Rural Electrification Administration telephone borrowers were using microwave on their systems and the interest and contemplated use was growing.

# Benefits for All

Frederick V. Waugh

SOME OF THE BENEFITS from improvements in farming and in agricultural marketing go to farmers. Some go to the millions of people who earn their livings by processing, transporting, storing, and distributing agricultural products. By far the greatest benefits go to consumers—that is, to every person in the Nation. Anything that affects food and fiber affects us all.

But today—when only one person among eight Americans lives on a farm—the average consumer may not feel very directly concerned with the great achievements in agricultural technology. The taxi driver may not realize that he has benefited from hybrid corn. The insurance salesman may not understand how farm tractors have helped him. The automobile worker may not know how much he has gained from improvements in the transportation and refrigeration of foods.

BETTER TECHNOLOGY provides more food and clothing for domestic consumers. Food supplies have increased faster than the growth of population. Our population has increased more than 50 percent since 1925, but the per capita civilian domestic use of food has gone up 11 percent, and the per capita use of nonfood products of agriculture has gone up 12 percent.

This is due not only to greater production on the farm. It is due in part to new techniques of food manufacturing, to better storage and refrigeration, and to speedier distribution.

New methods of canning, freezing, and dehydrating have given us year-round supplies of perishable foods. New markets have been opened up for farmers.

Better technology gives us better products. It gives us foods that are cleaner, fresher, healthier, prettier, easier to prepare. It gives us fabrics that are stronger, warmer, more comfortable.

Today, we are sure to get healthful, disease-free milk and meats because modern techniques of food inspection are so accurate. Rigorous enforcement of our pure food laws protects us from adulteration and misrepresentation.

Better fabrics, too, come from the new technology. Many of these so-called miracle fabrics are nonagricultural.

Research is developing better fabrics from cotton and wool, which have certain natural advantages over any synthetic materials that are yet known. Improved techniques of production are giving us cotton and wool of a higher and more uniform quality.

The new technology has supplied agricultural products needed to win a major war and to help other countries since the war.

Today our agricultural export programs are important arms of our international policy. Modern technology has put us in a position where we can supply greater amounts of food and fiber to our friends overseas. We can afford to make it available to them on favorable terms as long as we are careful not to disrupt ordinary commercial markets.

Efficient methods of production and distribution have provided consumers with food at reasonable prices.

Consumers sometimes fail to realize this fact because food prices now are higher than they were before the war. This is mainly because inflation has pushed up practically all costs, prices, and incomes.

Food prices are not high in relation to wages and other incomes. An hour's factory labor in 1959 would buy 11.3 pounds of bread, compared to 8.0 pounds in 1939; or 2.6 pounds of pork chops, compared to 2.1 pounds; or 9.0 quarts of milk, compared to 5.2 quarts.

Costs and prices are relative things. The important fact is that the rise in food prices has been much less than the rise in wages and in other costs.

THE BIGGEST benefits are indirect—as is often the case in economics. These indirect benefits grow out of labor efficiency—out of rising productivity of labor in agricultural production and marketing.

The basic change in agricultural production and marketing has been the substitution of capital for labor.

Machines and power have taken over much of the work that was formerly done by people. The big effect of these changes has been to save labor on the farm and in the marketing system. The gains in productivity of farm labor have been especially striking. One example is that the average amount of human labor needed to produce a bushel of corn in 1910 to 1912 was 75 minutes; by 1955–1958 it had been reduced to fewer than 14 minutes.

MANY examples could be given of increases in labor productivity in agricultural marketing. Several wholesale grocery warehouses recently increased their tonnage per man-hour by 26 percent by improved work methods and equipment. New methods, materials, equipment, and layout for handling meat in certain retail stores got 25 percent more productivity from labor.

The volume of food marketed went up 71 percent from 1938 to 1958. In this same period, the hours of labor in food marketing went up 17 percent. This indicates a rise of more than 45 percent in labor productivity in agricultural marketing.

We may often overlook these important gains because marketing charges have continued to creep upward since the end of the war. The rise in these charges, however, is a reflection of higher wages, higher freight rates, and higher costs of materials. The substantial increase in labor productivity has kept food margins from going higher.

Our great modern industries of manufacturing and commerce would have been impossible without the technological revolution in agriculture, which made available the necessary manpower for factories, banks, stores.

Agriculture has helped put the foundation under manufacturing as well as commerce.

Primitive societies must use most of their resources in primary production—in farming, fishing, forestry, and mining. Very few people can be spared to work in manufacturing, trade, services, the arts and sciences, which must wait until labor becomes more productive in the primary industries.

The opposite has happened in the United States. As our farm labor has become more productive, a smaller and smaller percentage of our workers can feed and clothe our whole population. Millions of farm boys and girls have moved to the cities and have found industrial jobs. Industries have moved out into the rural areas where they can find supplies of labor. Displaced farm labor has always been a major source of industrial labor.

The prosperity of the United States is based upon balanced growth. Efficiency in agriculture has helped industry and commerce. And the development of nonagricultural industries has provided an ever-increasing demand for farm products.

All parts of our economy are interdependent, almost like parts of a human body. Any important change for good or for bad in one part of the economy soon spreads to all other parts.

We would not claim that the prosperity of this country depends upon agriculture alone. We do believe that agricultural research and education have led to a great increase in the productivity of labor in agriculture. That increase and the high birth rates on farms have assured an unfailing and necessary supply of industrial labor, which was indispensable to the balanced growth of our economy.

The direct effects of better agricultural technology are seen in more and better food and fiber. The indirect effects are in more automobiles, television sets, roads, schools, and all sorts of nonagricultural goods and services.

Taking the direct effects and the indirect effects together, the technological revolution in agriculture has contributed a great deal to the prosperity and well-being of all our people.

Everyone has a stake in continued technological improvements in the future. The past gains have been great, but there is still much room for further improvements in efficiency on the farm and in the marketing system.

BETTER agricultural technology has also contributed to certain economic problems. Two of these problems will be noted here: The family farm and surpluses.

The family farm still is characteristic of American agriculture, but it is becoming bigger, more mechanized, and much more expensive. An investment of more than 100 thousand dollars is needed for a commercial farm in the Corn Belt—a good, modern commercial family farm, an efficient unit that should make a fairly good living for the operator and his family.

Perhaps it is unfortunate that more efficient technology often calls for larger investment in plant, machinery, and equipment. But it seems to be a fact. To take full advantage of mechanization and economies of scale, our commercial farms probably will grow still larger and still more expensive in the future.

This does not necessarily mean the passing of the family farm. So far, the corporation farm has made little headway in the United States. The prospect is that, at least for many years, most of our commercial farms will still be owned and operated by individual families with occasional hired labor. It is true, though, that many young men will find it increasingly hard to buy a good productive farm, with the necessary machinery and equipment. They will need credit and sound guidance in farm management if they are to succeed.

Moreover, as our best commercial farms become more profitable, they dramatize the plight of the small, under-capitalized, noncommercial farm with a chronically low income. This, too, is a family farm, and one that is still all too common.

So far, the technological revolution has not reached them. Even if they hear about the marvelous new farm machinery, they cannot afford to buy it. Often their farms are too small to use modern machinery efficiently. They get little, or no, benefit from Government price supports because they have little, or nothing, to sell.

As our technology continues to improve, we must strengthen our programs to help low-income farmers. Some can be helped by education and credit to become efficient commercial farmers. Some can be helped by education, by better employment services, and by promotion of local businesses to make a better living in nonagricultural industry.

It would be a great mistake to impede progress by trying to slow up the trend toward commercial farming. The Nation, as well as farmers, will benefit from greater efficiency in agriculture that can come through still greater mechanization and commercialization. Conceivably great disparity in farm incomes could be lessened by reducing the incomes of our most prosperous commercial farms. But how much better it is to do it by increasing the incomes of those who are on the low end of the scale!

The other problem to be noted here is that of agricultural surpluses. The Nation has become more and more aware of them as stocks in storage have mounted and as Government costs go up.

Of course, a food surplus is much better than a food shortage. Technology has, so far at least, rescued us from the threat of shortages. How grand it would be if only someone would save us from the threat of surpluses! Then farm incomes would be high, and taxpayers could get some relief.

This line of thought occasionally leads someone to suggest that we postpone further technological improvements in agriculture until demand catches up with supply.

It is not so simple as that. First, it would be very inefficient to turn research off and on again, whenever there was a change in the surplus situation. The most important research findings grow out of years and even decades of continuous study. Second, even a temporary postponement of research in agricultural technology would confront us with the danger of future shortages.

We are living in a world where adequate stocks of farm products could suddenly become vital. We need to be prepared to step up our production speedily. We need to have ready a modern, efficient system of food processing and distribution. To do this, we need still more improvements in agricultural technology.

Our basic trouble here is not that production and marketing are too efficient. Rather, it is that our social engineering has not kept pace with our physical and biological engineering. We know better how to manage machines and cows than how to deal with people. Our programs to safeguard farm income, vital as they are, may sometimes foster overproduction and sometimes may hold down consumption. These unintended results are signs of poor social engineering.

To avoid unwanted surpluses, we need more accurate, more timely, and more detailed statistics and information to distribute among farmers and the food trades. We need careful and realistic adjustments in price-support levels.

We need even more to develop more effective ways of making our surpluses available to those who now need them at home and abroad.

Such a program will not weaken private free enterprise. It will supplement and strengthen the ordinary forces of the market. A free market does not mean the absence of Government. It requires active assistance from the Government.

The greatest national benefit requires further that the agricultural program be geared into a sound national program to promote stability and progress throughout the whole economy. To this end, we must encourage stability in agricultural output, in farm employment, and in the level of agricultural prices.

The progress of the Nation depends in no small degree upon still further advances in technology, particularly in production and marketing. Any country over the years consumes about as much as it produces. Its output depends on its population, the number of persons in its work force, the average number of hours worked, and the productivity of its labor. This is simple arithmetic.

THUS, SOUND ECONOMIC policy in the long run calls for continued efforts to encourage efficiency throughout the whole economic system. But this is not all. In the modern world of large corporations and strong labor unions, we naturally look to our Government to see that the benefits of increased efficiency are shared by all the people, including workers, businessmen, and farmers. Only through Government can we protect ourselves against inflation and business depression.

There is still room for greater efficiency in agricultural production and in the marketing of farm products. Further gains in agricultural efficiency could be of immense benefit to the whole Nation, including farmers. But

the benefits—particularly those to farmers—may not come about automatically. We are now faced with large surpluses of a few commodities. If all production controls and price-supporting measures were eliminated suddenly, farm income would be drastically cut. This would not only harm farmers; in the long run it would hurt the whole economy.

We should continue to push market expansion vigorously at home and abroad. However, this alone is not likely to be enough to get rid of present surpluses of wheat, corn, and cotton in a reasonable time.

Some economists advocate a renewed effort to control agricultural production and marketings. This is a very difficult problem. Past efforts in this field have not been notably successful. The Conservation Reserve has helped. It should be expanded—not only as a means of reducing present surplus output but also as a means of conservation of future food supplies. In addition, we need to step up programs to develop rural industry and to train rural workers for industrial jobs, whether in the country or in the city.

Finally, our future agricultural programs must continue to wrestle with the difficult problems of the farmer's bargaining power. The individual farmer is at a disadvantage in competing with organized business and labor. Some farmers' cooperative associations have been able to attain a certain degree of bargaining power. Many local groups of dairymen and vegetable growers have been helped through Federal marketing agreements and orders. There is real merit in the general idea of truly "self-help" programs in agriculture, with appropriate safeguards to protect the interests of all groups, whether in other agricultural industries or engaged in nonagricultural business.

The agricultural program of the future doubtless will continue to be some combination of programs aimed at adjusting production, expanding markets, and strengthening the bargaining power of farmers.

# The Contributors

Wallace Ashby, Chief, Livestock Engineering and Farm Structures Research Branch, Agricultural Engineering Research Division, Agricultural Research Service.

Kenneth K. Barnes, Professor of Agricultural Engineering, University of Arizona: formerly Professor of Agricultural Engineering, Iowa State University.

Layne Beaty, Chief, Radio and Television Service, Office of Information.

Donald T. Black, Agricultural Engineering Research Division, Agricultural Research Service.

B. D. Blakely, Head Agronomist, Soil Conservation Service.

T. E. Bond, Agricultural Engineer, Livestock Engineering and Farm Structures Research Branch, Agricultural Engineering Research Division, Agricultural Research Service, Davis, Calif.

Ross D. Brazee, Agricultural Engineer, Agricultural Engineering Research Division, Agricultural Research Service, Ohio Agricultural Experiment Station, Wooster, Ohio.

Arthur E. Browne, Assistant to the Director, Fruit and Vegetable Division, Agricultural Marketing Service.

William M. Bruce, Agricultural Engineer, Agricultural Engineering Research Division, Agricultural Research Service.

Earl L. Butz, Dean, School of Agriculture, Purdue University.

L. E. Childers, Chief, Current Information Branch, Agricultural Research Service.

Harold T. Cook, Assistant Director, Market Quality Research Division, Agricultural Marketing Service.

A. W. Cooper, Director, National Tillage Machinery Laboratory, Agricultural Engineering Research Division, Agricultural Research Service, the United States Department of Agriculture, Auburn, Ala.

James J. Coyle, Engineering Division, Soil Conservation Service.

William C. Crow, Director, Transportation and Facilities Research Division, Agricultural Marketing Service.

S. S. DeForest, Development Representative, U.S. Steel Corporation, Pittsburgh, Pa.

E. M. Dieffenbach, Agricultural Engineer, Agricultural Engineering Research Division, Agricultural Research Service.

William W. Donnan, Principal Agricultural Engineer, Western Soil and Water Management Research Branch, Soil and Water Conservation Research Division, Agricultural Research Service, the United States Department of Agriculture, Pomona, Calif.

Richard F. Dudley, Agricultural Engineer, Crop Production Engineering Research Branch, Agricultural Engineering Research Division, Agricultural Research Service.

T. W. Edminster, Assistant Chief, Eastern Soil and Water Management Research Branch, Soil and Water Conservation Research Division, Agricultural Research Service.

William H. Elliott, Head, Handling and Facilities Research Section, Transportation and Facilities Branch, Marketing Research Division, Agricultural Marketing Service.

G. R. Free, Associate Professor of Soil Technology, Agricultural Research Service, Cornell University.

Fred L. Garlock, Head, Farm Credit Section, Farm Economics Research Division, Agricultural Research Service.

Henry Giese, Professor of Agricultural Engineering, Iowa State University.

Robert O. Gilden, Extension Agricultural Engineer, Federal Extension Service.

Wylie D. Goodsell, Assistant Chief, Costs, Income, and Efficiency Research Branch, Farm Economics Research Division, Agricultural Research Service.

R. B. Gray, at his retirement in 1954, Head of the former Farm Machinery Section, Agricultural Engineering Research Branch, Agricultural Research Service.

R. L. Green, Head, Department of Agricultural Engineering, College of Agriculture, University of Maryland.

Carl W. Hall, Professor, Department of Agricultural Engineering, Michigan State University.

Lowell S. Hardin, Head, Department of Agricultural Economics, Purdue University.

Reuben W. Hecht, Agricultural Economist, Costs, Income, and Efficiency Research Branch, Farm Economics Research Division, Agricultural Research Service.

Orve K. Hedden, Senior Agricultural Engineer, Agricultural Engineering Research Division, Agricultural Research Service, Ohio Agricultural Experiment Station, Wooster, Ohio.

T. E. Hienton, Chief, Farm Electrification Research Branch, Agricultural Engineering Research Division, Agricultural Research Service.

Emma G. Holmes, Family Economist, Household Economics Research Division, Agricultural Research Service.

Elmer B. Hudspeth, Jr., Agricultural Engineer, Crop Production Engineering Research Branch, Agricultural Engineering Research Division, Agricultural Research Service, Bushland, Tex.

W. V. Hukill, Agricultural Engineer, Agricultural Research Service, Iowa State University.

David A. Isler, Senior Agricultural Engineer, Agricultural Engineering Research Division, Agricultural Research Service.

Marvin E. Jensen, Head, Irrigation, Drainage and Water Storage Facilities Section, Western Soil and Water Management Research Branch, Agricultural Research Service, the United States Department of Agriculture, Fort Collins, Colo.

C. F. Kelly, Professor, Agricultural Engineering Department, University of California.

L. L. Kelly, Hydraulic Engineer, Soil and Water Conservation Research Division, Agricultural Research Service.

W. E. Larson, Associate Professor of Soils, Agricultural Research Service, Iowa State University.

N. L. LeRay, Agricultural Economist, Farm Economics Research Division, Agricultural Research Service.

Jordan H. Levin, Head, Fruit and Vegetable Harvesting Section, Harvesting and Farm Processing Research Branch, Agricultural Engineering Research Division, Agricultural Research Service, the United States Department of Agriculture, East Lansing, Mich.

M. M. Lindsey, Agricultural Economist, Cost, Income, and Efficiency Research Branch, Farm Economics Research Division, Agricultural Research Service, Stoneville, Miss.

W. G. Lovely, Agricultural Engineer, Agricultural Research Service, Iowa State University.

R. W. Lynn, Chief, Telephone Engineering and Operations Division, Rural Electrification Administration.

Howard F. McColly, Professor, Department of Agricultural Engineering, Michigan State University.

Earl C McCracken, Physicist, Institute of Home Economics, Agricultural Research Service.

Eugene G. McKibben, Director, Agricultural Engineering Research Division, Agricultural Research Service.

R. M. Marshall, Assistant Director, Soil Survey Operations, Soil Conservation Service.

Howard Matson, Head, Engineering and Watershed Planning Unit, Soil Conservation Service, Fort Worth, Tex.

William H. Metzler, Agricultural Economist, Farm Economics Research Division, Agricultural Research Service.

Herbert F. Miller, Jr., Chief, Harvesting and Farm Processing Research Branch, Agricultural Engineering Research Division, Agricultural Research Service.

M. L. Nichols, Retired Director, National Tillage Machinery Laboratory, Agricultural Engineering Research Division, Agricultural Research Service, the United States Department of Agriculture, Auburn, Ala.

Lyman J. Noordhoff, Information Specialist, Federal Extension Service.

K. H. Norris, Agricultural Engineer, Market Quality Research Division, Agricultural Marketing Service.

J. E. O'Brien, Chief, Electric Engineering Division, Rural Electrification Administration.

W. T. Pentzer, Director, Market Quality Research Division, Agricultural Marketing Service.

Harold E. Pinches, Assistant to Administrator, Agricultural Research Service.

H. B. Puckett, Agricultural Engineer, Farm Electrification Research Branch, Agricultural Research Service, University of Illinois.

Tyler H. Quackenbush, Irrigation Engineer, Engineering Division, Soil Conservation Service.

W. A. Raney, Head, Irrigation and Drainage Section, Eastern Soil and Water Management Research Branch, Soil and Water Conservation Research Division, Agricultural Research Service.

F. G. Renner, Head Range Conservationist, Soil Conservation Service.

Henry J. Retzer, Agricultural Engineer, Crop Production Engineering Research Branch, Agricultural Engineering Research Division, Agricultural Research Service.

C. B. Richey, Chief Research Engineer, Tractor and Implement Division, Ford Motor Co.

John H. Rixse, Jr., Assistant Chief, Engineering Division, Rural Electrification Administration.

J. S. Robins, Soil Scientist, Western Soil and Water Management Research Branch, Agricultural Research Service, Fort Collins, Colo.

J. W. Rockey, Agricultural Engineer, Livestock Engineering and Farm Structures Research Branch, Agricultural Engineering Research Division, Agricultural Research Service.

Dorothy R. Rush, Publications Editor, Office of Information.

G. E. Ryerson, Director, Administrative Division, Soil Conservation Service.

L. L. Sammet, Agricultural Economist and Agricultural Engineer, Agricultural Experiment Station, University of California.

J. K. Samuels, Director, Marketing Division, Farmer Cooperative Service.

Robert A. Saul, Agricultural Engineer, Agricultural Research Service, Iowa State University.

J. P. Schaenzer, Electro-Agricultural Engineer, Electric Operations and Loans Division, Rural Electrification Administration.

Leonard G. Schoenleber, Head, Special Crops Harvesting and Processing Section, Harvesting and Farm Processing Research Branch, Agricultural Engineering Research Division, Agricultural Research Service, the United States Department of Agriculture, Stillwater, Okla.

Orlin J. Scoville, Chief, Costs, Income, and Efficiency Research Branch, Farm Economics Research Division, Agricultural Research Service.

Fred C. Simmons, Specialist in Logging and Primary Processing, Northeastern Forest Experiment Station, Forest Service, the United States Department of Agriculture, Upper Darby, Pa.

Mark E. Singley, Professor, Department of Agricultural Engineering, Rutgers University.

Dwight D. Smith, Soil and Water Conservation Research Division, Agricultural Research Service.

Paul E. Strickler, Agricultural Economist, Mechanization and Structures Section, Farm Economics Research Division, Agricultural Research Service.

John Sutton, Principal Drainage Engineer, Head, Drainage Branch, Engineering Division, Soil Conservation Service.

Daniel W. Teare, Rural Electrification Administration.

Norman C. Teter, Head, Cooperative Farm Building Plan Exchange Section, Agricultural Engineering Research Division, Agricultural Research Service.

Harry C. Trelogan, Assistant Administrator, Marketing Research, Agricultural Marketing Service.

Roy N. Van Arsdall, Agricultural Economist, Agricultural Adjustments Research Branch, Farm Economics Research Division, Agricultural Research Service, University of Illinois.

James Vermeer, Head, Cost Analysis Section, Farm Economics Research Division, Agricultural Research Service.

Frederick V. Waugh, Director, Agricultural Economics Division, Agricultural Marketing Service.

E. C. Weitzell, Deputy Assistant Administrator, Rural Electrification Administration.

John C. Winter, Chief, Transportation Branch, Agricultural Marketing Service.

Avis M. Woolrich, Housing Specialist, Clothing and Housing Research Division, Agricultural Research Service.

# Index

474

478

479

Turnip harvesters, 177
Twine, baling, 171
Twine binders, 165
Two-way plow, 134

U-dozer, 108
UL approval, 409
Ultraviolet light, 77
Underwriter's Laboratories, Inc., 408
Unheated-air drying, 186, 187
United Fresh Fruit and Vegetable Association, 301
United Press International, 95
United States Weather Bureau, 90
Upright silo, 230
Utility poles, 72, 457

Vacuum cleaners, 403, 405
Vacuum coolers, 202
Vacuum cooling, produce, 201, 313
Vacuum tube, telephone, 460
Van Arsdall, Roy N., 79, 359–369
Van Duzen Gas and Gasoline Engine Co., 31
Van trucks, 48
Vane shear testers, 129
Variable costs, 339, 372
Vegetables, automation in handling, 421, 425; frozen, 206; vacuum cooling, 313
Veihmeyer tube, 114
Veneer bolts, 213
Ventilation, poultry houses, 229
Venturi tube, 157
Venturi meter, 121
Vermeer, James, 339–346
Vertical integration, 279, 383
Video-tape, 93
Viscous paints, 223
Voice repeaters, 460
Voltage, 71, 407

Wages, and food prices, 463; and mechanization, 394
Wagner, R. E., 148
Wagons, 48

Wagon-wheel layout, dairy, 259, 266
Walkways, cattle, 269
Wallis Tractor Co., 32, 43
Walnut harvester, 177
Walton, H. V., 80
Warehouses, food, 284; public refrigerated, 294; wholesale, 295
Washing machines, 78, 403, 404
Wastes, disposal of, 80, 265
Water, electric pump, 78; livestock, 246; range livestock, 269
Water control, in irrigation, 120
Water heaters, houses, 82; livestock, 83; milk production, 246; milkhouses, 84; poultry, 83
Water pipes, 264
Water pump, 264
Water system, farmstead, 259, 263
Water table survey, 114
Water transmission, 114
Water transportation, and marketing, 305
Water wheels, 2
Waterers, livestock, 83; poultry, 83
Waterloo Gasoline Engine Co., 42
Watersheds, remaking, 128–132
Watershed Protection and Flood Prevention Act, 130
Waugh, Frederick V., 462–466
Weather, animal protection, 231; combating, 183–199; grain drying, 188
Weather reports, radio, 90; TV, 92
Webb, Walter Prescott, 393
Webster, Daniel, 132
Weed control, burners, 155; chemical, 146; machinery, 153–157; through tillage, 141
Weed hooks, 134
Weirs, 121

Weitzell, E. C., 86–88
Wells, 263, 269
Westinghouse, George, 69
Wheat, drying of, 185; quality tests, 310
Wheat farms, mechanization, 370
Wheel scraper, 108, 110
Wheel-track planting, 149
Wheel tread, power adjusted, 37
Wheelbarrow, 50
Wheeled vehicles, 46
Wheels, in farm power, 45–51
Wholesale markets, changes, 283
Wilkinson, J., 219
Williams, W. H., 31
Williamson, E. B., 148
Wilson, W. O., 237, 263
Winch, 215
Wind, effect on beef cattle, 238
Wind erosion, deep plowing for, 125
Windbreaks, livestock protection, 270
Windmills, 2
Windrower machines, 167
Winter, John C., 297–307
Wire-pen housing, 263
Witzell, S. A., 239
Wood, Jethro, 133
Wood, physical properties of, 62
Woodard, A. E., 263
Woodlands, harvesting, 212–217
Woolrich, Avis M., 403–415
Wooten, O. B., 148
Worcester, Chuck, 92
Work simplification, 395–403
Workers, nonfarm agricultural, 324
Worstell, D. M., 237

Yeck, Robert G., 240
Young, E. C., 397
Yuba Manufacturing Co., 33

Zero pasture, 445
Zingg conservation bench terrace, 110

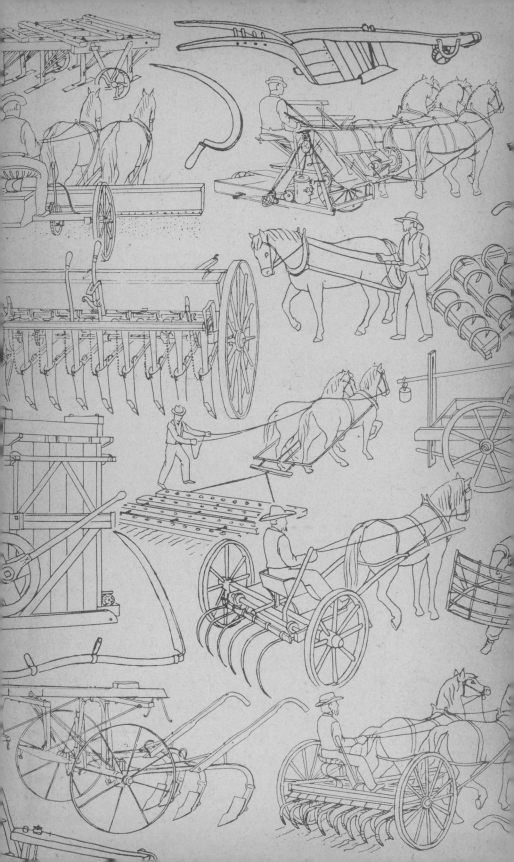